ELECTROMAGNETIC FIELDS AND INTERACTIONS

A BLAISDELL BOOK IN THE PURE AND APPLIED SCIENCES

CONSULTING EDITOR

Bernard T. Feld, *Massachusetts Institute of Technology*

ELECTROMAGNETIC FIELDS AND INTERACTIONS

RICHARD BECKER

EDITED BY PROFESSOR FRITZ SAUTER
TRANSLATED BY IVOR DE TEISSIER

VOLUME II

Quantum Theory of Atoms and Radiation

Revised by Prof. Günther Leibfried, Technische Hochschule, Aachen
and Dr. Wilhelm Brenig, Technische Hochschule, Munich

BLAISDELL PUBLISHING COMPANY
NEW YORK · LONDON
A DIVISION OF GINN AND COMPANY

This is the only authorized English translation of the original German Theorie der Elektrizität *published by permission of the B. G. Teubner Verlagsgesellschaft mbH, Stuttgart, Germany*

PUBLISHED IN NEW YORK BY BLAISDELL PUBLISHING COMPANY
AND SIMULTANEOUSLY IN GREAT BRITAIN BY BLACKIE AND SON LIMITED

Library of Congress Catalog Card Number 64–7001

PRINTED IN GREAT BRITAIN BY BLACKIE & SON LIMITED · GLASGOW

FOREWORD

Richard Becker intended that the second volume of *Electromagnetic Fields and Interactions* should contain an introduction to the quantum theory of radiation and the electron in its new edition. He considered that the following two provisions were essential for this purpose: firstly, the presentation should be complete in itself, and should include the detailed mathematical basis of quantum mechanics and, in particular, a summary of the theory of Hilbert space. Secondly, this volume should lay the foundations for the treatment of the properties of matter in electromagnetic fields, which is dealt with in the third volume. Becker himself considered the latter point to be of secondary importance; it does, however, determine the scope of the present volume. Even supposing that the quantum mechanical approach were unnecessary for the applications treated in the third volume, a knowledge of the formal basis of the quantum theory and an understanding of its methods are still indispensable for anyone who wishes to have a proper comprehension of the subject.

Richard Becker was unable to complete his *Quantum Theory*: at the time of his death about half this volume was in a more or less completed state. We have endeavoured to continue the presentation in a manner which, we hope, would have satisfied the author. Our task was rendered easier by many fruitful discussions with Becker over a number of years, as a result of which we felt able to convey his intentions and his approach to the subject.

The only knowledge assumed here is a familiarity with the basic principles of classical theoretical physics; we hope, therefore, that this volume will constitute a useful introduction for students. A revision of the classical properties of electrons is followed by a detailed presentation of the principles of the quantum theory. Later chapters are chiefly concerned with the application of the theory to problems involving respectively one and more than one electron. Finally, the principles of quantum field theory are developed to a stage sufficient to permit the treatment of the quantum theory of the Maxwell field and the Dirac field theory of the electron.

A number of exercises is included in each chapter, the solutions of which are given at the end of the book. They should help the reader to grasp the subject matter, since they offer him the opportunity of solving real problems, and enable him to make sure that he understands what he has read. Several important applications are treated in these exercises; we therefore recommend their study, together with their solutions, even for those readers who do not intend to work out the problems in the first instance.

Frau H. Geib and Fräulein F. Albus have been responsible for most of the work involved in the preparation of the manuscript. We have received considerable help from Dr. W. Ludwig in the preparation of the text, and from Dr. G. Süssmann and Dipl.-Ing. K. Fischer, who undertook a critical revision of the manuscript. Our sincere thanks are due to them.

G. LEIBFRIED
W. BRENIG

AACHEN and MUNICH, *September*, 1958

GERMAN EDITOR'S FOREWORD

Messrs. Leibfried and Brenig were the last colleagues of R. Becker to work in close contact with him. They are therefore most qualified to complete his posthumous half-finished manuscript of the second volume of *Electromagnetic Fields and Interactions*, which he had planned as a work of three volumes. The present volume shows how successful they have been in this task, and I should like to express my warmest thanks to them and to their collaborators.

My own participation in this volume has been limited to some suggestions, and to co-ordination with the other two volumes of this work. We have tried to ensure that this textbook in three volumes should have a uniform character in spite of the multiplicity of collaborators.

A few changes and corrections have been made in the ninth edition.

My special thanks are due to Messrs. B. G. Teubner, publishers, whose co-operation was much appreciated.

F. SAUTER

COLOGNE, 1964

CONTENTS

PART E. The theory of radiation

Chapter E I. Black-body radiation

Chapter E II. Absorption and emission

PART F. The relativistic theory of the electron

Chapter F I. Relativistic classical mechanics

Chapter F II. Relativistic quantum mechanics

A

The classical principles of electron theory

CHAPTER AI

Motion of an electron in electric and magnetic fields

§1. The equation of motion

From the fundamental experiments of P. E. A. Lenard (cathode rays), R. A. Millikan (measurement of the elementary charge), and J. J. Thomson (motion of electrons in electromagnetic fields) it is clear that we may conceive the electron as a charge distribution concentrated in a very small region of space, with total charge* e and mass m. Then the force $\mathbf{F}$ acting on an electron moving with velocity $\mathbf{v}$ in an electric field $\mathbf{E}$ and a magnetic field $\mathbf{H}$ is given by†

$$\mathbf{F} = e\mathbf{E} + \frac{e}{c}\mathbf{v} \times \mathbf{H} \tag{1.1}$$

It is assumed that $\mathbf{E}$, $\mathbf{H}$ and $\mathbf{v}$ are practically constant within the region of the charge distribution; $\mathbf{E}$ and $\mathbf{H}$ may then be taken as the fields at the electron's "position". For normal applications the precise charge distribution is unimportant, provided that the fields do not vary appreciably within the region occupied by the electron.

The force $\mathbf{F} = m d\mathbf{v}/dt$ in accordance with Newton's law (force = mass × acceleration). Substituting in (1.1), we obtain the equation of motion

$$m\frac{d\mathbf{v}}{dt} = e\mathbf{E} + \frac{e}{c}\mathbf{v} \times \mathbf{H} \tag{1.2}$$

$$m\ddot{\mathbf{r}} = e\mathbf{E} + \frac{e}{c}\dot{\mathbf{r}} \times \mathbf{H} \tag{1.2a}$$

where $\mathbf{r}(t) = [x(t), y(t), z(t)]$ represents the position of the electron. This equation is sufficient in most cases to describe the motion of an electron in a given field $\mathbf{E}$, $\mathbf{H}$.

* In this work e always represents the actual electron charge: it therefore has the negative value $e = -e_0$, where $e_0 = 4{\cdot}8 \times 10^{-10}$ e.s.u. $= 1{\cdot}6 \times 10^{-19}$ coulomb (C).

† Cf. Vol. I, §§18 and 44. As in Vol. I the Gauss system of measurement is used in all formulae. The force on a charged particle in a vacuum may therefore be expressed by $\mathbf{H}$ instead of $\mathbf{B}$.

It should be mentioned, however, that neither side of equation (1.2) is strictly correct. The left side is incorrect because the mass is no longer constant at very great velocities, but becomes infinitely large as v approaches the velocity of light c. Instead of $d m\mathbf{v}/dt$ we should strictly put $\dfrac{d}{dt}\dfrac{m\mathbf{v}}{\sqrt{(1-v^2/c^2)}}$. On the right side of the equation a further term is required to take account of the fact that the accelerating field which acts on an electron moving with non-uniform velocity can no longer be considered constant over the region occupied by the latter. An accelerated electron is a source of electromagnetic radiation, the energy of which must be drawn from the electron's kinetic energy. This "reaction of the electron with itself" will be discussed in §4 (radiation damping). This term plays no part in our immediate applications, however, and we may therefore consider the external fields **E** and **H** to be constant in the electron region.

We see firstly, from (1.2), that the magnetic field has no influence on the magnitude of the velocity. The scalar product with **v** gives

$$\frac{d}{dt}(\tfrac{1}{2}mv^2) = e(\mathbf{E}\,.\,\mathbf{v})$$

A change in kinetic energy is produced by the electric field alone. For an electrostatic field **E** represented by a potential ϕ ($\mathbf{E} = -\operatorname{grad}\phi$)

$$\frac{d}{dt}(\tfrac{1}{2}mv^2) = -e\left(\frac{\partial\phi}{\partial x}\frac{dx}{dt}+\frac{\partial\phi}{\partial y}\frac{dy}{dt}+\frac{\partial\phi}{\partial z}\frac{dz}{dt}\right) = -e\frac{d\phi}{dt}$$

This expression transforms the potential ϕ, which is a function of position alone, into a time-dependent function taken at the position of the electron. The theorem of the conservation of energy

$$\tfrac{1}{2}mv^2 + e\phi = \text{constant}$$

or

$$\tfrac{1}{2}mv_2^2 - \tfrac{1}{2}mv_1^2 = e(\phi_1 - \phi_2) \tag{1.3}$$

is therefore also valid in the presence of a steady magnetic field.

We now consider the effect of a uniform steady magnetic field alone, the direction of which is taken to be parallel to the positive z-axis of the system of coordinates: $\mathbf{H} = (0, 0, H)$. For this case the equations of motion are

$$m\ddot{x} = \frac{e}{c}\dot{y}H \qquad m\ddot{y} = -\frac{e}{c}\dot{x}H \qquad m\ddot{z} = 0 \tag{1.4}$$

The third equation shows that the component of motion in the direction of **H** is unaffected by the field. We therefore only need to consider the projection of the motion on the *xy*-plane (the component of **r** perpendicular to **H**.)

To integrate the first two equations of (1.4) we describe the motion in the complex plane *x-iy* by the introduction of the quantity

$$\zeta = x+iy$$

If the second equation of (1.4) is multiplied by i and added to the first, we obtain the following equation for ζ:

$$\ddot{\zeta} = -i\frac{eH}{mc}\dot{\zeta} = -i\omega\dot{\zeta} \qquad (1.4a)$$

where $\omega = \dfrac{eH}{mc}$.

Taking initial values $\zeta_{t=0}=\zeta_0$ and $\dot{\zeta}_{t=0}=\dot{\zeta}_0$, the first integral of (1.4*a*) is

$$\dot{\zeta} = \dot{\zeta}_0\, e^{-i\omega t}$$

and the second,

$$\zeta(t) = \zeta_0+\int_0^t \dot{\zeta}\, dt = \zeta_0+\frac{\dot{\zeta}_0}{i\omega}(1-e^{-i\omega t}) \qquad (1.5)$$

The vector $\zeta(t)$ then appears in the complex plane as the sum of the three complex vectors

$$\zeta_0 \qquad +\frac{\dot{\zeta}_0}{i\omega} \qquad -\frac{\dot{\zeta}_0}{i\omega}e^{-i\omega t}$$

In figure 1, let A be the initial position of the electron ($\overrightarrow{\text{OA}}=\zeta_0$), and $\overrightarrow{\text{AA}'}$ the direction of its initial velocity. The direction of $\mathbf{R} = \overrightarrow{\text{AB}} = \dot{\zeta}_0/i\omega$ is at right angles to $\overrightarrow{\text{AA}'}$, measured in a counter-clockwise sense, because ω is negative for an electron. Finally, $\overrightarrow{\text{BC}} = -\mathbf{R}e^{-i\omega t}$. The electron therefore describes an orbit with centre B and radius

$$R = v\left|\frac{mc}{eH}\right| \qquad (1.6)$$

with the constant angular velocity

$$\omega = \frac{eH}{mc} \qquad (1.6a)$$

Equation (1.6) also follows directly from the fact that, for circular motion, the centrifugal force mv^2/R must be balanced by the "Lorentz force" evH/c.

Equation (1.6) suggests a valuable method for the production of cathode rays of precisely determined velocity. If a series of small

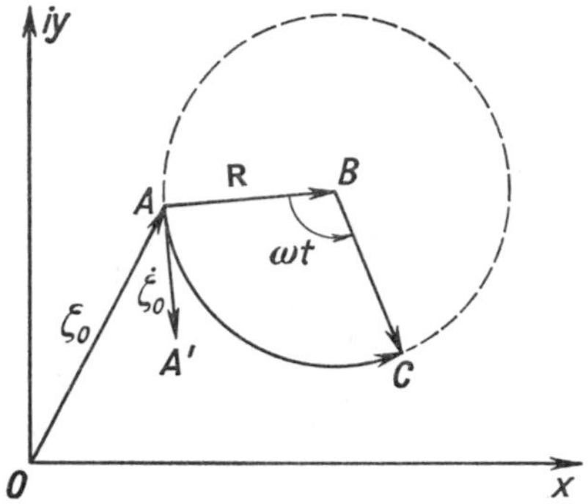

Fig. 1.—Electron track AC in a uniform magnetic field, with initial position ζ_0 and initial velocity $\dot{\zeta}_0$ (ω is negative as in (1.6*a*), because e is negative)

apertures is arranged along a circle of radius R, perpendicular to a magnetic field **H**, and a beam of cathode rays (also perpendicular to **H**) is directed on to the first aperture, the only beam electrons to pass through the apertures will be those whose velocity exactly satisfies the relation

$$v = \left|\frac{eH}{mc}\right| R$$

In a steady electric field, the acceleration is in the direction of the field. For initial values of position $\mathbf{r}_0$ and of velocity $\dot{\mathbf{r}}_0$ at time $t = 0$, the solution of (1.2) is

$$\mathbf{r}(t) = \mathbf{r}_0 + \dot{\mathbf{r}}_0\, t + \frac{e}{2m}\mathbf{E}t^2 \qquad (1.7)$$

The equation of motion and the electron path are identical with those of a particle in a uniform gravitational field acting in the direction of **E**. Figure 2 shows the parabolic track of an electron in a steady electric field acting along the x-axis $[\mathbf{E} = (E, 0, 0)]$, the initial velocity of which, $\mathbf{v}_0$, is normal to $\mathbf{E}$.

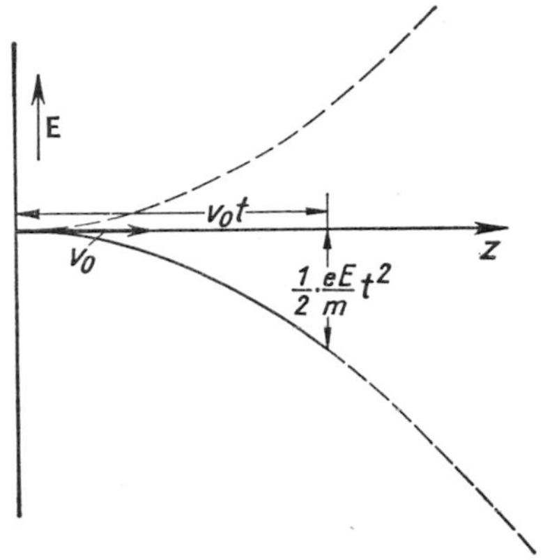

Fig. 2.—In a uniform electric field the track is a parabola

§2. The charge-mass ratio

The charge-mass ratio e/m can be determined from an investigation of the paths described by electrons acted upon by electric and magnetic fields in accordance with equation (1.2). It must be emphasized that such experiments can never permit the values of the charge or the mass to be separately determined, since only the quotient e/m occurs in the fundamental equation (1.2).

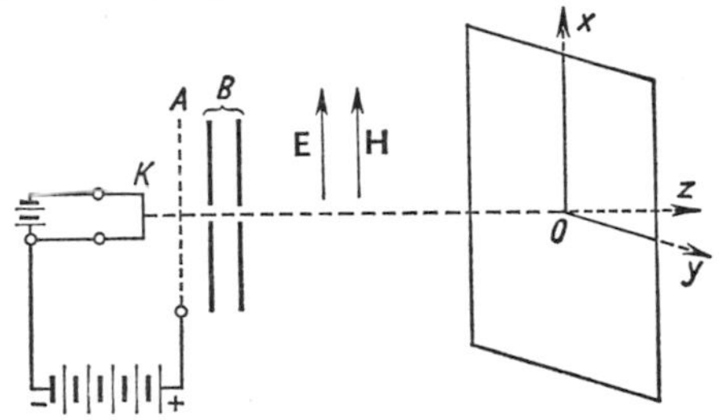

Fig. 3.—Measurement of e/m by simultaneous deflection in uniform electric and magnetic fields

We now consider the application of the equation of motion (1.2) to the case of a cathode-ray beam of velocity v (parallel to the z-axis), acted upon simultaneously by steady electric and magnetic fields, the directions of which are parallel to the x-axis (figure 3). The beam is laterally defined by suitable apertures, and in the absence of deflecting fields would strike the point O of a screen placed perpendicular to it at a distance l from the apertures. We choose this point as the origin of a coordinate system x, y on the screen. If the beam consists of negatively charged particles, its point of impact will be displaced parallel to the negative x-axis under the influence of the electric field, and parallel to the negative y-axis under that of the magnetic field. Under the simultaneous effect of both fields, therefore, the beam will strike the screen at a point (x, y) the coordinates of which we will now calculate. We assume that the deflections x and y are very small compared with the distance l, and that an approximate method of calculation will therefore be satisfactory. The field **E** acts only along the x-coordinate:

$$m\frac{d^2x}{dt^2} = eE$$

The time is reckoned from the instant the electron passes the aperture; therefore $x=0$ and $\dot{x}=0$ at $t=0$, and

$$mx = \tfrac{1}{2}eEt^2$$

The time taken by the electron to travel from the aperture to the screen is l/v, so that

$$x = \frac{1}{2}\frac{e}{m}\frac{El^2}{v^2}$$

For the deflection y we have

$$m\frac{d^2y}{dt^2} = \frac{e}{c}v_z H \approx \frac{e}{c}v H$$

For small deflections integration therefore yields

$$y = \frac{1}{2}\frac{e}{mc}\frac{Hl^2}{v}$$

Measurement of the deflections x and y accordingly yields values for e/m and v, as follows:

$$\frac{y}{x} = \frac{H}{E}\frac{v}{c} \quad \text{and} \quad \frac{y^2}{x} = \frac{1}{2}\frac{e}{m}\frac{H^2l^2}{c^2E}$$

The tracks of particles of the same velocity but of different charge-mass ratios lie on a straight line through the origin of the coordinates. From the experimental point of view, however, the second case is of greater importance: if the beam is composed of particles of one type only, all with the same charge-mass ratio, but with different velocities, the resultant image on a photographic plate (replacing the screen) will be a parabola, known as the Thomson parabola (figure 4).

On performing the above experiment in as many different ways as possible, the theoretically predicted parabolas were always obtained, provided that the velocities of the cathode rays were not too great.

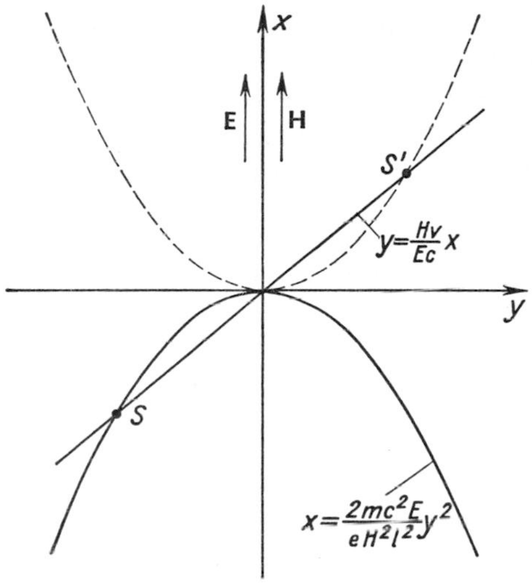

Fig. 4.—Evaluation of results of the deflection experiment. The electrons meet the photographic plate at S. For positively charged particles such as canal rays, the point of impact is given by the intersection S′ of the straight line with the broken parabola

The experiments proved that these rays consist of a single type of particle, negatively charged. Measurements of the important ratio $-e/m$ yielded the value $1{\cdot}76 \times 10^8$ C/g, which is about 1800 times greater than that attributable to the proton (96,500 C/g).

For very fast cathode rays, the velocities of which approach that of light, experiments yield a curve which departs appreciably from a parabola in the neighbourhood of the vertex (see §3). At this stage the increase in the inertial mass with velocity becomes apparent, an effect which we did not take into account in the above analysis.

Another method of measurement of the charge-mass ratio is based on the fact that, according to equation (1.6*a*), the angular velocity ω

with which an electron describes an orbit in the magnetic field is independent of the radius. The orbital period is

$$\tau = \frac{2\pi}{\omega} = \frac{2\pi mc}{eH}$$

H. Busch has shown that this fact may be used to focus a beam of cathode rays by means of a longitudinal magnetic field. The arrangement is shown diagrammatically in figure 5.

Electrons emitted by an incandescent filament are accelerated along the z-axis of the figure by means of a potential difference V. Having attained the velocity v (given by $\frac{1}{2}mv^2 = eV$), they pass through an aperture B and impinge on a fluorescent screen S, which is situated perpendicular to the z-axis at a distance l from the aperture. In the first instance the beam produces a diffuse spot on the screen, since it has left the hole B with a finite angular aperture. If a uniform magnetic

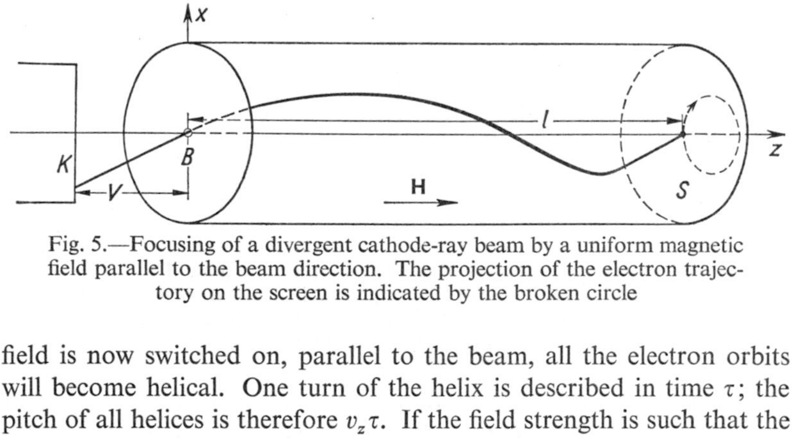

Fig. 5.—Focusing of a divergent cathode-ray beam by a uniform magnetic field parallel to the beam direction. The projection of the electron trajectory on the screen is indicated by the broken circle

field is now switched on, parallel to the beam, all the electron orbits will become helical. One turn of the helix is described in time τ; the pitch of all helices is therefore $v_z\tau$. If the field strength is such that the pitch is exactly equal to the interval l, all electrons will have executed precisely one revolution, and will therefore be concentrated on the screen into a spot of the same size as the aperture. The resultant focusing condition is $l = v_z\tau$, or, since

$$v_z \sim v = \sqrt{\frac{2eV}{m}}, \qquad \frac{e}{m} = \frac{8\pi^2 c^2 V}{H^2 l^2}$$

In order to determine the charge-mass ratio, given the potential difference V and the path length l, it is therefore only necessary to determine the field strength H at which the spot first becomes sharp. This method has also been developed to a stage of great accuracy.

The fundamental importance of the deflection experiments described above is illustrated by the fact that, in addition to the determination of the charge-mass ratio for slow electrons, they also permit the measurement of the relativistic variation of mass, an analysis of the velocity distribution of electrons occurring in radioactive decay processes, and the determination of the charge-mass ratio for canal rays, or positively charged ions.

Following the above description of procedures for determining the charge-mass ratio of cathode rays, we now give a short account of the methods of determining atomic and molecular masses by deflection experiments in electric and magnetic fields. The direct determination of e/m for individual groups of charged particles (ions) is particularly important, since it afforded the first means of isotope investigation; chemical methods of determining atomic weights only give average values for

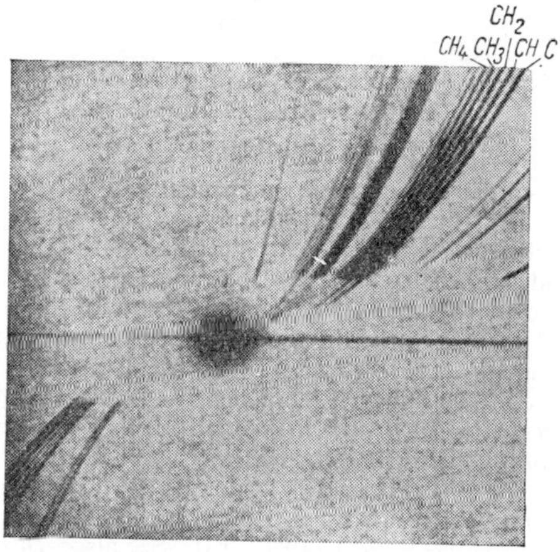

Fig. 6.—Parabolic spectrum of methane [O. Eisenhut and R. Conrad, *Z. Elektrochem.* 36, (1930) 654]

large numbers of particles. Using deflection methods, J. J. Thomson was the first to demonstrate the existence of isotopes, by showing that ordinary neon, the chemically determined atomic weight of which is 20·2, consists in fact of a mixture of two isotopes of atomic masses 20·0 and 22·0.

Thomson performed his experiments using the "parabola method" described above, in which the charged particles are subjected to parallel electric and magnetic fields. The points at which the particles meet a plate perpendicular to the beam give rise to parabolas; the points of impact of all particles with the same charge-mass ratio lie along a single parabola, the faster and therefore less easily deflected particles striking nearer the vertex (figure 6).

An essentially different method was employed by Thomson's pupil F. W. Aston, who passed a beam of ions first through an electric field, and then through a magnetic field at right angles, which compensated the deflection produced by the first field. The arrangement of Aston's apparatus is shown diagrammatically in figure 7. A collimated beam of ions is passed between the plates of a capacitor, which deflects the individual particles to an extent dependent on their masses and velocities and so produces a fan-like dispersion of the beam. A narrow pencil of rays is selected from the wide beam by means of the slit B and passed through a magnetic field, which deflects it in the reverse direction. In figure 7 the magnetic field is at right

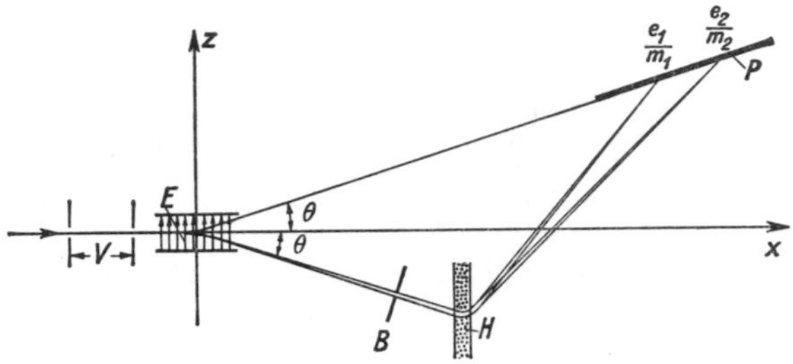

Fig. 7.—Aston's mass spectrograph. Trajectories are shown for two different values of e/m

angles to the plane of the paper. If the magnetic field is of the correct strength relative to the electric field, the beam diverging from the slit B is rendered convergent; the rays most strongly deflected by the capacitor also suffer the greatest deflection in the magnetic field, and the tracks of all particles having the same charge-mass ratio converge to a definite point. The essential feature of Aston's method is that the "image points" of rays with different values of e/m lie approximately in a straight line (cf. Exercise 2, p. 16). Hence, if a photographic plate P is placed along this line, a set of sharp images is obtained which correspond to the individual points of convergence of the rays and so enable the separate charge-mass ratios to be determined. A *mass spectrum* is thus obtained of the atoms contained in the primary rays.

A description of a modern mass spectrograph, with detailed references, has been given by H. Ewald, *Z. Naturforsch.* 1 (1946), 131. See also: *Handbuch der Physik*, Vol. XXXIII, p. 546ff., Berlin, 1956.

§3. Variability of mass at high velocities

We now wish to see how the Thomson parabolas change their shape when allowance is made for the relativistic variation of mass with speed (cf. Vol. I, §89). The momentum $\mathbf{p}$ of an electron moving with velocity $\mathbf{v}$ is now

$$\mathbf{p} = \frac{m\mathbf{v}}{\sqrt{(1-\beta^2)}} \quad \text{where} \quad \beta = \frac{v}{c} \tag{3.1}$$

From Newton's basic equation (force = rate of change of momentum) and equation (1.1) we obtain the relativistic equation of motion of the electron

$$\frac{d\mathbf{p}}{dt} = \frac{d}{dt}\frac{m\mathbf{v}}{\sqrt{(1-\beta^2)}} = e\mathbf{E} + \frac{e}{c}\mathbf{v}\times\mathbf{H} \tag{3.2}$$

Hence we have for the equations of motion applicable to Thomson's experiment, where $\mathbf{E}=(E, 0, 0)$ and $\mathbf{H}=(H, 0, 0)$:

$$\frac{d}{dt}\frac{mv_x}{\sqrt{(1-\beta^2)}} = eE \qquad \frac{d}{dt}\frac{mv_y}{\sqrt{(1-\beta^2)}} = \frac{e}{c}Hv_z$$
$$\frac{d}{dt}\frac{mv_z}{\sqrt{(1-\beta^2)}} = -\frac{e}{c}Hv_y \tag{3.3}$$

If the deflections along the x- and y-axes are very small, i.e. v_x and v_y are always very small compared to v_z, then $v = \sqrt{(v_x^2+v_y^2+v_z^2)}$ may be taken as practically constant and equal to v_z; the rate of change of v_z itself is only a small quantity of higher order, as may easily be seen from the third equation of motion. Then both the other equations may be approximately integrated; the first yields the following expression for the deflection along the x-axis:

$$x = \frac{1}{2}\frac{eE}{m}\frac{l^2}{v^2}\sqrt{(1-\beta^2)} \tag{3.3a}$$

where $t = l/v_z = l/v$ is the time interval from the slit to the plate.

The deflection along the y-axis is

$$y = \frac{1}{2}\frac{eH}{mc}\frac{l^2}{v}\sqrt{(1-\beta^2)} \tag{3.3b}$$

If we once more form the quotient

$$\frac{y}{x} = \frac{H}{E}\frac{v}{c} \tag{3.4}$$

we see that the traces of particles of equal velocity but different charge-mass ratios still lie on a straight line through the origin. If, however, we now investigate the traces made by a single type of particle (i.e. of fixed charge-mass ratio), we find that the results of the two cases differ. If the velocity v is eliminated from both expressions (3.3), we no longer obtain a parabola as in the case for which $\beta \ll 1$, but parabola-like curves of the fourth degree, similar to the solid curve shown in figure 8 (the broken curve is the parabola of figure 4). The fact of chief interest is that these curves do not meet the y-axis tangentially, but intersect it at a definite angle α. Since the smaller values of x and y correspond to the higher values of v/c, the neighbourhood of the origin

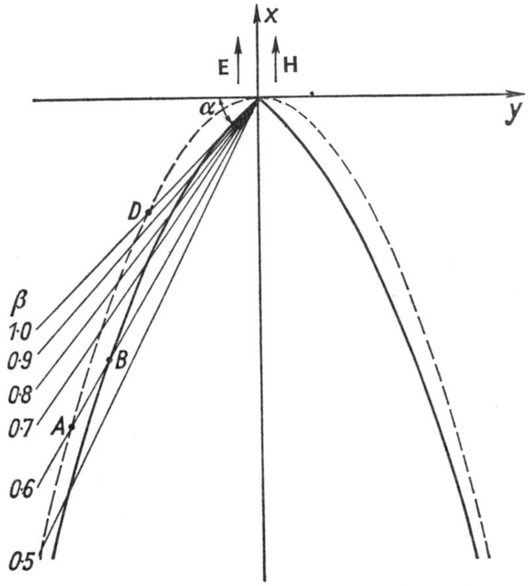

Fig. 8.—Increase of mass with velocity. The experimental arrangement of figure 3 yields the solid curve in place of the Thomson parabola (broken curve)

illustrates the differences between the old and new theories. The non-relativistic theory predicts that only particles of infinite velocity would strike the origin; the present theory, however, indicates that this would be achieved by particles with the limiting velocity of light. From equation (3.4), the angle α is seen to be given by

$$\tan\alpha = \lim_{v\to c}\frac{y}{x} = \frac{H}{E}$$

The effect of the variation of mass may be demonstrated by means of the following construction. In figure 8, the broken curve denotes a parabola calculated from the formula $\dfrac{y^2}{x} = \dfrac{1}{2}\dfrac{e}{m}\dfrac{H^2}{E}\dfrac{l^2}{c^2}$, assuming constant mass; this parabola represents the trace that would be produced by particles of a single type but with different velocities. Further, according to the relation (3.4), the traces of particles of different masses lie on straight lines through the origin; in figure 8, for example, these lines are drawn for $v/c = 0{\cdot}5$, $0{\cdot}6$, etc. In order to find a point on the modified curve, for a given velocity, the intersection of the appropriate straight line with the parabola is marked, and the distance along the line to this point is shortened in the ratio $\sqrt{(1-\beta^2)}:1$. For example, the point A, corresponding to $\beta = 0{\cdot}6$, is transformed to the point B by means of the factor $\sqrt{[1-(0{\cdot}6)^2]} = 0{\cdot}8$. In particular, it is evident from this construction that the point of intersection D of the line $\beta = 1$ with the original parabola is transferred to the origin.

The experiments described above indicate that the mass of a rapidly moving electron does in fact increase in the manner predicted by equation (3.1).

Exercises

1. *Rutherford's scattering formula*

Calculate the deflection of an electron with initial velocity $\mathbf{v}_0$ by a proton considered to be at rest at the origin of the coordinates. The equation of motion of the electron is $m\ddot{\mathbf{r}} = -\dfrac{e^2}{r^3}\mathbf{r}$.

(*a*) Verify that the following three conservation theorems are valid, by reason of the equation of motion:

1. Energy: $$\frac{dE}{dt} = \frac{d}{dt}\left(\tfrac{1}{2}m\dot{\mathbf{r}}^2 - \frac{e^2}{r}\right) = 0$$

2. Angular momentum: $$\frac{d\mathbf{M}}{dt} = \frac{d}{dt}m\mathbf{r}\times\dot{\mathbf{r}} = 0$$

3. $$\frac{d\mathbf{e}}{dt} = \frac{d}{dt}\left\{\dot{\mathbf{r}}\times\mathbf{M} - e^2\frac{\mathbf{r}}{r}\right\} = 0$$

(*b*) The electron's initial velocity is $\mathbf{v}_0$, and $\mathbf{v}_e$ is its velocity after scattering, at a great distance from the proton. The magnitudes of these velocities are the same, in virtue of the conservation of energy. It follows from the theorem on conservation of angular momentum that the orbit is plane, and normal to **M**. The deflection angle θ depends on the impact parameter b (see figure 9). Show the vector **e** in a graphical construction, using the initial and final velocity vectors, and the fact that **e** is invariable with respect to time. Derive a relation between θ and b from this construction.

(*c*) The elementary effective cross-section dQ producing scattering in the element of solid angle $d\Omega$ is defined as follows (cf. figure 9). Imagine a large number of electrons all with the same velocity $\mathbf{v}_0$, and of uniform density, travelling towards the proton. A surface dQ is placed across this electron stream, such that all particles passing through dQ are deflected into the element of solid angle $d\Omega$. Calculate the elementary effective cross-section from the relation between b and θ which was

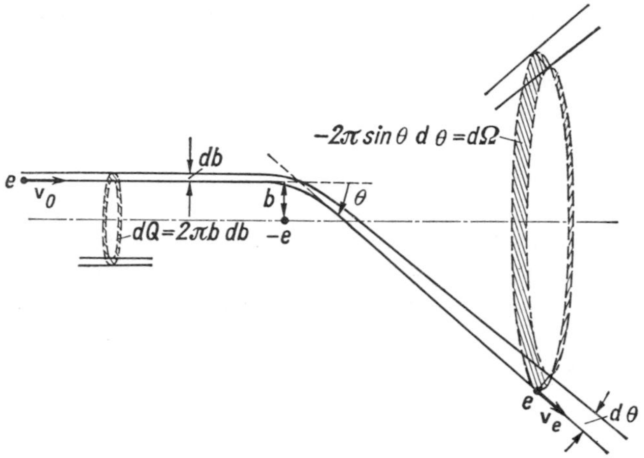

Fig. 9.—Derivation of the Rutherford scattering formula

derived in (*b*) above. Here $dQ = 2\pi b\,db$ and $d\Omega = -2\pi \sin\theta\, d\theta$ (because $d\theta$ is negative). (Since the geometry is cylindrically symmetrical about the direction of incidence, dQ does not depend on the azimuthal angle.)

2. *Aston's mass spectrograph*

In Aston's mass spectrograph (figure 10), particles of charge e are first of all accelerated by a potential difference V. All those particles with the same kinetic energy $\frac{1}{2}mv^2$ are then deflected through the same angle θ by the electric field E.

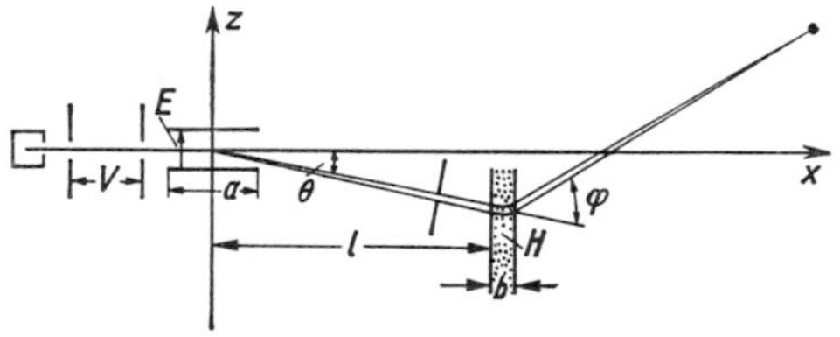

Fig. 10.—The focusing conditions for Aston's mass spectrograph

As a result of the distribution of the particle velocities v about the average value $\bar{v}$, the beam diverges slightly; this deflection is cancelled out by the succeeding deflection through the angle ϕ, which is produced by the magnetic field H ("velocity focusing"). At what point (x_f, z_f) does focusing occur? What is the position of the registering photographic plate?

CHAPTER A II

The classical model of the atom

§4. Free oscillation of the elastically bound electron

One of the most important objectives of theoretical physics consists in the detailed description of the structure of the atom. How may we construct an atomic model from positive and negative charges so that its properties, when calculated from the fundamental electrodynamic equations, agree with experimentally observed phenomena? Historically, three steps must be distinguished, corresponding to successive approximations to the required objective: they are represented, firstly, by the atomic models due to J. J. Thomson (until 1912), secondly, by the model due to N. Bohr (1912–25), and finally, by the statements of quantum mechanics (W. Heisenberg, E. Schrödinger, since 1925). Each step in turn was so successful in its applications that it was permissible to consider previous conceptions to be definitely superseded. Today the axioms of quantum mechanics are accepted as the point of departure in the systematic representation of atomic phenomena. We shall, however, analyse in some detail the properties of Thomson's model of the atom; our justification is that this model affords a particularly clear and simple means of understanding a number of important electrical and magnetic properties of atoms. We must be prepared for the introduction of corrections of varying degree into the results obtained in this manner when the stricter methods of Bohr's theory and of quantum mechanics are applied. The latter make no attempt to give a clear picture of the atom, but many of their conclusions may be interpreted by postulating that the atom behaves as though it contained elastically bound charges as assumed in Thomson's model. In any case, a knowledge of the properties of this model is essential, because the terms used to interpret the formulae of quantum mechanics have largely been drawn from the concepts developed with the aid of Thomson's simple model.

The existence of (nearly) sharp spectral lines, characteristic of each type of atom, provides the experimental starting-point of modern atomic research. (Spectra of this type are produced, for example, by the rare gases when rendered luminous in a Bunsen burner flame or a discharge tube.) In accordance with the electromagnetic theory of light, any given spectral line must be assumed to originate from an emitter oscillating with a frequency ν corresponding to the colour of the line. The simplest emitter of this type would consist of an electron bound to an equilibrium position in such a manner as to permit it to execute harmonic oscillations of just this frequency. Its equation of motion along the axis Ox would then be

$$m\ddot{x}+m(2\pi\nu)^2x = 0$$

for which the general solution is

$$x = A\cos 2\pi\nu t+B\sin 2\pi\nu t$$

In order that the electron should perform oscillations of frequency ν it must be bound to the equilibrium position $x=0$ in such a manner that, when displaced from the latter by a distance x, it is drawn back towards it by a restoring force $-m(2\pi\nu)^2x$. A model of this sort was proposed by Thomson, as follows.

Let an electron of charge e move within a sphere of radius a which is filled with a uniformly distributed positive charge of total value $-e$. We wish to calculate the force acting on the electron when it is at a distance $r<a$ from the centre of the sphere. The charge outside the sphere of radius r makes no contribution to this force. The charge inside this sphere is $-e(r/a)^3$, and acts on the electron as though it were concentrated at the centre. The force on the electron is therefore

$$\mathbf{F} = -\frac{e^2\mathbf{r}}{a^3}$$

This gives rise to harmonic oscillations of frequency

$$\nu = \frac{1}{2\pi}\sqrt{\frac{e^2}{a^3m}}$$

If we introduce the known values of e and m into the above expression, together with the order of magnitude of the characteristic optical frequencies of free gas atoms ($10^{15}\,\mathrm{s}^{-1}$), we obtain a value of about 10^{-8} cm for the radius of the positive sphere. This is precisely the order of magnitude of atomic radii as determined from the kinetic theory of gases.

This result could be considered to provide support for the Thomson model of the atom. Later, however, Rutherford's experiments on the scattering of α-particles were to afford direct proof that the positive charge of atoms is concentrated into a space no greater than 10^{-12} to 10^{-13} cm; its dimensions are therefore about 100,000 times smaller than is required to account for the optical spectral lines by Thomson's theory. The very result, $a \sim 10^{-8}$ cm, previously considered to be supporting evidence for this theory, now made it quite untenable as a result of Rutherford's experiments. The latter, in fact, constitute the starting-point of Bohr's quantum theory.

Without going further into the details of Thomson's model, let us now consider the motion of an electron acted on by a force of magnitude $-f\mathbf{r}$. From mechanics alone, its equation of motion would be

$$m\ddot{\mathbf{r}}+f\mathbf{r}=0 \tag{4.1}$$

with the general solution

$$\mathbf{r}=\mathbf{a}\cos\omega t+\mathbf{b}\sin\omega t, \quad \text{where} \quad \omega^2=\frac{f}{m} \tag{4.2}$$

The constants of integration are the arbitrary vectors **a** and **b**: they may, for instance, serve to specify the initial position and velocity.

The energy W of this mechanical system is

$$W=\tfrac{1}{2}m\dot{\mathbf{r}}^2+\tfrac{1}{2}f\mathbf{r}^2$$

From (4.2), therefore,

$$W=\tfrac{1}{2}m\omega^2(\mathbf{a}^2+\mathbf{b}^2) \tag{4.3}$$

Now, since an electron possesses charge as well as mass, it emits electromagnetic radiation in the course of its oscillations, transmitting radiation energy to space at a definite rate as it does so. Equation (4.3) shows the total amount of energy that can be emitted for given initial values of **a** and **b**. It would therefore be a contradiction of the theorem of the conservation of energy if the equation of motion (4.1) were to be taken as strictly correct; on the contrary, we expect the amplitudes **a** and **b** to decrease with time in proportion to the emitted radiation.

In Vol. I, §67ff. we deduced an expression for the radiation energy S emitted per second by an oscillating electric charge. It is

$$S=\frac{2e^2}{3c^3}\overline{\ddot{\mathbf{r}}^2} \tag{4.4}$$

The conservation theorem requires that this should be equal to the rate of decrease of energy of the oscillating electron:

$$\frac{dW}{dt} = -S = -\frac{2e^2}{3c^3}\overline{\ddot{\mathbf{r}}^2} \tag{4.5}$$

Equations (4.4) and (4.5) are only significant if the energy ST emitted during a single period $T = 2\pi/\omega$ is small compared with the existing energy W or, in other words, if the oscillations are lightly damped. With this restriction in mind, we can immediately obtain an expression for the damping from equation (4.5). From equation (4.2)

$$\overline{\ddot{\mathbf{r}}^2} = \tfrac{1}{2}\omega^4(\mathbf{a}^2 + \mathbf{b}^2)$$

From (4.4) and (4.3), therefore,

$$S = \frac{e^2\omega^4}{3c^3}(\mathbf{a}^2 + \mathbf{b}^2) = \frac{2e^2\omega^2}{3mc^3}W$$

The expressions for emission and damping are therefore

$$S = \gamma W = -\dot{W}; \quad W = W_0\, e^{-\gamma t} \quad \text{where} \quad \gamma = \frac{2e^2\omega^2}{3mc^3} \tag{4.6}$$

The time

$$\tau = \frac{1}{\gamma} = \frac{3mc^3}{2e^2\omega^2} \tag{4.7}$$

is the period required for the energy of the radiating atoms to decrease to a fraction $1/e$ of the initial value. Its approximate values are given for

$$\frac{\omega}{2\pi} = 10^{14}\,\mathrm{s}^{-1}; \quad \tau = 4 \times 10^{-7}\,\mathrm{s}$$

$$\frac{\omega}{2\pi} = 10^{15}\,\mathrm{s}^{-1}; \quad \tau = 4 \times 10^{-9}\,\mathrm{s}$$

The range of application of the above analysis depends on the ratio of the energy radiated in each period to the total energy, $ST/W = \gamma T = T/\tau$. Light damping occurs when γT is much smaller than unity. Now $\gamma T = \frac{4\pi}{3}\frac{e^2\omega}{mc^3} = (8\pi^2/3) \times R_{el}/\lambda$ if we introduce the classical "electron radius"* $R_{el} = e^2/mc^2 = 2{\cdot}8 \times 10^{-13}\,\mathrm{cm}$ and

* The classical electron radius is that radius R_{el} which a uniformly distributed charge e must possess, in order that the electrical energy ($\approx e^2/R_{el}$) of this distribution should be equal to the relativistic rest energy mc^2 of a stationary particle of mass m.

the wavelength $\lambda = 2\pi c/\omega$. Provided, therefore, that the wavelength is large compared with R_{el}, the oscillation is very lightly damped. Since λ is always much greater than R_{el} for atomic radiation, the application of equations (4.4) and (4.5) is justified.

The corresponding expressions for the attenuation of the amplitudes **a** and **b** are

$$\mathbf{a} = \mathbf{a}_0 \exp -\tfrac{1}{2}\gamma t, \qquad \mathbf{b} = \mathbf{b}_0 \exp -\tfrac{1}{2}\gamma t$$

the logarithmic decrement of which is

$$\delta = \frac{\gamma}{2}\frac{2\pi}{\omega} = \frac{2\pi e^2\omega}{3mc^3}$$

We do not violate the principle of the conservation of energy if we replace equation (4.2) by

$$\mathbf{r} = (\mathbf{a}_0 \cos \omega t + \mathbf{b}_0 \sin \omega t) \exp -\tfrac{1}{2}\gamma t \tag{4.8}$$

Naturally, equation (4.8) is not a solution of the original equation of motion (4.1), but is merely the result of a subsequent and therefore unsatisfactory correction to the solution of this equation.

It is natural to go one stage further, and to investigate the possibility of introducing a supplementary force **F** into equation (4.1) in order to avoid violating the principle of conservation of energy. Provided that we confine ourselves to nearly periodic motion we can indeed find a possible expression for such a force. Introducing it into equation (4.1):

$$m\ddot{\mathbf{r}} + f\mathbf{r} = \mathbf{F}$$

which, after multiplication by $\dot{\mathbf{r}}$ may be written as

$$\frac{d}{dt}(\tfrac{1}{2}m\dot{\mathbf{r}}^2 + \tfrac{1}{2}f\mathbf{r}^2) = \mathbf{F}\,.\,\dot{\mathbf{r}}$$

On the left-hand side we have the rate of change of energy, which is prescribed by equation (4.5); the force **F** must therefore be such that

$$\mathbf{F}\,.\,\dot{\mathbf{r}} = -\frac{2e^2}{3c^3}\ddot{\mathbf{r}}^2 \tag{4.9}$$

This equation cannot in general be solved by simple methods. Here, however, we shall limit ourselves to satisfying the conservation principle as a time average during nearly periodic motion. Using the identity

$$\frac{d}{dt}(\dot{\mathbf{r}}\,.\,\ddot{\mathbf{r}}) = \ddot{\mathbf{r}}^2 + \dot{\mathbf{r}}\,.\,\dddot{\mathbf{r}}$$

we may write
$$\mathbf{F}.\dot{\mathbf{r}} = \frac{2e^2}{3c^3}\left[\dot{\mathbf{r}}.\dddot{\mathbf{r}} - \frac{d}{dt}(\dot{\mathbf{r}}.\ddot{\mathbf{r}})\right]$$

If we now take the average value of the above expression, say from time $t=0$ to $t=t_1$, then

$$\overline{\mathbf{F}.\dot{\mathbf{r}}} = \frac{2e^2}{3c^3}\overline{(\dot{\mathbf{r}}.\dddot{\mathbf{r}})} - \frac{2e^2}{3c^3}\frac{[(\dot{\mathbf{r}}.\ddot{\mathbf{r}})_{t=t_1} - (\dot{\mathbf{r}}.\ddot{\mathbf{r}})_{t=0}]}{t_1}$$

If t_1 is sufficiently great, the second term is small compared with the first, and may be neglected. We may then satisfy our equation by putting

$$\mathbf{F} = \frac{2e^2}{3c^3}\dddot{\mathbf{r}} \tag{4.10}$$

and thus obtain for the corrected equation of motion of the elastically bound electron

$$m\ddot{\mathbf{r}} + f\mathbf{r} - \frac{2e^3}{3c^3}\dddot{\mathbf{r}} = 0 \tag{4.11}$$

This equation must of course lead to the solution (4.8). If we put

$$\mathbf{r} = \mathbf{A}\,e^{i\omega t}$$

where **A** is a complex vector, (4.11) yields the following equation for ω:

$$-\omega^2 + \frac{2e^2}{3mc^3}i\omega^3 + \frac{f}{m} = 0$$

Putting $\sqrt{\dfrac{f}{m}} = \omega_0$ and $\dfrac{2e^2\omega^2}{3mc^3} = \gamma$ the equation becomes

$$-\omega^2 + i\omega\gamma + \omega_0^2 = 0$$

If we limit ourselves to the case for which $\gamma \ll \omega$, the two approximate solutions are

$$\omega_1 = \omega_0 + \tfrac{1}{2}i\gamma, \qquad \omega_2 = -\omega_0 + \tfrac{1}{2}i\gamma$$

We thus obtain for the general solution of (4.11)

$$\mathbf{r} = \mathbf{A}\exp-(\tfrac{1}{2}\gamma - i\omega_0)t + \mathbf{B}\exp-(\tfrac{1}{2}\gamma + i\omega_0)t \tag{4.12}$$

which is identical with (4.8), apart from its complex form. Since **r** is real it must equal its complex conjugate $\mathbf{r}^*$; therefore $\mathbf{B} = \mathbf{A}^*$, and there are only six arbitrary constants in (4.12)—three each for the real and the imaginary parts of the vector **A**.

It must be emphasized that the expression (4.10) for the radiation damping is only valid for nearly periodic motion, for which

$$\frac{2e^2}{3c^3}\dddot{\mathbf{r}} \approx -\frac{2e^2\omega_0^2}{3c^3}\dot{\mathbf{r}} \tag{4.10a}$$

Absurd results are obtained if (4.10) is applied to other forms of motion, such as the retardation of a free electron in a constant opposing field. In this case only the second time derivative would be different from zero, and equation (4.11) would therefore predict no radiation damping at all.

The above derivation of the radiation damping is unsatisfactory, because it is not at all clear how the emitted spherical wave influences the electron's motion. In order to gain a closer understanding of the nature of this "self reaction" it is necessary to compute the resultant force on all electron volume elements.

This "self force" $\mathbf{F}_s$ is given by $\mathbf{F}_s = \int \rho\left(\mathbf{E} + \frac{\mathbf{v}}{c} \times \mathbf{H}\right) dV$ where the charge density ρ and the velocity $\mathbf{v}$ of the moving electron are functions of x, y, z, and t, and **E** and **H** represent the field strengths produced by the charge and current distributions at the point x,y,z, as shown in Vol. I, §66. If we consider the limiting or non-relativistic case, for which $|\mathbf{v}| \ll c$, then $\mathbf{F}_s = \int \rho \mathbf{E} dV$ approximately.

Consider the particular case of an electron moving along the x-axis as a rigid spherically symmetrical charge distribution with centre at $x_0(t)$. For the calculation of $\mathbf{F}_s$ and $\mathbf{E}$, we can confine ourselves to the x-components:

$$E_x = -\frac{\partial \phi}{\partial x} - \frac{1}{c}\dot{A}_x$$

where the retarded potentials ϕ, A_x are

$$\phi(x,y,z,t) = \int \frac{1}{r}\rho_0\left[\xi - x_0\left(t - \frac{r}{c}\right), \eta, \xi\right] d\xi\, d\eta\, d\zeta$$

$$A_x(x,y,z,t) = \frac{1}{c}\int \frac{1}{r}\dot{x}_0\left(t - \frac{r}{c}\right)\rho_0\left[\xi - x_0\left(t - \frac{r}{c}\right), \eta, \zeta\right] d\xi\, d\eta\, d\zeta$$

and $$r^2 = (x-\xi)^2 + (y-\eta)^2 + (z-\zeta)^2$$

$\rho_0(\xi, \eta, \zeta)$ is the rigid charge distribution of the electron at rest at the point $\xi, \eta, \zeta = 0$. If x_0 and ρ_0 can be developed as a power series, we may express

$$\{\rho_0\} = \rho_0[\xi - x_0(t - r/c), \eta, \zeta]$$

as a power series in terms of r/c:

$$\{\rho_0\} = \rho_0 + \frac{r}{c}\frac{\partial \rho_0}{\partial \xi}\dot{x}_0 - \left(\frac{r}{c}\right)^2\frac{1}{2}\left[\frac{\partial \rho_0}{\partial \xi}\ddot{x}_0 - \ldots\right] + \left(\frac{r}{c}\right)^3\frac{1}{6}\left[\frac{\partial \rho_0}{\partial \xi}\dddot{x}_0 + \ldots\right] + \ldots$$

to the third power of r/c, and leaving out terms that may be omitted for reasons of symmetry in the following integration for F_{sx}.

We then obtain the following expression for the contribution of ϕ to the force F_{sx}, after integration by parts to eliminate the derivative $\frac{\partial \rho_0}{\partial \xi}$:

$$\frac{1}{2c^2}\ddot{x}_0\int \rho_0(x,\ldots)\rho_0(\xi,\ldots)\left[\frac{1}{r}-\frac{(\xi-x)^2}{r^3}\right]d\xi\ldots dx\ldots$$

$$-\frac{1}{3c^3}\dddot{x}_0\int \rho_0(x,\ldots)\rho_0(\xi,\ldots)d\xi\ldots dx\ldots$$

Similarly, the contribution of A_x to the force F_{sx} is

$$-\frac{1}{c^2}\ddot{x}_0\int \rho_0(x,\ldots)\rho_0(\xi,\ldots)\frac{1}{r}\,d\xi\ldots dx\ldots$$

$$+\frac{1}{c^3}\dddot{x}_0\int \rho_0(x,\ldots)\rho_0(\xi,\ldots)\,d\xi\ldots dx\ldots$$

Now

$$U_0=\frac{1}{2}\int\frac{\rho_0(x,\ldots)\rho_0(\xi,\ldots)}{r}\,d\xi\ldots dx\ldots$$

is the electrical rest energy of the electron, and

$$X=\frac{1}{2}\int\frac{\rho_0(x,\ldots)\rho_0(\xi,\ldots)}{r}\frac{(x-\xi)^2}{r^2}\,d\xi\ldots dx\ldots=\frac{1}{3}U_0$$

since $X+Y+Z=U_0$, because ρ_0 is spherically symmetrical. The series expansion for the self-force F_{sx} is therefore

$$F_{sx}=-\frac{4}{3}\frac{U_0}{c^2}\ddot{x}_0+\frac{2}{3}\frac{e^2}{c^3}\dddot{x}_0+\ldots$$

The first term represents the familiar contribution, $\frac{4}{3}\frac{U_0}{c^2}$, to the electron mass (cf. Vol. I, §§65 and 91). The second term agrees exactly with expression (4.10) for the self-reactive force of the electron due to emitted radiation. The omitted terms contain higher derivatives of x_0.

In considering the useful range of application of the above series, we observe that it represents a development in powers of $R_{el}/c=e^2/mc^2$. Now if x_0 is expressed as a Fourier series terminating at ω_m, where ω_m corresponds to the highest significant frequency, and $\tau=1/\omega_m$, then, since $\left|\frac{d^n x_0}{dt^n}\right|\lesssim\tau^{-n}|x_0|$, F_{sx} may be expressed in powers of $R_{el}/c\tau$, interrupted after the term $\dddot{x}_0$, provided that

$$\tau\gg\frac{R_{el}}{c}=\frac{e^2}{mc^3}$$

This provision implies that the point x_0 should not have moved significantly during the time required by light to traverse the region occupied by the electron. For instance, if $x_0=ae^{i\omega t}$, we must have

$$\omega\ll\frac{mc^3}{e^2}$$

If this motion is caused by a light wave, then

$$\lambda \gg R_{\mathrm{el}} = \frac{e^2}{mc^2}$$

The formula derived for F_{sx} is applicable to radiation in the normal optical region, for which it predicts the damping effect discussed above.

In other cases, however, such as that of the free electron, it is not permissible to solve the equation $m\ddot{x}_0 + \frac{2}{3}\frac{e^2}{c^3}\dddot{x}_0 = 0$ by putting $x = ae^{\alpha t}$, $\alpha = mc^2/e^2$, because the omitted terms of the series expansion are of the same order of magnitude as the others.

Types of motion for which $\tau \lessapprox e^2/mc^3$ can only be treated in the light of a more precise knowledge of the "structure" of the electron, for which the primitive representation by means of a rigid sphere is quite inadequate.

More thorough analyses of the "self force" have been given by P. A. M. Dirac, *Proc. Roy. Soc.* Series A 167 (1938) 148, by F. Bopp, *Z. Naturforsch.* **1** (1946) 53, 237, and by H. Steinwedel, *Fortschr. d. Phys.* **I**, 1953 and 1954, 7.

§5. The width of the emitted spectral line

Pure monochromatic light would be equivalent to an infinitely long simple harmonic wave train of form $a \sin 2\pi(\nu t - x/\lambda)$. Any departure from this form results in the presence of a mixture of different frequencies ν, i.e. of different colours, as may be seen from spectral analysis. The frequencies contained in a given wave train may be determined by means of Fourier analysis; using this method, the wave train is represented as a linear superposition of infinitely long simple harmonic wave trains. The essence of Fourier's theorem is that any such wave form may be represented in this manner. In particular, if the wave train is approximately harmonic in form and has a definite frequency ν_0, its deviation from a strictly harmonic form is characterized by a definite widening $\delta\nu$ of the corresponding spectral line of frequency ν_0.

In many cases, the amount of broadening, $\delta\nu$, may be evaluated approximately almost without calculation. Consider, for instance, a wave train of finite length L, represented at a given instant (say $t = 0$) by

$$f = a \sin 2\pi \frac{x}{\lambda_0} \quad \text{for } 0 < x < L$$

$$f = 0 \qquad \text{for } x < 0 \text{ and } x > L$$

The number of wavelengths contained in the train is $n = L/\lambda_0$, where n is considered to be large compared to 1. In order to represent this train by a set of infinitely long waves, components are required of wavelengths such as to interfere destructively with the wave train λ_0 (considered here to be infinitely long) outside the interval L. For this purpose, constituents with $n+1$ and $n-1$ wavelengths in the interval are necessary; if these waves are in phase with the original wave in the middle of the interval, they are 180° out of phase at the boundaries. Hence, in the Fourier expansion, waves will occur whose wavelength is given by $n \pm 1 = L/\lambda'$. In terms of frequencies:

$$\nu_0 = \frac{nc}{L} \quad \text{and} \quad \nu' = \frac{(n \pm 1)c}{L}$$

We then obtain for the order of magnitude of the line width:

$$|\delta\nu| = \frac{c}{L} = \frac{1}{\tau}$$

where τ represents the time required by the wave train to pass a stationary observer. Expressed in terms of wavelength, the line width is

$$|\delta\lambda| = \frac{|\delta\nu|}{c}\lambda^2 = \frac{\lambda^2}{L}$$

The expression for the relative width is particularly simple:

$$\frac{|\delta\nu|}{\nu} = \frac{|\delta\lambda|}{\lambda} \approx \frac{1}{n}$$

which is the reciprocal of the number of wavelengths present in the wave train.

Now the wave emitted according to (4.11) by an oscillating electron is not suddenly chopped off but has the form of a damped wave train, the amplitude of which falls to $1/e$ of the original after a time $\tau = 2/\gamma$. We assume, however, that as regards line width it is comparable to a chopped wave of just this time interval. Then

$$\delta\nu \approx \tfrac{1}{2}\gamma \tag{5.1}$$

and the numerical value of the line width measured in terms of frequency is therefore given directly by the damping factor γ.

We now wish to verify the above treatment by means of the strict Fourier analysis of the oscillation equation (4.12). Since the field strengths of the wave region are linearly dependent on acceleration, the Fourier analysis of $\ddot{\mathbf{r}}$ is also directly valid for the emitted wave train.

For this purpose, let us consider an electron which is initially constrained. If it is released at time $t=0$, it moves according to equation (4.12), in which the amplitudes $\mathbf{A}$ and $\mathbf{A}^*$ are determined by the initial conditions $\mathbf{r}(0)=\mathbf{r}_0$, $\dot{\mathbf{r}}(0)=0$. Then

$$\ddot{\mathbf{r}}(t)=\begin{cases}(\tfrac{1}{2}\gamma-i\omega_0)^2\,\mathbf{A}\exp-(\tfrac{1}{2}\gamma-i\omega_0)t+ \\ \quad+(\tfrac{1}{2}\gamma+i\omega_0)^2\,\mathbf{A}^*\exp-(\tfrac{1}{2}\gamma+i\omega_0)t & \text{for } t>0 \\ 0 & \text{for } t<0\end{cases} \tag{5.2}$$

Confining ourselves initially to the first term of (5.2), we must seek a function $\mathbf{c}(\omega)$ such that

$$\int_{-\infty}^{\infty}\mathbf{c}(\omega)\,e^{i\omega t}\,d\omega=\begin{cases}(\tfrac{1}{2}\gamma-i\omega_0)^2\,\mathbf{A}\exp-(\tfrac{1}{2}\gamma-i\omega_0)t & \text{for } t>0 \\ 0 & \text{for } t<0\end{cases} \tag{5.3}$$

We know from Fourier's theorem that any function $f(t)$ for which $\int_{-\infty}^{\infty}|f(t)|\,dt$ exists may be represented by

$$f(t)=\int_{-\infty}^{\infty}c(\omega)\,e^{i\omega t}\,d\omega \quad \text{with} \quad c(\omega)=\frac{1}{2\pi}\int_{-\infty}^{\infty}f(t)\,e^{-i\omega t}\,dt$$

From this and from (5.3) it follows that

$$\mathbf{c}(\omega)=\frac{(\tfrac{1}{2}\gamma-i\omega_0)^2}{2\pi}\,\frac{\mathbf{A}}{\tfrac{1}{2}\gamma-i(\omega_0-\omega)} \tag{5.4}$$

The same treatment of the second term yields a similar expression with $-\omega_0$ instead of ω_0. We therefore obtain the result

$$\ddot{\mathbf{r}}(t)=\frac{1}{2\pi}\int_{-\infty}^{\infty}\left\{\frac{(\tfrac{1}{2}\gamma-i\omega_0)^2}{\tfrac{1}{2}\gamma-i(\omega_0-\omega)}\mathbf{A}+\frac{(\tfrac{1}{2}\gamma+i\omega_0)^2}{\tfrac{1}{2}\gamma+i(\omega_0+\omega)}\mathbf{A}^*\right\}e^{i\omega t}\,d\omega \tag{5.5}$$

When studying the distribution of intensity in a spectrogram we must bear in mind that we are not concerned with the relation between intensity and time; experimentally it is always the total intensity that is measured at any point of the spectrum. We are therefore interested in the spectral distribution of the quantity

$$\int_0^{\infty}S\,dt=\frac{2e^2}{3c^3}\int_0^{\infty}\ddot{\mathbf{r}}^2\,dt$$

such that

$$\int_0^{\infty}S\,dt=\int_0^{\infty}S(\omega)\,d\omega \tag{5.6}$$

Equation (5.5) may be written

$$\ddot{\mathbf{r}} = \int_{-\infty}^{+\infty} \mathbf{g}(\omega)\, e^{i\omega t}\, d\omega$$

$\ddot{\mathbf{r}}$ is a real number, therefore $\mathbf{g}(\omega) = \mathbf{g}^*(-\omega)$. We may therefore also write

$$\ddot{\mathbf{r}} = \int_{-\infty}^{+\infty} \mathbf{g}^*(\omega)\, e^{-i\omega t}\, d\omega$$

It follows that

$$\int_0^{\infty} \ddot{\mathbf{r}}^2\, dt = \int_{-\infty}^{+\infty} d\omega\, \mathbf{g}^*(\omega) \int_0^{\infty} \ddot{\mathbf{r}}(t)\, e^{-i\omega t}\, dt$$

From Fourier's theorem the time integral is $2\pi\mathbf{g}(\omega)$, therefore

$$\int_0^{\infty} \ddot{\mathbf{r}}^2\, dt = 2\pi \int_{-\infty}^{+\infty} \mathbf{g}(\omega)\mathbf{g}^*(\omega)\, d\omega = 4\pi \int_0^{\infty} \mathbf{g}(\omega)\mathbf{g}^*(\omega)\, d\omega$$

since the integrand is symmetrical in ω, as may be seen from (5.5). We have now accomplished our analysis and determined the amount of radiation energy arising from the elementary region $\omega, \omega + d\omega$ of the spectrum:

$$S(\omega)\, d\omega = \frac{2e^2}{3c^3} 4\pi \mathbf{g}(\omega)\mathbf{g}^*(\omega)\, d\omega \tag{5.7}$$

In order to evaluate (5.7) it is necessary to form the product $\mathbf{g}(\omega)\mathbf{g}^*(\omega)$, using (5.5), and this results in a rather long formula. A simpler expression is obtained if we confine ourselves to the neighbourhood of the frequency corresponding to ω_0. This simplification is satisfactory in practice, because almost the whole spectral intensity is distributed in a narrow band of frequencies of approximate width γ, as we saw in our earlier simplified treatment. We therefore restrict ourselves to frequencies such that $|\omega - \omega_0| \ll \omega_0$. In addition, γ is always much smaller than ω_0, as we saw in the last paragraph. On examining the expression for $\mathbf{g}(\omega)$ given by (5.5) we see that in this frequency region the first term is much larger than the second. Since we are only concerned with the value of the vector sum in (5.5) we may restrict ourselves to the first term. We then obtain

$$\mathbf{g}(\omega)\mathbf{g}^*(\omega) = \frac{\omega_0^4}{4\pi^2} \frac{\mathbf{A}\mathbf{A}^*}{(\omega - \omega_0)^2 + \frac{1}{4}\gamma^2} \tag{5.8}$$

(In the above expression we have neglected the quantity $\frac{1}{4}\gamma^2$ in the numerator, since it is much smaller than ω_0^2.) Inspection shows that equation (5.8) possesses a maximum of value $\omega_0^4 \mathbf{AA}^*/\pi^2\gamma^2$ at $\omega = \omega_0$. We also see that the intensity function has decreased to half its maximum value at a frequency separation given by $|\omega - \omega_0| = \frac{1}{2}\gamma$. The "half value" width of the line is therefore

$$\delta\omega = \gamma \quad \text{or} \quad \delta\nu = \frac{\gamma}{2\pi} \tag{5.9}$$

which agrees roughly with the earlier approximate estimate (5.1). It is now clear that we were justified in restricting our more complete analysis to the immediate neighbourhood of the spectral line.

As a check, we shall calculate the total radiated energy from its spectral distribution, using equations (5.6), (5.7) and (5.8):

$$\int_0^\infty S(t)\,dt = \int_0^\infty S(\omega)\,d\omega = \frac{2e^2}{3c^3}\frac{\omega_0{}^4}{\pi}\mathbf{AA}^* \int_0^\infty \frac{d\omega}{(\omega-\omega_0)^2+\frac{1}{4}\gamma^2}$$

Introducing the variable $x = \dfrac{2(\omega-\omega_0)}{\gamma}$

$$\int_0^\infty S(t)\,dt = \frac{2e^2}{3c^3}\frac{\omega_0{}^4}{\pi}\mathbf{AA}^* \frac{2}{\gamma}\int_{-2\omega_0/\gamma}^\infty \frac{dx}{x^2+1}$$

Since $\gamma \ll \omega_0$, the value of the integral is not appreciably altered if we substitute $-\infty$ for the lower limit. Then $\int_{-\infty}^\infty \frac{dx}{x^2+1} = \pi$, and inserting the value for the damping factor γ given by (4.6), we have for the total radiated energy

$$\int_0^\infty S(t)\,dt = 2m\omega_0{}^2\mathbf{AA}^*$$

which is necessarily equal to the total mechanical energy of the elastically bound electron at time $t = 0$:

$$W_0 = (\tfrac{1}{2}m\dot{\mathbf{r}}^2 + \tfrac{1}{2}f\mathbf{r}^2)_{t=0}$$

From the equations of motion (4.11) and (4.12), neglecting γ in comparison with ω_0:

$$W_0 = 2m\omega_0{}^2\mathbf{AA}^*$$

The total initial energy of oscillation therefore reappears as the total energy radiated.

For an understanding of the optical properties of matter it is particularly important to know how an elastically bound electron behaves in an alternating field, and in the field due to incident light waves in particular. We shall restrict ourselves to the consideration of a linearly polarized wave train, the field strength of which at the electron is $\mathbf{E} = \mathbf{E}_0 e^{i\omega t}$. The electron's equation of motion is

$$\ddot{\mathbf{r}} + \gamma\dot{\mathbf{r}} + \omega_0^2 \mathbf{r} = \frac{e}{m}\mathbf{E}_0 e^{i\omega t} \tag{5.10}$$

in which we allow for the loss of energy by radiation through the introduction of the damping term $\gamma\dot{\mathbf{r}}$, where γ is the damping factor given by equation (4.6).

The inhomogeneous equation (5.10) may be satisfied by putting

$$\mathbf{r} = \mathbf{r}_0 e^{i\omega t} \tag{5.11}$$

where

$$\mathbf{r}_0 = \frac{e}{m}\frac{\mathbf{E}_0}{\omega_0^2 - \omega^2 + i\omega\gamma} \tag{5.11a}$$

If we write $\mathbf{r}_0 = \mathbf{s}_0 e^{-i\phi}$, where $\mathbf{s}_0$ and ϕ are real quantities, we obtain the following result: the motion produced by the field $\mathbf{E} = \mathbf{E}_0 e^{i\omega t}$ may be described by the vector $\mathbf{r} = \mathbf{s}_0 e^{i(\omega t - \phi)}$, of amplitude

$$\mathbf{s}_0 = \frac{e}{m}\frac{\mathbf{E}_0}{\sqrt{[(\omega_0^2 - \omega^2)^2 + \omega^2\gamma^2]}} \tag{5.12a}$$

and phase

$$\phi = \frac{\omega\gamma}{\omega_0^2 - \omega^2} \tag{5.12b}$$

(The general integral of (5.10) is obtained by the addition of an arbitrary solution of the homogeneous equation; since this solution decays with time, after a sufficiently long period the electron is solely influenced by the light wave, and only the forced oscillation remains.)

For the amplitude and phase angle of the forced oscillation we obtain the familiar curves of figure 11. Outside the region of resonance (i.e. when $|\omega - \omega_0| \gg \gamma$), it is in phase with the exciting force at lower frequencies, and at very low frequencies its amplitude approaches the value applicable to steady fields, $\mathbf{r}_0 = e\mathbf{E}/m\omega_0^2$. On the other side of the resonance frequency the phase of the oscillation is opposed to the force. As the frequency increases without limit the amplitude tends to zero. In the region of resonance (i.e. when $|\omega - \omega_0| \approx \gamma$), the amplitude rises steeply, attaining a maximum value $\dfrac{e}{m}\dfrac{\mathbf{E}_0}{\omega_0\gamma}$ for $\omega \approx \omega_0$.

The "half-value width" for the square of the amplitude is once more $\delta\omega \approx \gamma$, as in the case of free oscillations.

In consequence of the "frictional term" in equation (5.10), work must be performed by the field on the electron in order to maintain

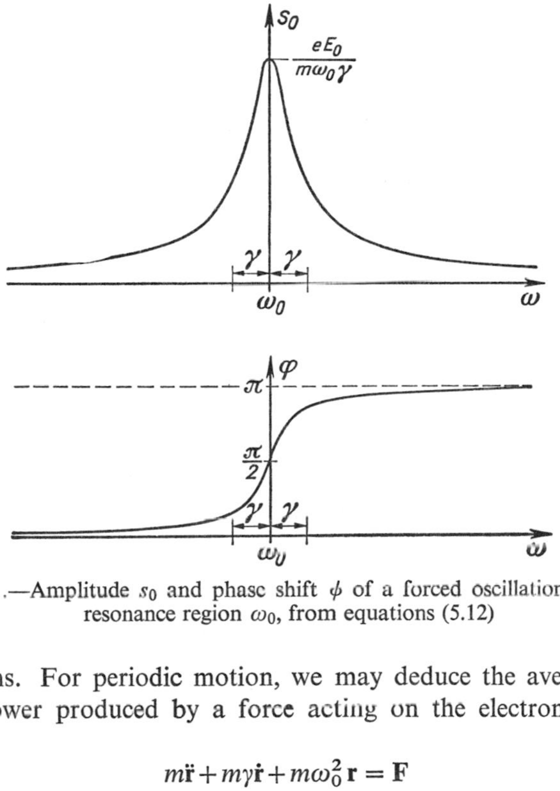

Fig. 11.—Amplitude s_0 and phase shift ϕ of a forced oscillation in the resonance region ω_0, from equations (5.12)

oscillations. For periodic motion, we may deduce the average value of the power produced by a force acting on the electron from the equation

$$m\ddot{\mathbf{r}} + m\gamma\dot{\mathbf{r}} + m\omega_0^2\mathbf{r} = \mathbf{F}$$

The power produced by $\mathbf{F}$ at any instant is $\mathbf{F}.\dot{\mathbf{r}}$. If we take the time average of the above expression, the terms $\dot{\mathbf{r}}.\ddot{\mathbf{r}} = \frac{1}{2}\frac{d\dot{\mathbf{r}}^2}{dt}$ and $\mathbf{r}.\dot{\mathbf{r}} = \frac{1}{2}\frac{d\mathbf{r}^2}{dt}$ drop out, and we obtain

$$\overline{\mathbf{F}.\dot{\mathbf{r}}} = m\gamma\overline{\dot{\mathbf{r}}^2} = \tfrac{1}{2}m\gamma\omega^2\mathbf{r}_0^2 \qquad (5.13)$$

in view of (5.11). If we are dealing with radiation damping alone, in which the electron loses energy only from emitted radiation, the value deduced above for the average power must correspond exactly to the energy radiated per second. From (4.4) this is

$$S = \frac{2e^2}{3c^3}\overline{\ddot{\mathbf{r}}^2} = \frac{2e^2}{3c^3}\frac{\omega^4 \mathbf{r}_0^2}{2}$$

If this expression is equated with (5.13) we obtain the correct value for γ, as given by equation (4.6).

The law of forced oscillations expressed by (5.12) corresponds experimentally to the finite width of the absorption lines observed when light is passed through a gas. If no other sources of disturbance are present, the half-value width due to radiation damping alone is

$$\delta\omega_{rad} = \gamma = \frac{2e^2\omega^2}{3mc^3}$$

When we discussed the emission from a freely oscillating electron we saw that the finite line width could be simply interpreted as the reciprocal of the electron's time constant for radiation; if τ_{rad} is the time required for the oscillation amplitude to decrease to a fraction $1/e$ of its original value, then

$$\gamma = \frac{2}{\tau_{rad}} \tag{5.14}$$

If the free oscillations are interrupted by collisions between atoms we must expect increased broadening of the spectral lines. This is obvious for the case of emission, since, as we have already seen, line width depends essentially upon the length of the individual wave trains and not on the cause of their limitation. If we designate by τ the average time between collisions, then a line width of order $\delta\omega \approx 1/\tau$ will be produced purely by the collisions. We shall now show that the same factor applies to the process of absorption, by considering the average motion, under the influence of an alternating electric field, of a large number of electrons bound to colliding atoms. Equation (5.10) is still valid for this average motion, provided that the supplementary term

$$g = \frac{2}{\tau} \tag{5.15}$$

is introduced and added to γ. We may thus describe the average motion of the electron by means of a damping constant $\gamma + g$ when both sources of damping are present.

For proof, we start from the general solution of equation (5.10)

$$\mathbf{r}(t) = \mathbf{r}_0\, e^{i\omega t} + (\mathbf{A}\, e^{i\omega_0 t} + \mathbf{B}\, e^{-i\omega_0 t})\, e^{-\frac{1}{2}\gamma t} \tag{5.16}$$

which includes the particular integral (5.11) and the two constants of integration **A** and **B**. The vector $\mathbf{r}_0$ is related to the (complex) amplitude vector $\mathbf{E}_0$ by the equation

$$\mathbf{r}_0 = \frac{e}{m} \frac{\mathbf{E}_0}{\omega_0^2 - \omega^2 + i\omega\gamma} \tag{5.11a}$$

Now assume that the atom under consideration suffered its latest collision at time t_1. If we were to know the values of $\mathbf{r}$ and $\dot{\mathbf{r}}$ immediately after collision, the constants **A** and **B** would be determined. Now we do not know these values for individual atoms; if, however, we consider a large number of such oscillators, all of which have been subjected to collision at time t_1, we can assert that immediately after t_1 all directions of the displacement $\mathbf{r}$ and the velocity $\dot{\mathbf{r}}$ are equally probable. The average value of $\mathbf{r}$ and $\dot{\mathbf{r}}$ at time t_1 will therefore be zero for all these oscillators. The equations determining the constants of integration are therefore, from (5.16),

$$\mathbf{r}_0\, e^{i\omega t_1} + (\mathbf{A}\, e^{i\omega_0 t_1} + \mathbf{B}\, e^{-i\omega_0 t_1})\, e^{-\frac{1}{2}\gamma t_1} = 0$$

$$i\omega \mathbf{r}_0\, e^{i\omega t_1} + \{(i\omega_0 - \tfrac{1}{2}\gamma)\mathbf{A}\, e^{i\omega_0 t_1} - (i\omega_0 + \tfrac{1}{2}\gamma)\mathbf{B}\, e^{-i\omega_0 t_1}\}\, e^{-\frac{1}{2}\gamma t_1} = 0$$

If we insert the resultant values for **A** and **B** into (5.16), and introduce the time elapsed since the last collision, $\theta = t - t_1$, we obtain

$$\mathbf{r}_\theta(t) = \mathbf{r}_0\, e^{i\omega t} \left\{ 1 - \frac{\omega_0 + \omega - \frac{1}{2}i\gamma}{2\omega_0} \exp\left[i(\omega_0 - \omega) - \tfrac{1}{2}\gamma\right]\theta - \right.$$
$$\left. - \frac{\omega_0 - \omega + \frac{1}{2}i\gamma}{2\omega_0} \exp - \left[i(\omega_0 + \omega) + \tfrac{1}{2}\gamma\right]\theta \right\}$$

If τ is the average time between collisions and N is the total number of oscillators present in the volume under consideration, then the number of these oscillators whose last collision took place during the time interval $\theta, \theta + d\theta$ is given by

$$\frac{N}{\tau}\, e^{-\theta/\tau}\, d\theta$$

The mean contribution of each individual oscillator to the resultant displacement is therefore

$$\overline{\mathbf{r}(t)} = \int_{\theta=0}^{\infty} \mathbf{r}_\theta(t)\, e^{-\theta/\tau} \frac{d\theta}{\tau} \tag{5.17}$$

Integration yields

$$\overline{\mathbf{r}(t)} = \mathbf{r}_0'\, e^{i\omega t} \tag{5.18}$$

where

$$\mathbf{r}_0' = \mathbf{r}_0 \frac{\omega_0^2 - (\omega - \frac{1}{2}i\gamma)^2}{\omega_0^2 - \left(\omega - \frac{1}{2}i\gamma - \dfrac{i}{\tau}\right)^2}$$

If we neglect the quadratic terms in γ, as before, then from the above expression and (5.11*a*) we have

$$\mathbf{r}_0' = \frac{e}{m} \frac{\mathbf{E}_0}{\omega_0^2 - \omega^2 + i\omega(\gamma + 2/\tau)}$$

Inspection shows that the original denominator of (5.11*a*) has been replaced by a new one, which differs from the first only through the addition of the collision damping constant $2/\tau$ to the radiation constant γ. Our previous statement is now proved.

Apart from the broadening of the spectral lines by radiation and collision damping there is also the Doppler effect, which is caused by the thermal motion of the emitting and absorbing atoms. For details of this broadening effect, see Exercise 1 below.

Exercises

1. *Broadening of spectral lines*

In addition to the effects of radiation and collision damping on line width, there is also the Doppler broadening effect arising from the thermal motion of the radiating atoms. Atoms moving towards the observer exhibit a shift towards the violet end of the spectrum; those moving away, a red shift. Compare the orders of magnitude of the three effects. How may these three effects be separated? (Note that the gas atoms possess a Maxwellian velocity distribution; the fraction of the N atoms, each of mass M, with an x-component of velocity lying between v_x and $v_x + dv_x$, is

$$N w(v_x)\, dv_x = N \exp -\frac{M v_x{}^2}{2kT}\, dv_x \Big/ \int_{-\infty}^{\infty} \exp -\frac{M v_x{}^2}{2kT}\, dv_x$$

2. *Radiation damping and the electron radius*

Let a plane linearly polarized light wave excite oscillations in a free electron. If we imagine the electron to be a sphere of radius R_{el}, then according to this conception R_{el} is determined from the fact that the power radiated by the electron is equal to the wave energy incident on this sphere in unit time.

Hint: Take a wave $\mathbf{E} = [E(t), 0, 0]$ polarized parallel to the x-axis, note the equation of motion $m\ddot{x} = eE$ when the Lorentz force is neglected, and the average value of the energy flow (Poynting vector) $S = c/4\pi E^2$.

CHAPTER AIII

The Hamiltonian form of the equations of motion

§6. The Hamiltonian theory in mechanics

The Hamiltonian form of the equations of motion is of proved value as a powerful general method employed in connection with many different physical problems. Two important applications are in statistical mechanics (with which we are only incidentally concerned

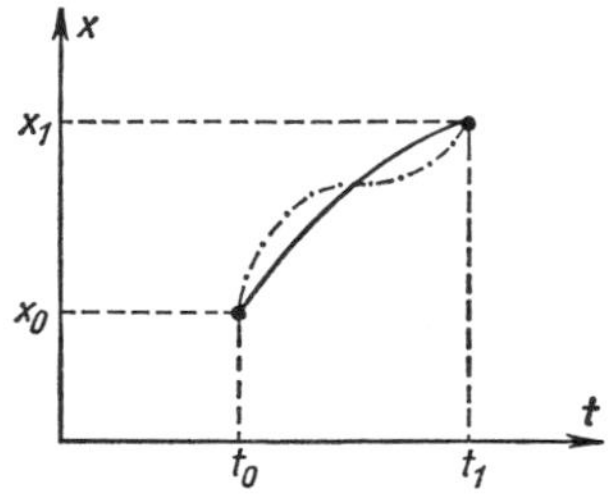

Fig. 12.—Determination of the correct path $x(t)$ (full line). A varied path is shown as a broken line. It must coincide with $x(t)$ at the end points.

here), and in the quantum theory. We shall begin our account of Hamiltonian theory with a mathematical digression on the calculus of variations.

Let us first consider a single function $x(t)$, and a function of the three variables x, $\dot{x}$, and t, $L(x, \dot{x}, t)$, designated the "Lagrange function". We may choose any function $x(t)$ (figure 12) with fixed initial and final values x_0 and x_1:

$$x(t_0) = x_0 \quad \text{and} \quad x(t_1) = x_1 \tag{6.1}$$

Using this function, which is arbitrary except for the above condition, we form the integral

$$G = \int_{t_0}^{t_1} L(x, \dot{x}, t)\, dt \tag{6.2}$$

Among all the possible functions $x(t)$ that satisfy condition (6.1) we seek the one that makes G an extremum; in doing so we must take account of $\dot{x} = dx/dt$ along all possible paths. We shall call this the "correct function", or in mechanical applications, the "correct path". Thus, let $x(t)$ be the correct function; we now form the varied function

$$x(t) + \alpha\eta(t)$$

where α is a numerical factor, and $\eta(t)$ is an arbitrary function vanishing at the terminal points:

$$\eta(t_0) = \eta(t_1) = 0 \tag{6.3}$$

G is now a function of α:

$$G(\alpha) = \int_{t_0}^{t_1} L(x+\alpha\eta, \dot{x}+\alpha\dot{\eta}, t)\, dt \tag{6.4}$$

The extremum condition is $(dG/d\alpha)_{\alpha=0} = 0$ for all functions $\eta(t)$ satisfying (6.3). Differentiating under the integral sign we obtain

$$\frac{\partial L}{\partial x}\eta + \frac{\partial L}{\partial \dot{x}}\dot{\eta} = \frac{\partial L}{\partial x}\eta - \left(\frac{d}{dt}\frac{\partial L}{\partial \dot{x}}\right)\eta + \frac{d}{dt}\left(\frac{\partial L}{\partial \dot{x}}\eta\right)$$

Therefore

$$\left(\frac{dG}{d\alpha}\right)_{\alpha=0} = \int_{t_0}^{t_1} \left(\frac{\partial L}{\partial x} - \frac{d}{dt}\frac{\partial L}{\partial \dot{x}}\right)\eta\, dt + \left(\frac{\partial L}{\partial \dot{x}}\eta\right)_{t=t_0} - \left(\frac{\partial L}{\partial \dot{x}}\eta\right)_{t=t_0}$$

The last two terms vanish on account of condition (6.3). In order that $dG/d\alpha$ should vanish for all functions η, $x(t)$ must satisfy the "Euler equation"

$$\frac{d}{dt}\left(\frac{\partial L}{\partial \dot{x}}\right) = \frac{\partial L}{\partial x} \tag{6.5}$$

The above treatment may clearly be extended to three functions. If we call these $x_1(t)$, $x_2(t)$, $x_3(t)$, the Lagrange function is $L(x_1, \dot{x}_1, x_2, \dot{x}_2, x_3, \dot{x}_3, t)$. We require that G should be an extremum for

$$G = \int_{t_0}^{t_1} L(x_j, \dot{x}_j, t)\, dt \tag{6.6}$$

for a variation of x_1, x_2, x_3,

$$x_j + \alpha_j \eta_j(t), \text{ where } \eta_j(t_0) = \eta_j(t_1) = 0 \quad (j = 1, 2, 3)$$

The Euler equations are

$$\frac{d}{dt}\left(\frac{\partial L}{\partial \dot{x}_j}\right) = \frac{\partial L}{\partial x_j} \quad (j = 1, 2, 3) \tag{6.7}$$

We now introduce the Hamiltonian function, which is related to the Lagrange function as follows: Let us introduce the "momenta"

$$p_j = \frac{\partial L}{\partial \dot{x}_j}$$

and assume these three equations to be solved for $\dot{x}_1$, $\dot{x}_2$, $\dot{x}_3$. Then the $\dot{x}_j$ appear as functions of the p_j and x_j. Using these functions $\dot{x}_j(p_j, x_j)$, we define the Hamiltonian function as

$$\mathscr{H}(p_j, x_j, t) = \sum_{j=1}^{3} p_j \dot{x}_j - L \tag{6.8}$$

From (6.7), it is clear that

$$\dot{x}_j = \frac{\partial \mathscr{H}}{\partial p_j} \qquad \dot{p}_j = -\frac{\partial \mathscr{H}}{\partial x_j} \qquad (j = 1, 2, 3) \tag{6.9}$$

If L, and hence $\mathscr{H}$, do not depend explicitly on t,

$$\frac{d\mathscr{H}}{dt} = 0$$

and from (6.9)

$$\frac{d\mathscr{H}}{dt} = \sum_j \left\{\frac{\partial \mathscr{H}}{\partial p_j}\dot{p}_j + \frac{\partial \mathscr{H}}{\partial x_j}\dot{x}_j\right\} + \frac{\partial \mathscr{H}}{\partial t} = \frac{\partial \mathscr{H}}{\partial t}$$

The value of $\mathscr{H}(p_j, x_j)$ therefore remains constant with respect to time if the "correct" path is chosen for the $p_j(t)$ and $x_j(t)$.

For physical applications $L(x_j, \dot{x}_j, t)$ must be so chosen that the Euler equations do in fact represent the correct equations of motion.

For a particle moving in a field of force of potential energy $V(x,y,z)$, L is equal to the difference between the kinetic and potential energies. In the non-relativistic case,* therefore (writing x, y, z instead of x_1, x_2, x_3)

$$L = \tfrac{1}{2}m(\dot{x}^2 + \dot{y}^2 + \dot{z}^2) - V(x, y, z) \tag{6.10}$$

* Cf. §55 for the relativistic Lagrangian and Hamiltonian functions.

The first of the equations (6.7) then states that

$$\frac{d}{dt}m\dot{x} = -\frac{\partial V}{\partial x}$$

This is the correct Newtonian equation of motion. The momenta are

$$p_x = \frac{\partial L}{\partial \dot{x}} = m\dot{x}, \text{ etc.}$$

From (6.8), the Hamiltonian function is

$$\mathscr{H} = \frac{1}{2m}(p_x^2 + p_y^2 + p_z^2) + V(x, y, z) \qquad (6.11)$$

which is the sum of the kinetic and potential energies. In this case, therefore, $\mathscr{H}$ is the total energy, expressed in terms of momenta and coordinates.

Equations (6.6) to (6.9) are clearly also valid for a system of N particles with coordinates $(x_1, x_2, \ldots, x_{3N})$; the index number j now runs from 1 to $3N$. Here too, if the forces between the particles can be represented by means of a potential energy $V(x_1, \ldots, x_{3N})$, L is the difference between the kinetic and potential energies and $\mathscr{H}$ is their sum.

We have seen that the Newtonian equations of motion (6.7) may be considered as Euler equations corresponding to the requirement that the function G should be an extremum for the "correct" paths.* This alternative concept is important, because it enables the equations of motion to be expressed in a form that is invariant with respect to the coordinates. The extremum requirement, known as Hamilton's principle, contains only physical quantities such as kinetic and potential energy, which are independent of the coordinate system. Equations (6.7) are therefore valid for any arbitrary system of coordinates, such as the polar form (cf. Exercise 1, p. 46). It is then only necessary to express L as the difference between the kinetic and potential energies in the coordinate system selected. The same applies to Hamilton's equations. For any arbitrary coordinate system, the "momenta" $p_j = \partial L/\partial \dot{x}_j$ do not in general have the dimensions of a true momentum (e.g. if the coordinate x_j is a dimensionless angular quantity); however, the product of any "momentum" p_j with its associated coordinate x_j always has the dimensions of action (energy $\times$ time). The momentum p_j and coordinate x_j are said to be canonically conjugate.

The Newtonian equations of motion for N particles form a system of $3N$ differential equations of the second order. Therefore, in order to specify a "path" uniquely, we require $6N$ initial conditions, namely the positions x_j and velocities $\dot{x}_j$ at a given time. The motion of the system may then be represented by a curve

* G does not always have to be a minimum, always a maximum, or a saddle point. There are cases in which G is a minimum for certain variations, and a maximum for other equally possible path changes. All that is required is that in the first approximation G should not change if a varied path is substituted for the correct path (cf. Exercise 3, p. 47).

in this space of $6N$ dimensions composed of position and velocity coordinates. One point in this space determines the course of the path; for if we define $\dot{x}_j$ as

$$\frac{d}{dt}x_j = \dot{x}_j \tag{6.12a}$$

then, in conjunction with the Euler equations

$$\frac{d}{dt}\frac{\partial L}{\partial \dot{x}_j} = \frac{\partial L}{\partial x_j} \tag{6.12b}$$

we have $\partial L/\partial \dot{x}_j = p_j = m\dot{x}_j$ for Cartesian coordinates. Hence, if $x_j(t)$ and $\dot{x}_j(t)$ are given, we can immediately determine $x_j(t+dt)$ and $\dot{x}_j(t+dt)$ from the above equations, from which it follows that the whole path can be constructed. In arbitrary coordinates p_j is no longer proportional to $\dot{x}_j$, but may depend on the other coordinates in a complicated manner. It therefore seems reasonable to introduce the p_j and the x_j as new variables, since their variation with respect to time is directly given by equation (6.12). The path can now be described in a "phase space" of $6N$ dimensions, the coordinates of which are the p_j and x_j. The Hamilton equations (6.9) enable the path to be constructed from an initial point in this space, provided that the Hamiltonian function is known. Newton's equations are replaced by (6.12) and (6.9), representing a system of $6N$ equations of the first order; the advantage of this substitution lies in the fact that the symmetrical form of Hamilton's equations makes them more suitable for the treatment of problems in any coordinate system.

Canonical transformations

In order to change from one pair of canonically conjugate variables p, x, to another pair $\bar{p}$, $\bar{x}$, we introduce a function of the old coordinate and the new momentum, $S(x, \bar{p})$, for which

$$p = \frac{\partial S}{\partial x} \quad \text{and} \quad \bar{x} = \frac{\partial S}{\partial \bar{p}} \tag{6.13}$$

The relation $\bar{p}(p, x)$, $\bar{x}(p, x)$ between the old and the new variables is given implicitly by (6.13). The functional determinant (Jacobian) of the transformation (6.13) is unity. This is most easily demonstrated by expressing the total differential $dS = p.dx + \bar{x}.d\bar{p}$ in terms of the new variables:

$$dS = \underbrace{p\frac{\partial x}{\partial \bar{x}}}_{\left(\frac{\partial S}{\partial \bar{x}}\right)_{\bar{p}}} d\bar{x} + \underbrace{\left(p\frac{\partial x}{\partial \bar{p}} + \bar{x}\right)}_{\left(\frac{\partial S}{\partial \bar{p}}\right)_{\bar{x}}} d\bar{p}$$

Then the criterion for integrability

$$\frac{\partial}{\partial \bar{p}}\left(p\frac{\partial x}{\partial \bar{x}}\right) = \frac{\partial}{\partial \bar{x}}\left(p\frac{\partial x}{\partial \bar{p}} + \bar{x}\right)$$

yields the functional determinant

$$\frac{\partial p}{\partial \bar{p}}\frac{\partial x}{\partial \bar{x}} - \frac{\partial p}{\partial \bar{x}}\frac{\partial x}{\partial \bar{p}} = \frac{\partial(p, x)}{\partial(\bar{p}, \bar{x})} = 1$$

Hamilton's equations are still valid in terms of the new variables introduced by the transformation (6.13), as we shall show. If we take an arbitrary function $b(p, x)$, its time rate of change is

$$\dot{b} = \dot{p}\frac{\partial b}{\partial p}+\dot{x}\frac{\partial b}{\partial x} = \frac{\partial \mathcal{H}}{\partial p}\frac{\partial b}{\partial x}-\frac{\partial b}{\partial p}\frac{\partial \mathcal{H}}{\partial x} = \frac{\partial(\mathcal{H}, b)}{\partial(p, x)}$$

Since the functional determinant of the transformation is unity, we also have

$$\dot{b} = \frac{\partial(\mathcal{H}, b)}{\partial(p, x)}\frac{\partial(p, x)}{\partial(\bar{p}, \bar{x})} = \frac{\partial(\mathcal{H}, b)}{\partial(\bar{p}, \bar{x})}$$

for any function b. If we now put b equal to $\bar{p}$ or to $\bar{x}$, we obtain Hamilton's equations in terms of the new variables and the old Hamiltonian function:

$$-\left(\frac{\partial \mathcal{H}}{\partial \bar{x}}\right)_{\bar{p}} = \dot{\bar{p}} \qquad \left(\frac{\partial \mathcal{H}}{\partial \bar{p}}\right)_{\bar{x}} = \dot{\bar{x}}$$

Equation (6.13) represents the most general form of canonical transformation of canonically conjugate quantities. We may obtain the special case of the "pure coordinate transformation" by putting $S(x, \bar{p}) = g(x)\bar{p}$, from which $\bar{x} = g(x)$ and $\bar{p} = p/g'(x)$. This result may clearly be generalized to several degrees of freedom.

§7. The electron in a given electromagnetic field

From equation (1.2) we know the electron's equation of motion

$$\frac{d}{dt}m\mathbf{v} = e\mathbf{E}+\frac{e}{c}\mathbf{v}\times\mathbf{H} \tag{7.1}$$

which we may consider to have been experimentally proved in the non-relativistic case. We now seek a Lagrangian function the Euler equation of which will agree with (7.1). For this purpose, let us introduce the potentials $\mathbf{A}$, ϕ (cf. Vol. I, §64) from which we may calculate the electric and magnetic fields

$$\mathbf{E} = -\operatorname{grad}\phi-\frac{1}{c}\dot{\mathbf{A}}, \qquad \mathbf{H} = \operatorname{curl}\mathbf{A}$$

If these expressions for $\mathbf{E}$ and $\mathbf{H}$ are inserted in (7.1), the x-component of this equation is

$$\frac{d}{dt}\left(m\dot{x}+\frac{e}{c}A_x\right) = \frac{\partial}{\partial x}\left\{-e\phi+\frac{e}{c}(\dot{x}A_x+\dot{y}A_y+\dot{z}A_z)\right\} \tag{7.2}$$

(For verification, we note that

$$\frac{dA_x}{dt} = \dot{A}_x+\frac{\partial A_x}{\partial x}\dot{x}+\frac{\partial A_x}{\partial y}\dot{y}+\frac{\partial A_x}{\partial z}\dot{z}$$

But (7.2) is the Eulerian form of the equation of motion for which

$$L = \tfrac{1}{2}m(\dot{x}^2+\dot{y}^2+\dot{z}^2) - e\phi + \frac{e}{c}(\dot{x}A_x+\dot{y}A_y+\dot{z}A_z) \tag{7.3}$$

The x-component of the momentum is

$$p_x = \frac{\partial L}{\partial \dot{x}} = m\dot{x} + \frac{e}{c}A_x, \quad \text{therefore} \quad \mathbf{p} = m\mathbf{v} + \frac{e}{c}\mathbf{A} \tag{7.4}$$

At first sight, this appears to be a strange result: the momentum is no longer equal to $m\mathbf{v}$, but contains an additional term $(e/c)\mathbf{A}$, the interpretation of which is not self-evident. The formal Hamiltonian treatment, however, compels us to designate $m\mathbf{v}+(e/c)\mathbf{A}$ as the momentum that is canonically conjugate to $\mathbf{r}$. If we now consider the Hamiltonian function as expressed by (6.8), we first obtain

$$(\mathbf{p}\,.\,\dot{\mathbf{r}}) = m\dot{\mathbf{r}}^2 + \frac{e}{c}(\dot{\mathbf{r}}\,.\,\mathbf{A})$$

If we use this equation together with (7.3) to form equation (6.8), we have

$$(\mathbf{p}\,.\,\dot{\mathbf{r}}) - L = \tfrac{1}{2}m(\dot{x}^2+\dot{y}^2+\dot{z}^2) + e\phi$$

This is again the sum of the kinetic and potential energies; the vector potential and hence the magnetic field have disappeared. The above expression, however, is not the Hamiltonian function, which must be obtained by expressing the $\dot{x}_j$ by means of the momenta p_j, according to the general rule. If we do this, using (7.4), we finally obtain the (non-relativistic) Hamiltonian function for a charged particle in a field specified by ϕ and $\mathbf{A}$:

$$\mathcal{H} = \frac{1}{2m}\left(\mathbf{p} - \frac{e}{c}\mathbf{A}\right)^2 + e\phi \tag{7.5}$$

We shall frequently have occasion to refer back to this expression.

§8. Some applications of Hamilton's theory

Hamiltonian theory is of fundamental importance in the transition from classical to quantum mechanics, as we shall see later on. In this section we shall consider some further problems of classical physics in which Hamiltonian theory is of value.

Statistical mechanics and the theory of heat are based in the first instance on the Hamiltonian form of the equations of motion. The fundamental statement of statistical mechanics may be expressed as follows:

"Consider a system of N particles with coordinates $\mathbf{r}_1,\ldots,\mathbf{r}_N$, momenta $\mathbf{p}_1,\ldots,\mathbf{p}_N$, the Hamiltonian function of which, $\mathscr{H}(\mathbf{p}_1,\ldots,\mathbf{r}_N)$, is invariant with respect to time. Assume that it is known only that the energy of the system lies between E and $E+\Delta E$. Then the probability $W d\mathbf{p}_1\ldots d\mathbf{r}_N$ of finding the system in an interval $(\mathbf{p}_1,\mathbf{p}_1+d\mathbf{p}_1;\ldots;\mathbf{r}_N,\mathbf{r}_N+d\mathbf{r}_N)$ is given by

$$W\,d\mathbf{p}_1\ldots d\mathbf{r}_N = C\,d\mathbf{p}_1\ldots d\mathbf{r}_N \quad \text{with} \quad E \leqq \mathscr{H} \leqq E+\Delta E \tag{8.1}$$

The constant C is determined by the normalization condition

$$\underset{E\leqq\mathscr{H}\leqq E+\Delta E}{\int\ldots\int} W\,d\mathbf{p}_1\ldots d\mathbf{r}_N = 1\text{"}$$

In order that normalization should be possible, the volume of phase space defined by $E\leqq\mathscr{H}\leqq E+\Delta E$ must exist. This may be achieved most simply by imagining the system to be enclosed in a container of volume V. Then the function $\mathscr{H}$ contains a share of the potential energy arising between the particles and the wall, which prevents the former from penetrating the latter. The volume V appears as a parameter in the Hamiltonian function. The energy indeterminacy may be arbitrarily small, and is only introduced for convenience in formulation.* The expression (8.1) is to be interpreted as a statistical statement of the course of the system in phase space. In virtue of the principle of conservation of energy, the system lies within the range $E\leqq\mathscr{H}\leqq E+\Delta E$. Equation (8.1) then implies that, for a sufficiently long period of observation, the time during which the phase point $\mathbf{p}_1(t),\ldots,\mathbf{r}_N(t)$ of the system remains within a small element of volume $d\mathbf{p}_1\ldots d\mathbf{r}_N$ lying in the range $E\leqq\mathscr{H}\leqq E+\Delta E$ is directly proportional to the size of this element.

If the system of particles is in contact with a heat source at temperature T, the course of the phase point can no longer be described by the Hamiltonian equations alone; the system is now coupled to a statistical ensemble defined solely by its temperature T, and because of the energy interchange with the heat source, the phase point path cannot be determined purely on mechanical grounds. In this case (8.1) is replaced by the "canonical distribution"

$$W\,d\mathbf{p}_1\ldots d\mathbf{r}_N = C\,e^{-\mathscr{H}/kT}\,d\mathbf{p}_1\ldots d\mathbf{r}_N \tag{8.2}$$

* If we wish to avoid the use of ΔE, and to consider E as an exact quantity, we may express W by means of the Dirac δ-function: $W = C\delta(\mathscr{H}-E)$ (cf. Exercise 1, p. 137).

where k is the Boltzmann constant.* Equations (8.1) and (8.2) are independent of the selected coordinate system.

If $f(\mathbf{p}_1,\ldots,\mathbf{r}_N)$ is an observable function of the "phase" $\mathbf{p}_1,\ldots,\mathbf{r}_N$, its average value, $\bar{f}$, is

$$\bar{f} = \frac{\int\ldots\int f W \, d\mathbf{p}_1 \ldots d\mathbf{r}_N}{\int\ldots\int W \, d\mathbf{p}_1 \ldots d\mathbf{r}_N} \tag{8.3}$$

or, with the particular value for W given by (8.2),

$$\bar{f} = \frac{\int\ldots\int f e^{-\mathscr{H}/kT} \, d\mathbf{p}_1 \ldots d\mathbf{r}_N}{\int\ldots\int e^{-\mathscr{H}/kT} \, d\mathbf{p}_1 \ldots d\mathbf{r}_N} \tag{8.4}$$

In the above expressions, $\bar{f}$ may be taken as the time average of f during the period of observation of the system, or as the average of simultaneous observations on a large number of identical systems.

In addition to the phase space volume, $\mathscr{H}$ may also contain as parameters the electric fields $\mathbf{E}$ and $\mathbf{H}$, represented by the potentials $\mathbf{A}(\mathbf{r})$ and $\phi(\mathbf{r})$. Then, generalizing from (7.5):

$$\mathscr{H} = \sum_{\nu=1}^{N} \left\{ \frac{1}{2m_\nu} \left(\mathbf{p}_\nu - \frac{e_\nu}{c} \mathbf{A}(\mathbf{r}_\nu) \right)^2 + e_\nu \phi(\mathbf{r}_\nu) \right\} + V(\mathbf{r}_1,\ldots,\mathbf{r}_N) \tag{8.5}$$

The above expression includes the mutual reaction between particles of mass m_ν and charge e_ν, V, and other possible mutual effects such as the reaction with the wall that defines the phase volume.

This definition is of particular importance in the investigation of the electric and magnetic moments of the atom, and of their dependence on temperature in the presence of external electric and magnetic fields. If an atom consists of N charges $e_1,\ldots,e_\nu,\ldots,e_N$ at positions $\mathbf{r}_1,\ldots,\mathbf{r}_\nu,\ldots,\mathbf{r}_N$, its electric and magnetic moments, $\bar{\mathbf{p}}_{el}$, $\bar{\mathbf{p}}_{magn}$, are given by the mean values of

$$\mathbf{p}_{el} = \sum_{\nu=1}^{N} e_\nu \mathbf{r}_\nu \tag{8.6a}$$

and†

$$\mathbf{p}_{magn} = \frac{1}{2c} \sum_{\nu=1}^{N} e_\nu \mathbf{r}_\nu \times \dot{\mathbf{r}}_\nu \tag{8.6b}$$

* (8.2) may be deduced from (8.1). For a thorough exposition of statistical mechanics and its bearing on the theory of heat, see R. Becker, *Theorie der Wärme* (Berlin, 1955).

† For (8.6*b*), cf. Vol. I, §47. Only the mean value of $\mathbf{p}_{magn}$ is significant. The closed orbit of an electron corresponds to a current round a closed circuit, and therefore gives rise to a magnetic moment.

Homogeneous electric and magnetic fields, **E** and **H**, are derived from potentials

$$\phi(\mathbf{r}) = -\mathbf{E}\,.\,\mathbf{r} \qquad -\operatorname{grad}\phi = \mathbf{E}$$

$$\mathbf{A}(\mathbf{r}) = \tfrac{1}{2}\mathbf{H}\times\mathbf{r} \qquad \operatorname{curl}\mathbf{A} = \mathbf{H}$$

The potentials appearing in (8.5) may therefore be written

$$\phi = \phi^0 - \mathbf{E}\,.\,\mathbf{r} \qquad \mathbf{A} = \tfrac{1}{2}\mathbf{H}\times\mathbf{r} \tag{8.7}$$

where the potential ϕ^0 is determined entirely by the mutual electrostatic forces between the individual charges in the atom. We may neglect the effect of the magnetic field due to a single electron on the orbits of the others, since it is very small compared to the electrostatic effect $e_\nu e_\mu/|\mathbf{r}_\nu - \mathbf{r}_\mu|$. In any case it could not be taken into account by means of the Hamiltonian function (8.5), since the vector potential **A** would not depend on the coordinates alone, but also on the momenta.

The following simple relationships may now be deduced from equations (8.5) and (8.6), using the values for the potentials given by (8.7):

$$\mathbf{p}_{el} = -\frac{\partial\mathcal{H}}{\partial\mathbf{E}} \tag{8.8a}$$

$$\mathbf{p}_{magn} = -\frac{\partial\mathcal{H}}{\partial\mathbf{H}} \tag{8.8b}$$

The derivation of equation (8.8*a*) is obvious; to prove (8.8*b*), we differentiate and substitute $m_\nu\dot{\mathbf{r}}_\nu$ for $\mathbf{p}_\nu - e_\nu\mathbf{A}(\mathbf{r}_\nu)/c$, in accordance with (7.4).

From (8.4) it follows that, with the thermodynamic "free energy"

$$\bar{\mathbf{p}}_{el} = -\overline{\frac{\partial\mathcal{H}}{\partial\mathbf{E}}} = kT\frac{\partial\ln Z}{\partial\mathbf{E}} = -\frac{\partial F}{\partial\mathbf{E}} \tag{8.9a}$$

where Z is the "phase integral", defined as

$$Z(\mathbf{E},\mathbf{H},T) = \int\dots\int e^{-\mathcal{H}/kT}\,d\mathbf{p}_1\dots d\mathbf{r}_N = e^{-F/kT} \tag{8.10}$$

Similarly,

$$\bar{\mathbf{p}}_{magn} = -\overline{\frac{\partial\mathcal{H}}{\partial\mathbf{H}}} = kT\frac{\partial\ln Z}{\partial\mathbf{H}} = -\frac{\partial F}{\partial\mathbf{H}} \tag{8.9b}$$

These relationships may be retained in the quantum theory, in which each system is characterized by its stationary energy value E_j. The probability W_j of finding the system in a state corresponding to E_j is

$$W_j = C \exp -\frac{E_j}{kT} \tag{8.11}$$

The energy values depend on the parameters **E** and **H**. Equations (8.9) remain valid in the quantum theory if the phase sum

$$Z(\mathbf{E}, \mathbf{H}, T) = \sum_j \exp -\frac{E_j(\mathbf{E}, \mathbf{H})}{kT} \tag{8.10a}$$

is introduced in place of the phase integral; the summation extends over all possible energy values E_j. We shall be particularly concerned with the application of equation (8.9*b*) in chapter C III.

In classical physics, however, equation (8.9*b*) is strictly speaking of no value, since it turns out that $\bar{\mathbf{p}}_{magn}$ always vanishes. This is because the phase integral

$$Z(\mathbf{E}, \mathbf{H}, T) =$$

$$\int \cdots \int \exp\left(-\frac{1}{kT}\left\{\left[\sum_\nu \frac{1}{2m_\nu}\left(\mathbf{p}_\nu - \frac{e_\nu}{c}\mathbf{A}(\mathbf{r}_\nu)\right)^2 + e_\nu \phi(\mathbf{r}_\nu)\right] + V\right\}\right) d\mathbf{p}_1 \ldots d\mathbf{r}_N$$

is independent of **A**, and hence of **H**. Integration over any $\mathbf{p}_\nu$ from $-\infty$ to $+\infty$ always results in a factor $(2\pi m_\nu kT)^{3/2}$ which is independent of $\mathbf{A}(\mathbf{r}_\nu)$. According to classical theory, therefore, no magnetism is present. By contrast the quantum theory is able to explain the magnetic properties of matter both qualitatively and quantitatively. The magnetic moment $\bar{\mathbf{p}}_{magn}$, when formed by means of the phase sum, does not generally vanish. For further discussion the reader is referred to chapter C III.

Exercises

1. *The Hamiltonian function in polar coordinates*

A particle is situated in a central field of force, for which the corresponding potential is $U(r)$. Express the kinetic energy in polar coordinates, and hence obtain the Hamiltonian function $\mathscr{H}(p_r, p_\theta, p_\phi, r, \theta, \phi)$ and the equations of motion in polar coordinates.

2. *The Lagrangian function and the conservation of momentum*

The Lagrangian function for N particles is

$$L(\dot{\mathbf{r}}_1, \ldots, \dot{\mathbf{r}}_N; \mathbf{r}_1, \ldots, \mathbf{r}_N) = \sum_{i=1}^{N} \tfrac{1}{2} m_i \dot{\mathbf{r}}_i^2 - V(\mathbf{r}_1, \ldots, \mathbf{r}_N)$$

If transformations $\mathbf{r}_i \to \mathbf{r}_i + \mathbf{R}_i$ are introduced that leave L unchanged, then $G = \int_{t_0}^{t_1} L\,dt$ also remains unchanged. If the potential depends only upon the distances between particles, then L is invariant for a "small" common displacement of all points $\mathbf{r}_i \to \mathbf{r}_i + \mathbf{R}_0$, and for a small common rotation $\mathbf{r}_i \to \mathbf{r}_i + \mathbf{n} \times \mathbf{r}_i$ ($\mathbf{n}$ is small). If the $\mathbf{R}_i$ are small, then $\mathbf{r}_i + \mathbf{R}_i$ may be looked on as variations of the correct paths. Since G does not change when these variations are introduced, show that the theorems on the conservation of linear and angular momentum may be obtained respectively from the invariance property of L with respect to displacement and rotation. (Note that the correct and the varied paths do not coincide at the limits t_0 and t_1.)

3. *Hamilton's principle of the extremum*

Discuss the bchaviour of $G = \int_{t_0}^{t_1} L(x, \dot{x})\,dt$ for arbitrary variations

(*a*) in the case of a free particle capable of motion along the x-axis, for which $L = \frac{1}{2}m\dot{x}^2$,

(*b*) in the case of a linear oscillator, for which $L = \frac{1}{2}m(\dot{x}^2 - \omega^2 x^2)$.

If $x(t)$ is the correct path, find G for the varied paths $x(t) + \gamma(t)$, for which $\gamma(t_0) = \gamma(t_1) = 0$. For what variations $\gamma(t)$ is G respectively a maximum and a minimum?

B

The principles of quantum mechanics

CHAPTER BI

The development of the quantum theory

§9. Planck's radiation formula

The first indication of the inadequacy of the concepts of classical physics appeared in the problem of radiation from an enclosure (black-body radiation). This subject will be treated in some detail in section E; at this stage we shall confine ourselves to the following short discussion.

According to G. R. Kirchhoff's analysis, if an enclosure is at a certain temperature, radiation must exist inside it. If u is the radiation energy density

$$u = \int_0^\infty u_\omega \, d\omega \tag{9.1}$$

then its spectral distribution function $u_\omega(T)$ must be independent (*a*) of the nature of the enclosure, (*b*) of the manner in which it is brought into contact with a heat source at temperature T, (*c*) of the nature of any emitting and absorbing materials present in the enclosure. If the enclosure contains a linear oscillator, such as an elastically bound charged particle oscillating at an angular frequency ω about its equilibrium position, and if $\varepsilon(T)$ is the mean energy of the oscillator at temperature T, then classical physics yields the following result for the equilibrium condition (see § 47):

$$u_\omega(T) = \varepsilon(T) \frac{\omega^2}{\pi^2 c^3} \tag{9.2}$$

According to the law of equipartition, $\varepsilon(T) = kT$. The energy density $u_\omega(T)$ would therefore be proportional to ω^2, and therefore infinitely large at all temperatures. This catastrophic prediction can only be avoided by drastic assumptions which have no foundation in classical physics. One of these is known as Planck's hypothesis, and assumes that the oscillator cannot take any arbitrary energy value, but only those values that differ by integral multiples of a finite energy ε_0.

In consequence of this assumption the following expression for ε is obtained in place of the classical value:*

$$\varepsilon = \frac{\varepsilon_0}{\exp(\varepsilon_0/kT)-1} \tag{9.3}$$

It was shown by W. Wien, from very general thermodynamical considerations, that $u_\omega(T)$ must have the form

$$u_\omega(T) = \omega^3 f\left(\frac{\omega}{T}\right)$$

where f is a function only of ω/T. This requirement is satisfied by (9.3) if we put $\varepsilon_0 = \hbar\omega$, where $\hbar$ is a new universal constant.† Then from (9.3)

$$\varepsilon = \bar{E}(T) = \frac{\hbar\omega}{\exp(\hbar\omega/kT)-1} \tag{9.4}$$

If we assume (9.2) to be correct, then

$$u_\omega(T) = \frac{\hbar\omega}{\exp(\hbar\omega/kT)-1}\frac{\omega^2}{\pi^2c^3} \tag{9.5}$$

This is Planck's radiation formula, which has been shown to give a perfect description of the radiation from a black body.

Two consequences of the greatest importance were deduced from the above considerations by Einstein. These were: the hypothesis of light quanta, and the extension of equation (9.4) to any number of oscillator degrees of freedom. If the oscillator can only gain or lose energy in integral multiples, the radiation field must be able to accept these energy quanta. Einstein expressed this postulate as follows:

"When radiation interacts with matter, it behaves as though it consisted of light quanta of energy $\hbar\omega$ which can only be emitted or absorbed as whole quantities."

* In order to derive this formula we start from the partition function Z. Writing $\beta = 1/kT$, Z is defined for a linear oscillator by $Z_{el} = \int_0^\infty e^{-\beta E}\,dE$ if all values of E are permitted, or by $Z_{qu} = \sum_{n=0}^{\infty} e^{-\beta n\varepsilon_0}$, if the only values allowed are $E_n = n\varepsilon_0$ ($n = 0, 1, 2, \ldots$). In each case

$$\varepsilon = \bar{E} = -\frac{\partial \ln Z}{\partial \beta}$$

† The experimental value is $\hbar = 1{\cdot}05 \times 10^{-27}$ erg s. $\hbar$ is often called the Dirac constant to distinguish it from Planck's constant $h = 2\pi\hbar = 6{\cdot}63 \times 10^{-27}$ erg s.

The first consequences of this hypothesis concerned the lower (short-wave) limit of X-ray spectra and the photoelectric effect. When an electron possessing energy $e\Phi$ strikes the anode of an X-ray tube, the highest angular frequency ω_{max} that can occur in the resulting radiation is given by

$$\hbar\omega_{max} = e\Phi$$

In the photoelectric case, if a light quantum strikes a metallic surface and transfers its whole energy $\hbar\omega$ to an electron, the latter can escape from the metal with kinetic energy $\hbar\omega - W$, where W is the work function (i.e. the work done by the electron in escaping). Both statements have been confirmed experimentally and have been used as the basis of precision methods for the determination of $\hbar$.

The extension of (9.4) to the natural modes of vibration of solid bodies forms the basis of the theory of the specific heats of crystals.

In its first stage (until about 1913) the quantum theory might be described as the theory of the linear oscillator, because it only recognized the "permitted" states given by the formula $E_n = n\hbar\omega$.

§10. The Rutherford-Bohr atomic model

The only "classical" model of the atom that could explain the occurrence of sharp spectral lines is due to J. J. Thomson; it was discussed in §4. Thomson assumed that the positive charge of the nucleus was approximately homogeneously distributed over a sphere of radius of order 10^{-8} cm. The electron is then bound to the nucleus by an elastic force and can execute oscillations, the frequency of which lies within the range of visible light.

Thomson's hypothesis became quite untenable as a result of the experiments of Rutherford, who investigated the deflection of α-particles by thin metal foils. Rutherford's results, in particular the occasional deflections through more than 90 degrees, forced him to the conclusion that the positive charge of individual metal atoms is concentrated in a space less than 10^{-12} cm. The atom accordingly consists of a positively charged nucleus of not more than 10^{-12} cm radius, around which the electrons revolve at distances* up to 10^{-8} cm.

* It would at first seem possible to attempt to preserve Thomson's model in the light of Rutherford's experiments, simply by interchanging the signs of the charges so that the electron is now regarded as distributed. This assumption leads to the same properties of an "atom"; it corresponds approximately to the results yielded by a quantum mechanical description (cf. §28). Such a model is of comparable value to Thomson's, but is incompatible with the fact that the electron must also be described by a charge distributed over a very small radius ($R_{el} \approx 10^{-13}$ cm).

It was impossible, however, to explain the sharpness of the spectral lines in terms of classical theory and the new model of the atom, as we may see for the simplest case of the hydrogen atom. An electron revolving around the nucleus at a distance of 10^{-8} cm must be continually radiating electromagnetic energy. In doing so it loses energy itself, and revolves in spirals round the nucleus which it gradually approaches, and by which it is finally captured. This model is therefore quite unstable, and in addition it cannot possibly radiate at a single well-defined frequency.

To provide a way out of this dilemma two postulates were put forward by N. Bohr:

1. There are definite orbits for the electron, in which it does not radiate. Let the energies of these orbits be

$$E_1, E_2, \ldots, E_n, \ldots \tag{10.1}$$

2. From time to time, the electron will cross from an orbit n to another orbit s, for which $E_s < E_n$. When such a transition occurs, the energy difference $E_n - E_s$ is radiated as a light quantum:

$$\hbar\omega_{ns} = E_n - E_s \tag{10.2}$$

If the electron is initially in orbit s, the same equation gives the frequency at which the transition from s to n can be induced by the absorption of a quantum $\hbar\omega_{ns}$.

In order to describe the optical properties of the atom we need a rule for the evaluation of the terms $E_1, \ldots, E_n, \ldots$. In this connection a hint is provided by the expression $E_n = n\hbar\omega$ for the permitted energy states of the linear oscillator, which we have already encountered. For an oscillator of mass m and angular frequency $2\pi\nu = \omega$, the Hamiltonian function is

$$\frac{1}{2m} p^2 + \tfrac{1}{2} m\omega^2 x^2 = \mathscr{H}(x, p)$$

where the momentum p is canonically conjugate to x. Consider the "orbit" in the xp-plane (figure 13) for which the energy is E. Since

$$\frac{1}{2m} p^2 + \tfrac{1}{2} m\omega^2 x^2 = E \tag{10.3}$$

it is an ellipse with semi-axes $a = \sqrt{(2mE)}$ and $b = \sqrt{(2E/m\omega^2)}$. The area Φ of the ellipse is

$$\Phi = \pi ab = 2\pi \frac{E}{\omega}$$

Our postulate $E_n = n\hbar\omega$ therefore states that the only orbits allowed are those for which $\Phi/2\pi = n\hbar$. Now the area is

$$\Phi = \oint p(E, x)\, dx$$

where p is expressed as a function of x and E according to (10.3), and the sign $\oint$ means the integration around a single orbital circuit.

We now have a starting-point for the calculation of the energy values, and one that is capable of considerable generalization. If we

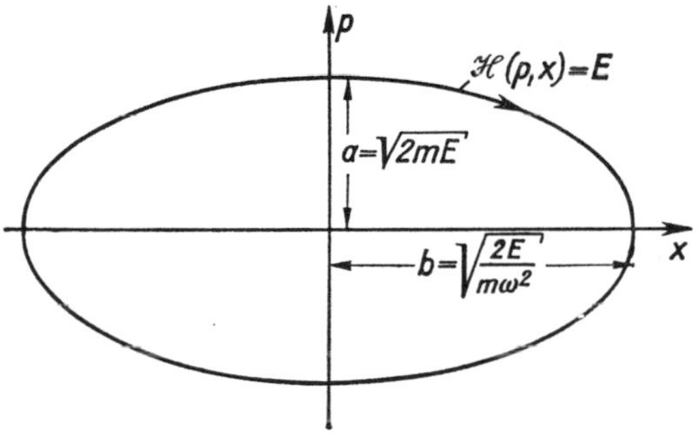

Fig. 13.—The path of a linear oscillator in phase space. The arrow indicates the direction of motion

restrict ourselves at first to one-dimensional motion, with a potential energy $V(x)$ (in place of the particular elastic energy of (10.3)), then (as did Bohr) we assume the following rule for the determination of E_n:

$$J(E) = \frac{1}{2\pi} \oint p(E, x)\, dx = n\hbar \qquad (10.4)$$

In the above expression $p = \sqrt{\{2m[E - V(x)]\}}$ is the momentum resulting* from the equation $p^2/2m + V(x) = E$.

If the system possesses f degrees of freedom, each orbit is specified by $f-1$ constants $c_1, c_2, \ldots, c_{f-1}$ in addition to the energy. If the coordinates $q_1, \ldots, q_f$ and the canonically conjugate momenta $p_1, \ldots, p_f$

* Expression (10.4) is invariant with respect to canonical transformations by means of the function S, since, by (6.13), $\bar{p}\, d\bar{x} = p\, dx - d(S - \bar{p}\bar{x})$.

are so chosen that each momentum p_r depends only on the conjugate coordinate q_r and the constants $E, c_1, \ldots, c_{f-1}$, then, as was shown by A. Sommerfeld, equation (10.4) may be generalized to give the quantum conditions

$$J_r = \frac{1}{2\pi}\oint p_r(q_r, E, c_1, \ldots, c_{f-1})\, dq_r = n_r \hbar \quad (r = 1, 2, \ldots, f) \qquad (10.5)$$

required for the determination of the constants $E, c_1, \ldots, c_{f-1}$ as functions of the quantum numbers $n_1, \ldots, n_f$.

We shall describe the procedure for the case of a particle moving within a spherically symmetrical potential $V(r)$. In spherical coordinates r, θ, ϕ, the Hamiltonian function is*

$$\mathcal{H}(r, \theta, \phi, p_r, p_\theta, p_\phi) = \frac{1}{2m}\left\{p_r^2 + \frac{1}{r^2}\left(p_\theta^2 + \frac{1}{\sin^2\theta} p_\phi^2\right)\right\} + V(r) \qquad (10.6)$$

The variables are already separated: from Hamilton's equations we have

$$\frac{d}{dt} p_\phi = 0, \qquad p_\phi = c_\phi$$

also

$$\frac{d}{dt}\left(p_\theta^2 + \frac{c_\phi^2}{\sin^2\theta}\right) = 0, \qquad p_\theta^2 + \frac{c_\phi^2}{\sin^2\theta} = c_\theta^2$$

and finally

$$\frac{d\mathcal{H}}{dt} = 0, \qquad \frac{1}{2m}\left(p_r^2 + \frac{c_\theta^2}{r^2}\right) + V(r) = E$$

It is evident that c_ϕ is the component of the angular momentum about the z-axis, and that $c_\theta{}^2$ is the square of the angular momentum.

In particular, if we put the potential $V(r)$ equal to the Coulomb energy $-e^2/r$, we have three phase integrals to evaluate. The results are

$$J_\phi = \frac{1}{2\pi}\oint p_\phi\, d\phi = c_\phi$$

$$J_\theta = \frac{1}{2\pi}\oint \sqrt{\left(c_\theta^2 - \frac{c_\phi^2}{\sin^2\theta}\right)}\, d\theta = c_\theta - c_\phi \qquad (10.7)$$

$$J_r = \frac{1}{2\pi}\oint \sqrt{\left(2mE + \frac{2me^2}{r} - \frac{c_\theta^2}{r^2}\right)}\, dr = \frac{me^2}{\sqrt{(-2mE)}} - c_\theta$$

* Cf. Exercise 1, p. 46.

If these equations are added together, c_ϕ and c_θ are eliminated:

$$J_\phi+J_\theta+J_r=\frac{me^2}{\sqrt{(-2mE)}} \quad \text{or} \quad E=-\frac{1}{2}\frac{me^4}{(J_\phi+J_\theta+J_r)^2}$$

If we now introduce the quantum condition (10.5), the energy E is found to be a function of the three quantum numbers n_ϕ, n_θ, n_r:

$$E=-\frac{1}{2}\frac{me^4}{\hbar^2}\frac{1}{(n_\phi+n_\theta+n_r)^2}$$

Putting $n_\phi+n_\theta+n_r=n$, we have

$$E_n=-2\pi\hbar cR\frac{1}{n^2} \tag{10.8}$$

where $R=\dfrac{1}{4\pi}\dfrac{me^4}{c\hbar^3}$ is known as the Rydberg constant. The only "allowed" energy values are those given by (10.8), with $n=1,2,3,\ldots$ From (10.2) it then follows that the wave numbers (reciprocal wavelengths) of the spectral lines are:

$$\frac{1}{\lambda_{nm}}=\frac{\omega_{nm}}{2\pi c}=\frac{E_n-E_m}{2\pi\hbar c}=R\left(\frac{1}{m^2}-\frac{1}{n^2}\right) \tag{10.9}$$

In particular,

$m=1$, $n=2,3,4,\ldots$ gives the "Lyman series"
$m=2$, $n=3,4,5,\ldots$ the "Balmer series"
$m=3$, $n=4,5,6,\ldots$ the "Paschen series"

of the hydrogen spectrum.

The quantum numbers are often referred to as follows:

$n_\phi+n_\theta+n_r=n$, the principal quantum number,
$n_\phi+n_\theta=l$, the angular-momentum quantum number,
$n_\phi=m$, the magnetic quantum number.

The above treatment of the hydrogen atom must be considered to be a provisional one; a consistent theory can only be obtained by means of quantum mechanics (e.g. the Schrödinger equation). The subject will be discussed in detail in §29, where it will be seen that many of the above results are confirmed.

In the quantum-mechanical treatment of the hydrogen atom, the energy, the angular momentum, and any arbitrary component of the latter are still subject to the quantum conditions, i.e. they can only assume certain discrete values.

§11. The correspondence principle

Bohr's assumptions of the existence of stationary energy values $E_1, \ldots, E_n, \ldots$ and the emission of light as quanta $\hbar\omega_{ns}$ of frequency

$$\omega_{ns} = \frac{E_n - E_s}{\hbar} \tag{11.1}$$

represent such a fundamental change from the concepts of classical physics that it seems hopeless to try to base them on a model, although this was often attempted during the period of currency of his theory (1913–25).

In spite of this difficulty, an attempt can be made to establish a relationship between the laws of classical physics and those of the

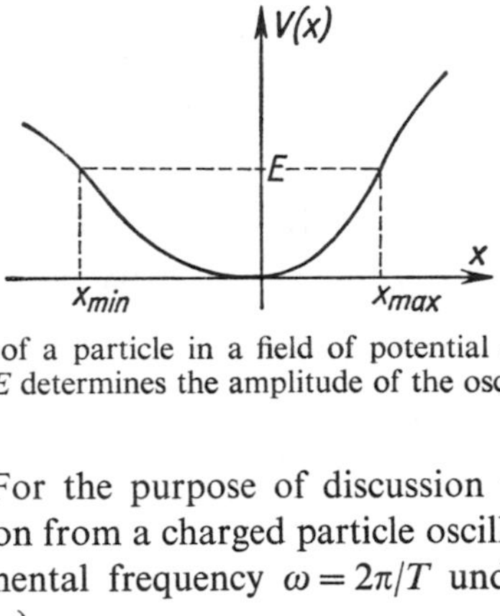

Fig. 14.—Motion of a particle in a field of potential energy $V(x)$. The energy E determines the amplitude of the oscillations

quantum theory. For the purpose of discussion we may take as an example the radiation from a charged particle oscillating parallel to the x-axis at a fundamental frequency $\omega = 2\pi/T$ under the influence of potential energy $V(x)$.

If E is the energy of the particle, the maximum and minimum amplitudes are given by $E = V(x_{max}) = V(x_{min})$ (figure 14). The motion can be described by a Fourier series containing the fundamental frequency ω and integral multiples thereof, $\tau\omega$. (Harmonics of the fundamental frequency are absent only in the case of the linear oscillator, where the potential is a parabolic function.) The oscillation can be expressed in terms of E, or in terms of J, in view of the relation (10.4). Then

$$x(t) = \sum_{\tau=-\infty}^{\tau=+\infty} x_\tau(J)\, e^{i\tau\omega t} \quad \text{and} \qquad x_{-\tau}(J) = x_\tau^*(J) \qquad (11.2)$$

Let the constant $J = n\hbar$ designate the state of the "atom". On classical theory we should expect the atom to emit spectral lines of angular frequencies $\omega, 2\omega, \ldots, \tau\omega, \ldots$, in virtue of (11.2), and that the intensity of the line $\tau\omega$ would be proportional to the square of the amplitude and therefore to $|x_\tau(J)|^2$, in accordance with Hertz's formula for the radiation from a dipole oscillator.

According to the quantum theory, an atom in state n can change to a lower state s, as a result of which it emits one of the lines

$$\omega_{ns} = \frac{E_n - E_s}{\hbar} \qquad (s = 1, 2, \ldots, n-1)$$

It is hopeless to try to establish a simple relationship between the classical and quantum theory predictions regarding the behaviour of an individual atom. The situation becomes more tractable, however, if we consider a gas consisting of a large number (say N) of identical independent atoms in a state $J = n\hbar$. According to classical theory, each of the N atoms will emit spectral lines $\omega, 2\omega, \ldots$ as described above. According to quantum theory, on the other hand, each atom is free to change to a lower energy level E_s. In general, therefore, all frequencies ω_{ns} can occur, and the intensity of each line depends on the number of atoms changing from state n to state s. This number, however, is proportional to the probability of the transition $n \to s$. It is therefore only when a large number of atoms are considered that the quantum theory predicts a spectrum of many lines, capable of comparison with the "classical" spectrum predicted by (11.2).

The correspondence principle was first enunciated by Bohr. It states that the experimentally realized predictions of the quantum theory must tend asymptotically to those of classical theory, for quantum numbers n increasing without limit and for transitions* $n - s = \Delta n$ for which $\Delta n \ll n$. An example would be a highly excited hydrogen atom, in which the electron revolves slowly round the nucleus at a great distance from it (about 10^{-8} cm). In this case the

* Another form of the principle states that in the limit as $\hbar \to 0$ the predictions of the quantum theory must coincide with those of the classical theory.

field could certainly be calculated according to the laws of classical electrodynamics. In the limiting case of large quantum numbers, therefore, the spectra of a great number of atoms calculated from the classical and from the quantum theories, should coincide asymptotically as regards all observable particulars, such as the position, intensity, and polarization of the individual spectral lines.

We must now establish a "correspondence" between the classical harmonic frequencies $\tau\omega$ and the Bohr frequencies ω_{ns} to which they tend at high quantum numbers. This may be achieved by means of a fundamental theorem of classical mechanics.

If the energy E is calculated as a function of J from the phase integral defined in (10.4)

$$J = \frac{1}{2\pi} \oint p(E, x)\, dx \tag{11.3}$$

the fundamental frequency of the motion is given by

$$\omega = \frac{dE}{dJ} \tag{11.4}$$

This is a generalization of the equation $E = J\omega$, which is restricted to the case of the linear oscillator. Equation (11.4) may be proved as follows. From the relation $p = \{2m[E - V(x)]\}^{1/2}$ we obtain $\partial p/\partial E = m/p = 1/v$. Therefore

$$\frac{dJ}{dE} = \frac{1}{2\pi} \oint \frac{dx}{v} = \frac{T}{2\pi} = \frac{1}{\omega}$$

since $\oint \frac{dx}{v}$ is the time required for one oscillation.

When there are several degrees of freedom, then instead of the one constant, E, we have f, say: $c_1, c_2, \ldots, c_{f-1}, E$. If we use these to construct the f phase integrals

$$J_j = \frac{1}{2\pi} \oint p_j(x_j, c_1, \ldots, c_{f-1}, E)\, dx_j \qquad (j = 1, 2, \ldots, f)$$

the latter may be used to calculate the constants c_j and hence the energy as functions of the J_j, as we did in the case of the hydrogen atom:

$$E = E(J_1, J_2, \ldots, J_f)$$

The variables x_j may then be expressed as Fourier series:

$$x_j(t) = \sum_{\tau_1, \tau_2, \ldots} x_{j\tau_1 \ldots \tau_f}(J_1, \ldots, J_f) \exp i(\omega_1 \tau_1 + \ldots + \omega_f \tau_f)t$$

where

$$\omega_j = \frac{\partial E}{\partial J_j}$$

Using equation (11.4), we may express the frequency $\tau\omega$ of the τth harmonic as

$$\tau\omega = \tau\frac{dE}{dJ} = \lim_{\varepsilon\to 0}\frac{E(J+\tau\varepsilon)-E(J)}{\varepsilon} \tag{11.5}$$

since the last expression is the definition of the differential coefficient.

In quantum theory, J can only assume integral values $n\hbar$; in place of the continuous curve $E(J)$ there occur the discrete energy values

$$E_n = E(n\hbar), \qquad E_{n+1} = E\{(n+1)\hbar\},\ldots$$

In view of the discontinuous nature of the J values, it seems reasonable to substitute a difference quotient for the derivative in (11.5). This means that we no longer pass to the limit $\varepsilon\to 0$, but that we put $\varepsilon = \hbar$. This is in fact the difference between successive values of J. From (11.5) we therefore obtain the correspondence*

$$\tau\omega \Leftrightarrow \frac{E_{n+\tau}-E_n}{\hbar} \tag{11.6}$$

When the quantum number changes by τ units, the emitted or absorbed frequency corresponds to the τth harmonic of the classical motion.

The recognition of this fact enables us to establish a relationship between each term of the Fourier expansion for the classical orbit in the state $J = n\hbar$, and the corresponding quantum transition:

$$x_\tau(J)\exp i\tau\omega t \Leftrightarrow x_{n+\tau,n}\exp i\frac{E_{n+\tau}-E_n}{\hbar}t \tag{11.7}$$

This relation may also be written in a slightly modified form:†

$$x_{m-n}(n\hbar)\exp i(m-n)\omega t \Leftrightarrow x_{mn}\exp i\omega_{mn}t \tag{11.7a}$$

In quantum theory, therefore, although Fourier coefficients associated with electron orbits may not appear, we nevertheless anticipate the existence of the corresponding "transition amplitudes" x_{mn}. We shall meet these amplitudes later as the elements of a matrix associated with the x-coordinate, and shall often have occasion to employ them.

* This correspondence is by no means unequivocal: we should, for instance, be equally justified in using the relation

$$\tau\omega \Leftrightarrow \frac{E_n - E_{n-\tau}}{\hbar}$$

† Here too, we are free to write either $x_{m-n}(n\hbar)$ or $x_{m-n}(m\hbar)$ for the left-hand side. From (11.2) we have $x_{nm} = x^*_{mn}$.

The correspondence must be interpreted to mean that at infinitely large values of n the amplitudes $x_{n+\tau,n}$ coincide with the Fourier coefficients $x_\tau(n\hbar)$ of the classical orbit. It is true that the quantum theory amplitudes have no significance for any single orbit, but the correspondence principle enables us to establish a relationship between the quantities $|x_{mn}|^2$ and the radiation from N atoms in the state $J = n\hbar$.

For this purpose, we make use of classical theory to calculate the energy radiated at frequency $\tau\omega$ by an electron oscillating in accordance with equation (11.2). The motion contributing to the energy at this frequency is

$$x_\tau(t) = x_\tau(J)\, e^{i\tau\omega t} + \{x_\tau(J)\}^*\, e^{-i\tau\omega t}$$

From (4.4) the radiated power is

$$S_{cl} = \frac{2e^2}{3c^3}\overline{\ddot{x}^2}$$

Substituting the value given above for $x(t)$:

$$S_{cl} = \frac{4e^2}{3c^3}(\tau\omega)^4\,|x_\tau(J)|^2$$

We assume that a gas consisting of N atoms in state n emits energy at angular frequency ω_{mn} at the following average rate per atom:

$$S_{qu} = \frac{4e^2}{3c^3}\,\omega_{mn}^4\,|x_{mn}|^2 \tag{11.8}$$

Also, a single atom emits energy $\hbar\omega_{mn}$ in the course of the transition $m \to n$.

Now if $A_{mn}\delta t$ represents the probability that an atom in state m radiates during the interval δt and thereby changes to state n (where $E_n < E_m$), then the number of atoms undergoing this transition will be $NA_{mn}\delta t$, and the total energy emitted will be $\hbar\omega_{mn}NA_{mn}\delta t$. The average emission from a single atom in this interval is therefore

$$S_{qu}\,\delta t = \hbar\omega_{mn}\,A_{mn}\,\delta t \tag{11.8a}$$

Comparison of the two equations for S_{qu} yields the following expression for the transition probability:

$$A_{mn} = \frac{4e^2\omega_{mn}^3}{3c^3\hbar}\,|x_{mn}|^2 \tag{11.9}$$

So far we have restricted ourselves to motion in one dimension. For the three-dimensional case, we must take account of the additional contributions $y_\tau(J)$ and $z_\tau(J)$, and the corresponding transition amplitudes y_{mn} and z_{mn}. The transition probability is then:

$$A_{mn} = \frac{4e^2}{3c^3}\frac{\omega_{mn}^3}{\hbar}(|x_{mn}|^2+|y_{mn}|^2+|z_{mn}|^2) \tag{11.9a}$$

We shall deduce this equation again by strict quantum methods, after having provided general methods for the evaluation of the amplitudes x_{mn}.

The foregoing analysis may be used to determine the "matrix elements" x_{mn} of the linear oscillator, for which the classical equation of motion is simple harmonic. Hence from (11.2)

$$x(t) = x_1(J)\,e^{i\omega t} + x_1^*(J)\,e^{-i\omega t} \tag{11.10}$$

In order to evaluate $x_1(J)$ we note, first, that $E = m\omega^2\overline{x^2} = J\omega$ for the oscillator. Also, if we take $x_1(J)$ to be real, then $\overline{x^2} = 2\,[x_1(J)]^2$ from (11.10). Hence

$$x_1(J) = x_1^*(J) = \sqrt{\frac{J}{2m\omega}}$$

According to the correspondence equation (11.7) we therefore have, for $J = n\hbar$,

$$x_1(n\hbar)\exp i\omega t \Leftrightarrow x_{n,n-1}\exp i\frac{E_n - E_{n-1}}{\hbar}t$$

$$x_1(n\hbar)\exp -i\omega t \Leftrightarrow x_{n-1,n}\exp -i\frac{E_n - E_{n-1}}{\hbar}t$$

The only matrix elements to occur are those for which $|n-m| = 1$. According to (11.9), therefore, this means that the only transitions that take place are those from n to $n-1$ for emission, and from n to $n+1$ in the case of absorption. Also,

$$x_{n,n-1} = x_{n-1,n} = \sqrt{\frac{n\hbar}{2m\omega}} \tag{11.11}$$

We shall often encounter the above equation.

We shall now calculate the transition probability $A_{n,n-1}$ in order to verify the above analysis. Using (11.9) and (11.11), we have

$$A_{n,n-1} = \frac{2e^2}{3mc^3}n\omega^2$$

If we now put $n\hbar\omega = E$, the energy radiated per second is

$$S = \hbar\omega A_{n,\,n-1} = \frac{2e^2\omega^2}{3mc^3}\,E$$

i.e. the fraction of the energy radiated per second, γ, is $2e^2\omega^2/3mc^3$. This agrees with the classical value.

An important application of the correspondence equations (11.6) and (11.7) is based on the assumption that only those quantum transitions occur for which a corresponding classical harmonic exists, and that all other transitions are "forbidden". We have already met the simplest example of this assumption in the case of the linear oscillator.

The correspondence principle has been of particular assistance in the determination of the "selection rules" of the atomic spectra. For instance, when we discussed the hydrogen atom in §10 we found that the state of the atom could be described by means of three quantum numbers, n, l, m. This classification may also be employed for many of the more complex atoms, such as those of the alkali metals. The selection rules state that in general, the only transitions to occur are those for which $\Delta l = \pm 1$ and $\Delta m = \pm 1$ or 0. We shall return to this subject later (in §24); at this stage we should merely note that the selection rules become comprehensible if we make the assumption that the corresponding harmonics of classical motion do not exist.

§12. Deduction of the Heisenberg form of the quantum theory

Heisenberg's approach to quantum mechanics involves the extension of the correspondence principle in a direction to which brief reference was made in §11. The basis of the method is briefly indicated in what follows. We shall again restrict ourselves to a single degree of freedom in order that the crucial aspects of the theory may be easily recognized.

(*a*) *Product formation.*—Consider a system of fundamental angular frequency ω, and assume that two quantities $a(t)$ and $b(t)$ depend on time as follows:

$$a(t) = \sum_\tau a_\tau(J)\,e^{i\tau\omega t} \quad \text{and} \quad b(t) = \sum_\tau b_\tau(J)\,e^{i\tau\omega t} \tag{12.1}$$

In §11 we showed that a "matrix element" in quantum theory corresponds to a single term of the Fourier expansion, thus:

$$a_\tau(J)\,e^{i\tau\omega t} \Leftrightarrow a_{nm}\,e^{i\omega_{nm}t}$$

where

$$n-m=\tau, \quad J=n\hbar \quad \text{or} \quad m\hbar, \quad \omega_{nm}=(E_n-E_m)/\hbar$$

In order to extend this correspondence to the product $a(t)b(t)$, we shall develop the latter in a Fourier series and then seek the matrix element corresponding to the factor of $e^{i\tau\omega t}$ in this expansion. By (12.1)

$$a(t)\,b(t)=\sum_{\tau}\left\{\sum_{s}a_s(J)\,b_{\tau-s}(J)\right\}e^{i\tau\omega t}=\sum_{\tau}(ab)_\tau e^{i\tau\omega t} \quad (12.2)$$

In the above expression we have so arranged the double summation that all terms with the same time factor $e^{i\tau\omega t}$ are collected together in the summation $\sum_s a_s b_{\tau-s}=(ab)_\tau$. Similarly, in the case of the quantum mechanical terms

$$a_{nm}\,e^{i\omega_{nm}t} \quad \text{and} \quad b_{nm}\,e^{i\omega_{nm}t}$$

we may seek to associate with the product ab a matrix element $(ab)_{nm}$ that also contains the time factor $e^{i\omega_{nm}t}$. The fact that

$$\omega_{nm}=\omega_{ns}+\omega_{sm}$$

for any value of s necessarily leads to the result

$$(ab)_{nm}\,e^{i\omega_{nm}t}=\sum_{s}a_{ns}\,e^{i\omega_{ns}t}b_{sm}\,e^{i\omega_{sm}t}$$

for the matrix element associated with the product ab and the transition from E_n to E_m. Hence we have the following rule for the multiplication of two quantum terms a_{nm} and b_{nm}:

$$(ab)_{nm}=\sum_{s}a_{ns}\,b_{sm} \quad (12.3)$$

This rule is the same as the multiplication rule for matrices; in this connection we should note that in general, matrix multiplication does not obey the commutative rule, i.e.

$$(ab)_{mn}\neq(ba)_{mn}$$

(*b*) *The Poisson bracket.*—If p and x are canonically conjugate variables as defined in Hamiltonian theory, and if $a(p,x)$ and $b(p,x)$ are any two functions of these variables, then the "Poisson bracket" $\{a,b\}$ is defined as

$$\{a,b\}=\frac{\partial a}{\partial p}\frac{\partial b}{\partial x}-\frac{\partial b}{\partial p}\frac{\partial a}{\partial x}=\frac{\partial(a,b)}{\partial(p,x)} \quad (12.4)$$

By the special choice of *a* and *b* we obtain

$$\{a,x\} = \frac{\partial a}{\partial p} \qquad \{a,p\} = -\frac{\partial a}{\partial x} \tag{12.5}$$

$$\{p,x\} = 1 \tag{12.6}$$

The Hamiltonian equations may also be expressed by Poisson brackets:

$$\{\mathscr{H},x\} = \frac{\partial \mathscr{H}}{\partial p} = \dot{x} \qquad \{\mathscr{H},p\} = -\frac{\partial \mathscr{H}}{\partial x} = \dot{p} \tag{12.7}$$

Hence it follows that for any arbitrary function* $b(p,x)$

$$\{\mathscr{H},b\} = \dot{b} \tag{12.7a}$$

According to (12.4) the Poisson bracket can be written as a Jacobian; its value therefore remains unchanged if new variables $\bar{p}$, $\bar{x}$ are introduced by means of the canonical transformation (6.13):

$$\{a,b\} = \frac{\partial(a,b)}{\partial(p,x)} = \frac{\partial(a,b)}{\partial(\bar{p},\bar{x})} \tag{12.4a}$$

since the Jacobian of the transformation is unity. For the same reason, equations (12.5,6) remain valid when expressed in the new coordinates.

At this stage it seems natural to introduce J (equation 10.4) as a new variable, because the quantum conditions can be very simply expressed in terms of this quantity. If we put $J = \bar{p}$, and if $w = \bar{x}$ is the coordinate† canonically conjugate to J, then

$$\{a,b\} = \frac{\partial(a,b)}{\partial(J,w)} = \frac{\partial a}{\partial J}\frac{\partial b}{\partial w} - \frac{\partial b}{\partial J}\frac{\partial a}{\partial w} \tag{12.8}$$

The function $S(x,J)$ that produces the required transformation is

$$S(x,J) = \int_0^x p\{E(J),x\}\,dx$$

* The function *b* does not depend explicitly on time; its variation with respect to time is merely the result of the time rate of change of the quantities *p* and *x*, of which it is a function.

† *J* and *w* are termed the action and angle variables. The corresponding transformations may also be performed for periodic motion in problems with several degrees of freedom: cf. the treatment of the hydrogen atom in §10. The Hamiltonian function then depends only on the action variables, and the canonically conjugate angle variables (usually angular quantities) are proportional to the time.

It may easily be shown that this function possesses the properties expressed in (6.13). The canonically conjugate quantity w is obtained by differentiating, taking into account the relation (11.4):

$$w = \frac{\partial S}{\partial J} = \omega \frac{\partial S}{\partial E} = \omega \int_0^x \frac{dx}{v} = \omega t$$

The Hamiltonian function is $\mathscr{H}(J, w) = E(J)$; the Hamiltonian equations $\dot{J} = 0$, $\dot{w} = dE/dJ = \omega(J)$ also give the result $w = \omega t$, as is to be expected. Using this last result, we may write $\dfrac{\partial b}{\partial w} = \dfrac{1}{\omega}\dfrac{\partial b}{\partial t}$; the τth Fourier component of $\partial b/\partial w$ is therefore

$$\left(\frac{\partial b}{\partial w}\right)_\tau = i\tau b_\tau$$

To find the corresponding expression for $\{a, b\}_\tau$ we put

$$\{a, b\}_\tau = i \sum_{r+s=\tau} \left\{ \left(\frac{\partial a}{\partial J}\right)_r s b_s - r a_r \left(\frac{\partial b}{\partial J}\right)_s \right\}$$

in accordance with (12.2). The derivatives with respect to J are replaced by appropriate difference quotients, so chosen as to eliminate the factors r and s:

$$\left(\frac{\partial a}{\partial J}\right)_r \Leftrightarrow \frac{a_r(J) - a_r(J - s\hbar)}{s\hbar} \qquad \left(\frac{\partial b}{\partial J}\right)_s \Leftrightarrow \frac{b_s(J) - b_s(J - r\hbar)}{r\hbar}$$

In the resulting expression

$$\frac{i}{\hbar} \sum_{r+s=\tau} \{a_r(J)\, b_s(J - r\hbar) - b_s(J)\, a_r(J - s\hbar)\}$$

let us put $J = \tau\hbar$, and let $r = m - l$, $s = l - n$ in the first term, and $s = m - l$, $r = l - n$ in the second. We then obtain the familiar correspondence

$$\{a, b\}_{m-n} \Leftrightarrow \frac{i}{\hbar}(ab - ba)_{mn} \tag{12.9}$$

The right-hand side of (12.9) may be termed a quantum-mechanical Poisson bracket.

A comparison with the special cases quoted above reveals that, for two canonically conjugate variables p and x, the corresponding analogue of (12.6) is

$$(px-xp)_{nm} \equiv [p,x]_{n,m} = \frac{\hbar}{i}\,\delta_{nm}$$

or

$$px-xp \equiv [p,x] = \frac{\hbar}{i}\mathbf{1} \tag{12.10}$$

where the symbol $\mathbf{1}$ represents the unit matrix

$$\begin{pmatrix} 1 & 0 & 0 & . & . \\ 0 & 1 & 0 & . & . \\ 0 & 0 & 1 & . & . \\ . & . & . & . & . \end{pmatrix}$$

Again, corresponding to (12.7*a*), we have the following relation for the rate of change of a quantum-mechanical term:

$$\left(\frac{db}{dt}\right)_{nm} = \frac{i}{\hbar}(\mathscr{H}b - b\mathscr{H})_{nm} \quad \text{and} \quad \frac{db}{dt} = \frac{i}{\hbar}[\mathscr{H},b] \tag{12.11}$$

In order to verify this last relation, we shall restrict ourselves to the case (tacitly assumed in §11) in which H_{nm} is a diagonal matrix, i.e. $H_{nm} = E_n\delta_{nm}$. Then

$$(\mathscr{H}b - b\mathscr{H})_{nm} = \sum_s (\mathscr{H}_{ns}\,b_{sm} - b_{ns}\,\mathscr{H}_{sm}) = (E_n - E_m)\,b_{nm}$$

$$\left(\frac{db}{dt}\right)_{nm} = i\omega_{nm}\,b_{nm}$$

Hence

$$b_{nm}(t) = b_{nm}(0)\,e^{i\omega_{nm}t}$$

which is the quantity we started with.

The relations (12.10) and (12.11), which have been derived somewhat intuitively from the correspondence principle, will be seen later to constitute the foundations of the whole quantum theory, in which they will be introduced as "axioms".

(*c*) *Stationary energy values.*—From the above considerations, Heisenberg, Born, and Jordan deduced the following procedure for the determination of the Bohr stationary energy values in a mechanical system with one degree of freedom and potential energy $V(x)$.

Consider the classical form of the Hamiltonian function

$$\frac{p^2}{2m}+V(x)=\mathscr{H}(p,x)$$

as a matrix equation

$$\left\{\frac{p^2}{2m}+V(x)\right\}_{nm}=\mathscr{H}_{nm} \tag{12.12}$$

We express the fact that the energy is constant with respect to time by the requirement that the matrix H_{mn} be diagonal, i.e. equal to $E_m\delta_{mn}$. The reason for this postulate is that a term nm of each matrix contains the time factor $e^{i\omega_{nm}t}$, which is only independent of time when $m=n$. We therefore require that the matrix $\mathscr{H}$ should have the form

$$\mathscr{H}=\begin{pmatrix} E_1 & 0 & 0 & . \\ 0 & E_2 & 0 & . \\ 0 & 0 & E_3 & . \\ . & . & . & . \end{pmatrix}$$

where the diagonal terms $E_1, E_2, \ldots$ are initially unknown. We can now formulate the problem precisely: Do matrices p_{nm} and x_{nm} exist, such that firstly

$$(px-xp)_{nm}=\frac{\hbar}{i}\delta_{nm} \tag{12.13a}$$

and secondly

$$\left\{\frac{p^2}{2m}+V(x)\right\}_{nm}=E_n\delta_{nm} \tag{12.13b}$$

becomes a diagonal matrix (with initially unknown numbers $E_1, E_2, \ldots$)?

It will be seen later that in the case of potentials for which the question has any significance, these two postulates serve to determine unambiguously the quantities x_{nm}, p_{nm}, and E_n. We shall perform the relevant calculation for the case of the linear oscillator in §15, to which the reader is now referred.

§13. De Broglie's hypothesis of the wave-like properties of the electron

(*a*) *De Broglie's hypothesis.*—We have shown how Heisenberg's form of the quantum theory was developed by means of an extension of the correspondence principle. An independent and formally simpler approach was presented by an extremely bold speculation by L. de Broglie, the main features of which we shall now describe.

The approach starts from Einstein's light quantum hypothesis, according to which monochromatic light of angular frequency ω interacts with matter as though it consisted of discrete light quanta of energy $\hbar\omega$. Without entering too deeply into the difficult subject of "wave corpuscles", we may describe the situation as follows:

A plane wave of angular frequency ω, amplitude vector **A**, and (vectorial) propagation constant **k** is represented by

$$\mathbf{A}\, e^{i(\mathbf{k}.\mathbf{r}-\omega t)} \tag{13.1}$$

The wavelength λ is derived directly from the magnitude k of the vector **k**:

$$k=\frac{2\pi}{\lambda}$$

Also, for propagation in a vacuum

$$\omega = ck$$

The light quantum associated with the wave described by (13.1) possesses an energy $E=\hbar\omega$. Introducing this energy into the phase factor in the wave equation, we may write it as

$$\exp\frac{i}{\hbar}(\hbar\mathbf{k}\,.\,\mathbf{r}-Et) \tag{13.2}$$

Since the phase of a light wave (i.e. the exponent $\hbar\mathbf{k}.\mathbf{r}-Et$) must be relativistically invariant, and according to the Special Theory of Relativity (Vol. I, §80) the quantities $\{x,y,z,ict\}$ constitute a four-vector, then the quantities $\{\hbar k_x,\hbar k_y,\hbar k_z,iE/c\}$ must also be the components of such a vector, since the exponent contains the scalar product of both vectors. But the quantity iE/c is the fourth component of the relativistic four-momentum $\{p_x,p_y,p_z,iE/c\}$. If $\hbar\omega$ is interpreted as the energy of the light quantum in (13.1), then the momentum associated with this quantum must be $\mathbf{p}=\hbar\mathbf{k}$. Hence we obtain the following familiar value for the magnitude of the momentum:

$$p=\frac{E}{c} \tag{13.3}$$

The above considerations led to de Broglie's hypothesis, which will now be described:

Since all attempts to interpret light quanta according to classical physics have failed, we must accept the fact that the same entity (in this case a light wave) behaves on some occasions as a wave and on others as a corpuscle, according to the experimental conditions. Now, if the unknown fundamental laws of nature are such as to permit this dualism, it would be unsatisfactory if they only applied in the case of light. On the other hand, if this dualism is really of a more general nature, applying also to an electron, for example, then we may employ the same argument that we have just used for the case of the light wave. This means that if we find that under suitable experimental conditions an electron of momentum **p** and energy E behaves like a light wave of angular frequency $\omega = E/\hbar$, then the following relation exists between the momentum and the propagation vector:

$$\mathbf{p} = \hbar \mathbf{k} \tag{13.4}$$

This equation is the well-known relation of de Broglie for momentum and wavelength. Putting $k = 2\pi/\lambda$, we have, from (13.4),

$$\lambda = \frac{2\pi\hbar}{p} = \frac{h}{p} \tag{13.5}$$

For an electron of rest mass m, we must replace equation (13.3) by the relation

$$E = c\sqrt{(p^2 + m^2c^2)} \tag{13.6}$$

The x-component of the velocity v_x, may now be derived:

$$v_x = \frac{\partial E}{\partial p_x} = \frac{cp_x}{\sqrt{(p^2 + m^2c^2)}} \tag{13.7}$$

Hence,

$$p = \frac{mv}{\sqrt{(1 - v^2/c^2)}} \quad \text{and} \quad E = \frac{mc^2}{\sqrt{(1 - v^2/c^2)}}$$

In the energy equation (13.6), two extreme cases are of particular importance:

1. The limiting case $p \gg mc$ leads to the relation for light quanta, $E = cp$, which is also obtained from the same equation if the rest mass m is allowed to become vanishingly small.

2. The non-relativistic case occurs when $p \ll mc$. Equation (13.6) then gives the approximation

$$E = mc^2 + \frac{p^2}{2m} \tag{13.8}$$

to which we shall confine ourselves in the first instance. We may then safely put $E = p^2/2m$ in the expression $\omega = E/\hbar$, since an additive constant is undetectable when the frequencies of matter waves are measured, and is therefore of no significance. If a particle of charge e falls through a potential difference Φ, it acquires kinetic energy $e\Phi$. Using the non-relativistic approximation (13.8), the corresponding momentum is $p = \sqrt{(2me\Phi)}$. De Broglie's relation (13.5) then predicts the following value for the associated wavelength:

$$\lambda = \frac{2\pi\hbar}{\sqrt{(2me\Phi)}}$$

This result may be experimentally verified. If we introduce the known values of $\hbar$, m, e, and measure Φ in volts, then

$$\lambda = \sqrt{\left(\frac{150}{\Phi_{(volts)}}\right)}\, 10^{-8}\ \text{cm} \tag{13.9}$$

This is the wavelength associated with an electron of kinetic energy $e\Phi$.

It is well known that a beam of electrons passing through a crystal gives rise to a diffraction pattern, the position of which can be calculated from the crystal lattice dimensions and the wavelength given by (13.9) in basically the same way as the X-ray diffraction pattern discovered by von Laue. At the time of de Broglie's hypothesis, however, nothing was known of the possibility of such experiments.

(*b*) *The free electron.*—De Broglie's hypothesis leads directly to the relation (13.4) between momentum and wavelength. The term $\exp \frac{i}{\hbar}(\mathbf{p}.\mathbf{r} - Et)$, however, is inadequate to describe a single electron, because its amplitude is unity everywhere in space. In order to obtain a spatially limited expression we make the assumption, essential to all wave theory, that waves may be superposed. Since E is given as a function of p, the most general superposition of such waves is

$$\psi(x, y, z, t) =$$

$$= \frac{1}{(2\pi\hbar)^{3/2}} \iiint\limits_{-\infty}^{\infty} g(p_x, p_y, p_z) \exp \frac{i}{\hbar}(p_x x + p_y y + p_z z - Et)\, dp_x\, dp_y\, dp_z$$

where $g(p_x, p_y, p_z)$ is an arbitrary function. (See figure 15 for the explanation of the factor $1/(2\pi\hbar)^{3/2}$.) In vectorial notation

$$\psi(\mathbf{r}, t) = \frac{1}{(2\pi\hbar)^{3/2}} \int g(\mathbf{p}) \exp \frac{i}{\hbar} (\mathbf{p}\cdot\mathbf{r} - Et)\, d\mathbf{p} \qquad (13.10)$$

We shall restrict ourselves at first to one dimension and discuss the function

$$\psi(x, t) = \frac{1}{(2\pi\hbar)^{1/2}} \int g(p) \exp \frac{i}{\hbar} (px - Et)\, dp \qquad (13.11)$$

We confine ourselves to a narrow frequency band by assuming that the function $g(p)$ is only appreciably different from zero in the neighbourhood of a given momentum p_0. We therefore put $g(p) = g(p_0 + q)$, where g is only different from zero for $|q| \ll |p_0|$. Then we can replace $E(p)$ in equation (13.11) by $E(p_0) + (dE/dp)_{p_0} q$, when we obtain

$$\psi(x, t) = \qquad (13.12)$$

$$= \frac{1}{(2\pi\hbar)^{1/2}} \exp \frac{i}{\hbar} [p_0 x - E(p_0)t] \int g(p_0 + q) \exp\left(\frac{i}{\hbar}\left[x - \left(\frac{dE}{dp}\right)_{p_0} t\right] q\right) dq$$

This is a plane wave $\exp i(p_0 x - E_0 t)/\hbar = \exp i(k_0 x - \omega_0 t)$ multiplied by an amplitude factor which is propagated along the x-axis with "group velocity" $v_g = (dE/dp)_{p_0}$. According to (13.7), however, v_g is identical with the velocity v_0 of a particle with momentum $p_0 = mv_0$.

For the further treatment of the wave packet represented by (13.12), we shall select for $g(p)$ the Gaussian function

$$g(p) = A \exp -\frac{(p - p_0)^2}{4s^2} = A \exp -\left(\frac{q}{2s}\right)^2 \qquad (13.13)$$

where A is an initially unimportant constant. Using this function g, the integral in (13.12) can be evaluated by elementary methods. We obtain

$$\psi(x, t) = s\left(\frac{2}{\hbar}\right)^{1/2} A \exp \frac{i}{\hbar} (p_0 x - E_0 t) \exp -\frac{(x - v_0 t)^2}{\hbar^2/s^2} \qquad (13.14)$$

It is important to realize that the expression (13.14) is an approximate solution for small time intervals. The exact determination of the integral in (13.11), using the value of g given by (13.13), leads to the result

$$\psi(x, t) = \frac{s(2/\hbar)^{1/2} A}{\left(1 + \frac{2s^2 it}{m\hbar}\right)^{1/2}} \exp \frac{i}{\hbar} (p_0 x - E_0 t) \exp -\frac{s^2}{\hbar^2} \frac{(x - v_0 t)^2}{1 + \frac{2s^2 it}{m\hbar}} \qquad (13.14a)$$

In particular, the amplitude factor no longer travels as a rigid entity with velocity v_0 as in (13.12), but becomes increasingly spread out: in effect, the wave packet breaks up. It is easy to understand the reason for the spreading of the originally compact wave packet: it occurs because ψ is composed of waves possessing different phase velocities, since E/p is not constant, and dispersion therefore arises. The wave packet must therefore become increasingly dispersed with time. The rate of this dispersion increases with the difference between the various phase velocities (cf. §16*c*).

(*c*) In attempting to explain the physical significance of the wave functions given by (13.10) or (13.11), we are inclined to interpret them in the first instance as "really" describing the spatial distribution of the electron; we might, for instance, consider $e|\psi(x)|^2$ to be proportional to the electron charge density expressed as a function of position. Alternatively, we might say that

$$\frac{|\psi|^2 \Delta x \Delta y \Delta z}{\iiint |\psi|^2 dx\, dy\, dz}$$

is the fraction of the electron charge contained in the volume $\Delta x \Delta y \Delta z$. Or again, we may say that the electron charge is distributed throughout space according to the charge density function $|\psi|^2$. Using this concept, we may interpret (13.10), for instance, as the "classical" equation for an electrically charged fluid in which there is no longer any question of localized electrons. This "wave concept" may be successfully applied to the interpretation of many experiments, and in particular to the diffraction of electron beams.

However, the fundamental difficulty of the quantum theory appears on further analysis of the above simple interpretation of the function ψ.

The concept that the electron is really distributed throughout space according to the function $|\psi|^2$ is obviously in complete contrast to the basis of electron theory, according to which only integral multiples of the elementary charge occur in all measurements of this quantity.

We met a somewhat similar difficulty in §11. We saw then that a proviso is necessary if we assume the existence of quantum transition elements x_{mn} which determine the intensities of the spectral lines in a similar manner to the Fourier coefficients $x_\tau(J)$ of classical physics; if we make this assumption, we can make no statement about the individual electron orbits. We must confine ourselves to the statistical statement that the quantities $|x_{mn}|^2$ are proportional to the probabilities of the transitions $m \rightarrow n$.

Similarly in the present case: if we wish to represent the electron by means of a wave function $\psi(x,t)$ in spite of the existence of discrete units of electric charge, this is only possible* if we restrict ourselves to a statistical statement. This requires that we should no longer say that the electron is "really" distributed throughout space according to $\psi(x,t)$, but that we should assume that $|\psi(x,t)|^2\Delta x$ is proportional to the experimental probability of finding the electron in the interval $x, x+\Delta x$. In a precisely similar manner, $|g(p)|^2\Delta p$ determines the experimental probability of finding a momentum the value of which lies between p and $p+\Delta p$.

This interpretation leads to consequences of great importance. In the first place we perceive that the coordinate and momentum probabilities are not independent:

$$\begin{aligned} |\psi(x,t)|^2 &= \frac{2s^2}{\hbar}|A|^2 \exp -\frac{(x-v_0 t)^2}{2(\hbar/2s)^2} \\ |g(p)|^2 &= |A|^2 \exp -\frac{(p-p_0)^2}{2s^2} \end{aligned} \qquad (13.15)$$

Both probabilities are represented by Gaussian functions (figure 15); the possible deviations from the most probable values $v_0 t$ and p_0

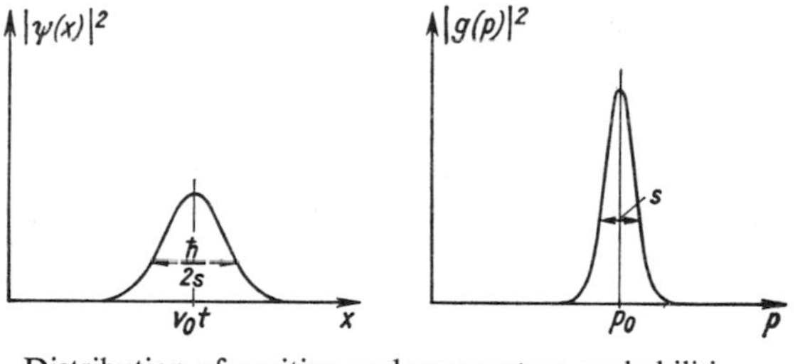

Fig. 15.—Distribution of position and momentum probabilities according to (13.15). The factor $1/\sqrt{(2\pi\hbar)}$ in (13.10) and (13.11) makes the areas under the curves the same for both distributions. [The area is unity for $A^2 = 1/s\sqrt{(2\pi)}$]

are approximately given by the widths $\Delta x = \hbar/2s$ and $\Delta p = s$ of the Gaussian functions. The indeterminacies are reciprocal; if the uncertainty in momentum Δp is small, then the uncertainty in position

* It might be thought that the electron could be represented by a comparatively concentrated wave packet. This is impossible, however, because such a packet would always spread throughout space in the course of time, as shown by (13.14*a*).

is large, and vice versa. However, the product $\Delta p \Delta x$ of the position and momentum uncertainties is constant:

$$\Delta p \Delta x = \tfrac{1}{2}\hbar \tag{13.16}$$

The indeterminacies may be somewhat more precisely formulated by introducing the mean square deviation. The average value of any function of the momentum, $f(p)$, is

$$\bar{f} = \frac{\int f(p)\,|g(p)|^2 dp}{\int |g(p)|^2 dp}$$

The average value of p is p_0. The square root of the mean square deviation $\overline{(p-\bar{p})^2}$ is a measure of the dispersion about the mean. If the indeterminacies are defined as $\Delta p = \{\overline{(p-\bar{p})^2}\}^{1/2}$ and $\Delta x = \{\overline{(x-\bar{x})^2}\}^{1/2}$, the required average values may easily be determined from (13.15):

$$\bar{p} = p_0,\ \overline{(p-\bar{p})^2} = s^2,\ \bar{x} = v_0 t,\ \overline{(x-\bar{x})^2} = (\hbar/2s)^2$$

from which (13.16) again follows.

Thus the simultaneous measurement of the position and momentum of an electron necessarily involves uncertainties which are related in accordance with equation (13.16).

This may be better understood if we consider how the measurement of the position of an electron might be accomplished in practice. The most direct method would be microscopical observation. For such an observation it would be necessary to illuminate the electron, say with light of wavelength λ. The position could then be determined with an accuracy Δx, of order of magnitude $\Delta x \approx \lambda = c/\nu$. But light of frequency ν has a momentum $p = h\nu/c$, of which an appreciable part must be transferred by the process of measurement to the electron, the momentum of which, after the measurement, is therefore unknown by an extent $\Delta p \approx h\nu/c$. In the final result, therefore,

$$\Delta p \Delta x \approx h$$

The more accurate the measurement of position (i.e. the smaller the value of Δx), the greater is the uncertainty in the value of the momentum of the electron after the measurement. This simple exposition of the "uncertainty relation" (13.16) and an analogous discussion of other possible methods of measurement were first given by W. Heisenberg.

The interpretation of the wave function ψ as a probability has a further consequence, not specifically related to quantum mechanics, but occurring in classical physics wherever probability theory must be employed.

Our interpretation implies that if we examine the elementary interval Δx for the presence of an electron we must expect one of two results: either the electron is completely contained in Δx, or not at all. If a measurement shows that the electron is contained in Δx, this statement only has meaning if the electron is "really" in Δx immediately after the measurement, as shown by a second measurement of its position immediately after the first. However, since the wave function

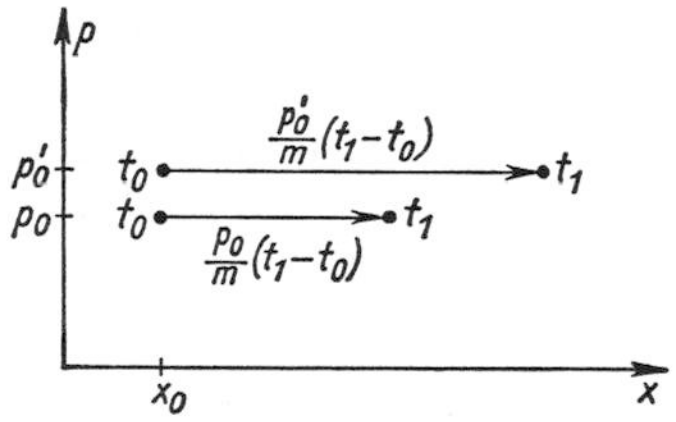

Fig. 16.—Paths in phase space for motion in the absence of external forces

$\psi(x,t)$ determines the probability of occurrence of the electron, it is necessary to postulate that the first measurement caused the ψ-function, previously distributed in space, to be concentrated in the elementary interval Δx.

Under certain circumstances, therefore, the process of measurement has a very drastic effect on the course of the state function designated by $\psi(x,t)$. This effect is called the "reduction of the wave function", by which is meant the reduction of ψ to the region Δx prescribed by the measuring equipment. The function is therefore provisionally transformed by the measurement into another function of state.

That there is nothing mysterious about this process may be illustrated by the simple example of a particle in uniform motion in the absence of external forces, according to classical mechanics. In phase space, this motion is represented by a line parallel to the x-axis. Figure 16 shows two such paths, both of which start from the same point x_0 at time t_0, but with different initial values of the momentum p_0 and p_0'. Each path will be traversed at a different velocity, according to the value of the corresponding momentum. If the initial position and momentum are not known exactly, but can only be measured with certain experimental or at any rate unavoidable errors, Δp and Δx, then the initial conditions are indeterminate and it is impossible to specify the path with complete precision. We can only say that every point within the element of phase space $\Delta p \Delta x$ represents a possible initial point of the path. Every initial point gives rise to a definite path, specified by the equations of motion; in the case of the point itself, however, we can only say that there is a probability $w(p,x)\,dp\,dx$ that it lies within the infinitesimal element of phase space $dp\,dx$. Then at time t_0 the value of w is constant within the rectangular area shown in figure 17, and zero outside this area. The probability at a later instant of time is found from the equations of motion; for instance $w(p,x,t_1)$ is constant within the parallelogram marked "t_1" in figure 17. The position uncertainty therefore increases with time because of the initial uncertainty in momentum. A new measurement of position at time t, with the same inherent error Δx, might show that the particle lies within the two limits shown as broken lines in the figure. This measurement consequently enables us to reduce the "probability distribution" from the broken-line area to the smaller region bounded by solid lines; the process is analogous to the reduction of the wave function. This sudden change in the probability distribution is not the result of any variations of a physical nature; it is important to realize that the function w merely describes the extent of our knowledge, or of our

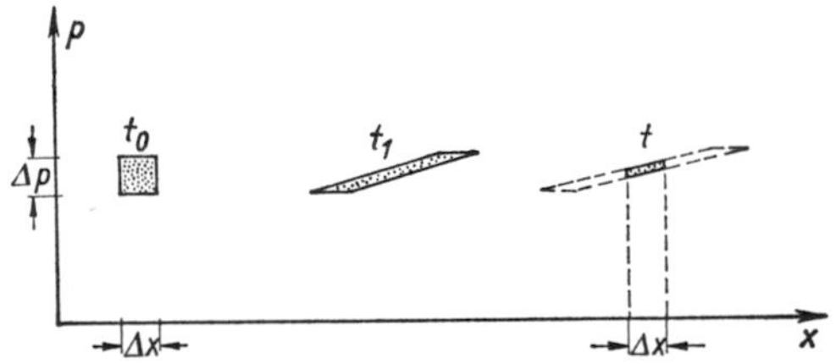

Fig. 17.—The probability distribution at different instants of time, for initial errors Δp and Δx. The distribution is reduced by a measurement of position at time t

information on the process. The information gained by a new measurement necessarily leads to a reduction in the area of the probability distribution.

As regards classical physics, it is clear from the above example that by means of a series of measurements we can continuously reduce the volume of phase space in which w is different from zero; in principle, therefore, it should ultimately be possible to specify the physical process with complete precision. In quantum theory the situation is different; in this case a measurement of position with error Δx necessarily entails a momentum uncertainty Δp according to the relation (13.16). This effect may be crudely represented in the classical model by postulating that the smallest physically significant element of phase space must be of order of magnitude $\hbar$.

There is a further essential difference between quantum and classical mechanics. In the latter case, if the function w is given for a certain definite time, it is known for all later instants of time. In quantum theory, the corresponding situation holds for the "probability amplitude" ψ, but not for the probability w itself.

§14. Schrödinger's wave equation for the electron

(*a*) *The wave equation for the free electron.*—We shall now derive a differential equation describing the properties of the function which we obtained in the case of the free electron (for motion in one dimension),

$$\psi(x,t) = \frac{1}{(2\pi\hbar)^{1/2}}\int_{-\infty}^{+\infty} g(p)\exp\frac{i}{\hbar}[px - E(p)t]\,dp \qquad (14.1)$$

We shall restrict ourselves to the non-relativistic approximation

$$E(p) = \frac{p^2}{2m} \qquad (14.2)$$

When the operator $-i\hbar\,\partial/\partial x$ acts upon the function $\phi = \exp\frac{i}{\hbar}(px - Et)$, it multiplies the latter by p. Similarly, the application of the operator $i\hbar\,\partial/\partial t$ multiplies the function by E. Therefore

$$\frac{\hbar}{i}\frac{\partial\phi}{\partial x} = p\phi \qquad -\hbar^2\frac{\partial^2\phi}{\partial x^2} = p^2\phi \qquad -\frac{\hbar}{i}\frac{\partial\phi}{\partial t} = E\phi$$

If these operators are applied to (14.1), we see that in virtue of (14.2)

$$-\frac{\hbar^2}{2m}\frac{\partial^2\psi}{\partial x^2} = -\frac{\hbar}{i}\frac{\partial\psi}{\partial t} \qquad (14.3)$$

The expression (14.3) only contains the first-order derivative with respect to t. Therefore, if $\psi(x, t)$ is given for time $t = 0$, the value of this function at all other times is given by (14.3). In fact, a function $\psi(x, 0)$ may always be expressed by the Fourier transform

$$\psi(x,0) = \frac{1}{(2\pi\hbar)^{1/2}}\int g(p)\exp\left(\frac{i}{\hbar}px\right)dp$$

The function $g(p')$ is obtained by multiplying $\psi(x, 0)$ by $\exp\left(-\frac{i}{\hbar}p'x\right)$ and integrating over all x:

$$g(p') = \frac{1}{(2\pi\hbar)^{1/2}}\int \psi(x, 0) \exp -\left(\frac{i}{\hbar}p'x\right) dx$$

If we now put
$$\psi(x, t) = \frac{1}{(2\pi\hbar)^{1/2}}\int g(p)c(t) \exp\left(\frac{i}{\hbar}px\right) dp$$

as the general solution (with $c(0) = 1$), (14.3) gives the following equation for $c(t)$:

$$\frac{p^2}{2m}c = -\frac{\hbar}{i}\dot{c}, \text{ from which } c(t) = \exp -\frac{i}{\hbar}\frac{p^2}{2m}t$$

Hence we obtain the original formula (14.1) for $\psi(x, t)$.

The same considerations apply to three-dimensional motion. The wave function

$$\phi = \exp\frac{i}{\hbar}(\mathbf{p}\,.\,\mathbf{r} - Et) \tag{14.4}$$

possesses the property that

$$\frac{\hbar}{i}\frac{\partial\phi}{\partial x} = p_x\phi, \quad \frac{\hbar}{i}\frac{\partial\phi}{\partial y} = p_y\phi, \quad \frac{\hbar}{i}\frac{\partial\phi}{\partial z} = p_z\phi, \quad -\frac{\hbar}{i}\frac{\partial\phi}{\partial t} = E\phi \tag{14.5}$$

It satisfies the two differential equations

$$-\frac{\hbar^2}{2m}\nabla^2\phi = -\frac{\hbar}{i}\frac{\partial\phi}{\partial t} \tag{14.6}$$

and
$$-\frac{\hbar^2}{2m}\nabla^2\phi = E\phi \tag{14.7}$$

Of these two equations, (14.7) is only valid for those values of p that satisfy the relation $p^2/2m = E$ for the initially assumed energy value. On the other hand the time-dependent equation (14.6) is of much more general application. Its solution is provided by the general expression for a wave packet with any arbitrary function $g(\mathbf{p})$,

$$\psi(\mathbf{r}, t) = \frac{1}{(2\pi\hbar)^{1/2}}\int g(\mathbf{p}) \exp\frac{i}{\hbar}\left(\mathbf{p}\,.\,\mathbf{r} - \frac{p^2}{2m}t\right) d\mathbf{p}$$

The solution of the differential equations (14.6) *and* (14.7):

When there are no external forces, the classical Hamiltonian function is

$$\frac{p_x^2 + p_y^2 + p_z^2}{2m} = \mathscr{H} \tag{14.8}$$

The quantities **p** and $\mathscr{H}$ occurring in this function are replaced by the operators

$$p_x \to \frac{\hbar}{i}\frac{\partial}{\partial x}, \ldots, \qquad \mathscr{H} \to -\frac{\hbar}{i}\frac{\partial}{\partial t} \tag{14.9}$$

The Hamiltonian function $p^2/2m$ thus becomes the Hamiltonian operator $-(\hbar^2/2m)\nabla^2$. The energy equation (14.8) is transformed into an operator equation, which gives the differential equation (14.6) when applied to a function $\phi(\mathbf{r}, t)$:

$$-\frac{\hbar^2}{2m}\nabla^2\phi = -\frac{\hbar}{i}\frac{\partial\phi}{\partial t}$$

On the other hand, if E is again a given quantity, we obtain the particular equation (14.7)

$$-\frac{\hbar^2}{2m}\nabla^2\phi = E\phi$$

(*b*) *The derivation of the Schrödinger equation*

From the above procedure, we can see how the differential equation (14.6) must be modified to take account of a potential energy $V(\mathbf{r})$ in addition to the kinetic energy $p^2/2m$. In this case, the classical form of the Hamiltonian function is

$$\frac{p^2}{2m} + V(\mathbf{r}) = \mathscr{H} \tag{14.10}$$

where $\mathscr{H} = E$, the total energy, which is constant. We again consider the Hamiltonian function as an operator in accordance with (14.9), and take $V(\mathbf{r})$ to mean an operator signifying "multiply by $V(\mathbf{r})$". We then have the two forms of the Schrödinger equation: the general equation is

$$-\frac{\hbar^2}{2m}\nabla^2\psi + V(\mathbf{r})\psi = -\frac{\hbar}{i}\frac{\partial\psi}{\partial t} \tag{14.11}$$

If we introduce the trial solution

$$\psi(\mathbf{r}, t) = u(\mathbf{r})\exp -\frac{i}{\hbar}Et$$

into (14.11), we obtain the particular equation

$$-\frac{\hbar^2}{2m}\nabla^2 u + V(\mathbf{r})u = Eu \tag{14.12}$$

In the above equations ψ depends on **r** and t, but u depends on **r** alone.

The solution of the general equation (14.11) expresses $\psi(\mathbf{r},t)$ as a function of time, for a given initial value $\psi(\mathbf{r},0)$. Integration of equation (14.12), on the other hand, yields the particular function $u(\mathbf{r})$ corresponding to a prescribed value of the energy E.

If we interpret (14.11) according to the crude wave concept discussed on page 74, then the function

$$\rho = e\psi^*\psi \tag{14.13}$$

represents a charge density. We shall now investigate the variation of ρ with respect to time:

$$\frac{\partial\rho}{\partial t} = e(\psi^*\dot{\psi}+\dot{\psi}^*\psi)$$

Written in terms of the complex conjugate, equation (14.11) becomes

$$-\frac{\hbar^2}{2m}\nabla^2\psi^*+V(\mathbf{r})\psi^* = \frac{\hbar}{i}\dot{\psi}^* \tag{14.11a}$$

If we now multiply equations (14.11) and (14.11a) respectively by $-e\dfrac{i}{\hbar}\psi^*$ and $e\dfrac{i}{\hbar}\psi$ and add, we obtain

$$\begin{aligned}\frac{\partial\rho}{\partial t} &= -e\frac{\hbar}{2im}(\psi^*\nabla^2\psi-\psi\nabla^2\psi^*)\\ &= -\operatorname{div}\left\{e\frac{\hbar}{2im}(\psi^*\operatorname{grad}\psi-\psi\operatorname{grad}\psi^*)\right\}\end{aligned} \tag{14.14}$$

This is the equation of continuity* for the electric charge: $\partial\rho/\partial t = -\operatorname{div}\mathbf{j}$. The current density† corresponding to the charge density defined by (14.13) is

$$\mathbf{j} = e\frac{\hbar}{2im}(\psi^*\operatorname{grad}\psi-\psi\operatorname{grad}\psi^*) \tag{14.15}$$

Since $\psi^*\psi\, d\mathbf{r}$ represents the probability of finding the electron in the volume element $d\mathbf{r}$, we must postulate that

$$\int\psi^*\psi\, d\mathbf{r} = 1$$

* The existence of the equation of continuity shows that it is physically justifiable to interpret $e\psi^*\psi$ as a charge density.

† In this volume, the current density is designated by j, in contrast to Vol. I, where it was designated by g. The former notation is the usual one employed in quantum theory.

because the electron must certainly be present somewhere in space. When this condition is fulfilled the function is said to be *normalized.* By (13.10), g is also normalized. Equation (14.14) then states that this normalization is conserved, since from this expression

$$\frac{d}{dt}\int \psi^* \psi \, d\mathbf{r} = 0 \tag{14.16}$$

if $\mathbf{j}$ vanishes at infinity.

The energy equation (14.12) possesses the fundamental property that no solutions exist for which $\int |u|^2 d\mathbf{r} = 1$ for arbitrary values of E. Only when E assumes certain definite values $E_1, E_2, \ldots, E_n, \ldots$ do the solutions $u_1, u_2, \ldots, u_n \ldots$ exist. Using the Hamiltonian operator

$$\mathscr{H} = -\frac{\hbar^2}{2m}\nabla^2 + V(\mathbf{r})$$

we may express this situation concisely as follows:

$$\mathscr{H} u_n = E_n u_n \qquad n = 1, 2, 3, \ldots \tag{14.17}$$

The E_n are called the eigenvalues of the Hamiltonian operator, and the u_n are termed the eigenfunctions belonging to the eigenvalues E_n. In this case we say that the eigenvalues are distributed according to a point spectrum. Equation (14.12) may also be soluble for a continuous range of energy values, as in the case of the free electron; we refer to this as a line spectrum. In this case the normalization condition is not fulfilled (cf. §17ff.).

Schrödinger discovered the important fact that the eigenvalues of $\mathscr{H}$ given by (14.17) are identical with Bohr's postulated energy levels, from which the frequencies of the absorbed and emitted spectral lines may be calculated by means of the relation $\omega_{mn} = (E_m - E_n)/\hbar$.

This fact, which at first sight appears most remarkable, may be better understood if the method described in §12 for the calculation of the stationary energy levels is expressed in a somewhat different manner. As originally given, the procedure consisted in finding matrices $p = (p_{mn})$ and $x = (x_{mn})$ that satisfy the commutation relation

$$[p, x] \equiv px - xp = \frac{\hbar}{i}$$

and for which the matrix

$$\mathscr{H} = (\mathscr{H}_{mn}) = \frac{p^2}{2m} + V(x)$$

only possesses diagonal elements, for which $m = n$.

This procedure may be carried out as follows: we first seek any matrices satisfying the commutation relation, and use them to form the matrix $(\mathscr{H}_{mn})$, on which we then perform an orthogonal transformation. As we know from matrix algebra, this is equivalent to finding the eigenvectors u_n of $\mathscr{H}$. The eigenvectors so found satisfy the equation (14.17).

In each case, therefore, we have a problem to solve that involves eigenvalues. The formal agreement between the two procedures is seen to be complete when we note that the differential operators $p = -i\hbar\, \partial/\partial x$ and x satisfy the commutation relation

$$px - xp = \frac{\hbar}{i}$$

If for instance we apply the operator $px - xp$ to a function $f(x)$, we obtain

$$(px - xp) f(x) = \frac{\hbar}{i}\left\{\frac{\partial}{\partial x}(xf) - x\frac{\partial f}{\partial x}\right\} = \frac{\hbar}{i} f(x)$$

Chapter B II of this book is devoted to a general investigation of these relationships, which at first sight appear so remarkable.

In the next section we shall analyse in some detail the important special case of the linear oscillator, using both the Heisenberg and the Schrödinger methods described in §§12 and 14 respectively.

§15. The Schrödinger and Heisenberg treatments of the linear oscillator

Before proceeding to the abstract formulation of the quantum theory in the next chapter, we shall apply the above procedures to the treatment of a particular example. Our starting-point is the classical Hamiltonian function of a linear harmonic oscillator of angular frequency ω:

$$\frac{p^2}{2m} + \tfrac{1}{2} m\omega^2 x^2 = \mathscr{H} \tag{15.1}$$

In the Schrödinger treatment, p is replaced by $-i\hbar\,\partial/\partial x$. In order to determine the function $\phi(x)$ corresponding to a fixed energy E, we must seek solutions of the differential equation

$$-\frac{\hbar^2}{2m}\frac{d^2\phi}{dx^2}+\tfrac{1}{2}m\omega^2x^2\phi = E\phi \qquad (15.2)$$

for which

$$\int_{-\infty}^{+\infty} |\phi(x)|^2\,dx = 1 \qquad (15.3)$$

A preliminary qualitative discussion of this equation is relevant. Let us put (15.2) in the form

$$\frac{d^2\phi}{dx^2} \equiv \phi'' = \frac{2m}{\hbar^2}(\tfrac{1}{2}m\omega^2x^2 - E)\phi$$

and consider this equation as a formula for the graphical construction of the curve $\phi(x)$. We see that the curvature of $\phi(x)$ changes sign both upon a change of sign of $\phi(x)$ itself and when x takes the value x_g defined by $\frac{1}{2}m\omega^2x_g^2 = E$. (The values $\pm x_g$ represent the classical path limits.)

If we begin the construction with $\phi(0)=1$ and $\phi'(0)=0$, for instance, then ϕ'' is negative at first for small x, and the curve is concave towards the x-axis, like a cosine curve. We now choose E and hence the initial curvature to be so small that the point x_g is reached before ϕ can become zero. Then for $x > x_g$, ϕ can follow one of three possible courses (figure 18):

1. $E = E_1$ is so small that the consequent change of curvature prevents the curve of ϕ from reaching the x-axis beyond x_g, and it tends instead to $+\infty$ (curve 1).

2. $E = E_2$ is so large that the curve cuts the x-axis beyond x_g in spite of the change of curvature. The curvature then changes again and ϕ tends to $-\infty$ (curve 2).

3. In between these two cases we must expect to find a limiting case when $E = E_0$, for which the curve of ϕ tends asymptotically to the x-axis. E_0 is an "eigenvalue" of the differential equation (15.2) (curve 3).

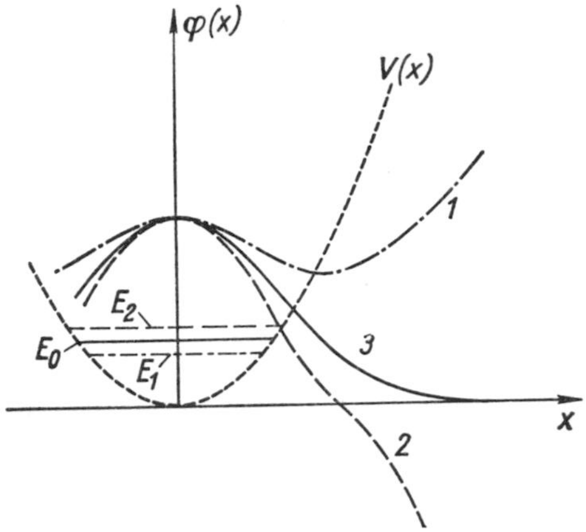

Fig. 18.—Graphical construction for the proper function of a linear oscillator in the lowest energy state. The solid curve is associated with the proper value E_0

We shall now calculate one such eigenvalue. Let us try the Gaussian curve

$$\phi = e^{-\frac{1}{2}\alpha^2 x^2}$$

as a solution of (15.2): this choice is prompted by the shape of curve 3 in figure 18. Then

$$\phi' = -\alpha^2 x\, e^{-\frac{1}{2}\alpha^2 x^2} \qquad \phi'' = (-\alpha^2 + \alpha^4 x^2)\phi$$

Substituting for ϕ'' in (15.2), we have

$$-\frac{\hbar^2}{2m}(-\alpha^2 + \alpha^4 x^2) + \tfrac{1}{2}m\omega^2 x^2 = E$$

In order that the equation should hold for all values of x, we must have

$$\alpha^2 = \frac{m\omega}{\hbar} \quad \text{and} \quad E = E_0 = \tfrac{1}{2}\hbar\omega$$

We have now obtained the lowest eigenvalue, and the associated eigenfunction which, when normalized, is

$$\phi = \phi_0 = \frac{1}{(\alpha\sqrt{\pi})^{1/2}}\, e^{-\frac{1}{2}\alpha^2 x^2}$$

We shall meet this solution again in the course of the analysis.

The quantity α has the dimension $(\text{length})^{-1}$, and is defined by the equation

$$\alpha^2 = \frac{m\omega}{\hbar} \tag{15.4}$$

Equation (15.2) may be written in terms of α, as follows:

$$\frac{1}{2}\left(\alpha^2 x^2 - \frac{1}{\alpha^2}\frac{d^2}{dx^2}\right)\phi = \frac{E}{\hbar\omega}\phi \tag{15.5}$$

The usual method for the solution of (15.5) requires the use of Hermite polynomials. We shall adopt another course, which will also prove useful for the treatment of the problem by Heisenberg's method.

We introduce the new operators

$$b = \frac{1}{\sqrt{2}}\left(\alpha x + \frac{1}{\alpha}\frac{d}{dx}\right) \qquad b^+ = \frac{1}{\sqrt{2}}\left(\alpha x - \frac{1}{\alpha}\frac{d}{dx}\right) \tag{15.6}$$

which possess the following properties. When the operators are applied in turn to an arbitrary function x,

$$b^+ b\phi = \frac{1}{2}\left(\alpha^2 x^2 - \frac{1}{\alpha^2}\frac{d^2}{dx^2}\right)\phi - \frac{1}{2}\phi \tag{15.7}$$

$$bb^+ \phi = \frac{1}{2}\left(\alpha^2 x^2 - \frac{1}{\alpha^2}\frac{d^2}{dx^2}\right)\phi + \frac{1}{2}\phi$$

Hence for any function ϕ

$$(bb^+ - b^+ b)\phi = \phi$$

and in particular, we may put

$$bb^+ - b^+ b = 1 \tag{15.8}$$

Now, for any two functions f and g that vanish at infinity

$$\int f(x)\frac{dg(x)}{dx}\,dx = -\int \frac{df(x)}{dx}g(x)\,dx$$

Hence

$$\int f(x)\,bg(x)\,dx = \int [b^+ f(x)]\,g(x)\,dx \tag{15.9}$$

b^+ is said to be the *adjoint operator* to b.

If we now put $\lambda = E/\hbar\omega - \frac{1}{2}$ as a temporary abbreviation, the Schrödinger equation assumes the form

$$b^+ b\phi = \lambda\phi \tag{15.10}$$

If ϕ is normalized, then from (15.9) and (15.10)

$$\lambda = \int \phi b^+ b\phi \, dx = \int (b\phi)^2 \, dx \tag{15.11}$$

In general, therefore, λ is positive, and only equal to zero if $b\phi = 0$.

If the operator b is applied to (15.10), then in virtue of (15.8)

$$bb^+ b\phi = (b^+ b + 1) b\phi = \lambda b\phi$$

Therefore

$$b^+ bb\phi = (\lambda - 1) b\phi \tag{15.12a}$$

Similarly

$$b^+ bb^+ \phi = (\lambda + 1) b^+ \phi \tag{15.12b}$$

Equation (15.12*a*) implies that if ϕ is an eigenfunction belonging to the eigenvalue λ, then either $b\phi$ is an eigenfunction belonging to $\lambda - 1$, or $b\phi = 0$. Repeated application of the operator b could yield eigenfunctions belonging to $\lambda - 1, \lambda - 2, \ldots, \lambda - v$, and would therefore finally give an eigenfunction belonging to a negative eigenvalue, which is in contradiction to (15.11). This conflict can only be avoided if the series $\lambda - v$ terminates in such a manner that one function ϕ_0 occurs in the series $b\phi, b^2\phi, b^3\phi, \ldots$ for which $b\phi_0 = 0$. But $\lambda - v = 0$ for this function ϕ_0.

There is an element ϕ_0, therefore, for which $b\phi_0 = 0$ and hence $b^+ b\phi_0 = 0$; the corresponding eigenvalue is $\lambda = 0$. The other eigenvalues of (15.10) are the whole numbers $\lambda = n = 1, 2, \ldots$. The eigenvalues E_n of the oscillator are therefore

$$E_n = (n + \tfrac{1}{2})\hbar\omega \qquad n = 0, 1, 2, \ldots$$

The eigenfunction ϕ_0 is a solution of the equation $b\phi_0 = 0$. From (15.6), therefore,

$$\frac{d\phi_0}{dx} = -\alpha^2 x \phi_0$$

from which

$$\phi_0 = C e^{-\frac{1}{2}\alpha^2 x^2}$$

or after normalization,

$$\phi_0 = \frac{1}{(\alpha\sqrt{\pi})^{1/2}}\, e^{-\frac{1}{2}\alpha^2 x^2} \tag{15.13}$$

as we deduced from our original trial solution.

We shall now make use of equation (15.12*b*), according to which an eigenfunction belonging to $\lambda = n+1$ is obtained as a result of the application of the operator b^+ to the eigenfunction belonging to $\lambda = n$. Hence

$$b^+\,\phi_n = N\phi_{n+1}$$

where the constant N is determined by the requirement that ϕ_{n+1} be normalized if ϕ_n is normalized. Hence

$$N^2 = \int (b^+\,\phi_n)(b^+\,\phi_n)\,dx = \int (bb^+\,\phi_n)\phi_n\,dx = n+1$$

since $bb^+\phi_n = b^+b\phi_n + \phi_n$ (from 15.8) $= (n+1)\phi_n$. Therefore

$$b^+\,\phi_n = (n+1)^{1/2}\phi_{n+1} \quad \text{and} \quad b\phi_n = n^{1/2}\phi_{n-1} \tag{15.14}$$

We can now obtain all the eigenfunctions by the repeated application of the operator b^+ to ϕ_0:

$$\phi_n(x) = \frac{1}{\sqrt{(n!)}}(b^+)^n\phi_0 \tag{15.15}$$

These functions $\phi_n(x)$ are normalized and orthogonal, since

$$\int \phi_n^*(x)\,\phi_m(x)\,dx = \delta_{nm} \tag{15.15a}$$

In order to determine the $\phi_n(x)$ explicitly we make use of the identity

$$b^+ f(x) = \frac{1}{\sqrt{2}}\left(\alpha x - \frac{1}{\alpha}\frac{d}{dx}\right) f(x) = -\frac{1}{\alpha\sqrt{2}}\, e^{\frac{1}{2}\alpha^2 x^2}\frac{d}{dx}(e^{-\frac{1}{2}\alpha^2 x^2} f)$$

If we now insert in (15.15) the value of ϕ_0 given by (15.13), we obtain

$$\phi_n(x) = \frac{(-1)^n}{(n!\,2^n\,\alpha\sqrt{\pi})^{1/2}}\, e^{\frac{1}{2}\alpha^2 x^2}\left(\frac{1}{\alpha}\frac{d}{dx}\right)^n (e^{-\alpha^2 x^2}) \tag{15.16}$$

The Hermite polynomials are defined by

$$H_n(y) = (-1)^n \exp(-y^2)\left(\frac{d}{dy}\right)^n \exp(-y^2)$$

Putting $\alpha x = y$ and substituting in (15.16), we obtain the following alternative and common form of ϕ_n:

$$\phi_n(y) = \frac{1}{(n!\,2^n\alpha\sqrt{\pi})^{1/2}} \exp\left(-\tfrac{1}{2}y^2\right) H_n(y)$$

Although (15.16) represents the explicit solution of equation (15.2), it is a most inconvenient formula for purposes of calculation. For instance, if we wish to evaluate the "matrix element"

$$x_{mn} = \int_{-\infty}^{\infty} \phi_m x \phi_n \, dx$$

this can admittedly be done by the direct use of (15.16). The following method, however, is much more convenient. From (15.6),

$$x = \frac{1}{2^{1/2}\alpha}(b + b^+)$$

From (15.14), therefore,

$$x\phi_n = \frac{1}{2^{1/2}\alpha}(n^{1/2}\phi_{n-1} + (n+1)^{1/2}\phi_{n+1})$$

If the above expression is multiplied respectively by ϕ_{n-1} and ϕ_{n+1} and integrated, then in view of (15.15*a*) the only matrix elements different from zero are

$$x_{n-1,n} = \frac{1}{\alpha}\sqrt{(\tfrac{1}{2}n)} \qquad x_{n+1,n} = \frac{1}{\alpha}\sqrt{[\tfrac{1}{2}(n+1)]} \tag{15.17}$$

We shall now describe the treatment of the linear oscillator by Heisenberg's matrix method. We take the equation (15.1) to be a matrix equation, and require the right-hand side to be diagonal, so that

$$\left\{\frac{p^2}{2m} + \tfrac{1}{2}m\omega^2 x^2\right\}_{nm} = E_n \delta_{nm} \tag{15.18}$$

We then have the following commutative relations between the matrices p and x:

$$(px - xp)_{nm} = \frac{\hbar}{i}\delta_{nm} \tag{15.19}$$

If the quantity α, defined as before by (15.4), is introduced into (15.18), then

$$\frac{1}{2}\left(\alpha^2 x^2 + \frac{1}{\hbar^2\alpha^2}p^2\right)_{nm} = \frac{E_n}{\hbar\omega}\delta_{nm} \tag{15.20}$$

We now consider the matrices

$$b_{nm} = \frac{1}{\sqrt{2}}\left(\alpha x_{nm} + \frac{i}{\hbar\alpha} p_{nm}\right) \qquad (b^+)_{nm} = \frac{1}{\sqrt{2}}\left(\alpha x_{nm} - \frac{i}{\hbar\alpha} p_{nm}\right) \quad (15.21)$$

Since $x^*_{mn} = x_{mn}$ and $p_{mn} = p^*_{mn}$ (cf. footnote †, p. 61),

$$(b^+)_{nm} = b^*_{mn} \quad (15.22)$$

As in the case of the operators b and b^+, the product of the matrices is

$$b^+ b = \frac{1}{2}\left(\alpha^2 x^2 + \frac{1}{\hbar^2\alpha^2} p^2\right) - \frac{1}{2}$$

in virtue of (15.19), and

$$bb^+ - b^+ b = 1 \quad (15.23)$$

Putting $E_n/\hbar\omega - \frac{1}{2} = \lambda_n$, as before, the matrix equation (15.20) becomes

$$b^+ b = \lambda \quad (15.24)$$

where λ is taken to be a diagonal matrix the elements of which are $\lambda_{nn} = \lambda_n$. For these elements

$$\lambda_n = \sum_s b^+_{ns} b_{sn} = \sum_s |b_{sn}|^2 = \sum_s |b^+_{ns}|^2 \quad (15.25)$$

If (15.24) is multiplied by b^+, we obtain $b^+b^+b = b^+\lambda$; from (15.23), $b^+bb^+ - b^+ = b^+\lambda$. Consequently $\lambda b^+ - b^+\lambda = b^+$. The element nm of the matrix equation (15.24) is

$$b^+_{nm}(\lambda_n - \lambda_m - 1) = 0$$

Hence, either

$$\lambda_n - \lambda_m = 1, \quad \text{or} \quad b^+_{nm} = 0. \quad (15.26)$$

If we imagine the λ_n to be arranged in order of magnitude, then non-zero matrix elements of b^+ exist only for $\lambda_n - \lambda_{n-1} = 1$; for a given n, all elements b^+_{ns} are zero except $b^+_{n,n-1}$. Equation (15.25) thus reduces to

$$\lambda_n = |b^+_{n,n-1}|^2 \quad (15.27)$$

If we begin the numbering of the matrix elements with $n = 0, 1, 2, \ldots$ and $m = 0, 1, 2, \ldots$, then it follows from (15.27) that $\lambda_0 = 0$. Hence we again obtain $\lambda_n = n$, where $n = 0, 1, 2, \ldots$, and if we choose the elements b_{nm} to be real, then

$$b^+_{n,n-1} = b_{n-1,n} = \sqrt{n} \quad (15.28)$$

The complete matrices are:

$$
b^+ = \begin{array}{c|ccccc} {}_n\diagdown^m & 0 & 1 & 2 & 3 & . \\ \hline 0 & 0 & 0 & 0 & 0 & . \\ 1 & \sqrt{1} & 0 & 0 & 0 & . \\ 2 & 0 & \sqrt{2} & 0 & 0 & . \\ 3 & 0 & 0 & \sqrt{3} & 0 & . \\ . & . & . & . & . & . \end{array}
\qquad
b = \begin{array}{c|ccccc} {}_n\diagdown^m & 0 & 1 & 2 & 3 & . \\ \hline 0 & 0 & \sqrt{1} & 0 & 0 & . \\ 1 & 0 & 0 & \sqrt{2} & 0 & . \\ 2 & 0 & 0 & 0 & \sqrt{3} & . \\ 3 & 0 & 0 & 0 & 0 & . \\ . & . & . & . & . & . \end{array}
\qquad
\lambda = \begin{array}{c|ccccc} {}_n\diagdown^m & 0 & 1 & 2 & 3 & . \\ \hline 0 & 0 & 0 & 0 & 0 & . \\ 1 & 0 & 1 & 0 & 0 & . \\ 2 & 0 & 0 & 2 & 0 & . \\ 3 & 0 & 0 & 0 & 3 & . \\ . & . & . & . & . & . \end{array}
$$

In addition, we have the matrix x_{nm}. From (15.21)

$$x = \frac{1}{\alpha\sqrt{2}}(b+b^+)$$

Hence

$$x_{n,n-1} = x_{n-1,n} = \frac{\sqrt{n}}{\alpha\sqrt{2}} = \sqrt{\frac{n\hbar}{2m\omega}} \tag{15.29}$$

which agrees with (15.17) and with the value (11.11) previously deduced from the correspondence principle.

§16. The wave equation of the electron considered as a classical equation

(*a*) *The constants of the wave equation*

We saw in §14 that the existence of discrete units of electric charge necessitates a statistical interpretation of the ψ-function. On the other hand, if we ignore the corpuscular properties of particles such as electrons, the Schrödinger equation (14.11) may be conceived to be a classical wave equation, which may for instance be used to represent the electron radiation from a cathode as a purely wave-like phenomenon. It is permissible to conjecture that, if diffraction phenomena had been observed when cathode rays were first discovered, this would necessarily have led to the representation of the latter as a wave phenomenon, and hence to equation (14.11). As a classical equation, (14.11) is comparable to Maxwell's equations: like them, it predicts only wave properties and gives no information about the corpuscular nature of the radiation. As in the case of light, the particle-like properties appear only as a result of the quantum theory.

In this case, either the wave or the particle aspect may be chosen, with equal justification. In the domain of classical physics it is necessary to employ either the particle or the wave representation, since these descriptions are mutually exclusive. Each of these classical models leads to the same quantum-mechanical representation; it is a matter of indifference, therefore, whether we "quantize" the classical wave theory or the classical corpuscular theory. The quantum theory is able to describe corpuscular and wave-like properties simultaneously, in so far as the wave representation provides statistical information about the properties of the particles.*

Many phenomena may be most simply expressed in terms of classical wave theory, so that it is important to be fully aware of the classical interpretation of the de Broglie-Schrödinger wave equation, which we shall also attempt to express simultaneously in the language of the quantum theory.

In the first instance we must realize that the Schrödinger equation (14.11) makes no reference to the corpuscular nature of electrons. We may express this otherwise by saying that equation (14.11) contains constants that can be determined from the wave-like properties of the radiation alone. The equation may be written in the form

$$-\frac{\hbar^2}{2m}\nabla^2\psi + e\Phi\psi = i\hbar\dot{\psi} \tag{16.1}$$

where $\Phi(\mathbf{r})$ represents an electric potential. If we divide by $\hbar^2/2m$ and introduce the new constants

$$\alpha = \frac{2m}{\hbar} \qquad \beta = \frac{2me}{\hbar^2} \tag{16.2}$$

(16.1) assumes the form

$$-\nabla^2\psi + \beta\Phi\psi = i\alpha\dot{\psi} \tag{16.1a}$$

The wave equation now contains two constants α and β which are completely determined by the wave properties of the electron radiation. In the present discussion we shall restrict ourselves to one dimension: $\psi = \psi(x,t)$, $\Phi = \Phi(x)$. The wave equation then takes the form

$$-\psi'' + \beta\Phi\psi = i\alpha\dot{\psi} \tag{16.3}$$

If the potential Φ is constant, the solution $\psi = ae^{i(kx-\omega t)}$ gives the following relation between the angular frequency ω and the wave number k, corresponding to the wavelength $\lambda = 2\pi/k$:

$$k^2 + \beta\Phi = \alpha\omega \tag{16.4}$$

* When there are several particles, all their coordinates must be included as variables in the ψ function; the wave theory must then apply in a multi-dimensional space.

The group velocity of the radiation is

$$v_g = \frac{d\omega}{dk} = \frac{2}{\alpha}k \tag{16.5}$$

The constant α therefore establishes a connection between group velocity and wavelength: equation (16.5) is in fact the de Broglie relation.

Equation (16.4) is also valid if the potential is piecewise constant. In this case the angular frequency ω remains constant, otherwise the boundary conditions for ψ could not be satisfied (cf. §16*d*). It follows from equation (16.4) that the quantity $k^2+\beta\Phi$ remains unchanged when the radiation travels from a region of potential Φ_1 to one of potential Φ_2:

$$k_1^2+\beta\Phi_1 = k_2^2+\beta\Phi_2 \quad \text{or} \quad k_1^2-k_2^2 = \beta(\Phi_2-\Phi_1) \tag{16.6}$$

The constant β therefore connects the change in wavelength of the radiation with the potential difference $\Phi_2-\Phi_1$. Equation (16.5) represents the theorem of conservation of energy for particles, expressed in terms of wave theory.

The constants α and β may therefore be obtained from measurements of wavelengths, group velocities, and potential differences. But α and β are in fact the experimental data corresponding to pure wave theory, and in this connection it is somewhat misleading to represent them, as in (16.2), by means of the typical quantities e and m, that are associated with particles. However, the charge-mass ratio of the radiation can be determined by deflection experiments and expressed in terms of the constants associated with the wave representation ($e/m = 2\beta/\alpha^2$).

(*b*) *Physical quantities and conservation theorems*

It is clear that those experiments which are exclusively concerned with the wave-like nature of cathode rays will lead to the formulation of the wave equation (16.3) or (16.1*a*). This equation is not very informative, however, if we do not know the physical meaning of the wave function ψ. In order to endow the theoretical pattern with physical meaning, we must understand the relationship between the wave function and the various relevant physical quantities. The typical physical quantities in a theory of the continuum are densities (charge, mass, momentum, and energy densities) and associated current or flow densities. In general, these densities satisfy conservation theorems, one of which we encountered in §14 in the case of the charge density ρ_e:

$$\frac{\partial \rho_e}{\partial t} + \operatorname{div} \mathbf{j}_e = 0 \tag{16.7}$$

or in integral form, after integration over a volume V bounded by a surface S

$$\frac{d}{dt}\int_V \rho_e \, d\mathbf{r} = -\int_S \mathbf{j}_e \cdot d\mathbf{f} \tag{16.7a}$$

(Equation (16.7*a*) signifies that the charge contained in volume V decreases with time because an electric current flows out across the boundary surface S.) If the system is self-contained, that is, if the current density $\mathbf{j}_e$ vanishes at the boundary, the total charge remains constant:

$$\frac{d}{dt}\int_V \rho_e \, d\mathbf{r} = 0$$

These conservation theorems must be implicit in the wave equation. We may express this as follows:

"If the wave equation (16.1*a*) leads to conservation theorems in the form of (16.7), then with certain reservations it is permissible to interpret as physical quantities the densities and current densities occurring in equation (16.7)".

We must now determine whether the conservation theorems are in fact contained in (16.1*a*), and if so, in what form.

We now state without proof two possible conservation theorems for scalar quantities; it may be shown that these are deducible from equation (16.1*a*) and its complex conjugate equation.

$$\frac{\partial}{\partial t}\underbrace{\psi^* \psi}_{\rho} + \operatorname{div} \underbrace{\frac{1}{i\alpha}(\psi^* \operatorname{grad} \psi - \psi \operatorname{grad} \psi^*)}_{\mathbf{j}} = 0 \tag{16.8}$$

$$\frac{\partial}{\partial t}\underbrace{(\operatorname{grad} \psi^* \operatorname{grad} \psi + \beta \Phi \psi^* \psi)}_{\tilde{\rho}} + \operatorname{div} \underbrace{[-(\dot{\psi}^* \operatorname{grad} \psi + \dot{\psi} \operatorname{grad} \psi^*)]}_{\tilde{\mathbf{j}}} = 0 \tag{16.9}$$

In view of the above theorems, we interpret ρ as charge or mass density, both of which are proportional to each other, since $e/m = 2\beta/\alpha^2$. We may then look upon (16.8) as the equation of continuity for charge or mass, and (16.9) as the corresponding equation for energy. There is still one free factor available in these equations, so that ρ need only be proportional to the charge density. Since this factor is quite arbitrary we can put $\rho_e = e'\psi^*\psi$ for the electric charge density ρ_e, where e' represents an arbitrary unit charge. The only reason for choosing e' to be equal to the electron charge e is to provide a simple corpuscular interpretation of the physical quantities occurring in the wave theory. Further, we shall choose the factor in (16.9) in such a manner that the term $\beta\Phi\psi^*\psi$ may be replaced by $\Phi\rho_e$; this latter quantity is the energy density of a charge distribution ρ_e in an electric potential $\Phi(\mathbf{r})$. Hence we have*

Charge density	$\rho_e = e\rho$	Electrical current density	$\mathbf{j}_e = e\mathbf{j}$	
Mass density	$\rho_m = m\rho$	Mass flow density	$\mathbf{j}_m = m\mathbf{j}$	(16.10)
Energy density	$u = \dfrac{e}{\beta}\tilde{\rho}$	Energy flow density	$\mathbf{f} = \dfrac{e}{\beta}\tilde{\mathbf{j}}$	

It is of interest to deduce the forms of the above expressions in the simplest three-dimensional case of a plane wave $\psi = a \exp i(\mathbf{k}.\mathbf{r} - \omega t)$. This is a solution of the wave equation for constant Φ, if $\mathbf{k}^2 + \beta\Phi = \alpha\omega$. In the three-dimensional case the group velocity is $\mathbf{v}_g = \partial\omega/\partial\mathbf{k} = (2/\alpha)\mathbf{k}$. Then

$$\begin{aligned} \rho_e &= e\,|a|^2 & \mathbf{j}_e &= \rho_e \mathbf{v}_g \\ \rho_m &= m\,|a|^2 & \mathbf{j}_m &= \rho_m \mathbf{v}_g \qquad (16.11) \\ u &= \tfrac{1}{2}\rho_m \mathbf{v}_g^2 + \rho_e \Phi & \mathbf{f} &= u\mathbf{v}_g \end{aligned}$$

The densities and currents are constant with respect to time and position, and the fact that the currents simply transport the corresponding densities at group velocity $\mathbf{v}_g$ leads to the following statement:

"The plane wave describes a state of constant density ρ_e or ρ_m which moves at a constant velocity $\mathbf{v}_g$."

Clearly, therefore, the first term in the expression for u corresponds to kinetic energy density, and the second to potential energy density.

* Note that $\mathbf{j}_e$ vanishes when ψ is real.

Furthermore, $\mathbf{j}_m$ is also the wave momentum density* (cf. Exercise 5, p. 108). The corpuscular representation requires that $\rho=|a|^2$ be interpreted as the particle density; the plane wave is a process in which a statistically constant distribution of particles moves with velocity $\mathbf{v}_g$. The momentum per particle is $m\mathbf{v}_g=\hbar\mathbf{k}$, and the kinetic energy, $\frac{1}{2}m\mathbf{v}_g^2=\hbar^2k^2/2m$.

It is clear from the above considerations that the wave equation may justifiably be written in its original form (16.1); it is important to realize, however, that the equation contains only two essential constants, the third being given by the arbitrary choice $e'=e$.

(*c*) *The wave packet*

In §14*a* the wave function $\psi(x,t)$ was derived from the function at time $t=0$ for linear motion in the absence of external forces, for which $\Phi=0$. The solution for the case of an initially Gaussian distribution was discussed in §13. If we start with the normalized function

$$\psi(x,0)=\frac{1}{(b\sqrt{\pi})^{1/2}}\exp\left(-\frac{x^2}{2b^2}+ik_0x\right) \tag{16.12}$$

the necessary integrations can be evaluated by elementary methods and lead to the result (13.14*a*) for $\psi(x,t)$. The factor s in this expression is replaced below by $\hbar/b\sqrt{2}$.

The resulting densities are

$$\rho(x,0)=|\psi(x,0)|^2=\frac{1}{b\sqrt{\pi}}\exp-\frac{x^2}{b^2} \tag{16.13}$$

$$\rho(x,t)=|\psi(x,t)|^2=\frac{1}{b(t)\sqrt{\pi}}\exp-\frac{(x-v_0t)^2}{b^2(t)} \tag{16.14}$$

where ω_0 is the angular frequency associated with k_0 ($\alpha\omega_0=k_0^2$), and v_0 is the corresponding group velocity ($v_0=2k_0/\alpha$). The "width" or dispersion, $b(t)$, of the density distribution ρ is a function of the time:

$$b(t)=b\left\{1+\left(\frac{\hbar t}{mb^2}\right)^2\right\}^{1/2}=b\left\{1+\left(\frac{2t}{\alpha b^2}\right)^2\right\}^{1/2}$$

The above equations represent a charge distribution $\rho(x,t)$, of total charge e and mass m, the motion of which is described by the wave equation (16.3). The total momentum is independent of the

* There is also a conservation theorem for the momentum density (for constant potential), which we have not stated above.

time: $\int \mathbf{j}_m dx = mv_0 = \hbar k_0$; the total energy is also independent of time and includes kinetic energy only: $\int u\,dx = \frac{1}{2}mv_0^2(1+1/2b^2k_0^2)$. The solution can of course be multiplied by a factor a, in which case the total charge, the mass, the momentum, and the energy are multiplied by $|a|^2$.

If we can neglect the variation of $b(t)$ with time, we obtain the result expressed by (13.14). This is only permissible for small intervals of time, for which $t \ll \frac{1}{2}\alpha b^2$; for large intervals, the dispersion is proportional to the time: $b(t) = 2t/\alpha b$. The sides of the Gauss curve separate at a constant velocity $2/\alpha b = v_0/bk_0$. If b is large compared to the wavelength $\lambda_0 = 2\pi/k_0$, the rate of separation is small in comparison with the mean velocity v_0 of the wave packet; if this condition does not apply, the separation rate is the dominant factor. A measure of the dispersion rate of the wave packet is provided by the time τ at which $b(\tau) = 2b$, from which $\tau = \frac{1}{2}\alpha b^2\sqrt{3}$. If b is of atomic dimensions (10^{-8} cm), τ is about 10^{-16} s. This result makes it impossible to describe an electron as a particle and as a wave packet represented by (16.12); if we wish to take account of the corpuscular properties of the electron, we must interpret the wave function in a statistical sense, because, while a probability distribution can become increasingly dispersed, the particle itself certainly cannot.

The behaviour of the wave packet is illustrated in figure 19. It should perhaps be mentioned that the dispersion of the wave packet is not an irreversible process—it is true that (16.12) leads to a dispersion that increases with time, but this is simply the consequence of our choice of initial function. For instance, by choosing suitable phase relations between the individual waves composing the packet, it is possible to make the dispersion decrease initially with time. As a solution of the wave equation, (13.14*a*) holds for all values of the time; therefore, if we start, say, at time $t = -\tau$, the density distribution is halved after an interval τ (see figure 19, broken curve).

For a wave packet of form corresponding to (16.12) in three dimensions, the general solution is simply a product of three solutions in the form of (16.13), in which we are still free to choose the components of the width and velocity along each axis.

(*d*) *Reflection and transmission at potential barriers* (*wave theory*)

We shall now investigate the effect of the potential on the solution of the wave equation. We restrict ourselves to one dimension, so that $\psi = \psi(x,t)$, $\Phi = \Phi(x)$, and the wave equation assumes the form (16.3).

We shall consider only stationary states, which are defined as those states in which the densities and currents are independent of the time. Although the wave function $\psi(x,t)$ contains a time factor $e^{-i\omega t}$, it is clear that the densities and currents given by (16.9) and (16.10) are

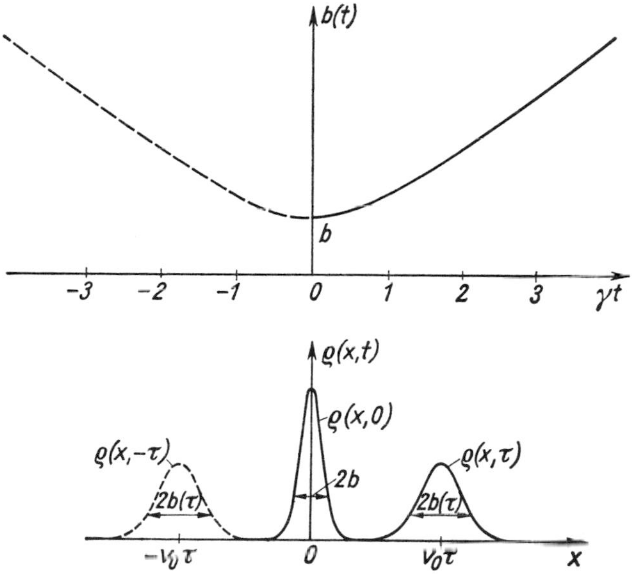

Fig. 19.—Density distribution $\rho(x,t)$ and width $b(t)$ of wave packet, from (16.14)

not functions of the time, since they include only factors of the form $\psi^*\psi$. We have already discussed the special case of the representation of a stationary state by means of a plane wave; the corresponding densities and currents are given by (16.11). If we now put $\psi = \phi(x)e^{-i\omega t}$ in (16.3), we obtain

$$-\phi'' + \beta\Phi\phi = \alpha\omega\phi \tag{16.15}$$

For constant potential Φ, the general solution* of this equation is

$$\phi(x) = a\, e^{ikx} + b\, e^{-ikx} \tag{16.16}$$

where a and b are arbitrary complex quantities, and

$$k^2 + \beta\Phi = \alpha\omega \tag{16.16a}$$

* When ω and k are positive (which we shall always assume to be the case), the first term in (16.16) represents a wave travelling to the right, while the second term represents one travelling to the left.

If the potential Φ is a continuous function of position, it follows from (16.15) that ϕ'' must exist; ϕ, ϕ', and ϕ'' are also continuous functions in this case. This is not so if potential steps are present, so that the potential is only piecewise continuous. At the step, ϕ and ϕ' are still continuous, while ϕ'' itself is obviously discontinuous. The continuity requirement may also be deduced from the fact that the mass (or charge) density must be continuous, which means that ϕ' must exist, and therefore that ϕ must be continuous. Further, ϕ' must also be continuous, in order that the current should be continuous and that mass should not accumulate at the barrier; this would lead to infinitely

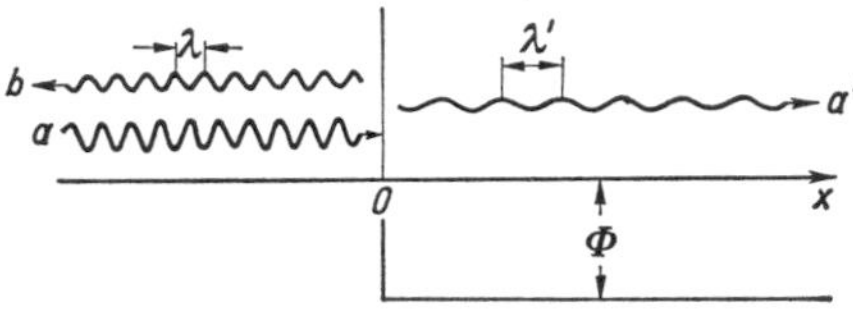

Fig. 20.—Reflection and transmission at a potential step

great densities, which would be physically absurd. This argument also holds for the energy flow, but not for the energy density, which is a discontinuous quantity.

As our first example, we shall consider the penetration of radiation through a potential barrier; the latter may be taken as a potential difference concentrated into a very small interval. We can picture this as follows. Let an initial plane wave $ae^{i(kx-\omega t)}$ be incident on the barrier from the left. At the barrier the wave will be partly reflected, partly transmitted; finally a steady state will be reached. The reason for the present investigation is that any given waveform, such as a wave packet incident from the left, can be created by superposing different stationary solutions with various angular frequencies.

When the system has reached a stationary state, we should expect to find an incident wave ae^{ikx} and a reflected wave be^{-ikx} to the left of the barrier, and a wave $a'e^{ik'x}$ to its right (figure 20). We wish to find the amplitudes b and a' in terms of the amplitude a of the incident wave. A unique solution is obtained if we impose the condition, on physical grounds, that no wave $b'e^{-ik'x}$ reaches the barrier from the right, although a wave travels towards the left from this point. Dropping the time factor $e^{-i\omega t}$, which is common to all the waves, we may now summarize the expressions for the wave functions and the mass flow in the regions to the right and left of the barrier:

$$\text{Left of the barrier } x<0 \quad \begin{cases} \phi = a\,e^{ikx} + b\,e^{-ikx} & k^2 = \alpha\omega \\ j_m = |a|^2 2k/\alpha - |b|^2 2k/\alpha \end{cases} \tag{16.17}$$

$$\text{Right of the barrier } x>0 \quad \begin{cases} \phi = a'\,e^{ik'x} & k'^2 = \alpha\omega - \beta\Phi = k^2 - \beta\Phi \\ j_m = |a'|^2 2k'/\alpha \end{cases} \tag{16.17a}$$

We see from (16.17) that the mass flow consists of an incident and a reflected component. The reflection coefficient R is defined as the ratio of the reflected to the incident flow density; the transmission coefficient D is the ratio of the transmitted to the incident flow density:*

$$R = \left|\frac{b}{a}\right|^2 \qquad D = \left|\frac{a'}{a}\right|^2 \frac{k'}{k} \tag{16.18}$$

As a result of the conservation of mass,

$$R + D = 1 \tag{16.18a}$$

ϕ and $\partial\phi/\partial x$ must be continuous at the point $x = 0$, hence

$$a + b = a' \qquad k(a-b) = k'a' \tag{16.19}$$

and

$$\frac{b}{a} = \frac{1 - k'/k}{1 + k'/k} \qquad R = \left|\frac{1 - k'/k}{1 + k'/k}\right|^2 \tag{16.20}$$

or

$$R = \left|\frac{1-n}{1+n}\right|^2 \tag{16.20a}$$

where the "refractive index" $n = k'/k$ is introduced, by analogy with optics; n is the ratio of the wavelengths in the two regions separated by the potential barrier.

From (16.17a)

$$n = (1 - \beta\Phi/k^2)^{1/2} = (1 - V/E_{kin})^{1/2} \tag{16.21}$$

The quantity $\beta\Phi/k^2$ may be replaced by V/E_{kin}, where $e\Phi = V$ is the jump in potential energy for an electron and $E_{kin} = \hbar^2 k^2/2m$ is the kinetic energy per electron in the incident wave. Figure 21 illustrates

* The quantities j_m and D deduced from (16.17a) and (16.18) are valid only for real values of k' For pure imaginary values of k', $j_m = 0$ ($D = 0$ and $R = 1$).

the variation of the reflection coefficient with the kinetic energy of the electron. In the region for which the kinetic to barrier potential energy ratio lies between 0 and 1, n and k' are pure imaginaries and total reflection takes place.* Expressed in terms of the corpuscular interpretation: the kinetic energy is insufficient to enable the electron to surmount the potential barrier V. At greater values of the kinetic energy R decreases gradually to zero. The full curve in figure 21 shows the reflection coefficient for positive values of $\beta\Phi$ or V, the broken

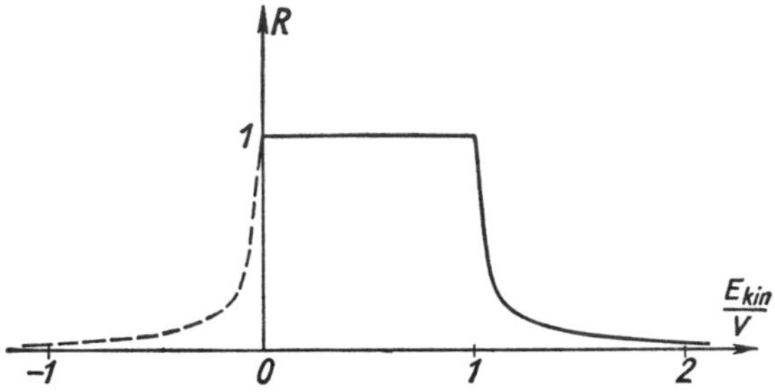

Fig. 21.—Reflection coefficient R at a potential step, shown as a function of E_{kin}/V. The broken line illustrates the variation of R for negative values of V.

curve, the coefficient at negative values. It is evident that, apart from the region of total reflection, we always find values of R and D that are different from zero.

According to classical corpuscular theory there are only two possible alternatives: if $E_{kin} > V$, the electron surmounts the barrier; if $E_{kin} < V$, it recoils. Classical wave theory, on the other hand, states that a certain fraction of the wave is reflected and that the remainder is transmitted through the barrier†. In order to describe particles and waves by means of a single model it is necessary once again to have recourse to the statistical interpretation: we may say, for instance, that

* When $x > 0$, $j_m \equiv 0$.

† In this connection, a remarkable situation appears to exist when V is negative and $|V| \gg E_{kin}$: this is the case when the radiation is highly accelerated by a large potential difference. According to the corpuscular theory, $R = 0$; according to wave theory, $R \approx 1$ because $n \gg 1$. The almost complete reflection predicted by wave theory appears to be strongly at variance with the classical behaviour of particles, and is not confirmed experimentally when cathode rays are accelerated. The answer is that such a sharp potential step cannot be realized experimentally; the solution under discussion applies only to the case where the wavelength of the radiation is large compared to the dimensions of the potential step. When we reflect that, according to (13.9), the wavelength of this radiation is generally less than 10^{-8}cm, we can appreciate that such dimensions cannot be realized in practice. For light waves the situation is different; in this case it is possible to arrange for the refractive index to change from one medium to the other within a small fraction of the wavelength.

R is the probability of recoil and D the probability of penetrating the barrier, or that on the average a fraction R of the incident particles is reflected and a fraction D transmitted.

Another important type of potential barrier is illustrated in figure 22. In this case there are four amplitudes, b, a', b', a'', which must be

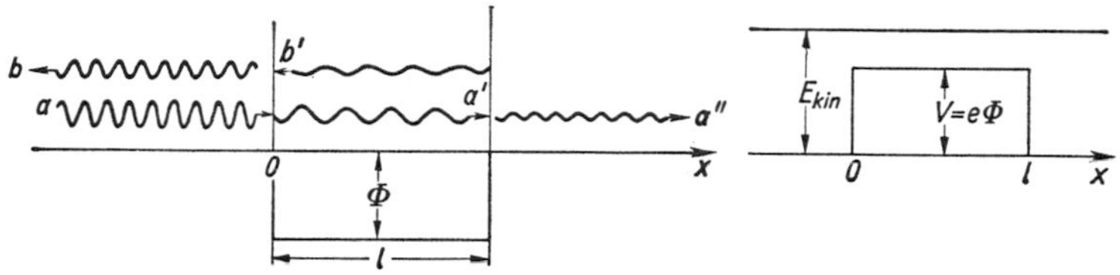

Fig. 22.—Amplitudes at a potential barrier

evaluated in terms of the amplitude a of the incident wave; for this purpose there are two boundary conditions at our disposal at each of the potential steps. The calculations are similar to those which we performed for the case of the potential step, and are omitted. The results are:

$$R = \left| \frac{\frac{1}{2}(n-1/n)\sin(nkl)}{\cos(nkl) - \frac{1}{2}i(n+1/n)\sin(nkl)} \right|^2 \tag{16.22}$$

where n is again defined by (16.21). If $E_{kin} > V$, n is real, and we obtain

$$R = \frac{\frac{1}{4}(n-1/n)^2 \sin^2(nkl)}{1+\frac{1}{4}(n-1/n)^2 \sin^2(nkl)}$$

$$D = \frac{1}{1+\frac{1}{4}(n-1/n)^2 \sin^2(nkl)} \tag{16.22a}$$

If $E_{kin} > V$, $n = i\bar{n}$ is a pure imaginary, and

$$R = \frac{\frac{1}{4}(\bar{n}+1/\bar{n})^2 \sinh^2(\bar{n}kl)}{1+\frac{1}{4}(\bar{n}+1/\bar{n})^2 \sinh^2(\bar{n}kl)}$$

$$D = \frac{1}{1+\frac{1}{4}(\bar{n}+1/\bar{n})^2 \sinh^2(\bar{n}kl)} \tag{16.22b}$$

Figure 23 illustrates the manner in which the reflection coefficient R depends on the ratio E_{kin}/V. It is of interest to note that R becomes zero at the points for which $nkl = \pi, 2\pi, 3\pi, \ldots$: this corresponds to the familiar interference phenomena in optics.

In classical physics, equation (16.22*b*) corresponds to the case of total reflection at the barrier; in the present treatment, this equation predicts almost total reflection provided that the width l of the barrier

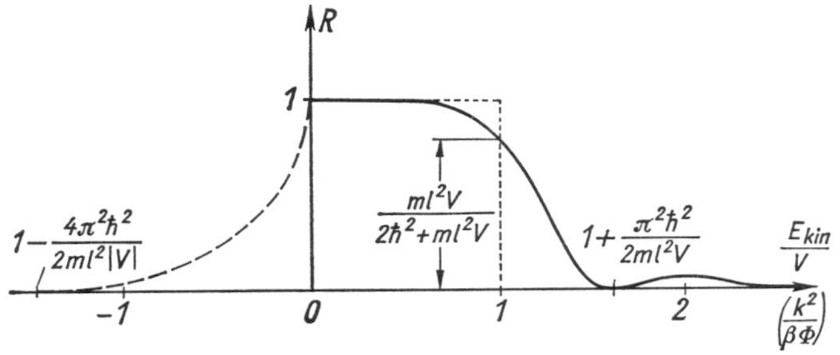

Fig. 23.—Reflection coefficient R at a potential barrier, shown as a function of E_{kin}/V. The figure is drawn for the case $\pi^2\hbar^2/ml^2|V| = 5/4$. The broken line illustrates the variation of R for negative values of V.

is sufficiently great (i.e. $\bar{n}kl \gg 1$). For smaller values of $\bar{n}kl$, however, we find that the barrier is appreciably "transparent" to the radiation, although according to classical corpuscular theory it should be insurmountable.

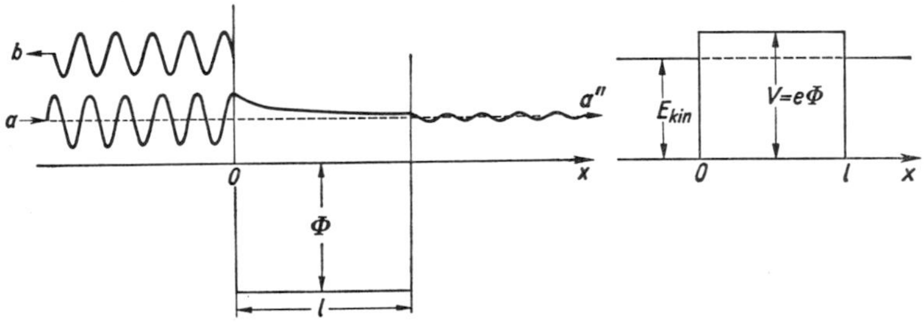

Fig. 24.—Amplitudes in the case of the tunnel effect

This result is easily explained in terms of the wave theory. If we restrict ourselves to the case for which $\bar{n}kl \gg 1$, then

$$D = \left(\frac{4\bar{n}}{\bar{n}^2+1}\right)^2 e^{-2\bar{n}kl} \ll 1$$

This implies that the wave amplitude decreases exponentially within the barrier according to the factor $e^{-\bar{n}kx}$; a small amplitude is still present at the right-hand boundary, however, and this gives rise to an outward-bound wave to the right of the barrier (figure 24).

The quantum theory again requires a statistical interpretation of this result: the transmission coefficient D represents the chance that an incident particle can pass through the barrier. A large number of phenomena are explained by this so-called "tunnel effect", according to which a particle has a chance of penetrating a barrier which, on classical theory, would be insurmountable. If we imagine the particle to be confined within two similar potential barriers then, according to classical mechanics, it cannot leave this region. If we now take into account the tunnel effect, we can estimate the escape probability approximately as follows. The particle strikes the wall of the enclosure at a definite frequency ν which depends on its velocity and on the enclosure dimensions. At each impact the chance that the particle will escape is D; the probability in a time dt is therefore equal to the number of attempts $\nu\, dt$ multiplied by D. If we now consider a system consisting of N confined particles, the average number escaping during the interval dt is $N\nu D\, dt$; this is equal to the decrease dN in the number of confined particles, therefore $dN/dt = -N\nu D$. It follows that the average number of remaining particles at time t is $N(t) = N(0)e^{-\nu Dt}$, where $N(0)$ is the number of particles present initially. This is the law of radioactive disintegration.

More precise quantum-mechanical calculations lead to a similar result, and afford a particularly satisfactory explanation of α-particle emission when the appropriate constants are introduced. For electrons, the tunnel effect is of importance in connection with

1. the ionization probabilities of atoms in an electric field (cf. §39),
2. the emission of electrons from metals in an electric field, in the absence of thermal excitation.

(e) *The "quantum conditions" applicable to the classical wave theory*

Bohr's hypothesis (10.1, 10.2), as applied to corpuscular theory, consists essentially of the following two postulates:

1. Stationary orbits exist, possessing energy values E_n.
2. The radiated frequencies are $\omega_{ns} = (E_n - E_s)/\hbar$.

It is clear that the condition of stationary non-radiating states is satisfied by the wave theory. As we have indicated in previous sections (in the case of the linear oscillator, for instance), every state $\psi(\mathbf{r}, t)$ may be developed in terms of a set of physically significant stationary solutions:

$$\psi(\mathbf{r}, t) = \sum_n a_n \phi_n(\mathbf{r}) e^{-i\omega_n t} \qquad (16.23)$$

In order to determine the emission of electric waves for a state represented by (16.23) let us investigate the motion of the centre of charge $e\mathbf{r}_s$, as in the case of radiation from a dipole:

$$ex_s(t) = \int \rho_e(\mathbf{r}) x \, d\mathbf{r} = e \int x \, |\psi(\mathbf{r}, t)|^2 \, d\mathbf{r}$$

or, from (16.23)

$$ex_s(t) = e \sum_{n,m} a_n^* a_m x_{nm} e^{i(\omega_n - \omega_m)t} \qquad (16.24)$$

where the "matrix element" x_{nm} is defined as

$$x_{nm} = \int \phi_n^* x \phi_m \, d\mathbf{r} \qquad (16.24a)$$

The radiation therefore contains the frequencies $\omega_{nm} = \omega_n - \omega_m$, provided $x_{nm} \neq 0$, in accordance with Bohr's theory.

The existence of the elementary charge e must clearly be allowed for in wave theory by the requirement* that $\int \rho \, d\mathbf{r}$ should be an integral number. In the case of the single electron this requirement implies that the wave function ψ be normalized. If the functions ϕ_n are normalized, it may be shown that the total energy $E_n = \int u \, d\mathbf{r}$ in the ϕ_n state is equal to $\hbar\omega_n$; the second Bohr postulate is therefore satisfied. In the single electron case, therefore, the quantum condition for wave theory is simply that the total charge be normalized to e. We then have an exact method for the treatment of single-electron problems.

There is one important matter, however, that we have not so far taken into consideration. The potential Φ appears in the wave equation; since the electron wave is electrically charged we must allow for the potential of its charge distribution. Φ then consists of a potential due to the external fields and a potential Φ_s due to the charge distribution ρ_e:

$$\Phi_s(\mathbf{r}) = \int \frac{\rho_e(\mathbf{r}')}{|\mathbf{r} - \mathbf{r}'|} \, d\mathbf{r}' \qquad (16.25)$$

If the wave is very tenuous Φ_s may be neglected, as we have tacitly assumed up to now. However, if we were to calculate again the energy

* If we had allowed the normalization charge e' to remain arbitrary, we should now have to postulate that $\int \rho_e dr = e' \int |\psi|^2 dr$ be an integral multiple of the elementary charge e.

levels of the hydrogen atom, using Φ_s, we should obtain a completely incorrect result,* since in this case Φ_s is by no means negligibly small. Clearly, we must postulate that Φ_s should vanish. This is the second quantum condition for wave theory—there can be no interaction of the electron with itself. Here again the statistical interpretation of ψ comes to the rescue, for the postulate would be quite incomprehensible if $\rho = |\psi|^2$ were a real density. The quantum postulates in the particle and wave theories are complementary, and the task of the quantum theory consists in finding a theoretical pattern that will take into account both the corpuscular and the wave concepts.

Exercises

1. *Planck's radiation formula interpolation*

The spectral distribution of radiation from an enclosure may be expressed in terms of the mean thermal energy $\varepsilon(\nu, T)$ of an oscillator whose frequency is ν. Before the discovery of Planck's radiation formula it was necessary to distinguish between two spectral regions, each characterized by a different mathematical relation: the Rayleigh-Jeans region for frequencies well below the maximum of the spectral distribution, and the Wien region lying well above this maximum.

$$\varepsilon(\nu, T) = \begin{cases} kT, & \text{Rayleigh-Jeans, "small" } \nu \\ \text{const.}\, \nu \exp -\dfrac{\alpha\nu}{T}, & \text{Wien, "large" } \nu \end{cases}$$

From thermodynamics, the mean square deviation Δ of the energy E of any system at temperature T is $\Delta = kT^2 \partial\bar{E}/\partial T$.

Express the mean square deviation in the Rayleigh-Jeans region, Δ_{RJ}, and in the Wien region, Δ_W, in terms of ε and ν. Verify that the sum $\Delta = \Delta_{RJ} + \Delta_W$ approximately represents the deviation in each region. This expression may be used as an interpolation formula for the mean square deviation throughout the whole spectral region. If this formula is assumed to be strictly correct, and equated to $\Delta = kT^2 \partial\varepsilon/\partial T$, a differential equation is obtained for ε, the solution of which is Planck's formula.

2. *Derivation of the hydrogen terms from the correspondence principle*

According to the correspondence principle, $dE/dn = \hbar\omega(E)$ for large quantum numbers n; $\omega(E)$ is the frequency of the classical motion. This is a differential equation for the function $E(n)$ in which n is to be taken as a continuously variable quantity. The possible energy values according to quantum theory are those for which n is a whole number. Calculate $\omega(E)$ and hence $E(n)$ for a linear oscillator, and for the hydrogen atom orbits.

3. *First approximation to the energy of an anharmonic linear oscillator*

Let the potential energy be $V(x) = \frac{1}{2}m\omega^2 x^2 + \lambda x^4$, where λ is "small". Calculate the energy values E_n from (10.4) to the first degree of approximation, by expanding in powers of λ. Neglect terms in λ of the second and higher degree.

* In the case of problems involving many electrons it is often possible to replace the strict quantum-mechanical treatment by wave theory, taking into account Φ_s. This corresponds somewhat to Hartree's "self-consistent field" treatment.

4. *Vibrations of solid bodies at the absolute zero of temperature*

When a linear oscillator is in its lowest state, at the absolute zero of temperature, the mean square deviation of its amplitude is $\overline{x^2} = \hbar/2M\omega$, where M is the mass of the oscillator and ω its angular frequency; this follows because the average values of the potential and kinetic energies are equal. This also applies in the case of atomic vibrations in a solid body. When calculating the vibration of an atom we may assume that the neighbouring atoms remain fixed, as in Einstein's model of a solid body. An atom in a cubical crystal lattice vibrates like a harmonic oscillator with a small amplitude in a definite direction. If the lattice constant (the distance between neighbouring atoms) is a, ω may be expressed approximately in terms of the velocity of sound c, thus $\omega \approx c/a$. This follows because the time a/c required for the transfer of an impulse from one atom to the next must be roughly equal to the period of an oscillation $1/\omega$. Evaluate the ratio $\overline{x^2}/a^2$, the root of which is a measure of the linear displacement of the atoms from their equilibrium positions at absolute zero. For aluminium, $a \approx 2 \times 10^{-8}$ cm, $c = 5 \times 10^3$ m/s, $M = 6 \times 10^{-23}$ g.

5. *Rate of change of total momentum in wave theory*

If $\mathbf{j}_m$ is correctly interpreted by (16.10), the rate of change of total momentum must be equal to the total force exerted by the electric field $\mathbf{E} = -\operatorname{grad}\Phi$ on the charge distribution ρ_e:

$$\frac{d}{dt}\int \mathbf{j}_m\, d\mathbf{r} = \int \rho_e \mathbf{E}\, d\mathbf{r}$$

Deduce the above equation from the equation of motion (16.1) on the assumption that $\psi(\mathbf{r}, t)$ vanishes at infinity.

6. *Motion of the centre of gravity of a wave packet*

The centre of gravity x_s of a wave packet is defined by

$$x_s = \int x\rho_m\, dx \Big/ \int \rho_m\, dx$$

Prove the following relation for motion in one dimension in the absence of external forces:

$$\dot{x}_s = \int j_m\, dx \Big/ \int \rho_m\, dx = v_0$$

(Total mass $\times$ velocity of centre of gravity = total momentum.) Show also that v_0 is the mean value of all the group velocities in the wave packet:

$$v_0 = \int \frac{d\omega}{dk}\, |g(k)|^2 dk \Big/ \int |g(k)|^2 dk$$

Hint: $\psi(x,t) = \int g(k,t)\, e^{ikx}\, dk/(2\pi)^{1/2}$, where $g(k,t) = g(k)\, e^{-i\omega(k)t}$. For any two functions $\phi_1(x) = \int g_1(k)\, e^{ikx}\, dk/(2\pi)^{1/2}$ and $\phi_2(x) = \int g_2(k)\, e^{ikx}\, dk/(2\pi)^{1/2}$:

$$\int \phi_1^*(x)\,\phi_2(x)\, dx = \int g_1^*(k)\, g_2(k)\, dk$$

7. *Energy according to wave theory, and the Hamiltonian operator*

Using integration by parts, prove that $\int u\, d\mathbf{r} = \int \psi^* \mathscr{H} \psi\, d\mathbf{r}$. u is the wave-theory energy density, $\mathscr{H}$ is the Hamiltonian operator of particle theory.

CHAPTER BII

The general basis of quantum mechanics

§17. Vectors and operators in Hilbert space

The separate lines of development of the quantum theory which were described in the last chapter lead to a common pattern, which we shall now examine.

To begin with, it is clear that both Heisenberg's and Schrödinger's quantum-mechanical formulations are formally similar to each other. For instance, Heisenberg's postulates (12.13) may also be expressed as follows: matrices must first be found, designated by $p_{\mu\nu}$ and $x_{\mu\nu}$, for which

$$(px-xp)_{\mu\nu} = \frac{\hbar}{i}\delta_{\mu\nu}$$

These matrices are then used to form the matrix

$$\mathscr{H}_{\mu\nu} = \left\{\frac{p^2}{2m}+V(x)\right\}_{\mu\nu}$$

which is then diagonalized by means of a "rotation". It is known from matrix algebra that diagonalization is equivalent to determining the eigenvectors $\phi(\nu)$ of the matrix $\mathscr{H}$:

$$\sum_{\nu} \mathscr{H}_{\mu\nu}\phi_n(\nu) = E_n\phi_n(\mu) \tag{17.1}$$

On the other hand, if we take the classical Hamiltonian function and replace the momentum p by the operator $-i\hbar\,\partial/\partial x$, we obtain the Schrödinger equation (14.12). Then for every differentiable $\phi(x)$:

$$(px-xp)\phi(x) = \frac{\hbar}{i}\phi(x)$$

The eigenvalues E_n are then obtained from the solution of the boundary-value equation

$$\mathscr{H}\phi_n(x) = E_n\phi_n(x) \quad \text{for} \quad \int\phi_n^*(x)\phi_n(x)\,dx \text{ finite} \tag{17.2}$$

It will now be shown that equations (17.1) and (17.2) are two equivalent forms of a single eigenvalue equation

$$\mathscr{H}\phi = E\phi$$

This means that the above equation may be represented in two different "coordinate systems" which can be transformed into each other by means of a "rotation" in so-called "Hilbert space".

Before this equivalence can be demonstrated certain preliminary mathematical concepts and propositions must be presented.

Hilbert space consists of a set of "elements" or "vectors", ϕ, $\chi, \psi, \ldots$, possessing the following properties:

(1). If a and b are any two complex numbers, $a\phi + b\psi$ is also an element in Hilbert space.

(2). Associated with any two elements ϕ and ψ there is a (generally complex) number (ϕ, ψ), which is termed the scalar or inner product of ϕ and ψ. The following relation is always true:

$$(\phi, \psi) = (\psi, \phi)^* \tag{17.3}$$

Further, if a is an arbitrary number, then

$$(\phi, a\psi) = a(\phi, \psi) \text{ and hence } (a\phi, \psi) = a^*(\phi, \psi) \tag{17.4}$$

In particular, if $(\phi, \psi) = 0$, ϕ and ψ are said to be *orthogonal* to each other.

(3). For any three elements ϕ, χ, ψ,

$$(\phi + \psi, \chi) = (\phi, \chi) + (\psi, \chi)$$

(4). From (17.3), we see that (ϕ, ϕ) is always a real number. We shall also stipulate that $(\phi, \phi) \geqq 0$. Elements for which (ϕ, ϕ) would be infinite are not admissible to Hilbert space.

The quantity (ϕ, ϕ) is called the norm of ϕ. If $(\phi, \phi) = 1$, the vector ϕ is said to be normalized. If $(\phi, \phi) = 0$, ϕ is said to be a null element of Hilbert space; $\phi = 0$.

If ϕ and ψ are given and are not null elements, then ϕ may be uniquely resolved into an element $a\psi$, proportional to ψ, and an element χ orthogonal to ψ, by means of the identity

$$\phi = \psi \underbrace{\frac{(\psi, \phi)}{(\psi, \psi)}}_{a} + \underbrace{\left\{\phi - \psi \frac{(\psi, \phi)}{(\psi, \psi)}\right\}}_{\chi} \tag{17.5}$$

Obviously, $(\psi, \chi) = 0$. If we now form the norm on both sides of (17.5), bearing in mind (17.4) and the fact that $(\psi, \chi) = 0$, we get

$$(\phi, \phi) = \frac{|(\phi, \psi)|^2}{(\psi, \psi)} + (\chi, \chi)$$

This leads to Schwarz's inequality*

$$(\phi, \phi)(\psi, \psi) \geqq |(\phi, \psi)|^2 \tag{17.6}$$

in which the equality sign only applies if $\chi = 0$, when $\phi = a\psi$.

The elements $\phi_1, \ldots, \phi_r$ are said to be linearly dependent if any of the ϕ can be expressed as a linear combination of the others, i.e. if coefficients $c_1, \ldots, c_r$ exist that are not all zero, such that

$$c_1 \phi_1 + \ldots + c_r \phi_r = 0 \tag{17.7}$$

If this is not the case the elements are said to be linearly independent.

A system of elements $\alpha_1, \ldots, \alpha_n, \ldots$ in Hilbert space is said to be *normalized* if $(\alpha_n, \alpha_n) = 1$ for each α_n. It is *orthogonal*, if $(\alpha_n, \alpha_m) = 0$ for all $n \neq m$. It is *complete* if each Hilbert space element ϕ may be expressed as a linear combination of the α_n:

$$\phi = \sum_n a_n \alpha_n \tag{17.8}$$

If the α_n fulfil all three conditions, the system is said to be *complete and orthogonal*. In future we shall employ only basic systems of this type. Then

$$(\alpha_n, \alpha_m) = \delta_{nm}$$

and from (17.8)

$$a_n = (\alpha_n, \phi) \equiv \phi(n)$$

We therefore have the following identity for every ϕ:

$$\phi = \sum_n (\alpha_n, \phi)\alpha_n = \sum_n \phi(n)\alpha_n \tag{17.8a}$$

We may say that the α_n span the whole Hilbert space, or that every element of Hilbert space may be represented by a linear combination of the α_n. The elements α_n are therefore said to form a basis α in Hilbert

* Equation (17.6) ensures the validity of postulate (1): if the norms of ϕ and ψ exist, so does the norm of any linear combination of these two elements.

space, and the components $\phi(n)$ of the vector ϕ in this coordinate system constitute the representation of ϕ referred to the basis α.

If

$$\phi = \sum_n \phi(n)\alpha_n \qquad \psi = \sum_n \psi(n)\alpha_n$$

the inner product is defined as

$$(\phi, \psi) = \sum_{n,m} \phi^*(n)\psi(m)(\alpha_n, \alpha_m) = \sum_n \phi^*(n)\psi(n) \qquad (17.9)$$

where

$$(\alpha_n, \alpha_m) \equiv \alpha_m(n) = \delta_{mn}$$

The numbers m are often continuous variables; in this case the summations in the above formulae are replaced by integrals. If α_a are the orthogonal basis vectors, then

$$\phi = \int (\alpha_a, \phi)\alpha_a \, da = \int \phi(a)\alpha_a \, da$$

If we now form the scalar product with $\alpha_{a'}$, we get

$$\phi(a') = \int \phi(a)(\alpha_{a'}, \alpha_a) \, da \qquad (17.10)$$

The function $\delta_{aa'} = (\alpha_{a'}, \alpha_a)$ is called the Dirac delta function; it corresponds in the continuous case to the Kronecker symbol δ_{nm} that occurs in the discrete case. This function has the property* that $\int \phi(a)\delta_{aa'} da = \phi(a')$ for all $\phi(a)$. It may be pictured as a function vanishing when $a \neq a'$, but tending to infinity in such a manner at $a = a'$ that $\int \delta_{aa'} da = 1$.

The Dirac function is obviously not a function in the ordinary sense, just as the vectors α_a do not really belong to Hilbert space because $(\alpha_a, \alpha_a) = \delta_{aa} = \infty$; however, we shall include it in our treatment for the sake of completeness of presentation. We shall encounter the function in (20.11) (cf. also Exercises 1 and 2, p. 137).

The eigenvectors $\phi_n(v)$ are a typical example of the representation of discrete vectors in Hilbert space. Examples of continuous quantities are provided by the wave functions $\phi(x)$ or their Fourier transforms $g(p)$, the scalar products of which are $(\phi, \psi) = \int \phi^*(x)\psi(x)dx$ and $(g_1, g_2) = \int g_1{}^*(p)g_2(p)dp$. In these cases Hilbert

* This property may be taken as the definition of the δ-function. Then clearly

$$\int \phi(a)\delta_{a+d,\,a'+d} da = \int \phi(a-d)\delta_{a,\,a'+d} \, da = \phi(a')$$

i.e. $\delta_{a+d,\,a'+d} = \delta_{a,\,a'}$. Then $\delta_{a,a'}$ only depends on the difference $a - a'$; for this reason, the function is also written as $\delta(a - a')$.

space consists of all functions $\phi(x)$ the squares of whose absolute magnitudes are integrable.

The beginner should familiarize himself with these concepts in three-dimensional space, bearing in mind that Hilbert space possesses an infinite number of dimensions. In vector calculus it is usual to represent a complete and orthonormal system by means of the unit vectors **i**, **j**, **k**, parallel to the axes x, y, z. Any vector **a** can then be represented as

$$\mathbf{a} = a_x\mathbf{i}+a_y\mathbf{j}+a_z\mathbf{k} \tag{17.10a}$$

The norm of the vector **a** is equal to the square of its magnitude a. The scalar product of two vectors **a**, **b** is

$$(\mathbf{a}, \mathbf{b}) \equiv \mathbf{a}.\mathbf{b} = ab \cos \phi$$

where a and b are the magnitudes of the vectors and ϕ is the angle they make with each other. The inequality (17.6) becomes simply

$$a^2b^2 \geq (ab \cos \phi)^2, \quad \text{i.e.} \ \cos^2 \phi \leqq 1$$

The analogue of equation (17.9) is

$$(\mathbf{a}, \mathbf{b}) = a_x b_x+a_y b_y+a_z b_z$$

If **e** is a normalized vector, then $(\mathbf{a}, \mathbf{e}) = a \cos \phi$ is the projection of **a** in the direction of **e**.

The importance of the Hilbert space vectors lies in the fact that they can be used to represent the physical states of quantum-mechanical systems. This means that, in principle, it is possible to calculate the result of any measurement on a system in a given state if we know the vector ϕ associated with that state. It remains to be seen how this calculation may be accomplished.

We saw in the last chapter that operators, such as matrices and differential operators, are associated in quantum theory with physically observable quantities such as position, momentum or energy.

In Hilbert space, an operator A represents a rule for transforming any vector ϕ into another vector ψ: $A\phi = \psi$. A is said to be linear if

$$A(a\phi+b\psi) = aA\phi+bA\psi \tag{17.11}$$

for any two elements ϕ, ψ, and complex numbers a and b. In what follows we shall only be concerned with linear operators.

The sum of two operators is defined as follows:

$$(A+B)\phi = A\phi+B\phi \tag{17.12}$$

and the product as

$$(AB)\phi = A(B\phi) \tag{17.13}$$

in which B is first applied to ϕ, then A to $B\phi$. The adjoint operator to A, A^+, is defined by the relation

$$(\phi, A\psi) = (A^+\phi, \psi) \tag{17.14}$$

for all ϕ and ψ. It follows immediately that

$$(A^+)^+ = A, \quad (aA)^+ = a^*A^+, \quad (AB)^+ = B^+A^+ \tag{17.15}$$

An operator is said to be Hermitian or self-adjoint if

$$A^+ = A \tag{17.16}$$

The unitary operator is defined by

$$U^+U = UU^+ = 1 \tag{17.17}$$

We shall see later that Hermitian operators always correspond to physical quantities. Unitary operators are important for such purposes as the representation of the variation of a state ϕ with respect to time.

We shall now describe the matrix representation of the above operator relations. The representation in the basis $\{\alpha_1, \ldots, \alpha_n, \ldots\}$ of the equation

$$A\phi = \psi$$

is obtained by forming the inner product with α_m:

$$(\alpha_m, A\phi) = \sum_n (\alpha_m, A\alpha_n)\phi(n) = \sum_n A_{mn}\,\phi(n) = \psi(m) \tag{17.18}$$

The operation of A on ϕ is represented in matrix form by multiplying $\phi(n)$ by the matrix $A_{mn} = (\alpha_m, A\alpha_n)$. The matrix A_{mn} is said to represent the operator A. The matrix representation of $A+B$ is

$$(A+B)_{mn} = A_{mn} + B_{mn} \tag{17.19}$$

The product of two operators is represented by the product of two matrices:

$$(AB)_{mn} = \sum_l (\alpha_m, AB_{ln}\,\alpha_l) = \sum_l A_{ml}\,B_{ln} \tag{17.20}$$

Finally, the matrix of the adjoint operator is the conjugate complex of the original transposed matrix:

$$(A^+)_{mn} = (\alpha_m, A^+\alpha_n) = (A\alpha_m, \alpha_n) = A^*_{nm} \tag{17.21}$$

For a Hermitian operator, therefore,

$$A_{mn} = A^*_{nm}$$

The analogue of matrix representation in the continuous case is provided by integral operators: for instance, if ϕ is represented by wave functions $\phi(x), A\phi = \psi$ is represented by

$$\int A(x, x')\phi(x')\, dx' = \psi(x)$$

Differential operators are of greater importance, however; among these, we encountered the momentum operator $-i\hbar\, \partial/\partial x$ in §14. Multiplication by x (or by a function* $V(x)$) represents another simple and important operation.

We shall now derive a relation between two different matrix representations of the same Hilbert space vector ϕ: if these are designated by $\phi(n)$ and $\tilde{\phi}(\nu)$ referred to bases α and β respectively, we have

$$\phi = \sum_n \phi(n)\alpha_n = \sum_\nu \tilde{\phi}(\nu)\beta_\nu \tag{17.22}$$

Forming the inner products with α_n and β_ν:

$$\phi(n) = \sum_\nu (\alpha_n, \beta_\nu)\tilde{\phi}(\nu) = \sum_\nu U_{n\nu}\, \tilde{\phi}(\nu) \tag{17.23a}$$

$$\tilde{\phi}(\nu) = \sum_n (\beta_\nu, \alpha_n)\phi(n) = \sum_n U^*_{n\nu}\, \phi(n) \tag{17.23b}$$

The transformation of one matrix representation into another is therefore effected by means of a matrix $U_{n\nu}$, which is unitary because

$$\sum_\nu U_{n\nu}\, U^*_{m\nu} = \sum_\nu (\alpha_n, \beta_\nu)(\beta_\nu, \alpha_m)$$

$$= \sum_\nu \alpha^*_n(\nu)\alpha_m(\nu) = (\alpha_n, \alpha_m) = \delta_{nm} \tag{17.24a}$$

and

$$\sum_m U^*_{m\mu}\, U_{m\nu} = \delta_{\mu\nu} \tag{17.24b}$$

The transformation of matrix elements is most simply effected by first expressing the elements β_ν in terms of the α_n:

$$\beta_\nu = \sum_n (\alpha_n, \beta_\nu)\alpha_n = \sum_n \beta_\nu(n)\alpha_n = \sum_n U_{n\nu}\alpha_n$$

* When the Dirac δ-function is introduced, multiplication and differentiation become equivalent to integration:

$$V(x)\phi(x) = \int V(x')\delta_{xx'}\phi(x')dx' \quad \text{and} \quad \frac{\partial\phi(x)}{\partial x} = \int \delta_{xx'}\frac{\partial\phi(x')}{\partial x'}dx' = -\int \frac{\partial\delta_{xx'}}{\partial x'}\phi(x')dx'$$

If this expression is now introduced into $\tilde{A}_{\mu\nu} = (\beta_\mu, A\beta_\nu)$ we obtain:

$$\tilde{A}_{\mu\nu} = \sum_{mn} U^*_{m\mu} A_{mn} U_{n\nu}$$

similarly

$$A_{mn} = \sum_{\mu\nu} U_{m\mu} \tilde{A}_{\mu\nu} U^*_{n\nu} \tag{17.25}$$

Since the elements α_n and β_ν each constitute an orthonormal basis in Hilbert space we may say that they transform into each other by means of a rotation, since the relations between them are similar to those governing the transformation of coordinate systems in three-dimensional space.

We shall still retain the concept of a rotation even when one of the two orthogonal systems, say β_ν, is continuous. It is true that in this case we cannot say strictly that each vector α_n belonging to the discrete basis is transformed by a unitary operation in Hilbert space into a corresponding vector β_ν in the continuous basis. The matrix $U_{n\nu}$ is now replaced by a generalized unitary "matrix" $U_{n\nu}$, possessing one discrete and one continuously variable index. The unitary relations then become

$$\sum_m U^*_{m\nu} U_{m\mu} = \delta(\mu - \nu) \qquad \int U_{n\mu} U^*_{m\mu} \, d\mu = \delta_{mn} \tag{17.26}$$

The above relations are similar to those expressed by (17.24) and suggest, therefore, that we may also refer to this class of transformation as a "rotation".

This obliteration of the difference between continuous and discrete manifolds is of somewhat doubtful mathematical validity; it is on a par with our introduction of the Dirac δ-function and is justified in so far as it is impossible to discriminate physically between a continuous basis β_ν and a discrete set β_{ν_n} if the ν_n lie close enough to each other. (A relevant example is provided by the frequent cases in which a Fourier integral is replaced by a summation.)

§18. Average value and standard deviation

The concepts so far introduced provide an extremely concise means of formulating the quantum theory, and one that is independent of the particular form of representation selected. We shall now describe in some detail the relations between vectors, operators, states, and physical quantities.

Let us measure a quantity A which is an attribute of a large number of identical systems, all of which are in the state ϕ. If the mean of all the measurements is formed, this is the expectation value of A, denoted by $\bar{A}$. This value may be calculated from the associated Hilbert space vector ϕ and the operator A according to the formula

$$\bar{A} = \frac{(\phi, A\phi)}{(\phi, \phi)} \tag{18.1}$$

Thus a relation has been established for the first time between the abstract quantities A, ϕ and a directly measurable quantity $\bar{A}$. Equation (18.1) obviously remains unchanged if ϕ is replaced by $a\phi$, where a is any complex number; ϕ and $a\phi$ represent the same state. It is often useful, but not essential, to assume ϕ to be normalized. Then the expectation value is simply

$$\bar{A} = (\phi, A\phi)$$

The significance of equation (18.1) may be made clearer if we can show that it provides a statistical interpretation of the normalized wave function $\phi(x)$ and its Fourier transform $g(p)$, which were discussed in §13. If for instance we take ϕ as the wave function $\phi(x)$ and A as the operator "multiply by x", we obtain

$$\bar{x} = \int x\,|\phi(x)|^2\,dx \tag{18.2}$$

This is of course just what we should put for the average value of x if we interpreted $|\phi(x)|^2\,dx$ to be the probability of finding the particle between x and $x+dx$. Similarly for the momentum:

$$\bar{p} = \int p\,|g(p)|^2\,dp \tag{18.3}$$

If we wish to determine $\bar{p}$, we might proceed by first finding the Fourier transform of $\phi(x)$ and using this to evaluate the integral (18.3). Equation (18.1) relieves us of this necessity, however: we require only the representation of the operator p in the coordinate system in which the state vector is represented as $\phi(x)$, and can then put

$$\bar{p} = \int \phi^*(x)p\phi(x)\,dx \tag{18.4}$$

From § 14, we should expect that the momentum p could be replaced in (18.4) by the operator $-i\hbar\partial/\partial x$. We shall leave it to the reader to show that, since $\phi(x) = \int g(p) e^{ipx/\hbar} dp/\sqrt{(2\pi\hbar)}$, (18.3) is identical with (18.4).

Since the operators A correspond to physical quantities, they must obviously be of such a form that $\bar{A}$ is always real; if $(\phi, \phi) = 1$, this means that

$$\bar{A} = \bar{A}^* = (\phi, A\phi)^* = (A\phi, \phi) = (\phi, A^+\phi)$$

Since this must be true for all states ϕ, A must be equal to A^+; in other words, Hermitian operators must always correspond to the physical quantities.

If A is an observable quantity in the state ϕ, where $(\phi, \phi) = 1$, the dispersion ΔA is defined as the mean square deviation

$$(\Delta A)^2 = \overline{(A - \bar{A})^2} = \overline{A^2} - \bar{A}^2 \tag{18.5}$$

where $\overline{A^2} = (\phi, A^2\phi)$. If we now define a vector χ by

$$A\phi - \bar{A}\phi = \chi \tag{18.6}$$

it follows immediately from the fact that A is Hermitian that

$$\overline{A^2} - \bar{A}^2 = (\chi, \chi) \tag{18.7}$$

Therefore $(\Delta A)^2$ vanishes only when $\chi = 0$, and the dispersion of A in the state ϕ is only zero if

$$A\phi = \bar{A}\phi = a\phi$$

where a is real. In this case ϕ is said to be an eigenvector of A, and the corresponding eigenvalue is a. If the system is therefore in an eigenstate of A for which the corresponding eigenvalue is a, each measurement of A will always yield the value a.

The measured values of other quantities relating to the system in state ϕ will in general be dispersed about their mean values.

As we have already seen, it is impossible to find states in which position and momentum each have a definite value at the same time. We shall now prove the generalized uncertainty relation $\Delta A \Delta B \geqq \frac{1}{2}\hbar$ for any canonically conjugate operators A and B:

Two Hermitian operators A and B are connected by the relation

$$AB - BA = \hbar/i \tag{18.8}$$

with which we are already familiar for the case when $A = p$ and $B = x$. We shall show that

$$(A\phi, A\phi)(B\phi, B\phi) \geqq |(A\phi, B\phi)|^2 \geqq \tfrac{1}{4}\hbar^2 \tag{18.9}$$

for all ϕ, where $(\phi, \phi) = 1$. The first inequality follows directly from (17.6) when ϕ is replaced by $A\phi$ and ψ by $B\phi$; the equality only holds when

$$A\phi = \lambda B\phi \tag{18.10}$$

The second inequality in (18.9) follows from (18.8). If we put

$$(A\phi, B\phi) = (\phi, AB\phi) = a+ib$$

where a and b are real, then

$$(\phi, BA\phi) = a-ib$$

Subtracting: $2b = -\hbar$, in view of (18.8), hence $|(\phi, AB\phi)|^2 = a^2+b^2 = a^2+\tfrac{1}{4}\hbar^2$. The second equality sign in (18.9) holds only if $a=0$, when $(A\phi, B\phi)$ is a pure imaginary quantity. In order to satisfy both the possible equalities in (18.9), therefore, λ in (18.10) must be a pure imaginary, and

$$A\phi = i\gamma B\phi, \text{ where } \gamma \text{ is real} \tag{18.11}$$

If A and B are replaced by their deviations from the expectation values, $A-\bar{A}$ and $B-\bar{B}$, the commutation relations (18.8) are preserved, and since $(A\phi, A\phi) = (\phi, A^2\phi)$, etc., it follows from (18.9) that

$$\overline{(A-\bar{A})^2(B-\bar{B})^2} \geqq \tfrac{1}{4}\hbar^2, \text{ i.e. } \Delta A \Delta B \geqq \tfrac{1}{2}\hbar \tag{18.12}$$

where the equality holds if

$$(A-\bar{A})\phi = i\gamma(B-\bar{B})\phi \tag{18.13}$$

In particular, if we now put $A = p = -i\hbar\,\partial/\partial x$ and $B = x$, (18.13) gives the differential equation for the function of ϕ with the minimum uncertainty product,

$$\frac{\hbar}{i}\frac{\partial\phi}{\partial x} - \bar{p}\phi = i\gamma(x-\bar{x})\phi$$

the solution of which is

$$\phi(x) = \exp\left(\frac{i}{\hbar}\bar{p}x\right)\exp\left(-\frac{\gamma}{2\hbar}(x-\bar{x})^2\right) \tag{18.14}$$

This is the equation of the wave packet* that was discussed in §§13 and 16. The constant γ shows how the indeterminacy is distributed between x and p:

$$\Delta x = \sqrt{\frac{\hbar}{2\gamma}} \qquad \Delta p = \sqrt{\left(\tfrac{1}{2}\gamma\hbar\right)}$$

* In the previous treatment, the uncertainty was found to be a minimum at time $t = 0$; this corresponds to the equality condition in (18.12).

§ 19. Eigenvalues and eigenvectors

(a) *Determination of the eigenvalues and eigenvectors*

If a vector ϕ remains unchanged apart from a numerical factor a when acted on by an operator A, i.e.

$$A\phi = a\phi \tag{19.1}$$

ϕ is said to be an eigenvector of A, and a is the associated eigenvalue.

An equation for the possible eigenvalues of A is obtained if (19.1) is expressed in any orthogonal system $\alpha_1, \alpha_2, \ldots$:

$$\sum_n A_{mn}\,\phi(n) = a\phi(m) \quad \text{for} \quad m = 1, 2, 3, \ldots \tag{19.2}$$

If the Hilbert space consists of a finite number of dimensions only (say N),* (19.2) contains N linear homogeneous equations for the N coefficients $\phi(1), \ldots, \phi(N)$. A solution of these equations exists if the determinant

$$\begin{vmatrix} A_{11}-a & A_{12} & A_{13} & \cdots \\ A_{21} & A_{22}-a & A_{23} & \cdots \\ \vdots & \vdots & \vdots & \end{vmatrix} \tag{19.3}$$

vanishes. This is an algebraic equation of the Nth degree in a, known as the secular equation. The N roots of this equation are therefore the eigenvalues of a; their existence follows from the fundamental theorem of algebra. Hilbert space often has an infinite number of dimensions, however; in this case the investigation of the existence of the eigenvalues is a much more difficult problem, for which we shall not give a general treatment.

In the infinite case, the eigenvalues might perhaps be determined as successive approximations by breaking off the infinite determinant (19.3) at a given finite value of N, equating to zero, and solving; N would then be increased and the procedure repeated in the hope that it would lead to convergent values.

Generally, however, more elegant procedures exist for the solution of the eigenvalue problems that are of importance in physics. In many cases the latter may be expressed as boundary conditions associated with differential equations (e.g. Schrödinger's eigenvalue equation in

* Examples of such space occur in §26 (perturbation theory), §36 (Zeeman effect), and §39 (Stark effect).

§14); alternatively they may be solved independently of any particular basis as a result of special commutation properties of the operator A (e.g. in the treatment of the linear oscillator given in §15, in which the eigenvalues of $\mathscr{H}$ were determined from the commutation relations of b^+ and b; further examples are provided in §24 (angular momentum) and §53 (quantization of black-body radiation)).

We shall now consider the two important special cases, in which A is unitary or Hermitian.

The eigenvalues u of a unitary operator U have absolute value unity.

The scalar product of the equation $U\psi = u\psi$ with itself gives $(U\psi, U\psi) = u^*u(\psi, \psi)$; hence $(U\psi, U\psi) = (\psi, U^+U\psi) = (\psi, \psi)$. If $(\psi, \psi) \neq 0$, then $u^*u = 1$, as stated.

The eigenfunctions belonging to different eigenvalues of a unitary operator are orthogonal to each other.

If the scalar product of the two equations $U\psi_1 = u_1\psi_1$ and $U\psi_2 = u_2\psi_2$ is formed, it follows that

$$(\psi_1, \psi_2) = u_1^* u_2 (\psi_1, \psi_2) \tag{19.4}$$

But $u_1^* = 1/u_1$, therefore either $u_1 = u_2$ or $(\psi_1, \psi_2) = 0$.

The eigenvalues of a Hermitian operator A are real.

It follows from $A\psi = a\psi$ that $a = (\psi, A\psi)$. Hence from (17.14) and (17.16) $a^* = (A\psi, \psi) = (\psi, A\psi)$, and therefore $a = a^*$.

The eigenfunctions belonging to different eigenvalues of a Hermitian operator are orthogonal to each other.

It follows from $A\phi_1 = a_1\phi_1$ and $A\phi_2 = a_2\phi_2$ that

$$(A\phi_1, \phi_2) - (\phi_1, A\phi_2) = (a_1 - a_2)(\phi_1, \phi_2) \tag{19.5}$$

When A is Hermitian the left-hand side is equal to zero; therefore either $a_1 = a_2$ or $(\phi_1, \phi_2) = 0$.

In the case of a continuous spectrum of eigenvalues

$$A\phi_a = a\phi_a$$

It follows from equation (19.5) that $(a - a')(\phi_a, \phi_{a'}) = 0$, i.e. $(\phi_a, \phi_{a'}) = 0$ for $a \neq a'$. The behaviour at $a = a'$ depends on the normalization, which can be so chosen that

$$(\phi_a, \phi_{a'}) = \delta(a - a')$$

It also occurs very frequently that the eigenvalue spectrum is partly discrete and partly continuous. It is left to the reader to generalize the corresponding formulae.

(b) Degeneracy

An eigenvalue is said to be "r-fold degenerate" if there are r linearly independent eigenvectors corresponding to it. In the case of two-fold degeneracy, for instance,

$$A\phi_1 = a\phi_1 \quad \text{and} \quad A\phi_2 = a\phi_2$$

In this case every linear combination $\alpha\phi_1+\beta\phi_2$ is an eigenfunction corresponding to the same eigenvalue a; in other words, all elements of the subspace spanned by ϕ_1 and ϕ_2 are eigenfunctions of A corresponding to a. This subspace may also be spanned by two orthogonal elements χ_1 and χ_2, say

$$\chi_1 = \phi_1, \quad \chi_2 = \phi_2-(\phi_1,\phi_2)\phi_1 \tag{19.6}$$

where ϕ_1 and ϕ_2 are assumed to be normalized. Then $(\chi_1,\chi_2)=0$.

The "orthogonalization" process assumed in (19.6) may be performed for any number r of linearly independent elements $\phi_1,\phi_2,\ldots,\phi_r$. We may therefore state the following result:

In the case of an r-fold degenerate eigenvalue, the r eigenvectors may always be chosen in such a manner that they are mutually orthogonal.

If $\phi_1,\ldots,\phi_r$ are the original eigenvectors, there always exist linear combinations

$$\chi_k = \sum_{l=1}^{r} c_{kl}\,\phi_l \qquad k = 1,2,\ldots,r \tag{19.7}$$

such that the χ_k are orthogonal and normalized. When the eigenvectors of a Hermitian operator A are chosen in this manner they all form an orthogonal system.

In addition, this orthogonal system is complete—a fact that we state without proof.

(c) Commuting operators

Let $AB=BA$. Then since $A\psi = a\psi$, it follows that $AB\psi = BA\psi = aB\psi$. We may express this result as follows:

If B and A commute, then both ψ and $B\psi$ are eigenfunctions of A corresponding to the same eigenvalue a.

If the eigenvalue a is non-degenerate, $B\psi$ must be identical with ψ apart from a numerical factor; therefore ψ is also an eigenfunction of B. On the other hand, if the eigenvalue is r-fold degenerate, with orthonormal eigenvectors $\phi_1,\ldots,\phi_r$, we can only infer that all the $B\phi_j$ belong to the subspace spanned by the $\phi_1,\ldots,\phi_r$:

$$B\phi_j = \sum_{k=1}^{r} B_{kj}\,\phi_k \quad \text{where} \quad B_{kj} = (\phi_k, B\phi_j) \tag{19.8}$$

In this case, however, we can find a linear combination

$$\chi = \sum_{k=1}^{r} d_k\,\phi_k \tag{19.9}$$

such that χ is also an eigenfunction of B, i.e.

$$B\chi = b\chi$$

It follows that

$$\sum_{k=1}^{r} d_k\,B\phi_k = b\sum_{j=1}^{r} d_j\,\phi_j$$

Forming the scalar product with ϕ_j gives the result

$$\sum_{k=1}^{r} B_{jk}\,d_k = b\,d_j \tag{19.10}$$

The above expression represents r linear homogeneous equations for the coefficients d_k introduced in (19.9); a solution only exists if the determinant

$$\begin{vmatrix} B_{11}-b & B_{12} & \cdots \\ B_{21} & B_{22}-b & \cdots \\ \vdots & \vdots & \end{vmatrix} \tag{19.11}$$

vanishes. To each root $b^{(s)}$ of this equation of the rth degree there corresponds a solution $d_1^{(s)},\ldots,d_r^{(s)}$ of the equations (19.10), and a linear combination

$$\chi_s = \sum_{k=1}^{r} d_k^{(s)}\phi_k \qquad s = 1,2,\ldots,r \tag{19.12}$$

which is an eigenfunction both of A and of B, for which the eigenvalues are a and $b^{(s)}$ respectively. This result may be expressed as follows:

If A and B commute, there always exists an orthonormal system of eigenfunctions that is common to both operators.

With regard to the roots $b^{(s)}$ of (19.11), there are two cases to be distinguished:

1. The roots are all different. Then, when a and b are given, the eigenfunction χ_s is uniquely determined. The degeneracy is said to be completely removed.
2. The roots are not all different. Then there is certainly another operator C that commutes with A and B, and there is an orthogonal system, the elements of which are eigenfunctions of A, B, and C, with associated eigenvalues a, $b^{(s)}$, $c^{(n)}$. The degeneracy is considered to be removed if the eigenfunction is uniquely determined by the three eigenvalues.

This method of establishing a unique orthogonal system, by means of commuting Hermitian or unitary operators, is of great importance in connection with the description of atomic spectra.

(*d*) *Functions of Hermitian and unitary operators*

A function $f(A)$ of an operator A is defined as follows: firstly, $A^2, A^3, \ldots$ are interpreted as repeated applications of A. Hence $f(A)$ is defined, provided $f(x)$ is developed as a power series $\sum_n c_n x^n$. Then

$$f(A) = \sum_n c_n A^n$$

A general definition proceeds from the orthogonal system associated with A,

$$A\phi_n = a_n \phi_n$$

where the a_n are ordinary numbers. The operator $f(A)$ can then be defined by the requirement that

$$f(A)\phi_n = f(a_n)\phi_n$$

This defines $f(A)$ for all elements of the basis of the ϕ_n, and therefore for any linear combination $\psi = \sum_n c_n \phi_n$.

We should also note that, if A is Hermitian and possesses eigenvalues a_n, then $e^{iA} = U$ is unitary with eigenvalues e^{ia_n}. We shall require this result in connection with the integration of the Schrödinger equation in §22.

§20. The correspondence between matrix and wave mechanics

It was shown in the last section that a Hilbert space basis may be formed from the eigenfunctions of a Hermitian operator; we shall now illustrate this procedure in connection with some important physical examples.

In the first instance we shall consider the problem in one dimension: a particle with coordinate x. In quantum theory, this coordinate corresponds to an operator which we shall designate by X. The eigenstates of X, denoted by α_x, satisfy the equation

$$X\alpha_x = x\alpha_x \tag{20.1}$$

We shall now show that, in consequence of the commutation relation

$$PX - XP = \frac{\hbar}{i} \tag{20.2}$$

the eigenvalues x and p corresponding to the operators X and P extend over all real numbers. If (20.2) is multiplied by $-P/\hbar^2$ from the right and from the left, and the two products are added, the result is

$$\left(\frac{i}{\hbar}P\right)^2 X - X\left(\frac{i}{\hbar}P\right)^2 = 2\frac{i}{\hbar}P = \frac{\hbar}{i}\frac{d}{dP}\left(\frac{i}{\hbar}P\right)^2$$

If this procedure is continued, we obtain

$$\left(\frac{i}{\hbar}P\right)^n X - X\left(\frac{i}{\hbar}P\right)^n = \frac{\hbar}{i}\frac{d}{dP}\left(\frac{i}{\hbar}P\right)^n$$

If we now multiply by $(-x')^n/n!$ and sum over all n, the following result is obtained:

$$\exp\left(-\frac{i}{\hbar}Px'\right)X - X\exp -\frac{i}{\hbar}Px' = -x'\exp -\frac{i}{\hbar}Px' \tag{20.3}$$

If this equation is applied to α_x, then from (20.1):

$$X\left\{\exp\left(-\frac{i}{\hbar}Px'\right)\alpha_x\right\} = (x+x')\exp\left(-\frac{i}{\hbar}Px'\right)\alpha_x \tag{20.4}$$

$\exp[-(i/\hbar)Px']\alpha_x$ is therefore an eigenfunction of X, with the eigenvalue $x+x'$. Since x' can be any real number, our statement is proved for x; the proof for p is identical.

An eigenfunction α_x is derived from α_0 by putting

$$\alpha_x = f(x)\exp\left(-\frac{i}{\hbar}Px\right)\alpha_0$$

where $f(x)$ is an arbitrary normalization factor for which $f(0)=1$; this factor may be chosen in such a manner that $(\alpha_x, \alpha_{x'}) = \delta(x-x')$. Since $f(x)$ is a pure number it commutes with P; hence $f(x) = \exp i\gamma(x)$, where $\gamma(x)$ is an initially arbitrary real function of x for which $\gamma(0)=0$.

Any vector ϕ may be represented by

$$\phi = \int \phi(x)\alpha_x\,dx \tag{20.5}$$

$\phi(x)$ is termed the representation of ϕ in the basis spanned by the eigenfunctions of X, or simply, the x-representation of ϕ. The x-representation of X is obtained by applying the operator X to (20.5):

$$X\phi = \int \phi(x)X\alpha_x\,dx = \int x\phi(x)\alpha_x\,dx \tag{20.6}$$

In the x-representation, therefore, the application of X to ϕ simply means the multiplication of $\phi(x)$ by x. In order to obtain the simplest possible representation of P, we make the stipulation that the arbitrary function $\gamma(x)$ shall vanish identically. Then, since P commutes with the number x:

$$\alpha_x = \exp\left(-\frac{i}{\hbar}Px\right)\alpha_0 \quad \text{therefore} \quad \frac{\hbar}{i}\frac{\partial\alpha_x}{\partial x} = -P\alpha_x$$

Hence

$$P\phi = \int \phi(x)P\alpha_x\,dx = -\int \phi(x)\frac{\hbar}{i}\frac{\partial\alpha_x}{\partial x}dx = \int \frac{\hbar}{i}\frac{\partial\phi(x)}{\partial x}\alpha_x\,dx$$

when $\phi(x)$ vanishes at infinity. The x-representation of P is therefore the same as the Schrödinger form of the momentum operator

$$P\phi(x) = \frac{\hbar}{i}\frac{\partial}{\partial x}\phi(x) \tag{20.7}$$

Thus in principle we know the effect of all operators of the form $f(P, X)$ in their x-representation. In particular, the representation of the eigenvalue equation $\mathscr{H}(P, X)\psi_n = E_n\psi_n$ is found to be the Schrödinger equation

$$\mathscr{H}\left(\frac{\hbar}{i}\frac{\partial}{\partial x}, x\right)\psi_n(x) = E_n\psi_n(x) \tag{20.8}$$

The eigenvectors ψ_n of $\mathscr{H}$ may of course be taken as a basis instead of the α_x. The representation of an arbitrary vector ϕ then becomes

$$\phi = \sum_n \phi(n)\psi_n$$

(assuming a discrete spectrum for the sake of simplicity). This is called the E-representation. Just as the x-representation of X implies the multiplication of $\phi(x)$ by x when X is applied to ϕ, so the E-representation of $\mathscr{H}$ means the multiplication of $\phi(n)$ by E_n. The representations of the operators X and P now become matrices

$$X_{mn} = (\psi_m, X\psi_n), \qquad P_{mn} = (\psi_m, P\psi_n) \tag{20.9}$$

which satisfy both (20.2) and

$$\sum_n \mathscr{H}_{mn}(P, X)\phi(n) = E_m\phi(m) \text{ for all } \phi(n)$$

from which it follows that

$$\mathscr{H}_{mn} = E_m\delta_{mn} \tag{20.10}$$

This is precisely Heisenberg's quantum-mechanical formulation (cf. §12).

Since the elements $\phi(x)$ and $\phi(n)$ represent the same vector ϕ in two different orthogonal systems α_x and ψ_n, each set may be converted into the other by means of the transformation formulae (17.23) or (17.26):

$$\phi(x) = \sum_n U^*_{nx}\phi(n) = \sum_n (\alpha_x, \psi_n)\phi(n) = \sum_n \psi_n(x)\phi(n) \tag{20.11}$$

$$\phi(n) = \int U_{nx}\phi(x)\,dx = \int (\psi_n, \alpha_x)\phi(x)\,dx = \int \psi^*_n(x)\phi(x)\,dx$$

The correspondence between matrix and wave mechanics is now apparent: the Heisenberg and Schrödinger formulations correspond respectively to the energy and position representations of vectors in Hilbert space. The Schrödinger energy eigenfunctions $\psi_n(x)$ constitute a unitary matrix that affords a means of transforming from one representation to another. In particular, they serve to derive the matrix elements $X_{mn}=x_{mn}$ which are of importance in radiation theory:

$$x_{mn}=(\psi_m, X\psi_n)=\int \psi_m^*(x)x\psi_n(x)\,dx \tag{20.12}$$

The momentum representation is also important: its relation to the x-representation is given in the accompanying table, in which the verification of the results is left to the reader (cf. also Exercise 3, p. 138). In the table are included the x- and p-representations of the operators X and P, an arbitrary vector ϕ, and the eigenfunctions $\phi_{x'}$ and $\psi_{p'}$ of X and P.

	x-representation	p-representation
X	x	$i\hbar\,\partial/\partial p$
P	$-i\hbar\,\partial/\partial x$	p
ϕ	$\phi(x)$	$g(p)$
$\phi_{x'}$	$\delta(x-x')$	$\exp(-ipx'/\hbar)/\sqrt{(2\pi\hbar)}$
$\psi_{p'}$	$\exp(ip'x/\hbar)/\sqrt{(2\pi\hbar)}$	$\delta(p-p')$

It should be noted that the expressions $\delta(x-x')$ in the x-representation and $\exp(-ipx'/\hbar)/\sqrt{(2\pi\hbar)}$ in the p-representation, which are analytically quite different, represent the same physical situation, namely, a particle situated at x'; on the other hand, the analytically similar expressions $\exp(-ipx'/\hbar)/\sqrt{(2\pi\hbar)}$ and $\exp(ip'x/\hbar)/\sqrt{(2\pi\hbar)}$ denote physically different states. Physical quantities are denoted by abstract elements in Hilbert space, which can be represented by different real or complex numbers according to the choice of coordinate system.

From the above table, we may derive a possible representation of the δ-function:

$$(\phi_x, \phi_{x'})=\frac{1}{2\pi\hbar}\int_{-\infty}^{\infty}\exp\frac{i}{\hbar}p(x-x')\,dp=\delta(x-x')$$

Let us now integrate, not from $-\infty$ to ∞, but from $-A\hbar$ to $A\hbar$, after which A is allowed to increase without limit:

$$\delta(x-x') = \lim_{A\to\infty} \frac{1}{\pi} \frac{\sin A(x-x')}{(x-x')} = \lim_{A\to\infty} s_A(x-x') \qquad (20.13)$$

In order to verify this, let us take an arbitrary function $f(x)$ and form the integral

$$\int_{-\infty}^{+\infty} f(x)s_A(x)dx = \frac{1}{\pi}\int_{-\infty}^{+\infty} f(x)\frac{\sin Ax}{x}\,dx$$

Substituting $x = z/A$, we obtain

$$\int_{-\infty}^{+\infty} f(x)s_A(x)dx = \frac{1}{\pi}\int_{-\infty}^{+\infty} f\left(\frac{z}{A}\right)\frac{\sin z}{z}\,dz$$

If A is now allowed to tend to infinity, z/A tends to 0. Then since $\int_{-\infty}^{+\infty} \frac{\sin z}{z} = \pi$

$$\lim_{A\to\infty} \int f(x)s_A(x)dx = f(0) \qquad (20.14)$$

The above result is all that it is intended to express by defining the δ-function as

$$\lim_{A\to\infty} \frac{1}{2\pi}\int_{-A}^{+A} e^{ikx}\,dk = \delta(x)$$

since the only significant property of this "function" is that

$$\int_{-\infty}^{+\infty} f(x)\delta(x)dx = f(0) \text{ for any } f(x)$$

The derivative of the δ-function can be derived in a similar manner as

$$\delta'(x) = \lim_{A\to\infty} s'_A(x)$$

hence

$$\int f(x)\delta'(x)dx = -f'(0)$$

Other representations and properties of the δ-function will be found in Exercises 1 and 2, p. 137.

Note: For the sake of completeness, we must mention a notation due to P. A. M. Dirac, which is described in his book *The Principles of Quantum Mechanics*, and which is frequently employed in the literature on the subject. In this notation vectors are denoted by the brackets $|\rangle$ or $\langle|$, depending upon whether they occur on the right or the left side of the scalar product. The symbol $\langle|$ is called a "bra" vector, and $|\rangle$, a "ket" vector. The suffixes required to designate the vectors ϕ are written inside the brackets. The scalar product (ϕ_m, ϕ_n) is written $\langle m|n\rangle$, and $A\phi_m$ is represented as $A|m\rangle$.

Dirac's notation possesses no advantages over that which has been used so far in this book. Its usefulness first appears in connection with the completeness relation for an orthonormal system $|m\rangle$, which it expresses very concisely. The projection operator $|m\rangle\langle m|$ is introduced for this purpose: the condition for completeness is then denoted by $\sum_m |m\rangle\langle m| = 1$.

If this equation is multiplied by $|\rangle$, we obtain $|\rangle = \sum_m |m\rangle\langle m|\rangle$, which is the representation of $|\rangle$ in terms of the $\langle m|\rangle$. Similarly, an operator A may be represented in terms of its eigenvalues a_m and eigenvectors $|m\rangle$: $A = \sum_m a_m |m\rangle\langle m|$.

§21. Probability and the quantum theory

We saw in §18 that if the state ϕ of a system is known, the average value and dispersion of any set of observations can be calculated. We now wish to ascertain the probability of any given measurement. When an observable A is measured, the system passes from its original state to an eigenstate of A; therefore the only possible results of such measurements are the eigenvalues of A. We may therefore pose the following question: given a normalized state ϕ, what is the probability $w(a_n)$ of finding the eigenvalue a_n of A when the observable A is measured, or in the case of a continuous spectrum, what is the probability $w(a)\,da$ that the measured value will lie between a and $a+da$?

To find the answer, we express the equation $\bar{A} = (\phi, A\phi)$ in the A-representation:

$$\bar{A} = (\phi, A\phi) = \sum_n a_n |\phi(n)|^2 \tag{21.1}$$

where

$$A\psi_n = a_n\psi_n \qquad \phi(n) = (\psi_n, \phi)$$

Similarly, for a continuous spectrum:

$$\bar{A} = \int a\,|\phi(a)|^2\,da \tag{21.1a}$$

where

$$A\psi_a = a\psi_a \qquad \phi(a) = (\psi_a, \phi)$$

We obtain in the same way

$$\overline{A^2} = \sum_n a_n^2 |\phi(n)|^2 \quad \text{and} \quad \overline{A^2} = \int a^2 |\phi(a)|^2\,da \tag{21.2}$$

and for an arbitrary function of A

$$\overline{f(A)} = \sum_n f(a_n)|\phi(n)|^2 \quad \text{and} \quad \overline{f(A)} = \int f(a)|\phi(a)|^2\,da$$

Therefore, if ϕ is resolved into components $\phi(n)$ or $\phi(a)$ along the eigenvectors ψ_n or ψ_a of A, the required probabilities can be calculated from the formula

$$w(a_n) = |\phi(n)|^2 \quad \text{or} \quad w(a)\,da = |\phi(a)|^2\,da \tag{21.3}$$

If a measurement of A yields the value a_n or a, then after the measurement the system is in an eigenstate ϕ; this means that a further measurement of A would yield the same result. If B is an operator that commutes with A, and a_n or a are not degenerate, then ϕ is also an eigenvector of B, and the result of a subsequent measurement of the observable B is also uniquely determined. When degeneracy is present, it is only possible to say that ϕ lies somewhere in the Hilbert subspace spanned by the eigenvectors of a_n or a. After the measurement of B, ϕ is also an eigenfunction of the operator B, and if it is no longer degenerate with regard to this operator, then it is uniquely determined. If this is not the case, it is necessary to seek another operator that commutes with A and B. Thus in simple cases it is possible in principle to determine a state uniquely by means of measurements on a complete set of operators.

A much more difficult problem is inherent in the determination of the original state of a system. It is obviously insufficient to determine by many measurements the probability distribution $w(x_1, \ldots)dx_1 \ldots dx_f$ of the eigenvalues of a complete system of operators $X_1, \ldots, X_f$, because this does not yield the phase $S(x_1, \ldots)$ of the wave function $\phi = \sqrt{(w)}e^{iS}$, which is necessary to determine the mean values $\bar{p}$, $\overline{p^2}$, etc. It is not even enough to know the momentum distribution $\tilde{w}(p_1, \ldots)$ in addition to the distribution $w(x_1, \ldots)$. This is apparent in the example of the wave packet discussed in §16: in this case $\phi(x, t)$ and $\phi(x, -t)$ have the same distributions $w(x)$ and $\tilde{w}(p)$, but correspond to different states, as is clear from their representation in terms of time ($\phi(x, -t)$ converges, $\phi(x, t)$ diverges). In the case of a particle, $\phi(x, t)$ can be determined if $w(x, t)$ and $w(x, t+dt)$ are measured, since, from the continuity equation

$$\dot{w} = -\frac{\partial}{\partial x}\frac{\hbar}{2mi}\left(\phi^* \frac{\partial \phi}{\partial x} - \phi \frac{\partial \phi^*}{\partial x}\right) = -\frac{\hbar}{m}\frac{\partial}{\partial x}\left(w \frac{\partial S}{\partial x}\right)$$

from which the phase $S(x)$ is obtained by integrating twice.

If B and A do not commute, then in general an indeterminate result is obtained when B is measured after A. An eigenstate of A has several non-zero components in the basis spanned by the eigenvectors of B; the squares of their magnitudes give the probability of finding the corresponding eigenvalue of B, by (21.1 or 21.1*a*). In the case of canonically conjugate operators, an accurate measurement of one quantity necessarily involves a corresponding indeterminacy in the other, in accordance with the uncertainty relation.

In most cases, of course, it is impossible in practice to determine a state by a series of measurements, particularly for systems with many degrees of freedom, such as macroscopic bodies. For instance, if we assume that we have only measured the energy of a macroscopic system, and that we knew that it lay between E and $E+\Delta E$, then we only know in the first instance that the state ϕ of the system lies in the Hilbert subspace spanned by the eigenstates ϕ_ν of the energy shell ΔE. From statistical mechanics we then know that there is an equal probability w_ν of finding any given state ϕ_ν out of all the states in the energy shell.

A system is called an *ensemble* if it consists of a set of states ϕ_ν, each of which occurs with a corresponding probability w_ν; this is in contrast to the so-called pure case, in which all the w_ν vanish except for one. If we assume that the ϕ_ν constitute a complete system, then when A is measured, the probability of finding the eigenvalue a_n is the product of the two probabilities, first, of finding ϕ_ν, and secondly, given ϕ_ν, of finding a_n, summed over all ν:

$$w(a_n) = \sum_\nu w_\nu |\phi_\nu(n)|^2 \tag{21.4}$$

i.e.

$$\bar{A} = \sum_\nu w_\nu (\phi_\nu, A\phi_\nu) \tag{21.5}$$

There is an essential difference between the various states ϕ_ν of an ensemble and the same states in a superposition $\phi = \sum_\nu c_\nu \phi_\nu$; in the latter case, the probability w_ν of finding the state ϕ_ν in ϕ is $|c_\nu|^2$. But from (21.3) the probability of finding the measured value a_n when the system is in the state ϕ is

$$\begin{aligned} w(a_n) = |\phi(n)|^2 &= \sum_{\nu\mu} c_\nu c_\mu^* \phi_\nu(n)\phi_\mu^*(n) \\ &= \sum_\nu w_\nu |\phi_\nu(n)|^2 + \sum_{\nu\neq\mu} c_\nu c_\mu^* \phi_\nu(n)\phi_\mu^*(n) \end{aligned}$$

Comparison with (21.4) indicates that in the pure case the ϕ_ν can interfere with each other, whereas the interference terms are absent in the case of the ensemble.

§22. The equation of motion in quantum mechanics

When we come to consider the problem of the time variation of a system, a new essential physical element appears in the concept of Hilbert space that we have used hitherto. If we refer back to Chapter B I, we see two solutions given which appear to be completely different, even though the Hamiltonian operator $\mathscr{H}$ appears in each of them.

In §12, the principles of Heisenberg's matrix mechanics were developed from the correspondence principle, and the following relation was obtained for the time variation of every quantum mechanical quantity that is represented by a matrix:

$$\left(\frac{dA}{dt}\right)_{nm} = \frac{i}{\hbar}(\mathscr{H}A - A\mathscr{H})_{nm} \tag{22.1}$$

This may be expressed as an operator equation:

$$\dot{A} = \frac{i}{\hbar}(\mathscr{H}A - A\mathscr{H}) \tag{22.2}$$

In §14, on the other hand, the Schrödinger wave equation for a state function ψ was established; in virtue of (14.10) and (14.11), it may be expressed in the form

$$-\frac{\hbar}{i}\dot{\psi} = \mathscr{H}\psi \tag{22.3}$$

where the operators corresponding to physical quantities such as x, p_x, etc., are introduced as time-independent quantities such as "multiplication by x", $-i\hbar\,\partial/\partial x$, etc.

It is important to realize that these two representations, known respectively as the Heisenberg and the Schrödinger picture (not to be confused with the E- and x-representations), lead to the same physical results in spite of their different viewpoints and their different initial equations.

The reason for this is that neither the vectors nor the operators A have any direct physical significance; this is a property of the expectation values $(\psi, A\psi)$ alone. The latter remain unchanged, however, if an arbitrary (and possibly time-dependent) unitary transformation $\psi \to \psi' = U\psi$, $A \to A' = UAU^+$ is applied to ψ and A:

$$(\psi', A'\psi') = (U\psi, UAU^+U\psi) = (\psi, A\psi) \tag{22.4}$$

For this reason, only the time dependence of the expectation values is physically defined; that of the vectors and operators themselves is not.*

In the Schrödinger picture, the operators A are assumed to be independent of time, and the vectors are expressed in terms of time by

* For the sake of brevity we shall assume here that the Hamiltonian operator $\mathscr{H}$ is independent of time. In the general case, when $\mathscr{H}$ depends explicitly on time, we have the situation described on p. 156.

integrating (22.3), in which $\mathscr{H}$ is taken to be constant with respect to time:

$$\psi(t) = \exp\left(-\frac{i}{\hbar}\mathscr{H}t\right)\psi(0) \tag{22.5}$$

For time-independent expectation values, therefore,

$$\{\psi(t), A\psi(t)\} = \left\{\psi(0), \exp\left(\frac{i}{\hbar}\mathscr{H}t\right)A\exp\left(-\frac{i}{\hbar}\mathscr{H}t\right)\psi(0)\right\} \tag{22.6}$$

It is easy to see that the operators

$$A(t) = \exp\left(\frac{i}{\hbar}\mathscr{H}t\right)A\exp\left(-\frac{i}{\hbar}\mathscr{H}t\right) \tag{22.7}$$

satisfy the "equations of motion" (22.2). Hence we have the following relationships between the Heisenberg and the Schrödinger pictures; in the former we are dealing with time-independent vectors $\psi = \psi(0)$, and the dependence upon time of the operators $A(t)$ is given by (22.7). The transition from the Schrödinger to the Heisenberg picture is effected by the unitary transformation

$$U = \exp\frac{i}{\hbar}\mathscr{H}t$$

The difference between the two pictures disappears in the case of vectors which may be represented by time-dependent bases. For instance, if we consider the identity

$$\begin{aligned}\psi(x,t) = \{\alpha_x, \psi(t)\} &= \left\{\alpha_x, \exp\left(-\frac{i}{\hbar}\mathscr{H}t\right)\psi(0)\right\}\\ &= \left\{\exp\left(\frac{i}{\hbar}\mathscr{H}t\right)\alpha_x, \psi(0)\right\}\\ &= \{U\alpha_x, \psi(0)\} = \{\alpha_x(t), \psi(0)\}\end{aligned} \tag{22.8}$$

we may say that

(1) $\psi(x,t)$ is the representation of the Schrödinger vector $\psi(t)$ in the system constituted by the eigenfunctions α_x of X (for which $X\alpha_x = x\alpha_x$), or

(2) $\psi(x,t)$ is the representation of the Heisenberg vector $\psi(0)$ in the system of eigenfunctions $\alpha_x(t)$ of $X(t)$ (for which $X(t)\alpha_x(t) = x\alpha_x(t) X(t) = UXU^+$).

We shall now investigate the variation with respect to time of the momentum and position expectation values. In the Heisenberg picture, from (22.2):

$$\dot{x} = \frac{i}{\hbar}(\mathscr{H}x - x\mathscr{H}) \qquad \dot{p} = \frac{i}{\hbar}(\mathscr{H}p - p\mathscr{H}) \tag{22.9}$$

Since $px - xp = \hbar/i$, it follows that for every function $F(x,p)$ of the operators x and p

$$Fx - xF = \frac{\hbar}{i}\frac{\partial F}{\partial p} \qquad Fp - pF = -\frac{\hbar}{i}\frac{\partial F}{\partial x} \tag{22.10}$$

To prove the above relations, let us expand $F(x,p)$ in the first equation (22.10) in powers of p, noting that

$$p^n x - x p^n = \frac{\hbar}{i} n p^{n-1} = \frac{\hbar}{i}\frac{\partial p^n}{\partial p} \tag{22.11}$$

for all n, as may be confirmed by proceeding step by step from the familiar commutation relation (for which $n = 1$). The second equation of (22.10) is proved in a similar manner from the commutation of x^n with p. Hence when $F \equiv \mathscr{H}$, (22.9) becomes the quantum-mechanical analogue of the Hamiltonian equations of motion

$$\dot{x} = \frac{\partial \mathscr{H}}{\partial p} \qquad \dot{p} = -\frac{\partial \mathscr{H}}{\partial x} \tag{22.12}$$

The equations (22.9) only assume physical significance in connection with the determination of the expectation values. In particular, if we put $p^2/2m + V(x)$ for $\mathscr{H}$, then for any state ψ in the Heisenberg picture

$$\frac{d}{dt}(\psi, x\psi) = \frac{1}{m}(\psi, p\psi) \qquad \frac{d}{dt}(\psi, p\psi) = -\left(\psi, \frac{dV}{dx}\psi\right) \tag{22.13}$$

from which we obtain the so-called Ehrenfest theorem

$$m\frac{d^2}{dt^2}(\psi, x\psi) = -\left(\psi, \frac{dV}{dx}\psi\right), \quad \text{i.e.} \quad m\ddot{\bar{x}} = -\overline{\left(\frac{\partial V}{\partial x}\right)} \tag{22.14}$$

This simple expression may be immediately extended to the case of motion in three dimensions.

The centre of gravity of a wave packet therefore moves in accordance with Newton's equation, if the acting force $-\text{grad}\, V$ is averaged over the wave packet. In particular, if the field of force is uniform (as in the deflection experiments for the measurement of e/m, for instance), the centre of gravity of the charge distribution moves exactly in accordance with the laws of classical physics.

The above statements only have obvious meaning if the wave packet remains fairly concentrated. For instance, if we consider a wave packet at a potential step, part of it is reflected and part transmitted. The packet divides into two separate portions travelling in different directions. The centre of gravity still moves according to (22.14), but it lies somewhere between the two parts and can no longer suggest that the charge is concentrated in its neighbourhood.

When magnetic fields are present the Hamiltonian operator no longer assumes the simple form $p^2/2m + V(x)$; it also contains product terms of the type $\mathbf{pA}(\mathbf{r}, t)$, where $\mathbf{A}$ is the vector potential. Although calculation is not quite as simple as in (22.13) it can still be performed, and gives the corresponding result to (22.14) (cf. Exercise 6, p. 138)

$$m\bar{\ddot{\mathbf{r}}} = \bar{\mathbf{F}}$$

where $\mathbf{F}$ is the operator of the Lorentz force,

$$\mathbf{F} = e\mathbf{E} + \frac{e}{2c}(\mathbf{v} \times \mathbf{H} - \mathbf{H} \times \mathbf{v})$$

$\mathscr{H}$ and $\mathbf{F}$ must be Hermitian operators; it is therefore necessary to pay attention to the included non-commuting operators, such as $\mathbf{p}$ and $\mathbf{A}$ in $\mathscr{H}$, $\mathbf{v}$ in (22.9), and $\mathbf{H}$ in $\mathbf{F}$.

In connection with Ehrenfest's principle, it is useful to give the quantum-mechanical form of the virial theorem. In classical mechanics this is obtained as follows: the equation of motion is first multiplied by $\mathbf{r}$: $m\ddot{\mathbf{r}}\mathbf{r} = -\mathbf{r}\,\mathrm{grad}\,V$.

The identity

$$\ddot{\mathbf{r}}\mathbf{r} = \frac{d}{dt}\dot{\mathbf{r}}\mathbf{r} - \dot{\mathbf{r}}^2$$

is now used to substitute for $\ddot{\mathbf{r}}\mathbf{r}$. If $\dot{\mathbf{r}}\mathbf{r}$ is finite, as is always the case for stationary atomic orbits, then on taking the time average:

$$\overline{2E_{kin}} = m\overline{\dot{\mathbf{r}}^2} = \overline{\mathbf{r}\,\mathrm{grad}\,V} \tag{22.15}$$

A similar result is obtained in quantum mechanics if the Schrödinger equation for stationary states, $\mathscr{H}\phi = E\phi$, is differentiated with respect to $\mathbf{r}$:

$$\mathscr{H}\,\mathrm{grad}\,\phi + \phi\,\mathrm{grad}\,V = E\,\mathrm{grad}\,\phi$$

Since

$$\mathscr{H}(\mathbf{r}\phi^*) = \mathbf{r}\mathscr{H}\phi^* - \frac{\hbar^2}{m}\operatorname{grad}\phi^*$$

if we multiply by $\phi^*\mathbf{r}$ and integrate with respect to $\mathbf{r}$, we obtain

$$-\frac{\hbar^2}{m}\int \operatorname{grad}\phi \operatorname{grad}\phi^* \, d\mathbf{r} + \int |\phi|^2 \mathbf{r} \operatorname{grad} V \, d\mathbf{r} = 0$$

after integration by parts. Now, since

$$\frac{\hbar^2}{2m}\int \operatorname{grad}\phi \operatorname{grad}\phi^* \, d\mathbf{r} = -\int \phi^* \frac{\hbar^2}{2m} \nabla^2 \phi \, d\mathbf{r} = \overline{E_{kin}}$$

we obtain the same result as in (22.15):

$$2\overline{E_{kin}} = \overline{\mathbf{r} \operatorname{grad} V} \tag{22.16}$$

although the average values in both equations are formed according to different rules (cf. Exercise 8, p. 138).

Exercises

1. *Various representations of the δ-function*

Represent the function $\delta(x)$ by means of the expression $\lim_{b\to 0} C_b S(x/b)$, in which the following functions S are to be used:

(1) $S = \exp -\frac{x^2}{b^2}$ (2) $S = \frac{1}{1+x^2/b^2}$ (3) $S = \begin{cases} 0 \text{ for } |x| > b \\ 1 \text{ for } |x| < b \end{cases}$ (4) $S = \frac{\sin^2 x/b}{x^2/b^2}$

The quantity b is taken to be the width of the distribution ($b > 0$). Determine the normalization constant C_b in each case so that the integral over the range $-\infty \leqq x \leqq +\infty$ gives the value unity. Illustrate the functions graphically. Show also that

$$\lim_{b\to 0} \int_{-a}^{a'} f(x) C_b S(x/b) \, dx = f(0)$$

provided that the integration takes place about the point $x = 0$, i.e. that $a', a > 0$.

2. *δ-function relations*

Prove the following relations:

(1) $\delta(Cx) = \frac{1}{C}\delta(x) \qquad C = \text{const}$

(2) $\delta\{(x-a)(x-b)\} = \frac{1}{|a-b|}\{\delta(x-a) + \delta(x-b)\} \qquad a \neq b \text{ const}$

(3) $\prod_{i=1}^{N} \delta\left(\sum_{k=1}^{N} \alpha_{ik} x_k\right) = \frac{1}{|\det \alpha_{ik}|} \prod_{k=1}^{N} \delta(x_k)$ where $\det \alpha_{ik} \neq 0$

Verify for the case of two variables x and y:

$$\delta(x+y)\delta(x-y) = \tfrac{1}{2}\delta(x)\delta(y)$$

3. *The Schrödinger equation in momentum space*

Express the Schrödinger equation $\mathscr{H}\phi = i\hbar\dot{\phi}$ in momentum space (*a*) as an integral equation, (*b*) as a differential equation where $x = -i\hbar\partial/\partial p$ and $V(x)$ is assumed to be given as a power series. (*c*) What is the form taken by the equation for the linear oscillator?

4. *One-dimensional potential well*

Let a particle move parallel to the x-axis in a potential field

$$V(x) = \begin{cases} 0 \text{ for } |x| > l \\ -V_0 \text{ for } |x| < l \end{cases}$$

Since $\mathscr{H} = p^2/2m + V(x)$ commutes with the reflection operator P (defined by $P\phi(x) = \phi(-x)$), the eigenfunctions of $\mathscr{H}$ can also be chosen as eigenfunctions of P, i.e. as odd or even functions. It will therefore be sufficient to consider the functions in the range $x \geqq 0$. For the even functions we shall put

$$\phi_g = \begin{cases} a \cos qx & \text{for } 0 < x < l \\ S_g(k)\, e^{-ikx} - e^{ikx} & \text{for } x > l \end{cases}$$

and for the odd functions,

$$\phi_u = \begin{cases} a \sin qx & \text{for } 0 < x < l \\ S_u(k)\, e^{-ikx} - e^{ikx} & \text{for } x > l \end{cases}$$

We also have

$$\frac{\hbar^2 k^2}{2m} + V_0 = \frac{\hbar^2 q^2}{2m}$$

Determine the functions $S_g(k)$ and $S_u(k)$ from the boundary conditions that ϕ and ϕ' are continuous at $x = l$. Where do the zero points of S lie along the positive imaginary axis of k? What is their significance?

5. *Potential in δ-function form*

Determine the eigenfunctions and eigenvalues for the potential $-\dfrac{\hbar^2}{2m\lambda}\delta(x)$ (*a*) from the previous exercise by passing to the limits

$$V_0 \to \infty, \; l \to 0, \text{ but with } 2V_0 l = \frac{\hbar^2}{2m\lambda}$$

(*b*) directly from the boundary condition for $x = 0$.
Are there any stationary states?

6. *Ehrenfest's theorem and the magnetic field*

Determine the equation for the time rate of change of the operators $\mathbf{r}$ and $\mathbf{p}$ in the presence of a magnetic field.

7. *Current and magnetic field*

Extend the continuity equation (14.15) to the case in which a magnetic field is present.

What is the current density $\mathbf{j}$ in this case?

8. *The virial theorem*

Discuss the virial equation (22.16) when the potential is (*a*) of the Coulomb type, (*b*) that of an oscillator.

CHAPTER BIII

Linear and angular momentum

§23. Translation and rotation as unitary operators

(a) Definitions

We saw in §20 that the operator $T_a = \exp(-iP_x a/\hbar)$ converts a Hilbert space basis vector α_x to α_{x+a}, and therefore displaces a state designated by x, by an amount equal to a. In the three-dimensional case, the unitary operator $T_{\mathbf{a}} = \exp(-i\mathbf{Pa}/\hbar)$ effects a similar translation of the states $\alpha_{\mathbf{r}}$ by an amount equal to the vector $\mathbf{a}$.

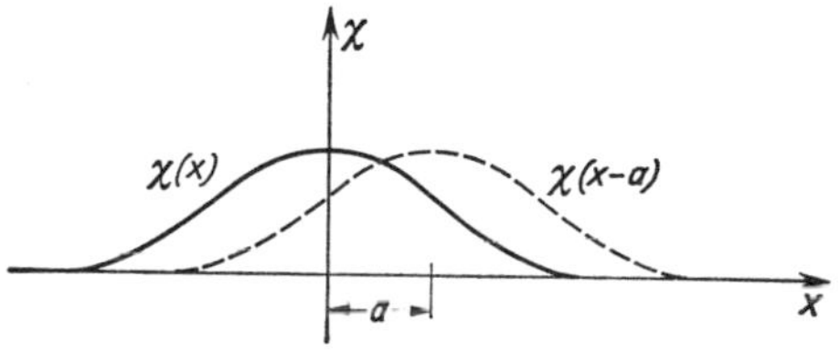

Fig. 25.—$\chi(x-a)$ represents a state $\chi(x)$ displaced by an amount a

In the $\mathbf{r}$-representation $\chi(\mathbf{r})$, $T_{\mathbf{a}}$ takes the form

$$T_{\mathbf{a}} = \exp\left(-\frac{i}{\hbar}\mathbf{pa}\right), \text{ where } \mathbf{p} = \frac{\hbar}{i}\frac{\partial}{\partial \mathbf{r}} = \frac{\hbar}{i}\,\text{grad} \tag{23.1}$$

Then

$$T_{\mathbf{a}}\chi(\mathbf{r}) = \chi(\mathbf{r}-\mathbf{a}) \tag{23.1a}$$

Equation (23.1*a*) can be immediately verified: if $T_{\mathbf{a}}$ is expanded in powers of $\mathbf{a}$, (23.1*a*) is clearly identical with the Taylor expansion of $\chi(\mathbf{r}-\mathbf{a})$. In particular, for the displacement in the x-direction (fig. 25):

$$T_a = \exp\left(-\frac{i}{\hbar}p_x a\right) = \exp\left(-a\frac{\partial}{\partial x}\right)$$

$$T_a\chi(x, y, z) = \chi(x-a, y, z) \tag{23.1b}$$

Similarly, the operator $\mathbf{M}$ of the angular momentum may be associated with a rotation $D_\mathbf{t}(\alpha)$ through an angle α about an axis $\mathbf{t}$ (where $\mathbf{t}^2 = 1$) through the origin of coordinates. In the $\mathbf{r}$-representation, the operator that rotates a state in this manner is

$$D_\mathbf{t}(\alpha) = \exp\left(-\frac{i}{\hbar}\mathbf{M}\mathbf{t}\alpha\right), \quad \text{where } \mathbf{M} = \mathbf{r} \times \mathbf{p} = \frac{\hbar}{i}\mathbf{r} \times \text{grad} \tag{23.2}$$

Then

$$D_\mathbf{t}(\alpha)\chi(\mathbf{r}) = \chi(\tilde{\mathbf{r}}), \quad \text{where } \tilde{\mathbf{r}} = D_\mathbf{t}(-\alpha)\mathbf{r} \tag{23.2a}$$

The vector $\tilde{\mathbf{r}}$ is produced from $\mathbf{r}$ by a rotation through the angle $-\alpha$, that is, by the reciprocal operation to $D_\mathbf{t}(\alpha)$. If we take the particular case of a rotation about the z-axis, and express this in polar coordinates:

$$\frac{i}{\hbar}M_z = (\mathbf{r} \times \text{grad})_z = x\frac{\partial}{\partial y} - y\frac{\partial}{\partial x} = \frac{\partial}{\partial \phi}$$

Therefore

$$D_z(\alpha) = \exp\left(-\alpha\frac{\partial}{\partial \phi}\right), \quad D_z(\alpha)\psi(r, \theta, \phi) = \psi(r, \theta, \phi - \alpha) \tag{23.2b}$$

Thus (23.2) is shown to be valid, since the z-axis can have any direction.

The above expressions for the translation and rotation operators are generally valid, even for the case of a number of particles, when $\mathbf{p}$ and $\mathbf{M}$ are the operators corresponding to the total linear and total angular momentum.

(*b*) *Eigenvalues and eigenfunctions*

Since $\mathbf{p}$ and $\mathbf{M}$ are Hermitian operators, $T_\mathbf{a}$ and $D_\mathbf{t}(\alpha)$ are unitary, and the eigenvalues of T_a and $D_z(\alpha)$ therefore have absolute value unity. In addition, $(T_a)^2 = T_{2a}$ and $[D_z(\alpha)]^2 = D_z(2\alpha)$. Further, if k and m are real numbers, and χ_k and ψ_m are eigenfunctions of T_a and $D_z(\alpha)$ respectively, then

$$T_a\chi_k = e^{-ika}\chi_k \quad \text{and} \quad D_z(\alpha)\psi_m = e^{-im\alpha}\psi_m \tag{23.3}$$

Comparison with (23.1*b*) shows that the function $\chi_k(x)$ satisfies the relation

$$\chi_k(x-a) = e^{-ika}\chi_k(x)$$

The solution of this functional equation is

$$\chi_k(x) = e^{ikx}u_k(x), \quad \text{where } u_k(x) = u_k(x-a) \tag{23.4}$$

$u_k(x)$ is therefore periodic, with period a. Similarly, ψ_m may be written

$$\psi_m(r,\theta,\phi) = e^{im\phi} w_m(r,\theta,\phi)$$

where
$$w_m(r,\theta,\phi) = w_m(r,\theta,\phi-\alpha) \qquad (23.5)$$

In order that ψ_m should be unique, m must be a whole number and $\alpha = 2\pi/n$ where n is an integer.

An infinitesimal translation or rotation is produced if a or α is made infinitesimally small. Then in virtue of (23.1*b*) and (23.2*b*) we may define

$$T_{inf} = \left(\frac{T_a - 1}{a}\right)_{a\to 0} = -\frac{i}{\hbar} p_x, \quad (D_z)_{inf} = \left\{\frac{D_z(\alpha)-1}{\alpha}\right\}_{\alpha\to 0} = -\frac{i}{\hbar} M_z$$

The relation (23.4) implies that when a is infinitesimal, u_k is quite independent of x. Similarly, w_m is independent of ϕ when α is infinitesimal. Then from (23.4) and (23.5) the eigenfunctions of T_{inf} and $(D_z)_{inf}$ are respectively

$$e^{ikx} u_k(y,z) \qquad e^{im\phi} w_m(r,\theta) \qquad (23.6)$$

The functions (23.6) are of course also eigenfunctions of p_x and M_z, corresponding to eigenvalues $\hbar k$ and $\hbar m$ respectively.

(*c*) *Commutability with* $\mathscr{H}$

If the Hamiltonian operator $\mathscr{H}$ commutes with a unitary operator U, then ϕ and $U\phi$ are both eigenfunctions of $\mathscr{H}$ corresponding to the same eigenvalue E. If E is non-degenerate, then ϕ is also an eigenfunction of U. On the other hand, if E is, say, s-fold degenerate with eigenfunctions $\phi_1,\ldots,\phi_s$, then $U\phi_j$ $(j = 1,2,3,\ldots,s)$ must be a linear combination of these eigenfunctions. In this case, however, new functions $\chi_j = \sum_{r=1}^{s} a_{jr}\phi_r$, $j = 1,\ldots,s$ may be formed, which are eigenfunctions of U; hence $U\chi_j = u_j\chi_j$. Each χ_j then belongs to the eigenvalue E of $\mathscr{H}$ and to the eigenvalue u_j of U. If a number of operators $U', U'',\ldots$ commute with $\mathscr{H}$ and with each other, then without restriction of generality the eigenfunctions of $\mathscr{H}$ can always be chosen so that they are also eigenfunctions of $U', U'',\ldots$ We shall now consider two applications of this fundamental theorem, which we have already discussed in §19*c*.

1. *Single electron functions in a metallic crystal lattice*

An electron moving through a metal is acted on by a spatially periodic potential due to the metal ions and the other conduction electrons in the metal lattice. If the sides of the elementary cell in the lattice are represented by the vectors $\mathbf{a}_1, \mathbf{a}_2, \mathbf{a}_3$, then the potential energy $V(\mathbf{r})$ of the electron takes the form

$$V(\mathbf{r}) = V(\mathbf{r}+n_1\,\mathbf{a}_1+n_2\,\mathbf{a}_2+n_3\,\mathbf{a}_3) \tag{23.7}$$

where n_1, n_2, n_3 are whole numbers. The Hamiltonian operator

$$\mathscr{H} = -\frac{\hbar^2}{2m}\nabla^2+V(\mathbf{r}) \tag{23.8}$$

then commutes with the translation operators $T_{\mathbf{a}_1}, T_{\mathbf{a}_2}, T_{\mathbf{a}_3}$. Indeed for any function $f(\mathbf{r})$

$$\begin{aligned} T_{\mathbf{a}_1}V(\mathbf{r})f(\mathbf{r}) &= V(\mathbf{r}-\mathbf{a}_1)f(\mathbf{r}-\mathbf{a}_1) = V(\mathbf{r})f(\mathbf{r}-\mathbf{a}_1) \\ &= V(\mathbf{r})T_{\mathbf{a}_1}f(\mathbf{r}) \end{aligned}$$

the commutability of T and ∇^2 is trivial.

Since the translation operators $T_{\mathbf{a}_1}, T_{\mathbf{a}_2}, T_{\mathbf{a}_3}$ also commute with each other, we may assume that the eigenfunctions ϕ of (23.8) are also eigenfunctions of the $T_{\mathbf{a}_j}$, and therefore, that (corresponding to (23.3))

$$T_{\mathbf{a}_j}\phi_{\mathbf{K}} = \exp(-i\mathbf{K}\,.\,\mathbf{a}_j)\,\phi_{\mathbf{K}} \qquad (j=1,2,3)$$

As in (23.4), the $\phi_{\mathbf{K}}$ may be written in the form

$$\phi_{\mathbf{K}} = \exp(i\mathbf{K}\,.\,\mathbf{r})\,u_{\mathbf{K}}(\mathbf{r})$$

where the $u_{\mathbf{K}}$ and $V(\mathbf{r})$ exhibit the period of the lattice.

2. *Electron in a central field of force*

In the case under consideration, the potential energy depends only on the distance r from a fixed centre; therefore

$$\mathscr{H} = -\frac{\hbar^2}{2m}\nabla^2+V(r) \tag{23.9}$$

$\mathscr{H}$ commutes with any rotation about this fixed centre: for instance, for $D_z(\alpha)$

$$D_z(\alpha)V(r)f(r,\theta,\phi) = V(r)f(r,\theta,\phi-\alpha) = V(r)D_z(\alpha)f(r,\theta,\phi)$$

Since this property of commutability also holds when α is infinitesimal, M_x, M_y, and M_z also commute with $\mathscr{H}$, and so does the sum of the squares

$$\mathbf{M}^2 = M_x^2 + M_y^2 + M_z^2$$

However, the individual components of $\mathbf{M}$ do not commute with each other; if we make use of the relations $p_x x - x p_x = \hbar/i$, etc., the following commutation relations may easily be verified:

$$\begin{aligned} M_x M_y - M_y M_x &= i\hbar M_z \\ M_y M_z - M_z M_y &= i\hbar M_x \\ M_z M_x - M_x M_z &= i\hbar M_y \end{aligned} \tag{23.10}$$

On the other hand, each component of $\mathbf{M}$ commutes with $\mathbf{M}^2$, e.g.

$$M_z \mathbf{M}^2 - \mathbf{M}^2 M_z = 0 \tag{23.11}$$

In the case of a central field, therefore, there are two operators, say $\mathbf{M}^2$ and M_z, that commute with $\mathscr{H}$ and with each other. It is therefore possible to choose the eigenfunctions of $\mathscr{H}$ in such a manner that they are also eigenfunctions of $\mathbf{M}^2$ and M_z.

We shall determine the eigenvalues and eigenfunctions of $\mathbf{M}^2$ and M_z in the next section, for which we shall require the following operators:

$$\vec{\Lambda} = \frac{1}{\hbar}\mathbf{M}, \quad \text{i.e.} \quad \begin{cases} \Lambda_x = \dfrac{1}{i}\left(y\dfrac{\partial}{\partial z} - z\dfrac{\partial}{\partial y}\right) \\ \Lambda_y = \dfrac{1}{i}\left(z\dfrac{\partial}{\partial x} - x\dfrac{\partial}{\partial z}\right) \\ \Lambda_z = \dfrac{1}{i}\left(x\dfrac{\partial}{\partial y} - y\dfrac{\partial}{\partial x}\right) \end{cases} \tag{23.12}$$

and

$$\Lambda_+ = \Lambda_x + i\Lambda_y \qquad \Lambda_- = \Lambda_x - i\Lambda_y \tag{23.13}$$

Since the M_l and Λ_l are Hermitian operators, Λ_+ and Λ_- are adjoint to each other:

$$\Lambda_+ = \Lambda_-^+$$

Equations (23.10) and (23.11) then become

$$\Lambda_x\Lambda_y - \Lambda_y\Lambda_x = i\Lambda_z, \ldots, \ldots \qquad \vec{\Lambda}^2\Lambda_z - \Lambda_z\vec{\Lambda}^2 = 0 \tag{23.14}$$

In addition, we have the following commutation rules for Λ_+ and Λ_-:

$$\Lambda_z\Lambda_+ - \Lambda_+\Lambda_z = \Lambda_+ \qquad \Lambda_z\Lambda_- - \Lambda_-\Lambda_z = -\Lambda_- \tag{23.15}$$

$$\Lambda_+\Lambda_- = \vec{\Lambda}^2 + \Lambda_z - \Lambda_z^2 \qquad \Lambda_-\Lambda_+ = \vec{\Lambda}^2 - \Lambda_z - \Lambda_z^2 \tag{23.16}$$

Equipped with these relations, we shall now determine the eigenvalues of Λ^2 and Λ_z from the commutation rules alone, without making use of (23.12).

§24. Eigenvalues of the angular momentum

We shall now consider an eigenfunction Y_λ corresponding to a fixed eigenvalue of $\vec{\Lambda}^2$. Since $(Y_\lambda, \vec{\Lambda}^2 Y_\lambda) = \sum_k (\Lambda_k Y_\lambda, \Lambda_k Y_\lambda) \geqq 0$, this eigenvalue cannot be negative. It may be written without restriction of generality in terms of a real number $\lambda \geqq 0$, in the form $\lambda(\lambda+1)$:

$$\vec{\Lambda}^2 Y_\lambda = \lambda(\lambda+1) Y_\lambda$$

In general, the eigenvalue $\lambda(\lambda+1)$ will be degenerate, since an electron with a given total angular momentum can have very different values for the components. We shall take the z-component as an example: since $\vec{\Lambda}^2$ and Λ_z commute, we may assume that Y_λ is also an eigenfunction of Λ_z, say with eigenvalue μ. Then we may write

$$\Lambda_z Y_{\lambda\mu} = \mu Y_{\lambda\mu} \tag{24.1}$$

$$\vec{\Lambda}^2 Y_{\lambda\mu} = \lambda(\lambda+1) Y_{\lambda\mu} \tag{24.2}$$

Since

$$(Y_{\lambda\mu}, \Lambda_z^2 Y_{\lambda\mu}) \leqq (Y_{\lambda\mu}, \vec{\Lambda}^2 Y_{\lambda\mu})$$

$$\mu^2 \leqq \lambda(\lambda+1)$$

Hence for any given λ there is always a maximum z-component $\bar{\mu}$ and a minimum $\underline{\mu}$.

We now multiply (24.1) by Λ_+ and make use of (23.15); then

$$\Lambda_z(\Lambda_+ Y_{\lambda\mu}) = (\mu+1)(\Lambda_+ Y_{\lambda\mu})$$

in other words $\Lambda_+ \boldsymbol{Y}_{\lambda\mu}$ either belongs to the eigenvalue $\mu+1$ or it vanishes.

In particular, we must have

$$\Lambda_+ Y_{\lambda\bar{\mu}} = 0$$

otherwise $\Lambda_+ Y_{\lambda\bar{\mu}}$ would belong to the eigenvalue $\bar{\mu}+1$, and $\bar{\mu}$ would not be the greatest value. It then follows from (23.16) that

$$\vec{\Lambda}^2 Y_{\lambda\bar{\mu}} = \lambda(\lambda+1)Y_{\lambda\bar{\mu}} = \{\Lambda_-\Lambda_+ + \Lambda_z(\Lambda_z+1)\} Y_{\lambda\bar{\mu}} = \bar{\mu}(\bar{\mu}+1)Y_{\lambda\bar{\mu}}$$

therefore, since $\lambda \geqq 0$,

$$\bar{\mu} = \lambda \tag{24.3}$$

In classical mechanics, the z-component of the electron's angular momentum would be a maximum if the latter vector were directed along the positive z-axis: we should then expect $M_x{}^2$ and $M_y{}^2$ to be zero, and $\mathbf{M}^2 = M_z{}^2 = \hbar^2\bar{\mu}^2$. The quantum-theory result, on the other hand, is $\hbar^2\bar{\mu}(\bar{\mu}+1) = \hbar^2\bar{\mu}^2+\hbar^2\bar{\mu}$. The reason is that, since M_x, M_y, and M_z do not commute, an eigenfunction of M_z cannot also be an eigenfunction of M_x and M_y. It is true that when $M_z = \hbar\bar{\mu}$ the expectation values of M_x and M_y are zero, but deviations occur about these mean values, the order of magnitude of which is $\overline{M_x{}^2} \approx \overline{M_y{}^2} \approx \hbar^2\bar{\mu}$. (Cf. Exercise 2, p. 152.) In the case of large quantum numbers, the relative deviation $\overline{M_x{}^2}/\mathbf{M}^2 \approx \frac{1}{\bar{\mu}}$ becomes vanishingly small and the classical formula is then valid.

It follows by a similar argument that $\Lambda_- Y_{\lambda\mu}$ either belongs to the eigenvalue $\mu-1$ of Λ_z or vanishes. If the operator Λ_- is applied to $Y_{\lambda\bar{\mu}}$ a number of times in succession, each successive eigenvalue of Λ_z is one less than the previous value. After a finite number of steps the eigenvalue $\underline{\mu}$ is reached, for which

$$\Lambda_- Y_{\lambda\underline{\mu}} = 0$$

Hence, in view of (23.16)

$$\vec{\Lambda}^2 Y_{\lambda\underline{\mu}} = \lambda(\lambda+1)Y_{\lambda\underline{\mu}} = \{\Lambda_+\Lambda_- + \Lambda_z(\Lambda_z-1)\} Y_{\lambda\underline{\mu}} = \underline{\mu}(\underline{\mu}-1)Y_{\lambda\underline{\mu}}$$

and therefore

$$\underline{\mu} = -\lambda \tag{24.4}$$

Now, since $Y_{\lambda\underline{\mu}}$ has been formed from $Y_{\lambda\bar{\mu}}$ by a finite number of operations in which successive eigenvalues are reduced by unity, $\bar{\mu}-\underline{\mu} = 2\lambda$ must be an integer:

$$\bar{\mu}-\underline{\mu} = 2\lambda = 0, 1, 2, 3, \ldots$$

In the case of the special angular-momentum operators (23.12), λ and μ must be whole numbers (cf. §25). However, by proceeding from the general commutation rules (23.14), half-integral values of λ and μ are also obtained; this case is important in connection with electron spin, although Λ_x, Λ_y, Λ_z can no longer be taken as differential operators or $Y_{\lambda\mu}$ as angle functions.

In describing the effect of the operators Λ_+ and Λ_- on the eigenfunctions we shall assume the $Y_{\lambda\mu}$ to be normalized. Then

$$\Lambda_+ Y_{\lambda\mu} = \alpha_{\lambda\mu} Y_{\lambda,\mu+1} \tag{24.5}$$

and by forming the inner product, remembering that $\Lambda_+ = \Lambda_-^+$, we obtain

$$|\alpha_{\lambda\mu}|^2 = (\Lambda_+ Y_{\lambda\mu}, \Lambda_+ Y_{\lambda\mu}) = (Y_{\lambda\mu}, \Lambda_- \Lambda_+ Y_{\lambda\mu})$$
$$= (Y_{\lambda\mu}, [\vec{\Lambda}^2 - \Lambda_z - \Lambda_z^2]\, Y_{\lambda\mu}) = \lambda(\lambda+1) - \mu(\mu+1)$$

We may therefore write

$$\Lambda_+ Y_{\lambda\mu} = \sqrt{[\lambda(\lambda+1) - \mu(\mu+1)]}\, Y_{\lambda,\mu+1}$$
$$= \sqrt{[(\lambda+\mu+1)(\lambda-\mu)]}\, Y_{\lambda,\mu+1} \tag{24.6}$$

and similarly

$$\Lambda_- Y_{\lambda\mu} = \sqrt{[\lambda(\lambda+1) - \mu(\mu-1)]}\, Y_{\lambda,\mu-1}$$
$$= \sqrt{[(\lambda-\mu+1)(\lambda+\mu)]}\, Y_{\lambda,\mu-1} \tag{24.7}$$

We next consider the case when $\lambda = \frac{1}{2}$: the only eigenfunctions that occur are

$$Y_{\frac{1}{2},\frac{1}{2}} = \alpha \quad \text{and} \quad Y_{\frac{1}{2},-\frac{1}{2}} = \beta$$

These two functions constitute a basis which spans the whole Hilbert space of the angular-momentum functions. Then from (24.6), (24.7), and (24.1)

$$\Lambda_+ \alpha = 0 \qquad \Lambda_+ \beta = \alpha$$
$$\Lambda_- \alpha = \beta \qquad \Lambda_- \beta = 0$$
$$\Lambda_z \alpha = \tfrac{1}{2}\alpha \qquad \Lambda_z \beta = -\tfrac{1}{2}\beta$$

A vector u in this Hilbert space is determined by two numbers a and b as follows:

$$u = \begin{pmatrix} a \\ b \end{pmatrix} = a\alpha + b\beta \quad \text{where} \quad \alpha = \begin{pmatrix} 1 \\ 0 \end{pmatrix}, \quad \beta = \begin{pmatrix} 0 \\ 1 \end{pmatrix}$$

The effect of the operators Λ_+, Λ_-, Λ_z on the vector u is represented by the following matrices:

$$\Lambda_+ = \begin{pmatrix} 0 & 1 \\ 0 & 0 \end{pmatrix} \qquad \Lambda_- = \begin{pmatrix} 0 & 0 \\ 1 & 0 \end{pmatrix} \qquad \Lambda_z = \frac{1}{2}\begin{pmatrix} 1 & 0 \\ 0 & -1 \end{pmatrix}$$

In the theory of electron spin, for which the above formalism will be required, the angular-momentum operator is written

$$\mathbf{M} = \hbar\vec{\Lambda} \equiv \mathbf{s} = \tfrac{1}{2}\hbar\vec{\sigma} \tag{24.8}$$

It follows from (23.13) that the components of the vector operator $\vec{\sigma}$ are

$$\sigma_x = \begin{pmatrix} 0 & 1 \\ 1 & 0 \end{pmatrix} \qquad \sigma_y = \begin{pmatrix} 0 & -i \\ i & 0 \end{pmatrix} \qquad \sigma_z = \begin{pmatrix} 1 & 0 \\ 0 & -1 \end{pmatrix} \tag{24.9}$$

These are the Pauli spin matrices, which we shall meet later. It can be verified by multiplying out that $\mathbf{s}$ is proportional to the unit matrix:

$$\mathbf{s}^2 = \tfrac{1}{4}\hbar^2(\sigma_x^2+\sigma_y^2+\sigma_z^2) = \tfrac{3}{4}\hbar^2\begin{pmatrix} 1 & 0 \\ 0 & 1 \end{pmatrix}$$

The constant of proportionality has the value $\hbar^2\lambda(\lambda+1)$ where $\lambda = \frac{1}{2}$.

We next consider the case in which the Λ-operators are given by the differential expressions (23.12). As we shall see in §25, λ and μ are whole numbers, usually designated by l and m; the eigenfunctions $Y_{lm} = Y_{lm}(\theta, \phi)$ are functions of the polar angles θ and ϕ. They are termed *spherical harmonics.*

§25. Spherical harmonics

Expressed in polar coordinates, (23.12) and (23.13) lead to the following results:

$$\Lambda_z = \frac{1}{i}\frac{\partial}{\partial\phi} \qquad \Lambda_+ = e^{i\phi}\left(\frac{\partial}{\partial\theta} + i\cot\theta\frac{\partial}{\partial\phi}\right)$$

$$\Lambda_- = e^{-i\phi}\left(-\frac{\partial}{\partial\theta} + i\cot\theta\frac{\partial}{\partial\phi}\right) \tag{25.1}$$

$$\vec{\Lambda}^2 = -\frac{1}{\sin^2\theta}\left(\sin\theta\frac{\partial}{\partial\theta}\sin\theta\frac{\partial}{\partial\theta} + \frac{\partial^2}{\partial\phi^2}\right) \tag{25.2}$$

We first determine Y_{ll} from the equations

$$\Lambda_+ Y_{ll} = 0 \qquad \Lambda_z Y_{ll} = lY_{ll}$$

From (25.1), the solution is

$$Y_{ll} = \alpha_l\, e^{il\phi} \sin^l \theta \tag{25.3}$$

as ϕ increases by 2π the solution is single-valued only for integral values of l.

The constants α_l are determined by the condition for normalization:

$$(Y_{ll}, Y_{ll}) = \int Y_{ll}^* \, Y_{ll}\, d\Omega$$

$$= \alpha_l^2 \int_0^{\pi}\int_0^{2\pi} \sin^{2l}\theta \sin\theta \, d\theta\, d\phi = 1 \tag{25.3a}$$

(It is assumed that α_l is a positive real number.) Evaluation of the integral by elementary methods yields the following result:

$$\alpha_l{}^2 = \frac{(2l+1)!}{2^{2l+1}(l!)^2 2\pi} \quad \text{or} \quad \alpha_l = \frac{1}{2^l l!}\sqrt{\frac{(2l+1)!}{4\pi}} \tag{25.3b}$$

The remaining spherical harmonics Y_{lm} are obtained from Y_{ll} by the repeated application of Λ_-, using (24.7). As a result of (24.1), Y_{lm} and hence $\Lambda_- Y_{lm}$ depend on ϕ through the factors $e^{im\phi}$ and $e^{i(m-1)\phi}$ respectively. Therefore

$$\sqrt{[(l-m+1)(l+m)]}\; Y_{l,m-1} = \Lambda_-\, Y_{lm} = e^{-i\phi}\left(-\frac{\partial}{\partial\theta} - m\cot\theta\right) Y_{lm}$$

$$= \frac{e^{-i\phi}}{\sin^{m-1}\theta}\frac{\partial}{\partial\cos\theta}(\sin^m\theta\; Y_{lm})$$

If $Y_{l,l-1}, Y_{l,l-2}, \ldots$, are calculated successively from Y_{ll}, we obtain the expression

$$Y_{lm} = \frac{1}{2^l l!}\left(\frac{2l+1}{4\pi}\right)^{1/2}\left(\frac{(l+m)!}{(l-m)!}\right)^{1/2}\frac{1}{\sin^m\theta}\frac{d^{l-m}(\sin^{2l}\theta)}{d\cos\theta^{l-m}}\,e^{im\phi} \tag{25.4}$$

In particular:

$$Y_{lo} = \frac{1}{2^l l!}\left(\frac{2l+1}{4\pi}\right)^{1/2}\frac{d^l \sin^{2l}\theta}{d\cos\theta^l} \tag{25.4a}$$

and

$$Y_{l,-l} = \frac{(-1)^l}{2^l l!}\left(\frac{(2l+1)!}{4\pi}\right)^{1/2}\sin^l\theta\, e^{-il\phi} \tag{25.4b}$$

Apart from the factor $(-1)^l$, it would have been possible to obtain this last formula in the same way as (25.3), directly from the equation $\Lambda_- Y_{l,-l}=0$, subject to the corresponding normalization condition. Conversely, we could have found the Y_{lm} from $Y_{l,-l}$ or from Y_{lo} by (24.6), by repeated application of Λ_+. In this case

$$\sqrt{[(l+m+1)(l-m)]}\, Y_{l,m+1} = \Lambda_+ Y_{lm} = -e^{i\phi} \sin^{m+1}\theta \frac{d}{d\cos\theta} \frac{Y_{lm}}{\sin^m\theta}$$

and from the above expression together with (25.4*a*) or (25.4*b*) we obtain

$$Y_{lm} = \frac{(-1)^m}{2^l l!}\left(\frac{2l+1}{4\pi}\right)^{1/2}\left(\frac{(l-m)!}{(l+m)!}\right)^{1/2} \sin^m\theta \frac{d^{l+m}\sin^{2l}\theta}{d\cos\theta^{l+m}} e^{im\phi} \qquad (25.5)$$

It can be verified by differentiation that the above formula agrees with (25.4).

The above relations constitute the usual definition of the spherical harmonics as given in the literature. Putting $\cos\theta=\eta$, the ordinary Legendre polynomials are defined as

$$P_l(\eta) = \frac{1}{2^l l!}\frac{d^l(\eta^2-1)^l}{d\eta^l}$$

and the associated Legendre functions as

$$P_l^m(\eta) = (-1)^m \sin^m\theta \frac{d^m}{d\eta^m} P_l(\eta) = \frac{(-\sin\theta)^m}{2^l l!}\frac{d^{l+m}(\eta^2-1)^l}{d\eta^{l+m}}$$

the latter expression is also valid for negative values of m. Formulae (25.4) and (25.5) may now be expressed in the following simplified forms:

$$Y_{lm} = (-1)^{l-m}\left(\frac{2l+1}{4\pi}\right)^{1/2}\left(\frac{(l+m)!}{(l-m)!}\right)^{1/2} P_l^{-m} e^{im\phi}$$

or

$$= (-1)^l\left(\frac{2l+1}{4\pi}\right)^{1/2}\left(\frac{(l-m)!}{(l+m)!}\right)^{1/2} P_l^m e^{im\phi}$$

As a result of the equivalence of these two expressions we have the familiar relation for associated Legendre functions:

$$P_l^{-m} = (-1)^m \frac{(l-m)!}{(l+m)!} P_l^m$$

The spherical harmonics corresponding to $l=0,1,2,3,4,\ldots$ are designated successively as the $s-,p-,d-,f-,g-,\ldots$ functions. Since m can assume a total of $2l+1$ different values between $-l$ and $+l$, there are one s-function, three p-functions, five d-functions, etc. The s- and p-functions are given below:

$$Y_{00}=\frac{1}{(4\pi)^{1/2}}$$

$$Y_{11}=\left(\frac{3}{8\pi}\right)^{1/2}\sin\theta\, e^{i\phi};\; Y_{10}=-\left(\frac{3}{4\pi}\right)^{1/2}\cos\theta;\; Y_{1,-1}=-\left(\frac{3}{8\pi}\right)^{1/2}\sin\theta\, e^{-i\phi}$$

The probability distributions $w(\theta,\phi)=|Y_{l,m}(\theta,\phi)|^2$ are of some interest, and are shown as polar diagrams in figure 26, apart from their normalization factors.

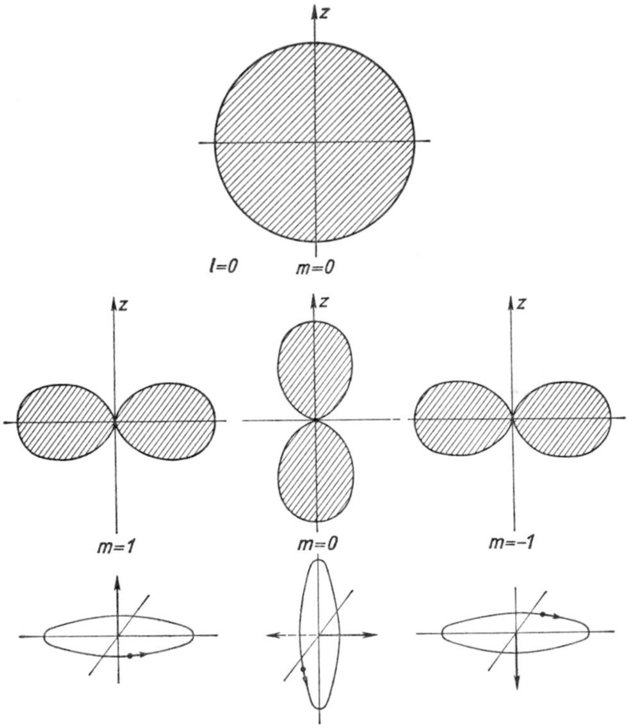

Fig. 26.—Probability distributions of the s-function and the three p-functions, and the three corresponding classical orbits

Since the effect of the operators Λ_+, Λ_- on the functions Y_{lm} is now known, the matrix elements $(Y_{l'm'}, \mathbf{M}Y_{lm})$ can be easily deduced, using (23.12). We now give another method of calculating the important matrix elements $(Y_{l'm'}, \mathbf{r}Y_{lm})$. For this purpose, we put

$$\mathbf{r}/r = \mathbf{a} = (\sin\theta\cos\phi, \sin\theta\sin\phi, \cos\theta)$$

and

$$a_\pm = a_x \pm i a_y = \sin\theta\, e^{\pm i\phi} \tag{25.6}$$

We can then easily verify the following commutation relations:

$$\Lambda_+ a_+ - a_+ \Lambda_+ = 0 \tag{25.7a}$$

$$\Lambda_- a_- - a_- \Lambda_- = 0 \tag{25.7b}$$

$$\Lambda_+ a_- - a_- \Lambda_+ = -(\Lambda_- a_+ - a_+ \Lambda_-) = 2a_z \tag{25.7c}$$

Also, from (25.4)

$$a_- Y_{ll} = -\left(\frac{2}{(2l+1)(2l+3)}\right)^{1/2} Y_{l+1,l-1} + \left(\frac{2l}{2l+1}\right)^{1/2} Y_{l-1,l-1} \tag{25.8}$$

Since a_- and Λ_- commute, if the latter operator is applied $(l-m)$ times to (25.8) we obtain

$$a_- Y_{lm} = -\left(\frac{(l-m+1)(l-m+2)}{(2l+3)(2l+1)}\right)^{1/2} Y_{l+1,m-1} + \left(\frac{(l+m)(l+m-1)}{(2l+1)(2l-1)}\right)^{1/2} Y_{l-1,m-1} \tag{25.9}$$

Similarly, when Λ_+ is applied to $a_+ Y_{l,-l}$,

$$a_+ Y_{lm} = \left(\frac{(l+m+1)\ (l+m+2)}{(2l+3)\ (2l+1)}\right)^{1/2} Y_{l+1,m+1} - \left(\frac{(l-m)(l-m-1)}{(2l+1)(2l-1)}\right)^{1/2} Y_{l-1,m+1} \tag{25.10}$$

Finally, from (25.9) and (24.6) and the commutation relation (25.7c):

$$a_z Y_{lm} = -\left(\frac{(l+m+1)(l-m+1)}{(2l+3)(2l+1)}\right)^{1/2} Y_{l+1,m} - \left(\frac{(l+m)(l-m)}{(2l+1)(2l-1)}\right)^{1/2} Y_{l-1,m} \tag{25.11}$$

We now have all the quantities required for the calculation of the angle-dependent portions of the matrix elements $\mathbf{r}_{l'm', lm}$. We should particularly note that these elements only differ from zero if $\Delta l = l' - l = \pm 1$ and $\Delta m = m' - m = 0, \pm 1$. These "selection rules" are extremely important in connection with the optical spectra of atoms. We might have guessed the condition for m immediately because the quantities $a_{\pm}$ include a factor $e^{\pm i\phi}$ and $a_z = \cos\theta$ is independent of ϕ. Hence in the calculation of the matrix elements integration over the range of ϕ always gives the value zero, provided that Δm is not equal to 0 or ± 1.

Exercises

1. *Parity of the spherical harmonics*

Let $P\phi(\mathbf{r}) = \phi(-\mathbf{r})$ represent the operation of reflection in the origin. Show that (1) The parity operator P has the eigenvalues $+1$ and -1;
(2) $PY_{lm}(\theta, \phi) = (-1)^l Y_{lm}(\theta, \phi)$.

2. *Angular momentum matrices*

Using (24.6) and (24.7), express the matrices M_x, M_y, M_z, and $\mathbf{M}^2$ in the l-, m-representation, for the subspace $l = 1$ (p-functions). Use the results to calculate the root mean square deviations ΔM_x and ΔM_y, and explain these deviations by means of the classical model of a precessing top.

3. *Eigenfunctions of the electron spin*

Determine the eigenvectors of the component of s in the direction θ, ϕ,
(a) when the eigenvectors of

$$s_{\theta,\varphi} = s_x \sin\theta \cos\phi + s_y \sin\theta \sin\phi + s_z \cos\theta$$

are directly determined by the relation

$$s_{\theta,\varphi}\begin{pmatrix} a \\ b \end{pmatrix} = \hbar\lambda\begin{pmatrix} a \\ b \end{pmatrix}$$

in which the eigenvalues λ are naturally independent of the direction and equal to $\pm\frac{1}{2}$;

(b) when the two eigenstates $\alpha = \begin{pmatrix} 1 \\ 0 \end{pmatrix}$ and $\beta = \begin{pmatrix} 0 \\ 1 \end{pmatrix}$ are rotated into the direction θ, ϕ in accordance with (23.2), in which $\mathbf{M} = \mathbf{s}$. (The first rotation is about the y-axis through an angle θ, the second, about the z-axis through an angle ϕ.)

(c) Compare the two results.

4. *Relation between* Λ_+ and Λ_-

Prove the relation $\Lambda_+ = \Lambda_-^+$, using (25.1) and the definition (25.3a) for the scalar product.

5. *A spherical harmonic relation*

Prove that
$$\sum_{m=-l}^{l} |Y_{lm}|^2 = \frac{2l+1}{4\pi}$$

CHAPTER B IV

Approximation methods

§26. Schrödinger's perturbation theory

There are not many cases in quantum theory for which exact solutions can be obtained, and it is therefore important to be able to have recourse to approximation procedures. The first to be discussed will be Schrödinger's method for the approximative determination of eigenfunctions and eigenvalues. For this purpose we assume that the Hamiltonian operator may be written in the form $\mathscr{H}_0 + W$, in which the solution of the eigenvalue problem

$$\mathscr{H}_0 \phi_m = \varepsilon_m \phi_m \tag{26.1}$$

is known, and W is a small "perturbation" of $\mathscr{H}_0$; $\mathscr{H}_0$ and W are Hermitian. The permissible magnitude of W will be more precisely specified later in this discussion. It is further assumed that the ϕ_m constitute a complete orthonormal system in which the required eigenfunctions ψ_μ of

$$(\mathscr{H}_0 + W)\psi_\mu = E_\mu \psi_\mu \tag{26.2}$$

can be expressed as follows:

$$\psi_\mu = \sum_m c_{m\mu} \phi_m \tag{26.3}$$

Provided that the term ε_m is non-degenerate and that W is not too great, there will be just one term in the "disturbed" (or exact) problem that can be said to have been generated from ε_m by the perturbation W. More precisely, the solution $\phi_m(\lambda)$ of

$$(\mathscr{H}_0 + \lambda W)\,\phi_m(\lambda) = \varepsilon_m(\lambda)\,\phi_m(\lambda)$$

is a continuous function of λ for which

$$\phi_m(0) = \phi_m \qquad \varepsilon_m(0) = \varepsilon_m$$

$$\phi_m(1) = \psi_\mu \qquad \varepsilon_m(1) = E_\mu$$

ψ_μ may then be denoted by the old quantum number m. In the degenerate case, however, when two or more terms ε_m almost or completely coincide,* it is no longer possible to find a relation of this sort between individual unperturbed and perturbed states; it is solely the group of coincident ε_m (denoted below by the index m') that is transformed into the corresponding group of perturbed terms E_μ. This is formally represented as follows:

$$\psi_\mu = \sum_{m'} c_{m'\mu}\phi_{m'} + P\psi_\mu \tag{26.4}$$

The operator P eliminates the terms in m' and is defined as follows:

$$P\psi = \sum_{m(\neq m')} \phi_m(\phi_m, \psi) \tag{26.4a}$$

The operator P is a projector, since it projects each state in the subspace of the ϕ_m for which $m \neq m'$: $P\phi_m = \phi_m$, $P\phi_{m'} = 0$. This operator commutes with $\mathscr{H}_0$. We now introduce the Schrödinger equation (26.2) in the form

$$\psi_\mu = \frac{1}{E_\mu - \mathscr{H}_0} W\psi_\mu$$

into the second term of (26.4), and obtain the equation

$$\psi_\mu = \sum_{m'} c_{m'\mu}\phi_{m'} + \frac{P}{E_\mu - \mathscr{H}_0} W\psi_\mu \tag{26.5}$$

the formal solution of which is

$$\psi_\mu = \left(1 - \frac{P}{E_\mu - \mathscr{H}_0} W\right)^{-1} \sum_{m'} c_{m'\mu}\phi_{m'} = \sum_{m'} c_{m'\mu}\Omega\phi_{m'} \tag{26.6}$$

The operator Ω may be expressed as a power series:

$$\begin{aligned} \Omega &= \left(1 - \frac{P}{E_\mu - \mathscr{H}_0} W\right)^{-1} \\ &= 1 + \frac{P}{E_\mu - \mathscr{H}_0} W + \frac{P}{E_\mu - \mathscr{H}_0} W \frac{P}{E_\mu - \mathscr{H}_0} W + \dots \end{aligned} \tag{26.7}$$

The necessary condition for the convergence of this series is that

$$\left|\left(\phi_m, \frac{P}{E_\mu - \mathscr{H}_0} W\phi_{m'}\right)\right| = \left|\frac{W_{mm'}}{E_\mu - \varepsilon_m}\right| < 1$$

* A criterion will be given later for the case in which two terms are to be considered as "almost" coincident.

for all $m \neq m'$. It is clear that the expansion (26.7) is only of value if $|W_{mm'}| \ll |E_\mu - \varepsilon_m|$, since only in this case can we restrict ourselves to the first few terms of the series.

From (26.7) it follows that

$$(\phi_{m'}, \Omega\phi_{n'}) = \delta_{m'n'}$$

In order to determine the coefficients $c_{m'\mu}$ we introduce (26.6) in (26.2) and form the scalar product with $\phi_{m'}$. We then obtain the equation

$$\sum_{n'} \{\varepsilon_{m'}\,\delta_{m'n'} + (W\Omega)_{m'n'}\}\, c_{n'\mu} = E_\mu\, c_{m'\mu} \tag{26.8}$$

This is a finite secular equation, the degree of which is determined by the number of coincident terms $\varepsilon_{m'}$.

It is disturbing at first sight to find that Ω depends on E_μ and that the solution of the secular equation does not therefore give E_μ explicitly. However, if the perturbation W is sufficiently small, Ω depends only slightly upon E_μ, and the latter quantity can be determined from (26.8) by iteration; the zero-order approximation $\varepsilon_{m'}$ is introduced in the left-hand side of (26.8), E_μ is determined as a first approximation and introduced in turn in the left-hand side, and so on.

If we introduce the zero-order approximation of (26.7), $\Omega \approx 1$, into (26.8), this equation simply becomes

$$\sum_{n'} (\varepsilon_{m'}\,\delta_{m'n'} + W_{m'n'})\, c_{n'\mu} = E_\mu\, c_{m'\mu} \tag{26.8a}$$

The E_μ are therefore the solutions of the algebraic equation

$$\det\{(\varepsilon_{m'} - E_\mu)\,\delta_{m'n'} + W_{m'n'}\} = 0 \tag{26.9}$$

In the non-degenerate case we obtain

$$E_\mu = \varepsilon_{m'} + W_{m'm'} = \varepsilon_{m'} + (\phi_{m'}, W\phi_{m'}) \tag{26.10}$$

in other words, the energy perturbation of first order in W is equal to the mean value of the perturbation operator W in the undisturbed state.

If we go one step further and introduce the zero-order approximation $\varepsilon_{m'}$ in (26.7), we obtain the following expressions for ψ_μ and E_μ:

$$\psi_\mu = \phi_{m'} + \frac{P}{\varepsilon_{m'} - \mathscr{H}_0} W\phi_{m'} = \phi_{m'} + \sum_{m(\neq m')} \frac{W_{mm'}}{\varepsilon_{m'} - \varepsilon_m}\phi_m \tag{26.11}$$

$$E_\mu = \varepsilon_{m'} + W_{m'm'} + \sum_{m(\neq m')} \frac{|W_{mm'}|^2}{\varepsilon_{m'} - \varepsilon_m} \tag{26.12}$$

It is evident that in the lowest state the second approximation to the energy perturbation is always negative, since $\varepsilon_m > \varepsilon_{m'}$.

The eigenfunctions of zero-order approximation belonging to each eigenvalue are obtained by determining the coefficients $c_{m'\mu}$ from (26.8*a*). Their evaluation is often facilitated if a Hermitian or unitary operator A exists that commutes with W and $\mathscr{H}_0$, and the eigenfunctions and eigenvalues a_l of which are known. In this case we choose the eigenfunctions of zero-order approximation in such a manner that they are also eigenfunctions of $\mathscr{H}_0$ and A. It can then be shown that $W_{m'n'} = 0$ when $\varepsilon_{m'} = \varepsilon_{n'}$, provided that $a_{m'} \neq a_{n'}$. The proof depends on the postulate that $AW - WA = 0$, from which it follows that

$$(\phi_{m'}, (AW - WA)\phi_{n'}) = (a_{m'} - a_{n'})W_{m'n'} = 0$$

The results of this section may be summarized as follows. If no degeneracy is present, to the zero-order approximation, a perturbation leads to a displacement of the original energy levels in accordance with (26.6). In the degenerate case, on the other hand, there are energy values that are originally equal, but which correspond to different "correct" eigenfunctions of zero-order approximation. These are in general displaced by different amounts; in other words, the perturbation causes the originally degenerate term to split. We shall encounter examples of such splitting in later chapters.

§27. Dirac's perturbation calculation

Dirac's procedure deals with time-dependent processes. The starting point is the time-dependent Schrödinger equation

$$\mathscr{H}\psi = i\hbar\dot{\psi} \tag{27.1}$$

in which the Hamiltonian operator $\mathscr{H}$ is resolved into an unperturbed operator $\mathscr{H}_0$ that is independent of time, and a small perturbation operator W that may be time-dependent:

$$\mathscr{H} = \mathscr{H}_0 + W \tag{27.1a}$$

The object is to determine the state $\psi(t)$ at time t from a given initial state $\psi(0)$ at time $t = 0$, assuming that the change with respect to time produced by W can be treated as a small perturbation.

Since $\mathscr{H}$ is a Hermitian operator, from (27.1) all scalar products remain constant with respect to time:

$$\frac{d}{dt}(\phi, \psi) = i\hbar\,\{(\phi, \mathscr{H}\psi) - (\mathscr{H}\phi, \psi)\} = 0$$

If $\psi(t)$ is related to $\psi(0)$ by means of an operator U:

$$\psi(t) = U(t)\,\psi(0),$$

hence
$$(\phi(t),\ \psi(t)) = (\phi(0),\ U^* U\psi(0)) \tag{27.2}$$

and U must consequently be unitary.

The operator $U(t)$ was introduced in §22 for the case in which $\mathscr{H}$ is independent of time. When $\mathscr{H}(t)$ depends on time we obtain an expression which is equally simple, at any rate in form:

$$U(t) = \sum_{\nu=0}^{\infty}\left(\frac{1}{i\hbar}\right)^{\nu}\int_{t\geqq\theta_1\geqq\theta_2\geqq\ldots\geqq\theta_\nu\geqq 0} d\theta_1\, d\theta_2 \ldots d\theta_\nu\, \mathscr{H}(\theta_1)\,\mathscr{H}(\theta_2)\ldots\mathscr{H}(\theta_\nu) \tag{27.3}$$

or written out in full,

$$U(t) = 1 + \frac{1}{i\hbar}\int_0^t d\theta_1\, \mathscr{H}(\theta_1) + \frac{1}{(i\hbar)^2}\int_0^t d\theta_1 \int_0^{\theta_1} d\theta_2\, \mathscr{H}(\theta_1)\,\mathscr{H}(\theta_2) + \ldots \tag{27.3a}$$

Differentiation of (27.3) with respect to time gives $i\hbar\dot{U} = \mathscr{H}U$, and $U(0) = 1$; hence (27.2) satisfies the Schrödinger equation and the initial condition.

The transformation may be expressed symbolically in a somewhat simpler form:

$$U(t) = T\exp\left(\frac{1}{i\hbar}\int_0^t \mathscr{H}(\theta)\, d\theta\right) \tag{27.4}$$

In the above expression the exponential operator is defined as a power series expansion of the exponential function:

$$\exp\left(\frac{1}{i\hbar}\int_0^t \mathscr{H}(\theta)\, d\theta\right) = \sum_{\nu=0}^{\infty}\frac{1}{\nu!}\left\{\frac{\int_0^t \mathscr{H}(\theta)\, d\theta}{i\hbar}\right\}^{\nu} =$$

$$= \sum_{\nu=0}^{\infty}\left(\frac{1}{i\hbar}\right)^{\nu}\frac{1}{\nu!}\int_0^t d\theta_1 \int_0^t d\theta_2 \ldots \int_0^t d\theta_\nu\, \mathscr{H}(\theta_1)\,\mathscr{H}(\theta_2)\ldots\mathscr{H}(\theta_\nu) \tag{27.4a}$$

The symbol T in (27.4) means that the operators $\mathscr{H}(\theta_1), \ldots, \mathscr{H}(\theta_\nu)$ are so arranged in terms of time that $\theta_1 \geqq \theta_2 \geqq \ldots \geqq \theta_\nu$. The complete range of integration $t \geqq \theta_1,\ \theta_2, \ldots, \theta_\nu \geqq 0$ can then be divided into ranges of the form $t \geqq \theta_1 \geqq \theta_2 \geqq \ldots \geqq \theta_\nu \geqq 0$. There are $\nu!$ such ranges, corresponding to the $\nu!$ permutations of the $\theta_1,\ldots,\theta_\nu$ among themselves. When the $\mathcal{H}(\theta)$ are arranged according to the conditions imposed by T each partial range of integration provides the same contribution, so that (27.4) is identical with the expression (27.3).

The symbol T is of no importance if the operators $\mathcal{H}(\theta)$ and $\mathcal{H}(\theta')$ commute:

$$U(t) = \exp\left(\frac{1}{i\hbar}\int_0^t \mathcal{H}(\theta)\,d\theta\right), \text{ if } [\mathcal{H}(\theta),\mathcal{H}(\theta')] = 0 \quad (27.5)$$

The simplest case of this sort occurs when $\mathcal{H}$ is independent of the time:

$$U(t) = \exp\frac{1}{i\hbar}\mathcal{H}t \text{ for } \dot{\mathcal{H}} = 0 \quad (27.5a)$$

If the perturbation $W = A f(t)$ consists of a time-dependent numerical factor and a time-independent operator A that commutes with $\mathcal{H}_0$:

$$U(t) = \exp\left[\frac{1}{i\hbar}\left\{\mathcal{H}_0 t + A\int_0^t f(\theta)\,d\theta\right\}\right]$$

$$= \exp\left(\frac{1}{i\hbar}\mathcal{H}_0 t\right)\exp\left(\frac{1}{i\hbar}A\int_0^t f(\theta)\,d\theta\right) \quad (27.5b)$$

In many cases it is expedient to separate the effect of the unperturbed operator $\mathcal{H}_0$ in order to show the variation due to the perturbation W alone. For this purpose we put

$$\psi = U_0(t)\tilde{\psi}, \text{ where } U_0(t) = \exp\frac{\mathcal{H}_0 t}{i\hbar} \quad (27.6)$$

Then

$$\dot{\psi} = \dot{U}_0\tilde{\psi} + U_0\dot{\tilde{\psi}} = \frac{1}{i\hbar}\mathcal{H}_0 U_0\tilde{\psi} + U_0\dot{\tilde{\psi}}$$

If no perturbation were present, $\tilde{\psi}$ would be constant with respect to time and equal to $\psi(0)$; the variation of $\tilde{\psi}$ with time is only due to the perturbation. If we introduce (27.6) into the Schrödinger equation we obtain

$$W U_0(t)\tilde{\psi} = i\hbar U_0(t)\dot{\tilde{\psi}} \quad (27.7)$$

or

$$\tilde{W}\tilde{\psi} = i\hbar\dot{\tilde{\psi}} \quad (27.7a)$$

where $\tilde{W} = U_0^+(t)\,W U_0(t) = \exp\left(-\frac{\mathcal{H}_0 t}{i\hbar}\right) W \exp\left(\frac{\mathcal{H}_0 t}{i\hbar}\right) = \tilde{W}^+$

(Note that if W and $\mathscr{H}_0$ do not commute, $\tilde{W}$ is time-dependent even though W is not a function of time.) This equation must be solved for the initial condition $\tilde{\psi}(0) = \psi(0)$; the result is

$$\tilde{\psi}(t) = T \exp\left(\frac{1}{i\hbar}\int_0^t \tilde{W}(\theta)\,d\theta\right)\psi(0) \tag{27.7b}$$

U has thus been split into two factors, only one of which contains the perturbation:

$$U(t) = \exp\left(\frac{1}{i\hbar}\mathscr{H}_0 t\right) T \exp\left(\frac{1}{i\hbar}\int_0^t \tilde{W}(\theta)\,d\theta\right) \tag{27.8}$$

Dirac's approximation consists in expanding the perturbation factor and retaining only the lowest powers. If we include only the linear terms in W or $\tilde{W}$, we have

$$U = U_0\left\{1 + \frac{1}{i\hbar}\int_0^t \tilde{W}(\theta)\,d\theta\right\} \tag{27.8a}$$

If the terms of the second degree are included,

$$U = U_0\left\{1 + \frac{1}{i\hbar}\int_0^t \tilde{W}(\theta)\,d\theta + \frac{1}{(i\hbar)^2}\int_0^t d\theta_1 \int_0^{\theta_1} d\theta_2\,\tilde{W}(\theta_1)\,\tilde{W}(\theta_2)\right\} \tag{27.8b}$$

Accordingly, when $\psi(t)$ is obtained from (27.2) by the use of (27.8*a*), it is represented by an expansion only to terms of the first order of the perturbation potential; the approximation (27.8*b*), on the other hand, provides an expansion to terms of the second order. If the function of first approximation $\psi^{(1)}(t)$ is used to obtain expectation values, it is of course permissible to retain terms only up to the first order of the perturbation potential, if the expectation values are required to the second degree of approximation they must be calculated from the second-order wave functions $\psi^{(2)}(t)$.

The above approximations may only be used if

$$\left(\psi(0), \left\{\frac{1}{\hbar}\int_0^t \tilde{W}(\theta)\,d\theta\right\}^2 \psi(0)\right) \ll 1 \tag{27.9}$$

This means that they are in general only valid for comparatively small time intervals. (Cf. however p. 162 and §41.)

In general equation (27.8) is expressed in the representation in which $\mathscr{H}_0$ is diagonal. $\psi(t)$ is therefore resolved into eigenfunctions ϕ_m of $\mathscr{H}_0$, the amplitudes of which are time-dependent:

$$\psi(t) = \sum_m a_m(t)\,\phi_m \tag{27.10}$$

In the above expression

$$a_m(t) = \sum_n U_{mn}(t)\,a_n(0)$$

where

$$U_{mn}(t) = \{\phi_m, U(t)\,\phi_n\} \tag{27.11}$$

Since $U_0(t)$ is also diagonal along with $\mathscr{H}_0$, i.e.

$$\mathscr{H}_{0mn} = E_m\,\delta_{mn} \quad \text{and} \quad U_{0mn}(t) = \exp\left(\frac{1}{i\hbar}E_m\,t\right)\delta_{mn}$$

it follows that

$$\widetilde{W}_{mn}(\theta) = \exp\left(-\frac{1}{i\hbar}E_m\,\theta\right)W_{mn}\exp\left(\frac{1}{i\hbar}E_n\,\theta\right)$$

Hence $U_{mn}(t)$ is given by the expression

$$\begin{aligned} U_{mn}(t) = \exp\left(\frac{1}{i\hbar}E_m\,t\right)\Bigg\{\delta_{mn} &+ \frac{1}{i\hbar}\int_0^t d\theta_1\,W_{mn}(\theta_1)\times \\ &\times\exp\left(-\frac{1}{i\hbar}(E_m-E_n)\theta_1\right)+ \\ &+\frac{1}{(i\hbar)^2}\int_0^t d\theta_1\int_0^{\theta_1} d\theta_2\sum_{m'} W_{mm'}(\theta_1)\times \\ &\times\exp\left(-\frac{1}{i\hbar}(E_m-E_{m'})\theta_1\right)W_{m'n}(\theta_2)\times \\ &\times\exp\left(-\frac{1}{i\hbar}(E_{m'}-E_n)\theta_2\right)+\ldots\Bigg\} \end{aligned} \tag{27.12}$$

The integration is easily performed in the particular case where the perturbation W is independent of time. The result is expressed in a form which enables the extension to higher orders of approximation to be easily deduced:*

$$U_{mn}(t) = \exp\left(\frac{1}{i\hbar} E_m t\right)\delta_{mn} + W_{mn}\left\{\frac{\exp\frac{1}{i\hbar}E_m t}{E_m - E_n} + \frac{\exp\frac{1}{i\hbar}E_n t}{E_n - E_m}\right\} +$$

$$+ \sum_{m'} W_{mm'} W_{m'n}\left\{\frac{\exp\frac{1}{i\hbar}E_m t}{(E_m - E_{m'})(E_m - E_n)} + \frac{\exp\frac{1}{i\hbar}E_{m'} t}{(E_{m'} - E_m)(E_{m'} - E_n)} + \right.$$

$$\left. + \frac{\exp\frac{1}{i\hbar}E_n t}{(E_n - E_m)(E_n - E_{m'})}\right\} + \ldots \qquad (27.12a)$$

If we proceed from the state "0" of the unperturbed operator $\mathscr{H}_0$, for which $a_m(0) = \delta_{m0}$, then the amplitude $a_m(t)$ is equal to $U_{m0}(t)$, and $|U_{m0}(t)|^2$ is the probability of encountering the state ϕ_m at time t. If we include terms up to the second degree in W, then

$$|U_{m0}(t)|^2 = |W_{m0}|^2 \frac{\sin^2\{\frac{1}{2}(E_m - E_0)t/\hbar\}}{\frac{1}{4}(E_m - E_0)^2} \quad \text{for } m \neq 0 \qquad (27.13a)$$

$$|U_{00}(t)|^2 = 1 - \sum_{m \neq (0)} |W_{m0}|^2 \frac{\sin^2\{\frac{1}{2}(E_m - E_0)t/\hbar\}}{\frac{1}{4}(E_m - E_0)^2} \qquad (27.13b)$$

In equation (27.13*a*) the only contribution is from the linear term in W, shown in equation (27.12*a*), since the first term of this latter equation vanishes; in (27.13*b*), on the other hand, the quadratic term of the expansion must be taken into account. Equations (27.13) simply express the fact that U is unitary to the second-order terms in W, provided that the quadratic terms in U itself are taken into account.† ($\sum_m |U_{m0}(t)|^2 = 1$ or $\sum_m |a_m(t)|^2 = 1$.) This approximation is obviously only permissible provided that $\sum_{m(\neq 0)} |U_{m0}(t)|^2$ in (27.13*a*) is small

* The individual terms of the expansion contain no singularities, although it appears at first sight that infinite terms would occur on the vanishing of differences such as $E_m - E_{m'}$. It may easily be verified that in all these cases the transition to the limit, $E_m \to E_{m'}$, produces a finite and correct result according to (27.12). Indeed, we can see immediately from this expression that any equal values of E_m that may occur simply give rise to a factor t.

† The relation (27.13*b*) can therefore be obtained from the unitariness property, without using the second approximation in (27.12*a*).

compared to 1 (see (27.9)), and that the initial state ϕ_0 is therefore still most likely to obtain.

As an example of Dirac's approximation method, we shall treat the problem of the scattering of a particle by a potential $W(\mathbf{r})$. The Hamiltonian operator of the free particle is $\mathscr{H}_0 = -(\hbar^2/2m)\nabla^2$. The treatment will be facilitated if we imagine the particle to be contained in a cubical enclosure of side L and volume $V = L^3$; this is done simply to obtain discrete eigenfunctions of $\mathscr{H}_0$. This restriction may be eliminated in the final result by allowing V to tend to infinity. The normalized eigenfunctions of $\mathscr{H}_0$ are

$$\phi_{\mathbf{k}} = \frac{1}{\sqrt{V}} \exp i\mathbf{kr}$$

where $\mathbf{k} = 2\pi\mathbf{n}/L$ and $\mathbf{n}$ is any vector the components of which have integral values. The energy values are $E_{\mathbf{k}} = \hbar^2\mathbf{k}^2/2m$. If the volume is large, the permissible values of $\mathbf{k}$ lie very close together; the number of possible values in an element $d\mathbf{k} = dk_x dk_y dk_z$ is $V d\mathbf{k}/(2\pi)^3$.

If we proceed from an initial state $\phi_{\mathbf{k}_0}$, in which a particle of momentum $\hbar\mathbf{k}_0$ is present in the enclosure, then from (27.13) the probability $w_{\mathbf{k}}(t)$ of finding a particle of momentum $\hbar\mathbf{k}$ after an interval t is

$$w_{\mathbf{k}}(t) = |W_{\mathbf{k}\mathbf{k}_0}|^2 \frac{\sin^2[\frac{1}{2}(E_{\mathbf{k}} - E_{\mathbf{k}_0})t/\hbar]}{\frac{1}{4}(E_{\mathbf{k}} - E_{\mathbf{k}_0})^2} \quad \text{for } \mathbf{k} \neq \mathbf{k}_0 \quad (27.14)$$

in which the matrix element $W_{\mathbf{k}\mathbf{k}_0}$ is given by the expression

$$W_{\mathbf{k}\mathbf{k}_0} = \frac{1}{V} \int_V \exp[i(\mathbf{k}_0 - \mathbf{k})\mathbf{r}]\, W(\mathbf{r})\, d\mathbf{r} = \frac{1}{V} \overline{W}_{\mathbf{k}\mathbf{k}_0} \quad (27.14a)$$

It is always possible to ensure that $\sum_{\mathbf{k}(\neq \mathbf{k}_0)} w_{\mathbf{k}}(t)$ is small compared to 1 by taking the volume V to be sufficiently large. In this case, therefore, the Dirac approximation is always applicable, however long the time interval; its value depends, however, on the extent to which it is possible to neglect the higher terms of the expansion.

The probability of finding the particle with values corresponding to $\mathbf{k}$ at time t in the element $d\mathbf{k}$ is clearly $w(\mathbf{k}, t)\, d\mathbf{k} = [V/(2\pi)^3]\, w_{\mathbf{k}}(t)\, d\mathbf{k}$. We can now define a differential effective cross-section dq for scattering in the element $d\mathbf{k}$, as follows. Let the current of particles associated with the primary wave, $\mathbf{j}_0 = \hbar\mathbf{k}_0/mV$, pass through an element of area

dq, normal to $\mathbf{j}_0$. The size of this element is such that all particles passing through it in the time t are scattered into the element $d\mathbf{k}$ of $\mathbf{k}$-space:*

$$\frac{\hbar k_0}{mV} t\, dq = w(\mathbf{k}, t)\, d\mathbf{k} \tag{27.15}$$

It is not immediately evident that dq is independent of time, since at first sight $w(\mathbf{k},t)$ is not proportional to the time; this difficulty is only apparent, however. If the time-dependent component of $w(\mathbf{k}, t)$ is plotted as a function of $E_\mathbf{k}$ (figure 27), we see that for large values of the time there is a maximum of magnitude $(t/\hbar)^2$ at the point

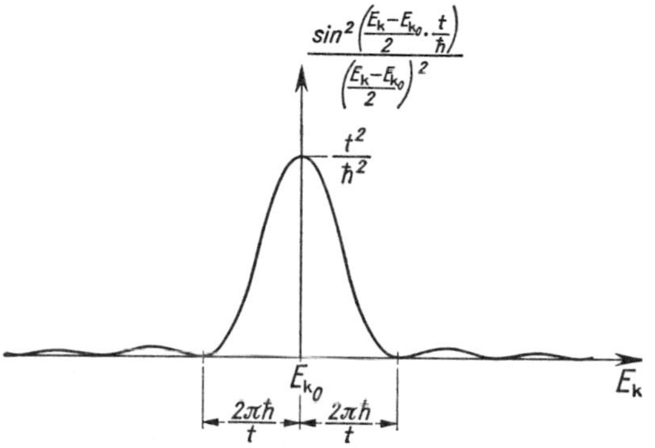

Fig. 27.—Relation between the probability $w_\mathbf{k}(t)$ and the energy, according to (27.14)

$E_\mathbf{k} = E_{\mathbf{k}_0}$, and that the interval in which this component is appreciable is of order of magnitude $|E_\mathbf{k} - E_{\mathbf{k}_0}| \approx \hbar/t$. Therefore over a sufficiently long interval the only scattered particles to appear are those for which $E_\mathbf{k} \approx E_{\mathbf{k}_0}$; hence $k \approx k_0$. The particles are scattered elastically, without change of energy. If the width $\hbar/t$ is small enough for $W_{\mathbf{k}\mathbf{k}_0}$ to remain virtually unchanged within this region, the time factor in (27.14) may be replaced by a δ-function of argument $E_\mathbf{k} - E_{\mathbf{k}_0}$ (cf. Exercise 1, p. 137), multiplied by the value of the integral

$$\int_{-\infty}^{+\infty} \frac{\sin^2\left[\frac{1}{2}(E_\mathbf{k} - E_{\mathbf{k}_0})t/\hbar\right]}{\frac{1}{4}(E_\mathbf{k} - E_{\mathbf{k}_0})^2}\, dE_\mathbf{k} = \frac{2\pi}{\hbar} t$$

* Since the wave function in the volume V is normalized to unity $\mathbf{j}_0$ is a probability current. The argument remains unchanged if we proceed from the initial function $(N/V)^{1/2} \exp i\mathbf{k}_0\mathbf{r}$ representing N particles of momentum $\hbar\mathbf{k}_0$. $N\mathbf{j}_0$ is the particle flux, and $Nw(\mathbf{k}, t)d\mathbf{k}$ the number of scattered particles of class $(\mathbf{k}, d\mathbf{k})$.

Hence

$$dq = \frac{mV}{\hbar k_0 t} w(\mathbf{k}, t)\, d\mathbf{k} = \frac{m}{(2\pi\hbar)^2} \cdot \frac{1}{k_0} \mid \overline{W}_{\mathbf{k}\mathbf{k}_0} \mid^2 \delta(E_{\mathbf{k}} - E_{\mathbf{k}_0})\, d\mathbf{k}$$

The differential cross-section will now be expressed in terms of polar coordinates in **k**-space. If we take $k^2 = 2mE_k/\hbar^2$, then $d\mathbf{k} = k^2\, dk\, d\Omega = (mk/\hbar^2) dE_k d\Omega$, where $d\Omega$ is the element of solid angle.

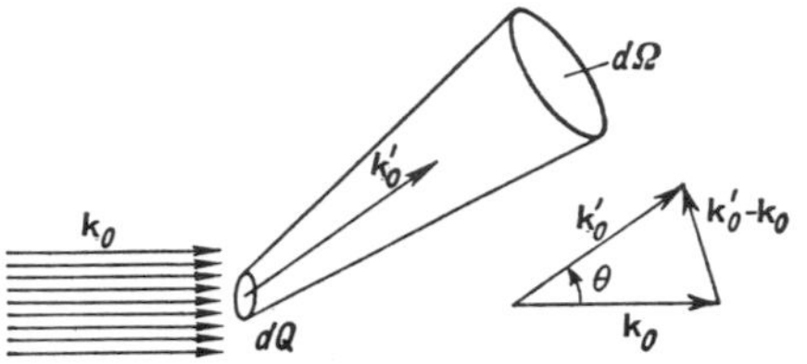

Fig. 28.—Effective scattering cross-section

Introducing a further vector $\mathbf{k}_0'$ parallel to the element of solid angle and of magnitude k_0 (figure 28), we obtain

$$dq = \left(\frac{m}{2\pi\hbar^2}\right)^2 \mid \overline{W}_{\mathbf{k}_0'\mathbf{k}_0} \mid^2 . \delta(E_k - E_{k_0})\, dE_k\, d\Omega$$

If we now integrate over E_k, we obtain the differential effective cross-section dQ for scattering into the element of solid angle $d\Omega$:

$$dQ = \left(\frac{m}{2\pi\hbar^2}\right)^2 \mid \overline{W}_{\mathbf{k}_0'\mathbf{k}_0} \mid^2 d\Omega \qquad (27.16)$$

The particles of the primary wave striking dQ are scattered into the element of solid angle $d\Omega$; $\mathbf{k}_0'$ is determined by the direction from which the particles are observed. For a spherically symmetrical potential $W(r)$,

$$\overline{W}_{\mathbf{k}_0'\mathbf{k}_0} = \int \exp\left[i(\mathbf{k}_0' - \mathbf{k}_0)\mathbf{r}\right] W(r)\, d\mathbf{r}$$

$$= \frac{4\pi}{\mid \mathbf{k}_0' - \mathbf{k}_0 \mid} \int_0^\infty dr\, .\, rW(r) \sin(\mid \mathbf{k}_0' - \mathbf{k}_0 \mid r)$$

depends only on $|\mathbf{k}_0' - \mathbf{k}_0|$; since $|\mathbf{k}_0' - \mathbf{k}_0| = 2k_0 \sin\frac{1}{2}\theta$ according to figure 28, $W_{\mathbf{k}_0'\mathbf{k}_0}$ depends only on the angle between the direction of observation and the direction of incidence.

The total effective cross-section is obtained by integrating throughout the complete range of solid angles. An example of the calculation is given in Exercise 4, p. 176.

For the Dirac approximation to be applicable, it must be possible to treat W as a small perturbation in comparison with the energy of the primary particles. The approximation procedure employed in the case of scattering is therefore typical of the treatment applicable to high energies. What is meant by "high energies" or "small W" can really be decided only from a knowledge of the higher approximations, whose further contribution must be small compared with the first approximations derived above.

In the Dirac approximation, the occurrence of the factor $\delta(E_m - E_0)$ for large time values is often taken to be an instance of the conservation of energy. This is very misleading, particularly as the impression is created that the conservation theorem holds only as an approximation for large values of the time, whereas in fact when the Hamiltonian operator is independent of time this theorem is strictly valid ($\dot{\mathscr{H}} = 0$). In fact, the δ-function expresses much more; it implies that the energy associated with the unperturbed operator is conserved over long time intervals. This may be expressed in another way: when the perturbation is small it is permissible to resolve the state $\psi(t)$ into the eigenfunctions of $\mathscr{H}_0$; it then contains functions practically all of which have the same unperturbed energy. If we now consider the wave aspect of the scattering process previously discussed, its significance is easily perceived. The scattering is detectable because the plane wave associated with the incident beam produces a spherical wave propagated from the scattering centre. While this spherical wave is within the effective range of the scattering potential it contains values of $\mathbf{k}$ that differ markedly from the value $\mathbf{k}_0$ for the plane wave. The situation is different when the spherical wave has travelled outwards a distance of many wavelengths, and only a small fraction lies within the effective range of the potential. In this case nearly all the $\mathbf{k}$-values occurring in the outer regions have the magnitude k_0, and the small portion within effective range of the potential may be neglected.*

Appendix: **The Born approximation for the time-independent treatment of scattering.**

In the scattering case which we discussed above, a stationary state will set in if we wait long enough. This problem may also be treated by means of Born's "time-free" approximation procedure. Putting $E = \hbar^2 k_0^2 / 2m$ for the energy, the Schrödinger equation becomes

$$\nabla^2 \psi + k_0^2 \psi = \frac{2m}{\hbar^2} W \psi \tag{27.17}$$

We shall now deduce the corresponding integral equation, which is easier to deal with. Since

$$(\nabla^2 + k_0^2) \frac{e^{ikr}}{r} = -4\pi \, \delta(\mathbf{r})$$

* In classical mechanics the scattered particles also regain their initial energy after passing through the scattering potential.

equation (27.17) is satisfied by

$$\psi(\mathbf{r}) = \psi_0(\mathbf{r}) - \frac{m}{2\pi\hbar^2}\int W(\mathbf{r}')\psi(\mathbf{r}')\frac{\exp(ik_0|\mathbf{r}-\mathbf{r}'|)}{|\mathbf{r}-\mathbf{r}'|}\,d\mathbf{r}' \tag{27.18}$$

if $\psi_0(\mathbf{r})$ represents a solution of the equation in the absence of the perturbation potential,

$$\nabla^2\psi_0 + k_0^2\psi_0 = 0 \tag{27.19}$$

It is true that the transition from (27.17) to (27.18) is not unique, since we could have put $\exp(-ik_0|\mathbf{r}-\mathbf{r}'|)$ instead of $\exp(+ik_0|\mathbf{r}-\mathbf{r}'|)$. The choice of the + sign resulted from the boundary condition that, at a great distance from the scattering centre, $\psi(\mathbf{r})$ must consist of a plane wave and a spherical wave diverging from the centre. The latter is provided for by the sign of the exponential function in (27.18), since the following approximation is valid when the distance r is large:

$$\frac{\exp(ik_0|\mathbf{r}-\mathbf{r}'|)}{|\mathbf{r}-\mathbf{r}'|} \to \frac{\exp\left[ik_0 r - ik_0\left(\mathbf{r}'\frac{\mathbf{r}}{r}\right)\right]}{r} = \frac{\exp(ik_0 r)}{r}\exp(-i\mathbf{k}_0'\mathbf{r}') \text{ for } |\mathbf{r}| \gg |\mathbf{r}'| \tag{27.18a}$$

In the above expression $\mathbf{k}_0' = k_0\mathbf{r}/r$. The first condition is satisfied by putting

$$\psi_0 = a\exp i\mathbf{k}_0\mathbf{r} \tag{27.19a}$$

Born's approximation consists in the iterative solution of the integral equation (27.18); the ψ-function under the integral sign is replaced by the whole right-hand side of (27.18), the ψ-function occurring again is replaced in turn, the procedure being continued as far as is necessary. If terms up to the second approximation are included we obtain the following result:

$$\psi(\mathbf{r}) = \psi_0(\mathbf{r}) - \frac{m}{2\pi\hbar^2}\int W(\mathbf{r}')\psi_0(\mathbf{r}')\frac{\exp(ik_0|\mathbf{r}-\mathbf{r}'|)}{|\mathbf{r}-\mathbf{r}'|}\,d\mathbf{r}' + \left(\frac{m}{2\pi\hbar^2}\right)^2\iint W(\mathbf{r}')W(\mathbf{r}'')\psi_0(\mathbf{r}'')\times \times\frac{\exp(ik_0|\mathbf{r}-\mathbf{r}'|)}{|\mathbf{r}-\mathbf{r}'|}\cdot\frac{\exp(ik_0|\mathbf{r}'-\mathbf{r}''|)}{|\mathbf{r}'-\mathbf{r}''|}\cdot d\mathbf{r}'\,d\mathbf{r}'' + \ldots \tag{27.20}$$

We shall now write down the first approximation, taking due account of (27.18*a*) and (27.19*a*) at great distances from the scattering centre. Then, making use of the abbreviation (27.14*a*), we obtain

$$\psi(\mathbf{r}) \to a\left\{\exp i\mathbf{k}_0\,\mathbf{r} - \frac{m}{2\pi\hbar^2}\frac{\exp ik_0 r}{r}\overline{W}_{\mathbf{k}_0'\mathbf{k}_0}\right\} \tag{27.21}$$

The first term of the above expression obviously represents the primary wave, and the second, the spherical wave diverging from the scattering centre.

The differential cross-section dQ is the ratio of the particle current through $d\Omega$ and the primary current across unit area:

$$dQ = \left(\frac{m}{2\pi\hbar^2}\right)^2 |\,\overline{W}_{\mathbf{k}_0'\mathbf{k}_0}|^2 d\Omega$$

This agrees exactly with the formula (27.16) which was obtained by means of Dirac's "time-dependent" approximation.

§28. The variational method for the determination of eigenvalues

The eigenvalues and eigenfunctions of a Hamiltonian operator $\mathscr{H}$ are determined by the equation

$$\mathscr{H}\phi = E\phi \tag{28.1}$$

Equation (28.1) possesses solutions, the norm of which (ϕ,ϕ) exists only for certain definite values of E. If ϕ is normalized,

$$(\phi,\phi) = 1 \tag{28.2}$$

then the energy

$$E = \overline{\mathscr{H}} = (\phi, \mathscr{H}\phi) \tag{28.2a}$$

is equal to the expectation value of $\mathscr{H}$ in the state ϕ. If ϕ is not normalized, then

$$E = \overline{\mathscr{H}} = \frac{(\phi,\mathscr{H}\phi)}{(\phi,\phi)} \tag{28.3}$$

Equation (28.1) may be formulated as the solution of a variational problem. The latter is defined as follows: ϕ is determined in such a manner that, when $\overline{\mathscr{H}}$ is given by (28.3), or by (28.2*a*) and the auxiliary condition (28.2), E possesses an extreme value. Let ϕ be a solution, and $\phi+\alpha\eta$ a small variation of the "correct" function ϕ, where α is a small complex number and η an arbitrary function, the norm of which

(η,η) exists. Then if $\bar{\mathscr{H}}(\alpha)$ is formed from $\phi+\alpha\eta$ according to (28.3), it must possess an extreme value when $\alpha=0$. This is expressed as follows:

$$\frac{\partial\bar{\mathscr{H}}(\alpha)}{\partial\alpha}=\frac{\partial}{\partial\alpha}\frac{[(\phi+\alpha\eta),\mathscr{H}(\phi+\alpha\eta)]}{[(\phi+\alpha\eta),(\phi+\alpha\eta)]}\to 0 \quad \text{as} \quad \alpha\to 0 \qquad (28.4)$$

If $\bar{\mathscr{H}}(\alpha)$ is expanded in powers of α for small α, then

$$\bar{\mathscr{H}}(\alpha)=E+\frac{1}{(\phi,\phi)}\{\alpha^*[\eta,(\mathscr{H}-E)\phi]+\alpha[\phi,(\mathscr{H}-E)\eta]\} \qquad (28.5)$$
$$+\text{ higher terms in } \alpha \text{ and } \alpha^*.$$

In the above expression E is introduced as an abbreviation for $(\phi,\mathscr{H}\phi)/(\phi,\phi)$. The condition (28.4) implies that the terms of the first degree in α and α^* must vanish in (28.5). When α is real, we have the result

$$[\eta,(\mathscr{H}-E)\phi]+[\phi,(\mathscr{H}-E)\eta]$$
$$=[\eta,(\mathscr{H}-E)\phi]+[\eta,(\mathscr{H}-E)\phi]^*=0 \quad (28.6a)$$

and when α is a pure imaginary quantity,

$$[\eta,(\mathscr{H}-E)\phi]-[\eta,(\mathscr{H}-E)\phi]^*=0 \qquad (28.6b)$$

It follows that for all η

$$[\eta,(\mathscr{H}-E)\phi]=0 \qquad (28.6c)$$

Since, however, the functions η are entirely arbitrary, and can for instance cover all functions of a complete system, it follows that $(\mathscr{H}-E)\phi$ must vanish, and therefore that ϕ is a solution of equation (28.1).

If we use the definitions (28.2, 28.2*a*), the auxiliary condition (28.2) implies that η must be orthogonal to ϕ: $(\eta,\phi)=0$. The extremum condition for (28.2*a*) leads to the result $(\eta,\mathscr{H}\phi)=0$ for all η, with $(\eta,\phi)=0$. Then $\mathscr{H}\phi$ must be proportional to ϕ, and we again obtain (28.1).

We may express the above facts as follows. If we proceed from the exact eigenfunctions, then in the first approximation the energy value $E=\bar{\mathscr{H}}$ remains unchanged if $\bar{\mathscr{H}}$ is formed from a slightly modified function $\phi+\alpha\eta$. The energy value itself is relatively unaffected by variations of ϕ; it is therefore possible to obtain good eigenvalues with comparatively poor eigenfunctions. Actually, this is just the way that the energy values behave in an ordinary perturbation calculation (§26).

The energy values are always better than the eigenfunctions by one degree of approximation; the energy in first approximation is $\overline{\mathscr{H}}$, formed from the unperturbed eigenfunctions, while the energy in second approximation is determined from the eigenfunctions of the first approximation, and so on.

The extreme values of $\overline{\mathscr{H}}$ do not necessarily have to be either minima, maxima, or saddle-points (cf. Exercise 3, p. 47). However, the lowest energy value, which is the energy E_0 of the ground state, is always the absolute minimum of $\overline{\mathscr{H}}$, since the contribution of eigenfunctions with higher energy values can only result in $\overline{\mathscr{H}}$ being greater than E_0.

The extremal property of $\overline{\mathscr{H}}$ can thus be used to determine the energy of the ground state, as follows. In cases where an exact solution is impossible or difficult, we choose an initial function ϕ which can be presumed to represent the ground state approximately. Let this function contain one or more parameters β_i. Then $\overline{\mathscr{H}}(\beta_1, \beta_2, \ldots)$ is determined as a function of the parameters, which are chosen in such a manner that $\overline{\mathscr{H}}$ is a minimum. This minimum value approximately represents the energy of the ground state, and it is the optimum approximation over the function range employed. The calculated energy is always greater than the exact value, since the latter is in fact the absolute minimum. The energies calculated in this manner are generally very good approximations, although the function used to determine $\overline{\mathscr{H}}$ may still be a relatively poor approximation to the eigenfunction of the ground state. There is of course an art in choosing physically suitable initial functions. The value of different types of approximation can only be judged by the results. The best approximations are obtained for the lowest energy values. Examples of the applications of approximation procedures are given in §§43 and 44.

For excited states, the application of the above method is not so simple. If the energy of the first excited state is to be determined in this manner, for instance, it is necessary to ensure that the chosen functions are orthogonal to the exact ground-state function, since any contribution from the ground state lowers the minimum energy, and it is then by no means clear whether the calculated energy is greater or less than the exact value. In many cases, however, the possibility of any contribution from the lower states can be excluded for reasons of symmetry.*

* The case of the atom in an electric field, described overleaf, provides another example in which the calculated state does not give the lowest value of the energy: when the distance x is very large, W is also very large, and negative. When the electron is removed to a great distance from the nucleus and W is negative, the corresponding state certainly has a lower energy. Actually, there are no stationary bound states when a homogeneous electric field is present; the calculation given overleaf refers to a metastable state corresponding to a relative minimum (cf. remarks in §39).

A simple example may serve to illustrate the applicability of the method of variations: we shall determine the ground-state energy of a hydrogen atom in an electric field F directed along the x-axis. The Hamiltonian operator in this case is

$$\mathcal{H} = \underbrace{\frac{\mathbf{p}^2}{2m} - \frac{e^2}{r}}_{\mathcal{H}_0} \underbrace{- eFx}_{W} \tag{28.7}$$

The electric field is assumed to be small enough for it to be permissible to neglect terms in F of higher degree than the second, in the expression for the energy. The eigenfunction ϕ_0 of the ground state in the absence of the field is given by

$$\mathcal{H}_0 \phi_0 = E_0 \phi_0, \; \phi_0 = \frac{e^{-r/a}}{\sqrt{(\pi a^3)}} \text{ where } a = \frac{\hbar^2}{me^2}, \; E_0 = -\frac{e^2}{2a} \tag{28.8}$$

The calculation of ϕ_0 and the proof that it is the eigenfunction of the ground state are given in the next section. It may easily be verified by differentiation that ϕ_0 is in fact an eigenfunction of $\mathcal{H}_0$ corresponding to the eigenvalue* E_0.

The electron charge density $\rho = e\phi_0^2$ is distributed about the nucleus with spherical symmetry and decreases exponentially with distance. The situation is similar to Thomson's model, though in this case the approximately homogeneous electron charge is distributed throughout a sphere of radius a while the point-like nucleus lies at the centre of this distribution. We can determine the polarizability and the energy change in the electric field if we can assume that the charge distribution remains unaltered when the field is applied (as in Thomson's model), and that it merely moves as a whole through a fixed distance $\tilde{x}$ relative to the nucleus.

For the Thomson model (§4) in a state of equilibrium we have the following relations:

$$\frac{e^2}{a^3}\tilde{x} = eF, \; e\tilde{x} = a^3 F; \text{ therefore } \alpha = a^3, \; E = E_0 - \tfrac{1}{2}\alpha F^2 \tag{28.9}$$

In the above expressions, a is the radius of the model sphere, $e\tilde{x}$ is the dipole moment, α is the polarizability, and $E - E_0$ is the energy change

* ϕ_0 is normalized. If we take ϕ_0 as an approximate solution and a as parameter, then since $(\phi_0, \mathcal{H}\phi_0) = \hbar^2/2ma^2 - e^2/a$ must be a minimum for the best estimate of a, it follows that a has the value $\hbar^2/me^2$.

caused by the field (i.e. the change in the electron's electrostatic energy as a result of the displacement $\tilde{x}$).

We shall now calculate the polarizability from the displacement of the rigid charge distribution relative to the nucleus, just as we did for the Thomson model; in this case, however, the charge is no longer homogeneously distributed. Nevertheless, for small displacements the result depends on the field strength and the charge density at short distances from the centre of the distribution; the latter is approximately constant in this region, and equal to $e/\pi a^3$. In the Thomson model the corresponding charge density is $\frac{3}{4}e/\pi a^3$. If we therefore replace a^3 in (28.9) by $\frac{3}{4}a^3$, we obtain the following values for the polarizability and the energy of the present model:

$$\alpha = \tfrac{3}{4}a^3 \qquad E = E_0 - \tfrac{1}{2}\alpha F^2 \tag{28.10}$$

where a is now the Bohr radius given by (28.8). Taking $a = 0{\cdot}53 \times 10^{-8}$ cm, we obtain the value $\frac{3}{4} \times 0{\cdot}15 \times 10^{-24}\,\text{cm}^3$ for the polarizability of the hydrogen atom; this result does not agree very well with the value $0{\cdot}66 \times 10^{-24}\,\text{cm}^3$ found by Wentzel and Waller* from a second-order perturbation calculation. The discrepancy is not surprising, however, in view of the crude approximations on which the present calculation is based.†

At this point the variational method will be found to be of assistance. So far, we have assumed that the charge distribution is rigid; this implies that the wave function $\phi_0(x, y, z)$ is replaced by $\phi_0(x - \beta_1, y, z)$, where β_1 is the displacement of the distribution. For small displacements this is equivalent to putting

$$\phi = \left(1 - \frac{i}{\hbar}\beta_1\, p_x\right)\phi_0 \tag{28.11}$$

If the above expression is used to calculate $\overline{\mathscr{H}}(\beta_1)$, and β_1 is determined from the minimum of $\overline{\mathscr{H}}$, the result, as might be expected, is identical with (28.10).

As has been shown by P. Gombás,‡ the trial solution

$$\phi = (1 + \beta_2\, W)\phi_0 \tag{28.12}$$

* G. Wentzel, *Z. f. Phys.* **38** (1927), 518; J. Waller, *Z. f. Phys.* **38** (1927), 635.

† The somewhat uncertain experimental value is given as $0{\cdot}66 \times 10^{-24}\,\text{cm}^3$ (Landolt-Börnstein I/1, Berlin 1955).

‡ Gombàs, P. *Theorie und Lösungsmethoden des Mehrteilchenproblems der Wellenmechanik* (Basel, 1950).

frequently leads to very good results in perturbation problems. In this case it leads to the better approximation $4a^3$ for α. Finally, if we combine both solutions in the form

$$\phi = \left(1 - \frac{i}{\hbar}\beta_1 p_x + \beta_2 W\right)\phi_0 \tag{28.13}$$

we obtain

$$\alpha = \tfrac{3}{4}a^3 = 0{\cdot}11 \times 10^{-24}\,\text{cm}^3 \text{ with } \beta_1 \text{ alone} \tag{28.11a}$$

$$\alpha = 4a^3 = 0{\cdot}60 \times 10^{-24}\,\text{cm}^3 \text{ with } \beta_2 \text{ alone} \tag{28.12a}$$

$$\alpha = (4+\tfrac{1}{8})a^3 = 0{\cdot}62 \times 10^{-24}\,\text{cm}^3 \text{ with } \beta_1 \text{ and } \beta_2 \tag{28.13a}$$

It is certain that the true polarizability is greater and the true energy value lower than the calculated value. The results show that the variational method is almost as good as the second-order perturbation calculation of Waller and Wentzel. The calculations using (28.13) are very simple, containing elementary integrals and merely requiring the solution of a linear system of equations for β_1 and β_2. When choosing trial functions it is of course necessary to ensure that they will lead to simple and completely integrable expressions.

The method of calculation will now be briefly described. The expectation value of the energy is formed from (28.3), using (28.13):

$$E = \frac{((1+O)\phi_0, \mathscr{H}(1+O)\phi_0)}{((1+O)\phi_0, (1+O)\phi_0)} = \frac{(\phi_0, (1+O^+)\mathscr{H}(1+O)\phi_0)}{(\phi_0, (1+O^+)(1+O)\phi_0)} \tag{28.14}$$

in which the abbreviations

$$O = \beta_2 W - \frac{i}{\hbar}\beta_1 p_x \qquad O^+ = \beta_2 W + \frac{i}{\hbar}\beta_1 p_x \tag{28.15}$$

have been introduced. (β_1 and β_2 are taken to be real numbers, while W and p_x are Hermitian operators.) Mean values over ϕ_0 are denoted by bars. Many of the terms in (28.14) vanish because of the radial symmetry of ϕ_0, e.g. $\overline{O}$, $\overline{O^+}$, $\overline{W}$, $\overline{O^+\mathscr{H}_0}$, $\overline{\mathscr{H}_0 O}$, $\overline{O^+WO}$. Hence from (28.14)

$$E = \frac{(\phi_0, (\mathscr{H}_0 + O^+W + WO + O^+\mathscr{H}_0 O)\phi_0)}{(\phi_0, (1+O^+O)\phi_0)} = \frac{E_0 + \overline{O^+W} + \overline{WO} + \overline{O^+\mathscr{H}_0 O}}{1+\overline{O^+O}} \tag{28.14a}$$

The terms containing O or W are linear in terms of the perturbation, and therefore proportional to the field strength F. It will appear later that β_1 is proportional to the field strength, while β_2 is independent of it. The expression (28.14a) contains quadratic terms only. If we require the expansion only as far as terms in F^2, the denominator can be expanded, and we obtain

$$E = E_0 + \overline{O^+W} + \overline{WO} + \overline{O^+\mathscr{H}_0 O} - E_0\overline{O^+O} \tag{28.14b}$$

The last two terms can be combined in the form $\overline{(O^+\mathcal{H}_0-\mathcal{H}_0O^+)O}$. If we now insert the expressions in (28.15) corresponding to O and O^+, we obtain

$$E = E_0-\beta_1 eF+\beta_2.2e^2F^2\overline{x^2}$$

$$-\beta_1{}^2\frac{ie^2}{\hbar}\overline{\frac{x}{r^3}p_x}+\beta_2{}^2.\frac{e^2F^2i\hbar}{m}\overline{p_x x}-\beta_1\beta_2\left\{e^3F\overline{\frac{x^2}{r^3}}+\frac{eF}{m}\overline{p_x{}^2}\right\} \qquad (28.14c)$$

The required mean values are as follows, in view of the spherical symmetry of ϕ_0:

$$\overline{r^2} = 3a^2 \qquad \bar{r} = \frac{3}{2}a \qquad \overline{\frac{1}{r}} = \frac{1}{a} \qquad \overline{\frac{1}{r^2}} = \frac{2}{a^2}$$

Then

$$E = E_0-\beta_1 eF+\beta_2.2e^2F^2a^2+\beta_1{}^2\frac{2e^2}{3a^3}+\beta_2{}^2\frac{e^2F^2\hbar^2}{2m}-\beta_1\beta_2\left\{\frac{e^3F}{3a}+\frac{eF\hbar^2}{3ma^2}\right\} \qquad (28.14d)$$

If we deal with each parameter separately, then at the minimum

$$\beta_1 = \frac{3a^3F}{4e} \text{ when } \beta_2 = 0, \text{ therefore } E = E_0-\tfrac{1}{2}\times\tfrac{3}{4}a^3F^2, \quad \alpha = \tfrac{3}{4}a^3 \qquad (28.15a)$$

$$\beta_2 = -\frac{2ma^2}{\hbar^2} \text{ when } \beta_1 = 0, \text{ therefore } E = E_0-\tfrac{1}{2}\times 4a^3F^2, \ \alpha = 4a^3 \qquad (28.15b)$$

These are the results given in (28.11*a*) and (28.12*a*). If we now take β_1 and β_2 together and determine the lowest value, we obtain a linear system of equations which serves to determine the optimum values:

$$\beta_1\frac{4e^2}{3a^3}-\beta_2\frac{2e^3F}{3a} = eF \qquad \beta_1\frac{2e^3F}{3a}-\beta_2\frac{e^2F^2\hbar^2}{m} = 2e^2F^2a^2 \qquad (28.16)$$

The solution gives the lowest energy:

$$\beta_1 = -\frac{3Fa^3}{8e} \qquad \beta_2 = -\frac{9ma^2}{4\hbar^2}$$

therefore $$E = E_0-\frac{1}{2}\left(4+\frac{1}{8}\right)a^3F^2 \qquad \alpha = \left(4+\frac{1}{8}\right)a^3 \qquad (28.15c)$$

From the above example it is clear that the choice of initial function is of decisive importance in the final result. If we refer back to the beginning of the previous analysis we can see that the assumption of a rigid unchanged electron structure was an unfortunate one. Judging from the satisfactory result provided by the trial function (28.12) it is evident that the outer part of the electron distribution is much more strongly influenced than the inner portion. (28.12) corresponds in effect to an additional term $x\phi_0$, whereas the corresponding quantity for (28.11) is $(x/r)\phi_0$. The two expressions therefore differ by the factor r which ensures that due weight is given to the perturbation in the outer regions where it is strongest.

When choosing trial functions it is also important to make sure that no unnecessary parameters are introduced, since they would have no effect on the result. In the above example, for instance, we might have introduced functions that were proportional to $y\phi_0$ or $\partial\phi_0/\partial y$. As we can see from the fact that the symmetry is cylindrical about the x-axis after the field is applied, the corresponding parameters would have vanished when the minimum value was derived, and we should have expended time and trouble for nothing. It is also evident that a variation of a, though possible in principle, would only provide contributions proportional to F^4, because $E_0(a)$ is already a minimum.

In many cases a superposition of independent linear functions $\phi_i(i=1,2,\ldots,n)$ can be used as a trial function:

$$\phi = \sum_{i=1}^{n} c_i \phi_i$$

The initial functions do not need to be either normalized or orthogonal. The optimum values of the coefficients c_i can then be determined by the method of variations.

Putting $\mathscr{H}_{ik} = (\phi_i, \mathscr{H}\phi_k)$ and $S_{ik} = (\phi_i, \phi_k)$, we obtain

$$\overline{\mathscr{H}}(c_1, \ldots, c_n) = \frac{\sum_{i,k} c_i^* c_k \mathscr{H}_{ik}}{\sum_{i,k} c_i^* c_k S_{ik}}$$

The derivatives with respect to the c_i and c_i^* must vanish. This gives the result

$$\sum_k \mathscr{H}_{ik} c_k = E \sum_k S_{ik} c_k$$

where the value of $\overline{\mathscr{H}}$ at the extremum is denoted by E. There is only one solution to this linear homogeneous equation if the determinant vanishes:

$$\det\left[\mathscr{H}_{ik} - ES_{ik}\right] = 0$$

The solution of this equation of the nth degree yields n quantities $E^{(s)}$ $(s=1,\ldots,n)$ which are the stationary energy values in the available function range. Associated with each value $E^{(s)}$ are coefficients $c_i^{(s)}$ and a function $\phi^{(s)}$, the expectation value of which is simply $E^{(s)}$:

$$(\phi^{(s')}, \mathscr{H}\phi^{(s)}) = E^{(s)}\,\delta_{ss'}$$

The functions $\phi^{(s)}$ can be chosen in such a manner that they are normalized and mutually orthogonal.

The above procedure is called Ritz's method after its originator. If the system of functions is complete, it yields all the exact eigenvalues. If this is not the case approximations are obtained, the degree of accuracy of which depends once more on a skilful choice of the functions ϕ_i.

A trial function of this type is often suitable as a starting-point for a perturbation calculation when degenerate terms are present. It is evident that this method gives energy values of first approximation and eigenfunctions of zero-order approximation, provided that we admit only orthonormal functions of the unperturbed Hamiltonian operator (for which $S_{ik} = \delta_{ik}$) corresponding to one definite energy value. These functions are in fact defined by the condition that $(\phi^{(s')}, \mathscr{H}\phi^{(s)})$ should have only diagonal elements, which are identical with the energy values of first approximation (cf. §26). However, the method of variations gives the optimum energy values even if the functions are not orthonormal, or if they are not eigenfunctions of a common unperturbed Hamiltonian operator. A relevant example is provided by the treatment of the hydrogen molecule in §44, in which the two functions chosen for the calculation of the ground state have approximately the same energy, but do not possess a common unperturbed operator.

If the functions ϕ_i contain additional parameters which are also varied, the energy values $E^{(s)}$ depend on these parameters as well. Since the extremum conditions are given by

$$\frac{\partial \overline{\mathscr{H}}(\ldots c_i \ldots, \ldots \beta_\lambda \ldots)}{\partial c_i} = 0 \quad \text{and} \quad \frac{\partial \mathscr{H}(\ldots c_i \ldots, \ldots \beta_\lambda \ldots)}{\partial \beta_\lambda} = 0$$

we obtain the further equations $\partial E^{(s)}/\partial \beta_\lambda = 0$

Exercises

1. *First-order perturbation calculation for an anharmonic oscillator*

Calculate the energy to the first degree of approximation in the case of an anharmonic oscillator for which $V(x) = \frac{1}{2}m\omega^2 x^2 + \lambda x^4$. Evaluate the matrix elements $(x^4)_{nn}$ according to the method given in §15. Compare the result with the "classical" calculation in Exercise 3, p. 107; the results should agree for high quantum numbers.

2. *Quadratic secular equation*

Let the Hamiltonian operator consist of the following matrix:

$$\mathscr{H} = \begin{pmatrix} \varepsilon_1 + \lambda W_{11} & \lambda W_{12} \\ \lambda W_{21} & \varepsilon_2 + \lambda W_{22} \end{pmatrix}$$

Determine the eigenvalues (*a*) exactly, by solving the quadratic equation $\text{Det}\,(\mathscr{H} - \varepsilon . 1) = 0$; (*b*) by perturbation theory, assuming that $|\lambda W_{12}/(\varepsilon_2 - \varepsilon_1)| \ll 1$.

(*c*) Expand the exact solution in powers of λ and compare it with (*b*). (*d*) Discuss the degenerate case when $\varepsilon_1 = \varepsilon_2$.

3. *A primitive model of the electron in a metal*

Assume that an electron moves freely along the x-axis, and that its wave function is

$$\phi(x) = e^{ikx}/\sqrt{l} \qquad k = 2\pi n/l \qquad (n \text{ integer})$$

Investigate the effect of a small perturbation in the form of a periodic potential

$$W(x) = W(x+a) = \sum_n W_{\frac{2\pi n}{a}} \exp\left(\frac{2\pi i n}{a} x\right)$$

using second-order perturbation theory. For which neighbourhoods does the perturbation theory fail? Find the correct functions of zero-order approximation at these points. What is the form of the energy spectrum in this case? (Answer: It is split into bands.) The calculation is facilitated by noting that

$$\mathscr{H} = -(\hbar^2/2m)\,\partial^2/\partial x^2 + V(x)$$

commutes with the displacement operator T_a of §23.

4. *Effective scattering cross-section for a screened Coulomb potential*

Calculate the differential and total cross-sections for a scattering potential $-(e^2/r)\exp(-r/a)$, using Dirac's approximation. This so-called "screened Coulomb potential" represents the interaction between an electron and a neutral hydrogen atom. The potential of the nucleus, $-e^2/r$, is screened by the electrons of the atom; a is of the order of magnitude of the Bohr radius. If a is allowed to tend to infinity a pure Coulomb potential is obtained. Compare the differential cross-section calculated in this manner with the classical scattering formula of Rutherford.

5. *Polarizability of a spherically symmetrical system*

Calculate the polarizability of a spherically symmetrical atom with N electrons (representing an inert gas), using the trial function $\phi = (1+\beta W)\phi_o$, where $W = -eF \sum_{i=1}^{N} x_i$. $\overline{W}$ vanishes because of the spherical symmetry, since $\Sigma \overline{x_i} = 0$. $\mathscr{H}_0$ contains kinetic and Coulomb energies only. Let ϕ_0 be the exact eigenfunction corresponding to H_0 and the eigenvalue E_0. Express the polarizability in terms of mean values corresponding to the state ϕ_0.

C

Problems involving one electron

CHAPTER CI

Stationary states

§29. The electron in a central field of force

We shall now describe the motion of an electron in the central field of force of an atom. Strictly speaking, such a field exists only in the cases of the hydrogen atom and of hydrogen-like ions, since all other atoms contain more than one electron. However, the atoms of many monovalent elements (in particular, the alkali and precious metals) may be represented as though they consisted of a rigid "hull" formed from the nucleus and the firmly bound inner electrons, around which a single valence electron revolves. This outer electron therefore moves in the Coulomb potential of the nucleus, although this potential is screened by the inner electrons. It is spherically symmetrical, acting at a great distance from the nucleus like the potential due to a nucleus with a single charge. At shorter distances the potential approaches that due to a nucleus of charge Z, where Z is the atomic number of the element in question. The energy levels of the valence electron are therefore determined from a Schrödinger equation of the form

$$\left\{-\frac{\hbar^2}{2m}\nabla^2+V(r)\right\}\phi(\mathbf{r}) = E\phi(\mathbf{r}) \tag{29.1}$$

Since the potential depends only on the magnitude of $\mathbf{r}$, the eigenfunctions may be chosen in accordance with §§24 and 25 in such a manner that they are eigenfunctions of the square of the angular momentum $\mathbf{M}$ and also of its z-component.

Equation (29.1) can be expressed in the following form, as may easily be verified.*

$$-\frac{\hbar^2}{2m}\frac{1}{r}\frac{\partial^2(r\phi)}{\partial r^2}+\left(\frac{\mathbf{M}^2}{2mr^2}+V(r)\right)\phi = E\phi \tag{29.2}$$

* In polar coordinates r, ϑ, ϕ,

$$\nabla^2 = \frac{1}{r}\frac{\partial^2}{\partial r^2}r + \frac{1}{r^2\sin^2\theta}\left\{\sin\theta\frac{\partial}{\partial\theta}\sin\theta\frac{\partial}{\partial\theta}+\frac{\partial^2}{\partial\phi^2}\right\}$$

Cf. expression (25.2) for $\mathbf{M}^2$, and Vol. I, equation (13.4*b*).

Since ϕ must be an eigenfunction of $\mathbf{M}^2$, it follows, if we put $r\phi = \chi(r) Y_{lm}(\theta, \phi)$, that

$$-\frac{\hbar^2}{2m}\chi'' + \left(\frac{l(l+1)\hbar^2}{2mr^2} + V(r)\right)\chi = E\chi \tag{29.3}$$

In this equation the term added to $V(r)$ comes from the centrifugal force F_r:

$$F_r = -\frac{\partial}{\partial r}\frac{l(l+1)\hbar^2}{2mr^2} = \frac{l(l+1)\hbar^2}{mr^3} = m\omega^2 r$$

if the associated classical angular velocity $\omega = \hbar\sqrt{[l(l+1)]}/mr^2$ is substituted for the angular momentum $\hbar\sqrt{[l(l+1)]}$.

We shall first consider equation (29.3) for the situations in which r is very small, and very large, distinguishing between the cases $E < 0$ and $E > 0$. When r is small, V and E are small compared with the potential of the centrifugal force $1/r^2$. Hence, approximately,

$$-\chi'' + \frac{l(l+1)}{r^2}\chi = 0$$

There are two independent linear solutions of the above equation:

$$\chi = ar^{l+1} \quad \text{and} \quad \chi = br^{-l}$$

The second solution must be excluded, since it leads to a singularity of the radial part of the wave function, $R = \chi/r$, as r tends to 0. Hence for small values of r we must have*

$$\chi = ar^{l+1} \tag{29.4}$$

For sufficiently large values of r, the terms in brackets in equation (29.3) become negligible compared with E, and we obtain the solution†

$$\chi = \begin{cases} A\sin kr + B\cos kr & \text{for } \dfrac{\hbar^2 k^2}{2m} = E > 0 \\[2ex] A\,e^{\beta r} + B\,e^{-\beta r} & \text{for } -\dfrac{\hbar^2\beta^2}{2m} = E < 0 \end{cases} \tag{29.5}$$

* Equation (29.4) is also valid for $l = 0$; in this case the singularity of the excluded solution is weak enough for the wave function to remain normalizable. The solution must still be excluded, however, since in this case $\nabla^2\phi$ in (29.1) would exhibit a singularity similar to that of the δ-function whereas $V\phi$ has a singularity of order $1/r^2$ only.

† When the Coulomb potential is expanded asymptotically the factor $1/r$ must still be retained: the relation (29.5) remains correct, in so far as A and B are now proportional to powers of r.

In the first case, $E > 0$, and the particle possesses sufficient energy to escape to infinity; this corresponds to the classical case in which a particle approaches from and flies away to infinity. By a suitable choice of the parameters A and B for each value of k we should expect to obtain a continuation of equation (29.4). The energy is therefore not quantized, the spectrum is continuous, and the eigenfunctions cannot be normalized.

In the second case, $E < 0$, and we obtain the closed orbits of classical theory, to which correspond the spatially limited bound states of quantum theory. It is necessary that $A = 0$ in order that the eigenfunctions should remain finite when r tends to infinity. A connection with equation (29.4) is established by means of the parameter B alone, but only for certain definite values of E; the energy is quantized, and the spectrum is discrete.

In the first instance we shall consider the case of the hydrogen atom, which provides a prototype of such a spectrum; the potential $V(r) = -e^2/r$. It is convenient to replace r and E by the dimensionless quantities

$$\rho = \frac{r}{\hbar^2/m e^2} = \frac{r}{a_0} \quad \text{and} \quad \varepsilon = \frac{E}{e^2/2a_0} \tag{29.6}$$

in other words, lengths are measured in terms of the Bohr radius

$$a_0 = \frac{\hbar^2}{m e^2} = 0{\cdot}53\,\text{A.U.}$$

and energies are expressed in terms of the Rydberg unit

$$\frac{e^2}{2a_0} = 13{\cdot}55\,\text{eV}$$

Then, from (29.3),

$$\frac{d^2\chi}{d\rho^2} + \left\{\varepsilon + \frac{2}{\rho} - \frac{l(l+1)}{\rho^2}\right\}\chi = 0 \tag{29.7}$$

Using (29.4) and (29.5), we can put χ in the form

$$\chi = \rho^{l+1}\left(\sum_{\nu=0}^{\infty} c_\nu \rho^\nu\right) e^{-\lambda\rho}, \quad \text{where } \lambda = \sqrt{(-\varepsilon)}$$

We then introduce the above expression into (29.7) and determine the coefficients of $\rho^{\nu+l}$:

$$c_{\nu+1}\left[(\nu+l+2)(\nu+l+1) - l(l+1)\right] - 2c_\nu\left[\lambda(\nu+l+1) - 1\right]$$

This expression must vanish for all values of v in order to satisfy (29.7):

$$c_{v+1} = 2\frac{\lambda(v+l+1)-1}{(v+l+2)(v+l+1)-l(l+1)}c_v \tag{29.8}$$

The above relation serves to determine the coefficients c_v in terms of c_0. The value of the latter coefficient is arbitrary, and is determined by the normalization condition. We may now draw the following alternative conclusions:

1. $\lambda = 1/(n_r+l+1) = 1/n$, where $n_r = 0,1,2,\ldots$ Then $c_v = 0$ when $v \geqq n_r+1$, i.e. the series terminates at $v = n_r$.

2. n_r is not an integer: in this case the series does not terminate. For large values of v, (29.8) gives

$$c_{v+1} \approx \frac{2\lambda}{v+1}c_v$$

therefore asymptotically,

$$c_v \approx \frac{(2\lambda)^v}{v!}c_0$$

hence

$$\sum_v c_v \rho^v \approx c_0 e^{2\lambda\rho}$$

As $\rho \to \infty$, χ would increase like $e^{\lambda\rho}$ and would not be normalizable; this case must therefore be excluded.

The result is, therefore, that the energy levels are given by the following relation:

$$E_n = -\frac{e^2}{2a_0}\frac{1}{n^2}, \quad \text{where } n \geqq l+1 \text{ is an integer} \tag{29.9}$$

We must now investigate the degree of degeneracy of E_n. Firstly, if we take the relation $n = n_r+l+1$, we always obtain the same value if we put in succession $l = 0,1,\ldots,n-1$ and $n_r = n-1, n-2,\ldots,1,0$.

From §25, we know that each value of l is associated with $2l+1$ different eigenfunctions $Y_{l,m}$, denoted by the quantum numbers l and $m = -l,\ldots,0,\ldots,l$. Thus the total degree of degeneracy is

$$\sum_{l=0}^{n-1}(2l+1) = n^2$$

If we denote the radial component by $R_{nl}(r) = \chi_{nl}/r$, corresponding to energy E_n and angular-momentum quantum number l, then

$$\phi_{nlm}(\mathbf{r}) = R_{nl}(r)Y_{lm}(\theta,\phi) \tag{29.10}$$

is the complete eigenfunction of $\mathscr{H}$, $\mathbf{M}^2$, and M_z. The first three radial components, with their appropriate normalization factors, are as follows:

$$R_{10} = \frac{2}{a_0^{3/2}} \exp -\frac{r}{a_0}$$

$$R_{20} = \frac{1}{(2a_0)^{3/2}}\left(2 - \frac{r}{a_0}\right) \exp -\frac{r}{2a_0} \tag{29.11}$$

$$R_{21} = \frac{1}{(24a_0^3)^{1/2}} \frac{r}{a_0} \exp -\frac{r}{2a_0}$$

In order to illustrate the above components we shall consider the functions

$$w_{nl}(r)\, dr = r^2 R_{nl}^2(r)\, dr$$

which represent the probability of finding the electron in a spherical shell of thickness dr at a distance r from the nucleus, when the atom is in the state R_{nl} (figure 29.) The maxima of these functions move outwards with each increase in the principal quantum number, and occur

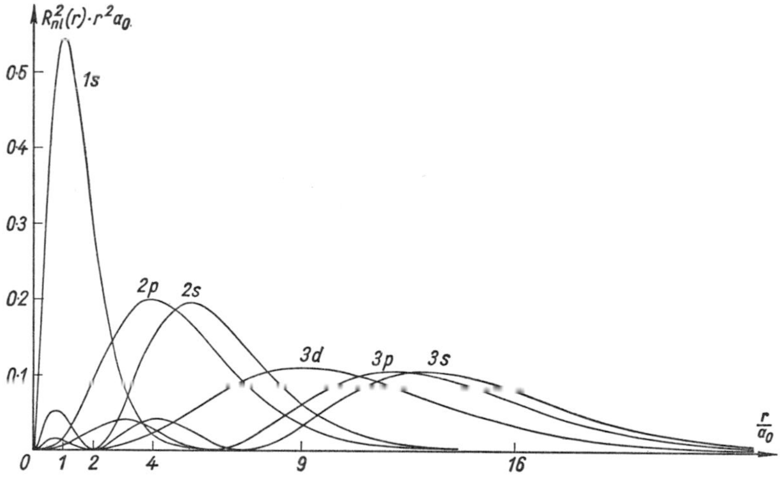

Fig. 29.—Radial probability distributions for the hydrogen atom

w_{10}: 1*s*-state	w_{21}: 2*p*-state	w_{31}: 3*p*-state
w_{20}: 2*s*-state	w_{30}: 3*s*-state	w_{32}: 3*d*-state

near the Bohr orbits of the old quantum theory. The maximum of the function

$$w_{10} = Cr^2 \exp -\frac{2r}{a_0}$$

occurs at $r = a_0$, the radius of the smallest Bohr orbit.

The mean values $\overline{1/r}$, $\overline{1/r^2}$, $\overline{1/r^3}$ are determined by means of the functions w_{nl}:

$$\overline{\frac{1}{r^\nu}} = \int_0^\infty R^2{}_{nl} \frac{1}{r^\nu} r^2 dr = \left(\chi_{nl}, \frac{1}{r^\nu} \chi_{nl}\right)$$

The mean value $\overline{1/r}$ follows from the virial theorem (22.16) for Coulomb forces: $\overline{V} = 2E = -e^2/n^2a = -\overline{e^2/r}$, from which

$$\overline{\frac{1}{r}} = \frac{1}{n^2} \frac{1}{a_0} \tag{29.12}$$

The mean value $\overline{1/r^2}$ may be determined by making use of the fact that the definition of the eigenvalues of (29.7) is applicable to integral and non-integral values of l. This equation may therefore be differentiated with respect to l. For this purpose it may be written as

$$\mathscr{H} \chi_{nl} = \varepsilon \chi_{nl}$$

where $$\mathscr{H} = \left\{-\frac{d^2}{d\rho^2} + \frac{l(l+1)}{\rho^2} - \frac{2}{\rho}\right\} \quad \text{and} \quad \varepsilon = -\frac{1}{(n_r+l+1)^2} = -\frac{1}{n^2}$$

Then $$\frac{\partial \mathscr{H}}{\partial l} \chi + \mathscr{H} \frac{\partial \chi}{\partial l} = \frac{\partial \varepsilon}{\partial l} \chi + \varepsilon \frac{\partial \chi}{\partial l}$$

therefore $$\left(\chi, \frac{\partial \mathscr{H}}{\partial l} \chi\right) + \left(\chi, \mathscr{H} \frac{\partial \chi}{\partial l}\right) = \frac{\partial \varepsilon}{\partial l} + \varepsilon \left(\chi, \frac{\partial \chi}{\partial l}\right)$$

Since $\mathscr{H}$ is Hermitian, it follows that

$$\left(\chi, \mathscr{H} \frac{\partial \chi}{\partial l}\right) = \left(\mathscr{H} \chi, \frac{\partial \chi}{\partial l}\right) = \varepsilon \left(\chi, \frac{\partial \chi}{\partial l}\right)$$

and hence $$\frac{\partial \varepsilon}{\partial l} = \frac{2}{n^3} = \overline{\frac{\partial \mathscr{H}}{\partial l}} = (2l+1) \overline{\frac{1}{\rho^2}}$$

Therefore $$\overline{\frac{1}{r^2}} = \frac{2}{(2l+1)n^3} \frac{1}{a_0{}^2} \tag{29.13}$$

If we differentiate (29.7) with respect to ρ, we obtain

$$\frac{\partial \mathscr{H}}{\partial \rho} \chi + \mathscr{H} \frac{\partial \chi}{\partial \rho} = \varepsilon \frac{\partial \chi}{\partial \rho}$$

Forming the scalar product with χ:

$$\left(\chi, \frac{\partial \mathscr{H}}{\partial \rho} \chi\right) = 0$$

Since

$$\frac{\partial \mathscr{H}}{\partial \rho} = -\frac{2l(l+1)}{\rho^3} + \frac{2}{\rho^2}$$

it follows that

$$\overline{\frac{1}{\rho^2}} = \overline{\frac{l(l+1)}{\rho^3}}$$

hence, when $l \neq 0$*

$$\overline{\frac{1}{r^3}} = \frac{2}{l(l+1)(2l+1)n^3} \frac{1}{a_0{}^3} \tag{29.14}$$

We have now determined all the mean values of interest to us in connection with later calculations.

In the case of other monovalent atoms, equation (29.3) cannot be exactly integrated. However, by means of Schrödinger's perturbation theory it is possible to deduce the extent of the displacement of the energy levels with respect to the hydrogen terms. For this purpose we shall put

$$V(r) = -\frac{e^2}{r} + S(r)$$

treating the deviation $S(r)$ of the potential $V(r)$ from the hydrogen atom potential as a perturbation. We then obtain the hydrogen terms as the zero-order approximation and, using the methods of §26, the following perturbed terms as a first-order approximation:†

$$E_{nl} = E_n + \int_0^\infty R_{nl}^2(r) r^2 S(r)\, dr \tag{29.15}$$

$S(r)$ is only appreciably different from zero in the neighbourhood of $r = 0$, and its sign is always negative. The perturbed energy terms are therefore lower than the corresponding values of E_n; the deviation increases with increased concentration of the wave function R_{ln} at small values of r. This energy diminution decreases as l increases, n being fixed, and as n increases at a fixed value of l.

In figure 30 the spectra of lithium and sodium are illustrated; these provide the simplest examples of spectra of monovalent atoms other than hydrogen. The term $n = 1$ does not appear in the case of lithium, because it is occupied by the electrons of the inner shell, and cannot

* For the s-term (for which $l = 0$), $\overline{1/r^3}$ is divergent.

†This is a degenerate case; however, R_{nl} and Y_{lm} are the correct initial functions of zero-order approximation, since they are eigenfunctions corresponding to different eigenvalues of the operators $\mathbf{M}^2$ and M_z, which commute with $\mathscr{H}$ and with S.

therefore be occupied by the outer electron in virtue of the Pauli exclusion principle. The same situation applies in the case of sodium for the terms $n=1$ and $n=2$.

The characteristic difference between the hydrogen spectrum and the spectra of the other monovalent elements consists in the removal of

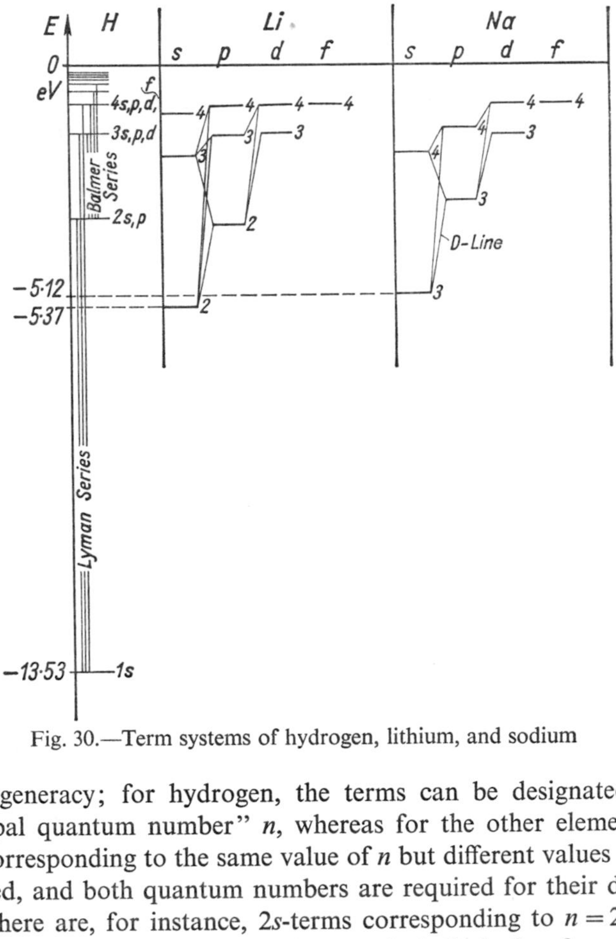

Fig. 30.—Term systems of hydrogen, lithium, and sodium

the l-degeneracy; for hydrogen, the terms can be designated by a "principal quantum number" n, whereas for the other elements the terms corresponding to the same value of n but different values of l are separated, and both quantum numbers are required for their designation. There are, for instance, $2s$-terms corresponding to $n=2$, $l=0$, $2p$-terms corresponding to $n=2$, $l=1$, and similarly $3s$-, $3p$-, and $3d$-terms with different energy values.

The intensity of the emitted radiation is given by the matrix elements of $\mathbf{r}$. The results obtained in §25 imply that the only spectral lines that occur are those corresponding to the transitions $\Delta l = \pm 1$ and $\Delta m = 0, \pm 1$. In the case of the hydrogen atom, transitions are possible between all terms, since for any two terms there are always two corresponding functions that do not violate the above selection rules. In the case of lithium and sodium the l-degeneracy is removed, and it is necessary to take account of the selection rule $\Delta l = \pm 1$. The only transitions occurring are those between p- and s-states, for instance, or between p- and d-states, as shown in figure 30. The selection rule $\Delta m = 0, \pm 1$ comes into effect only when the degeneracy is completely removed.

§30. The normal Zeeman effect

When a magnetic field is switched on, the m-degeneracy vanishes. In order to see this, let us express the Hamiltonian operator of the atom in a magnetic field as follows:*

$$\mathscr{H} = \frac{\left(\mathbf{p} - \frac{e}{c}\mathbf{A}\right)^2}{2m_0} + V(r) \approx \frac{\mathbf{p}^2}{2m_0} - \frac{e}{m_0 c}(\mathbf{A}, \mathbf{p}) + V(r) \tag{30.1}$$

The magnetic field is assumed to be homogeneous, and to be represented by the vector potential

$$\mathbf{A} = \tfrac{1}{2}\mathbf{H} \times \mathbf{r} \tag{30.2}$$

then, from (30.1)

$$\mathscr{H} = \frac{\mathbf{p}^2}{2m_0} - \frac{e}{2m_0 c}(\mathbf{M}, \mathbf{H}) + V(r)$$

The middle term represents the energy, in the field $\mathbf{H}$, of a magnetic moment

$$\vec{\mu} = \frac{e}{2m_0 c}\mathbf{M}$$

associated with an angular momentum† $\mathbf{M}$. If we take the z-axis of

* We omit the quadratic term in $\mathbf{A}$; this is permissible for sufficiently small magnetic fields (i.e. for those fields that can be realized in practice), provided that the contribution of the first-degree term in $\mathbf{A}$ is different from zero. The electron mass will be denoted here by m_0 in order to avoid confusion with the quantum number m. The charge of the electron, e, is equal to the negative elementary charge $-e_0$, and is therefore a minus quantity. Since $\operatorname{div} \mathbf{A} = 0$, $(\mathbf{p}, \mathbf{A}) = (\mathbf{A}, \mathbf{p})$, from which it follows that $\mathscr{H}$ is Hermitian.

† It is necessary to distinguish between the "canonical angular momentum" $\mathbf{M} = \mathbf{r} \times \mathbf{p}$ and the "mechanical angular momentum"

$$m\mathbf{r} \times \dot{\mathbf{r}} = \mathbf{M} - \mathbf{r} \times \frac{e}{c}\mathbf{A}$$

Strictly speaking, the magnetic moment is proportional to the mechanical angular momentum, but this can be neglected in the present approximation.

our coordinate system to be parallel to **H** we obtain the Schrödinger equation

$$\left\{-\frac{\hbar^2}{2m_0}\nabla^2+V(r)-\frac{e}{2m_0 c}M_z H\right\}\psi = E\psi \tag{30.3}$$

The solutions are the same as those in the absence of a magnetic field; the only difference is that the m-degeneracy is removed. We obtain

$$E_{nlm} = E_{nl}-\frac{e\hbar}{2m_0 c}mH \tag{30.4}$$

where E_{nl} is the energy of the atom in the absence of the magnetic field. The energy perturbation due to the magnetic field can be expressed as

$$\Delta E = \mu_B mH = -\mu_z H$$

where $\mu_B = -e\hbar/2m_0 c$ appears as the smallest unit of the magnetic moment, termed the *Bohr magneton.*

According to the Bohr frequency condition, the possible emission and absorption frequencies of the spectrum (30.4) are

$$\begin{aligned}\omega_{nlm,n'l'm'} &= \frac{E_{nl}-E_{n'l'}}{\hbar}-\frac{eH}{2m_0 c}(m-m')\\ &= \omega_0+\omega_L(m-m') \end{aligned}\tag{30.5}$$

where
$$\omega_L = -\frac{e}{2m_0 c}H$$

is the "Larmor frequency" (cf. §35).

The intensity and polarization of the spectral lines are obtained from the "correspondence" postulates of §11. These lead to the result that the radiation corresponding to the transition $nlm \rightarrow n'l'm'$ can be considered to be emitted by a Hertzian dipole of moment

$$e\mathbf{r}(t) = e(\tilde{\mathbf{r}}\, e^{i\omega t}+\tilde{\mathbf{r}}^*\, e^{-i\omega t})$$

where
$$\omega = \omega_0+\omega_L(m-m')$$

and
$$\tilde{\mathbf{r}} = (\phi_{nlm}, \mathbf{r}\phi_{n'l'm'})$$

is the transition element, with components $(\tilde{x}, \tilde{y}, \tilde{z})$. If (x, y, z) are replaced by the quantities

$$x\pm iy = r\sin\theta\, e^{\pm i\phi} \quad \text{and} \quad z = r\cos\theta$$

then, putting $\phi_{nlm} = R_{nl} Y_{lm}$,

$$\tilde{x} \pm i\tilde{y} = (R_{nl}, rR_{n'l'})(Y_{lm}, \sin\theta\, e^{\pm i\phi} Y_{l'm'}) \tag{30.6a}$$

$$\tilde{z} = (R_{nl}, rR_{n'l'})(Y_{lm}, \cos\theta\, Y_{l'm'}) \tag{30.6b}$$

We now consider the angular components of the wave function. According to the recurrence formulae (25.9) to (25.11) for the spherical harmonics, the latter vanish except when $l - l' = \pm 1$ and $m - m' = 0, \pm 1$. We then have the following selection rule: for the electric dipole radiation of an electron in a central field of force the following conditions always apply,

$$\Delta l = \pm 1 \qquad \Delta m = 0, \pm 1$$

When $m = m'$, it follows from (25.9) and (25.10) that $\tilde{x} = \tilde{y} = 0$, $\tilde{z} \neq 0$, and hence that

$$\tilde{\mathbf{r}}(t) = A(0, 0, \cos\omega_0 t)$$

where A is a constant.

In this case the dipole moment oscillates parallel to the z-axis with unchanged angular frequency ω_0; it therefore produces no radiation in the direction of the z-axis, and linearly polarized light in the plane normal thereto.

When $m = m' + 1$, $\tilde{x} + i\tilde{y} \neq 0$, $\tilde{x} - i\tilde{y} = \tilde{z} = 0$, therefore

$$\mathbf{r}(t) = B[\cos(\omega_0 + \omega_L)t,\ \sin(\omega_0 + \omega_L)t, 0]$$

where B is a constant. In this case the dipole moment rotates with increased frequency in a right-handed sense about the z-axis. The light emitted in the direction of the z-axis is circularly polarized in the right-handed sense; at right angles, in the xy-plane, the light is linearly polarized.

Similarly, when $m = m' - 1$,

$$\mathbf{r}(t) = C[\cos(\omega_0 - \omega_L)t,\ \sin(\omega_0 - \omega_L)t, 0]$$

where C is a constant. Therefore, if we observe the system along a direction parallel to the z-axis and the magnetic field, we find two circularly polarized components of angular frequencies $\omega_0 \pm \omega_L$; this is the longitudinal Zeeman effect. If the system is observed at right angles to the field we obtain the transverse Zeeman effect, which comprises one component (called the π-component) of frequency ω_0, linearly polarized parallel to the field, and two components (termed the σ-components) of frequencies $\omega_0 \pm \omega_L$, linearly polarized at right angles to the field (figure 31).

This phenomenon is the familiar Lorentz triplet of classical physics. In practice, the splitting of the spectral lines in the magnetic field is found to be much more complicated. Equation (30.3) cannot therefore be regarded as the correct representation of the electron motion in a

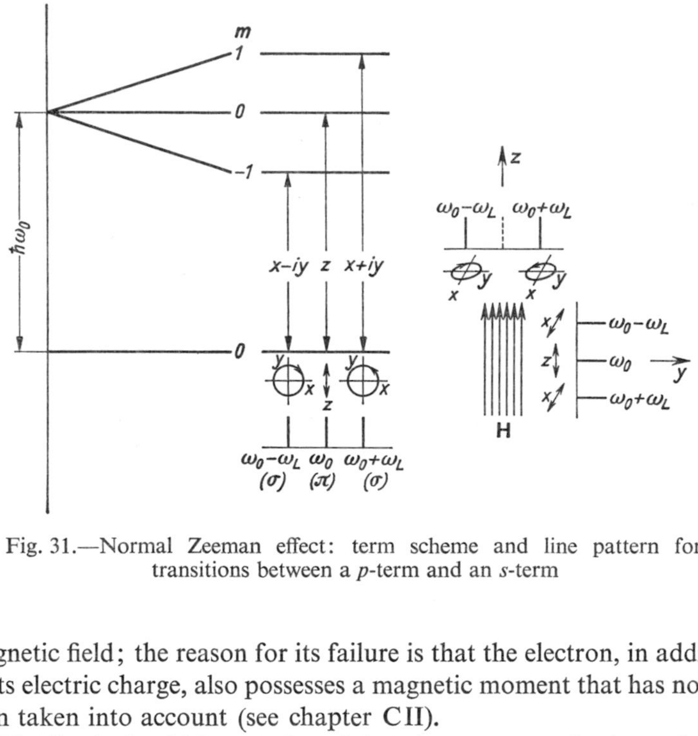

Fig. 31.—Normal Zeeman effect: term scheme and line pattern for transitions between a p-term and an s-term

magnetic field; the reason for its failure is that the electron, in addition to its electric charge, also possesses a magnetic moment that has not yet been taken into account (see chapter C II).

Finally, it should be mentioned that there are no selection rules for the radial component of (30.6), and hence for n. The evaluation of the integrals for these components is extremely laborious; the reader is referred to the literature.*

* W. Gordon, *Ann. Phys.* 2 (1929), 1031.

Exercises

1. *Energy terms and degree of degeneracy for a three-dimensional oscillator* *

Calculate the energy terms of a three-dimensional oscillator of potential $V(r) = \frac{1}{2}m\omega^2r^2$, in the same manner as was done for the case of the hydrogen atom. Determine the behaviour at short and at long distances from the centre, for which $\chi = r^{l+1}$ and $\exp -\frac{1}{2}\alpha r^2$ respectively; $\alpha = m\omega/\hbar$. For any distance, represent χ by the following general expression:

$$\chi = r^{l+1}\left[\exp -\tfrac{1}{2}\alpha r^2\right]\sum_{\nu=0}^{\infty} c_\nu r^\nu$$

The Schrödinger equation leads to a recurrence formula for the coefficients c_ν, from which it appears that the power series must terminate. Give the formula for the energy terms and represent each term by its appropriate spectroscopic symbol (s, p, d, f, g, h). Deduce a general formula for the degrees of degeneracy.

2. *Hermitian nature of the Hamiltonian operator expressed in polar coordinates*

Determine the adjoint operator p_r^+ of $p_r = -i\hbar\partial/\partial r$, and express the radial part of $(-\hbar^2/2m)\nabla^2$,

$$-\frac{\hbar^2}{2m}\cdot\frac{1}{r^2}\frac{\partial}{\partial r}r^2\frac{\partial}{\partial r} = -\frac{\hbar^2}{2m}\frac{1}{r}\frac{\partial^2}{\partial r^2}r$$

in terms of p_r and p^+, so that its Hermitian nature is evident.

3. *Probability function and Bohr orbits of the hydrogen atom*

Show that, in the case of a large principal quantum number n, and maximum angular-momentum quantum number $l = n-1$, an electron is to be found at a mean distance $\bar{r}$ from the nucleus with a corresponding small root mean square deviation Δr given by

$$(\Delta r)^2 = \overline{(r-\bar{r})^2} = \overline{r^2}-\bar{r}^2$$

$\bar{r}$ being given by the radius of the corresponding Bohr orbit. Compare the result with (29.12) and (29.13).

* In nuclear theory the term scheme of the three-dimensional oscillator is often employed for the representation of the nucleon terms. The degree of degeneracy is closely connected with the so-called "magic numbers" of the nuclear shell model. (cf. Mayer-Jensen, *Elementary Theory of Nuclear Shell Structure* (New York, 1955).

CHAPTER CII

Electron spin

§31. The Stern-Gerlach experiment

It was stated at the end of §30 that equation (30.3) fails to explain the experimental results of the Zeeman effect. The inadequacy of this equation becomes even more apparent when attempting to interpret the Stern-Gerlach experiment for the determination of atomic magnetic moments. An outline of this experiment is given below.

If a beam of neutral atoms of moment μ is passed through a homogeneous magnetic field $\mathbf{H}_0$, each atom is subjected to a couple $\vec{\mu} \times \mathbf{H}_0$, but not to any deflecting force. The magnetic moments therefore

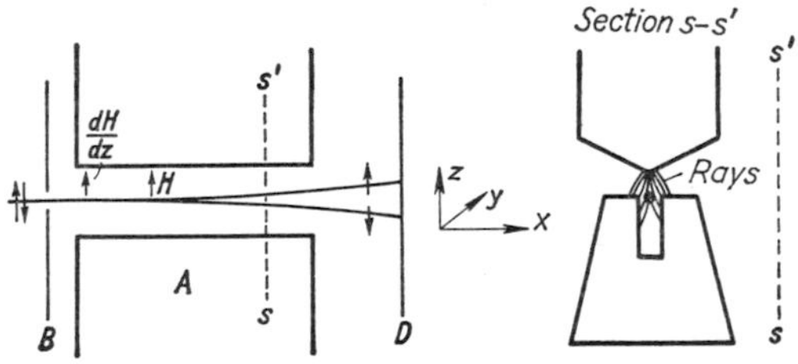

Fig. 32.—The Stern-Gerlach experiment

precess about the direction of the field in such a manner that their components in this direction remain constant; the motion of the atoms through the field, however, remains rectilinear.

The situation is different when the atomic beam is passed through an inhomogeneous magnetic field, as in the arrangement shown in figure 32. In the classical sense the magnetic moments still precess about the field direction; in addition, however, a force

$$\mathbf{F} = (\vec{\mu} \, . \, \nabla)\mathbf{H} = \left(\mu_x \frac{\partial}{\partial x} + \mu_y \frac{\partial}{\partial y} + \mu_z \frac{\partial}{\partial z} \right) \mathbf{H} \tag{31.1}$$

arises, which produces a deviation of the beam (cf. Vol. I, §31).

In order to deduce the magnetic moment of the individual atoms from the observed deflection, we must pass the beam through the magnetic field using the simplest possible geometrical arrangement. We take the x-axis parallel to the initial beam direction, the z-axis in the plane of symmetry of the magnet, and the y-axis perpendicular to it (figure 32). Then $H_x = 0$, and all derivatives with respect to x vanish. Hence from (31.1)

$$F_x = 0 \qquad F_y = \mu_y \frac{\partial H_y}{\partial y} + \mu_z \frac{\partial H_y}{\partial z} \qquad F_z = \mu_y \frac{\partial H_z}{\partial y} + \mu_z \frac{\partial H_z}{\partial z}$$

In particular, if the beam lies in the symmetry plane $y = 0$, $H_y = 0$ and $\partial H_y/\partial z = \partial H_z/\partial y = 0$; in the latter case because the magnetostatic field is irrotational. Further, since the field is solenoidal in the region of the beam, $\partial H_y/\partial y + \partial H_z/\partial z = 0$, and the components of the force are

$$F_x = 0 \qquad F_y = \mu_y \frac{\partial H_y}{\partial y} = -\mu_y \frac{\partial H_z}{\partial z} \qquad F_z = \mu_z \frac{\partial H_z}{\partial z}$$

We see, therefore, that deflecting components of the force exist in both the z- and y-directions.

Now the magnetic moment precesses about the direction of the field at any point, which is virtually parallel to the axis of z. The component μ_z is therefore practically constant, whereas μ_y oscillates about zero. If the magnetic field is so strong that the atomic magnet executes many precessional cycles during the flight of the particle, the mean value of F_y vanishes, and the only non-zero component of the force is

$$F_z = \mu_z \frac{\partial H_z}{\partial z} \qquad (31.2)$$

If the atoms in question are in a state corresponding to an azimuthal quantum number l, this force should cause the original beam to split into $2l+1$ constituent beams, corresponding to the $2l+1$ possible values of μ_z; each constituent beam would be associated with a definite value of the magnetic moment component

$$\mu_z = -\mu_B m = \frac{e\hbar}{2m_0 c} m \qquad (31.3)$$

In particular, no splitting should occur in the case of s-electrons. In fact, however, when beams of alkali and noble-metal atoms are observed it is found that they split into two component beams.

Since there is certainly no orbital angular momentum associated with the electrons of these atoms in the ground state, the observed moment can only be ascribed to the electron itself, possibly because it rotates about its own axis. The value of the magnetic moment is found from measurements to be one Bohr magneton.

The experimental fact of this splitting into two component beams, together with our analysis of the angular momentum in §24 (for the case $\lambda=\frac{1}{2}$), suggests the hypothesis that the magnetic moment is connected with a spin angular momentum, the z-component of which can assume only the values $\pm\hbar/2$. This hypothesis was first put forward by S. A. Goudsmit and G. E. Uhlenbeck; W. Pauli was responsible for the mathematical analysis of this concept, and in particular for the representation of the angular momentum operators by means of the matrices $(\sigma_x, \sigma_y, \sigma_z)$ (§24).

The ratio of the magnetic moment to the spin angular momentum is

$$\frac{e\hbar}{2m_0 c}\Big/\frac{\hbar}{2}=\frac{e}{m_0 c} \tag{31.4}$$

whereas the ratio of this moment to the orbital angular momentum is $e/2m_0 c$. This result makes it difficult to put forward a simple explanation of the magnetic moment in terms of electron spin; such an assumption would lead to the ratio $e/2m_0 c$ (cf. §35).

This discrepancy affords an interpretation of the magneto-mechanical anomaly in ferromagnetic materials, in the case of the Einstein-de Haas effect (Vol. III). In the study of this effect the ratio (31.4) was found experimentally; this leads necessarily to the assumption that ferromagnetism originates from electron spin, and not from the orbital angular momentum.

It will appear later that the assumption of electron spin provides an explanation of the multiplet structure (§34) and of the anomalous Zeeman effect (§36). It is found, for instance, that the energy levels of the alkali atoms, apart from the s-states, are split into two levels, called *doublets*, lying close together. A well-known example is the splitting of the yellow sodium D line into the two lines $D_1=5890$ A.U. and $D_2=5896$ A.U., which correspond to the transition $3p\to 3s$: this arises as a result of the separation of the $3p$-level into two neighbouring terms. The phenomenon may be explained as follows: the electrons orbiting the nucleus create a magnetic field with respect to which the spin takes up a parallel or an anti-parallel position, thus producing two different energy levels.

We shall go into the subject more thoroughly in §34, and will deal next with the motion of the spin in external fields.

§32. Spin in a steady magnetic field

According to the previous section the operators $(s_x, s_y, s_z) = \frac{1}{2}\hbar(\sigma_x, \sigma_y, \sigma_z)$ are associated with the spin angular momentum of the electron. The spin state of the electron is represented by a function χ, lying in a two-dimensional Hilbert space in which the operators $(\sigma_x, \sigma_y, \sigma_z)$ act, and which according to §24 may be considered to be spanned by the two eigenfunctions of σ_z, denoted by α, β. We may therefore write

$$\chi = a\alpha + b\beta \tag{32.1}$$

where a and b are complex numbers. χ is normalized if $(\chi, \chi) = |a|^2 + |b|^2 = 1$; $|a|^2$ and $|b|^2$ then represent the respective probabilities that the electron spin is parallel to the positive z-axis or in the opposite direction.

If we put $\alpha = \kappa_{+1}$, $\beta = \kappa_{-1}$, where $\sigma_z \kappa_s = s\kappa_s$, and $s = \pm 1$, then (32.1) may be written

$$\chi = \sum_{s=\pm 1} \kappa_s \chi(s), \text{ where } \chi(s) = (\kappa_s, \chi).$$

The spin function (or spin coordinate) $\chi(s)$ represents a combination of the two numbers (a, b), and can assume only the two values ± 1. An operator A may then be constructed from the Pauli matrices and represented by a two-row matrix $A_{ss'}$. Such an operator acts as follows:

$$A\chi(s) = \sum_{s'=\pm 1} A_{ss'}\chi(s')$$

The normalization condition is

$$(\chi, \chi) = \sum_s \chi^*(s)\chi(s) = 1$$

The state of an electron is completely represented by a function of the position and spin coordinates, $\chi(\mathbf{r}, s, t)$, or alternatively by the pair of functions $\chi(\mathbf{r}, 1, t) = a$ and $\chi(\mathbf{r}, -1, t) = b$. The position and spin probabilities are then determined by the product $\chi^*(\mathbf{r}, s, t)\chi(\mathbf{r}, s, t)d\mathbf{r}$. To begin with we shall neglect the dependence on position and concern ourselves only with the time relationship. For this purpose we shall assume that the spatial relationship for both spin settings is represented at any moment by a comparatively broad wave packet, the dispersion of which may be neglected, and which in other respects obeys the laws of motion of classical mechanics (cf. Exercise 1, p. 206, and 2, p. 207).

The magnetic moment associated with the spin is

$$\vec{\mu} = \frac{e\hbar}{2m_0 c}\vec{\sigma} = -\mu_B \vec{\sigma}$$

and its energy in a magnetic field **H** is $-\vec{\mu}\mathbf{H}$. Hence

$$-(\vec{\mu}\mathbf{H})\chi = -\frac{\hbar}{i}\dot{\chi} \tag{32.2}$$

Taking the field to be parallel to the z-axis, and using (24.9) to represent the Pauli matrix σ_z, we may write (32.2) in terms of its components:

$$\dot{a} = -i\omega_L a \qquad \dot{b} = i\omega_L b \qquad \text{where} \quad \omega_L = -\frac{eH}{2m_0 c} \tag{32.3}$$

The solution of these equations is

$$a(t) = a_0\, e^{-i\omega_L t} \qquad b(t) = b_0\, e^{i\omega_L t} \tag{32.4}$$

The normalization condition $|a_0|^2 + |b_0|^2 = 1$ is always satisfied if we put

$$a_0 = e^{i\gamma}\cos\tfrac{1}{2}\theta \qquad b_0 = e^{i\delta}\sin\tfrac{1}{2}\theta$$

It may easily be verified that

$$(\chi, \vec{\sigma}\chi) = (\bar{\sigma}_x, \bar{\sigma}_y, \bar{\sigma}_z)$$
$$= [\sin\theta\cos(2\omega_L t - \gamma + \delta), \sin\theta\sin(2\omega_L t - \gamma + \delta), \cos\theta] \tag{32.5}$$

The mean value of the angular momentum therefore precesses about the field direction, with twice the Larmor frequency, on account of the magneto-mechanical spin anomaly. The states $a_0 = 1$, $b_0 = 0$ and $a_0 = 0$, $b_0 = 1$ are eigenfunctions with energies

$$E = \mu_B H = \hbar\omega_L \quad \text{and} \quad E = -\mu_B H = -\hbar\omega_L \quad \text{respectively} \tag{32.6}$$

The Larmor precession (32.5) may perhaps be better understood if we consider the time-dependent operators

$$\vec{\sigma}(t) = \exp\left(\frac{i}{\hbar}\mathscr{H}t\right)\vec{\sigma}\exp\left(-\frac{i}{\hbar}\mathscr{H}t\right)$$

and their time derivatives

$$\frac{d\vec{\sigma}}{dt} = \frac{i}{\hbar}(\mathscr{H}\vec{\sigma} - \vec{\sigma}\mathscr{H}) \tag{32.7}$$

For instance, the x-component of (32.7) is

$$\frac{d\sigma_x}{dt} = -\frac{ie}{2m_0c}[(\mathbf{H}\vec{\sigma})\sigma_x - \sigma_x(\mathbf{H}\vec{\sigma})]$$

If we write out the scalar product in terms of the components and make use of the commutation rules

$$\sigma_x\sigma_y - \sigma_y\sigma_x = 2i\sigma_z, \ldots, \ldots,$$

we obtain

$$\frac{d\vec{\sigma}}{dt} = 2\vec{\omega}_L \times \vec{\sigma} \quad \text{where} \quad \vec{\omega}_L = -\frac{e}{2m_0\,c}\mathbf{H} \tag{32.8a}$$

or

$$\frac{d\mathbf{s}}{dt} = \vec{\mu} \times \mathbf{H} \quad \text{since} \quad \mathbf{s} = \tfrac{1}{2}\hbar\vec{\sigma} \tag{32.8b}$$

The latter equation may be expressed as in classical mechanics: the rate of change of angular momentum is equal to the mechanical torque. Since the equations (32.8) are linear as regards the operators σ_i, they may also serve to express the expectation values $(\chi, \sigma_i\chi)$ in the same form.

§33. Spin resonance in an oscillating magnetic field

The existence of the Larmor precession affords a means of determination of the magnetic moments of atoms and of atomic nuclei that is more accurate than that provided by the original Stern-Gerlach method. According to equation (32.6), a particle with spin $\frac{1}{2}\hbar$ and magnetic moment μ in a magnetic field of magnitude H is capable of assuming two different states, of energies

$$E_0 = \mu H = -\hbar\omega_L \qquad E_1 = -\mu H = \hbar\omega_L$$

If the spin and the magnetic moment are anti-parallel as in the case of the electron, then μ is negative and E_0 is the energy of the lower state.

If the particle is brought into a weak oscillating magnetic field normal to the constant field, transitions between the ground and the excited states can be produced, similar to those that occur in the case of an atom in the radiation field. These transitions are most easily brought about when the angular frequency ω_0 of the oscillating field satisfies the Bohr frequency condition $\hbar\omega_0 = E_1 - E_0 = 2\hbar\omega_L$.

This condition obviously implies that the oscillating field resonates with the spin precessional frequency in the constant magnetic field, since, according to (32.5), the latter is equal to twice the Larmor frequency. At resonance the vertex angle of the cone of precession is continuously increased by the oscillating field, and the spin is finally "switched round" from its original direction to the opposite one, provided that it is not impeded by any damping effects.

In atomic beams, in which the spin precesses practically undamped, the onset of resonance can be directly determined by measuring the

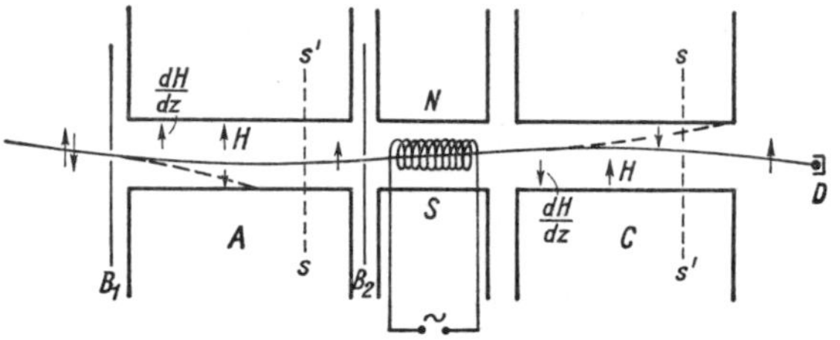

Fig. 33*a*.—Rabi's experiment

number of "switched spins" (I. I. Rabi, 1939). In fluids and solids strong damping forces exist as a result of interaction between spins and vibrations of the crystal lattice. For these materials, the oscillating field merely causes a precession of the spin about the constant field at the frequency of oscillation, and produces the usual resonance phenomena of a damped oscillator, such as a large increase in the amplitude of precession and a rise in absorption in the neighbourhood of the resonance frequency. Both these phenomena have been observed (F. Bloch, 1946; E. Purcell, 1946). Figure 33*a* shows the experimental arrangement of Rabi's method in diagrammatic form. A beam of atoms or molecules passes through the slit B_1 and enters the region of the inhomogeneous field due to the magnet A. A single direction of spin is selected by the screen B_2. In the succeeding homogeneous field NS, the field due to the coil excites additional Larmor precessions and "switches" spins. After a further splitting of the beam in the inhomogeneous magnetic field C, the unswitched spins are recorded by the detector D.

We shall now make a closer study of the Larmor precession and the deflection of the spin axis. For this purpose we shall again make use of equation (32.2), but with a magnetic field given by

$$H_x = H' \cos\omega_0 t \qquad H_y = H' \sin\omega_0 t \qquad H_z = H$$

We have assumed a rotating field instead of an oscillating one since this facilitates calculation and has little effect on the result; any oscillating field can be taken as a superposition of two rotating fields, the directions of rotation being clockwise and anti-clockwise respectively. If one of the rotating fields is in resonance with the Larmor precession, then as we shall see, the other is always far from resonance, and therefore hardly affects the precession at all. We shall take the solution of (32.2) to be

$$\chi = \begin{Bmatrix} a(t)\exp -i\omega_L t \\ b(t)\exp i\omega_L t \end{Bmatrix}$$

then, since $\hbar\omega_L = -\mu H$, $\hbar\omega'_L = -\mu H'$,

$$\begin{aligned} \dot{a} &= -i\omega'_L \exp i(2\omega_L - \omega_0)t \,.\, b \\ \dot{b} &= -i\omega'_L \exp -i(2\omega_L - \omega_0)t \,.\, a \end{aligned} \qquad (33.1)$$

If we differentiate the first equation and insert the value of b from the second, we obtain

$$\ddot{a} - i(2\omega_L - \omega_0)\dot{a} + \omega_L'^2 a = 0$$

If we put $a \sim e^{i\omega t}$, we obtain a quadratic equation in ω, the two solutions of which are

$$\omega_{1,2} = \omega_L - \tfrac{1}{2}\omega_0 \pm \sqrt{[(\omega_L - \tfrac{1}{2}\omega_0)^2 + \omega_L'^2]} \equiv \omega_r \pm \omega_K \qquad (33.2)$$

We are interested in the case in which the spins are parallel to the z-axis on leaving the slit B_2 at the instant $t = 0$; accordingly, we put $a(0) = 1$, $b(0) = 0$. Then at later instants of time

$$\begin{aligned} a &= \left(\cos\omega_K t - i\frac{\omega_r}{\omega_K}\sin\omega_K t\right)\exp i\omega_r t \\ b &= -i\frac{\omega'_L}{\omega_K}\sin\omega_K t \exp -i\omega_r t \end{aligned} \qquad (33.3)$$

Let τ be the time of transit through the oscillating field H': then at the end of the field region we find a fraction

$$|b|^2 = \frac{\omega_L'^2}{(\omega_L - \tfrac{1}{2}\omega_0)^2 + \omega_L'^2}\sin^2[\sqrt{\{(\omega_L - \tfrac{1}{2}\omega_0)^2 + \omega_L'^2\}}\,\tau]$$

of the atoms of the original beam with altered spins. The relation of $|b|^2$ to ω_0 exhibits the character of a resonance curve.

In order to change as many spins as possible at the resonance point $\omega_0 = 2\omega_L$, the parameters of the oscillating field are chosen to make $\tau\omega_L' = \frac{1}{2}\pi$. Rabi's method is chiefly used for the determination of nuclear magnetic moments $\mu \approx e\hbar/M_{\text{prot}}c$, when the moment of the electron shell vanishes. For $H' \approx 1\,\text{Oe}$ and a beam of atoms with

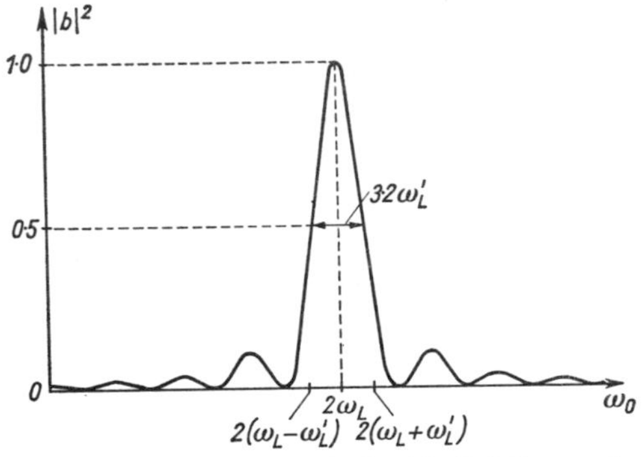

Fig. 33*b*.—Resonance curve obtained in Rabi's experiment

thermal velocities $v \approx 10^5\,\text{cm/s}$, this corresponds to a field dimension of a few centimetres. Figure 33*b* shows the form of the resonance curve. Its width is of order of magnitude ω_L'; since ω_L' is chosen to be much smaller than ω_L, the resonance point is very sharply defined.

In general, however, the lines are broadened by other effects, chief among which may be mentioned:

1. Dispersion of ω_L as a result of inhomogeneities in *H*, partly because of the dispersion of the external magnetic field, and also (in the case of solid and liquid materials) because *H* does not represent the external field alone, but also includes the field of the neighbouring atoms, which naturally varies from point to point.

2. In the Rabi method, the dispersion of τ as a result of the distribution of velocities in the atomic beam.

3. For solids and liquids, there is a further damping effect due to the transfer of spin precessional energy to neighbouring atoms through spin-spin or spin-lattice interaction. (In the frequency region of interest, radiation damping may be completely neglected.) This broadening is analogous to the normal broadening of the resonance curve of a forced oscillator as a result of the damping terms.

§34. Spin-orbit interaction and doublet splitting

Spin-orbit interaction is in itself a relativistic effect, the full treatment of which will be deferred until Section F. We shall content ourselves here with a semi-classical derivation, which is correct except for terms of order v^2/c^2. In the first place, we know from Vol. I, §87, that a magnetic dipole of moment $\vec{\mu}$, moving with velocity **v**, possesses an electric dipole moment

$$\vec{\pi} = \frac{\mathbf{v}}{c} \times \vec{\mu}$$

For the ordinary permanent electrostatic dipole moment the potential energy in a field **E** would be equal to $-\vec{\pi}.\mathbf{E}$, that is, equal to the work required to turn the dipole away from the direction of the field. In the present case, however, the dipole is associated with an angular momentum which produces a precessional motion that we must consider somewhat more closely. The equation for this motion is

$$\frac{d\mathbf{s}}{dt} = \vec{\mu} \times \mathbf{H} + \left(\frac{\mathbf{v}}{c} \times \vec{\mu}\right) \times \mathbf{E}$$

This equation is not obtained by adding the terms $-\vec{\mu}\mathbf{H} - \vec{\pi}\mathbf{E} = -\vec{\mu}(\mathbf{H} + \mathbf{E} \times \mathbf{v}/c)$ to the Hamiltonian function; according to §32, this would lead to the equation

$$\frac{d\mathbf{s}}{dt} = \vec{\mu} \times \left(\mathbf{H} + \mathbf{E} \times \frac{\mathbf{v}}{c}\right) = \vec{\mu} \times \mathbf{H} + \left(\frac{\mathbf{v}}{c} \times \vec{\mu}\right) \times \mathbf{E} + (\vec{\mu} \times \mathbf{E}) \times \frac{\mathbf{v}}{c}$$

which differs from the previous equation by the presence of a third term that is certainly not negligibly small. The first equation is obtained in an approximate manner, however, by adding the terms $-\vec{\mu}\mathbf{H} - \frac{1}{2}\vec{\pi}\mathbf{E}$ to the Hamiltonian function. These additional terms lead in the first place to the equation for spin

$$\frac{d\mathbf{s}}{dt} = \vec{\mu} \times \left(\mathbf{H} + \tfrac{1}{2}\mathbf{E} \times \frac{\mathbf{v}}{c}\right)$$

which differs from the initial equation by the expression

$$\left(\frac{\mathbf{v}}{c} \times \vec{\mu}\right) \times \mathbf{E} - \tfrac{1}{2}\vec{\mu} \times \left(\mathbf{E} \times \frac{\mathbf{v}}{c}\right) = \frac{1}{2}\left\{\frac{\mathbf{v}}{c} \times (\vec{\mu} \times \mathbf{E}) + \mathbf{E} \times \left(\vec{\mu} \times \frac{\mathbf{v}}{c}\right)\right\}$$

In our present approximation, we may take the equation of motion of the electron to be $m\dot{\mathbf{v}} = e\mathbf{E}$; the above expression may then be written in the form

$$\frac{m}{2ec}\left\{\mathbf{v} \times (\vec{\mu} \times \dot{\mathbf{v}}) + \dot{\mathbf{v}} \times (\vec{\mu} \times \mathbf{v})\right\} = \frac{m}{2ec}\frac{d}{dt}\{\mathbf{v} \times (\vec{\mu} \times \mathbf{v})\} - \frac{1}{2}\frac{\mathbf{v}}{c} \times \left(\dot{\mathbf{s}} \times \frac{\mathbf{v}}{c}\right)$$

In the present approximation this expression may be neglected, because the mean value of the time derivative over one cycle vanishes, and because the frequency of the spin precession is small compared with the orbital frequency of the electron.

The Hamiltonian function associated with the spin equation is therefore approximately

$$\mathscr{H} = \frac{\mathbf{p}^2}{2m} + V(\mathbf{r}) - \vec{\mu}\,\mathbf{H} - \tfrac{1}{2}\vec{\mu}\left(\mathbf{E}\times\frac{\mathbf{v}}{c}\right)$$

In particular, when $\mathbf{H} = 0$ and the electric field is centrally symmetrical

$$\mathbf{E}\times\frac{\mathbf{v}}{c} = -\frac{1}{e}\frac{dV(r)}{dr}\frac{\mathbf{r}}{r}\times\frac{\mathbf{v}}{c} = -\frac{1}{emc}\frac{dV(r)}{dr}\cdot\frac{\mathbf{L}}{r}$$

and

$$\mathscr{H} = \frac{\mathbf{p}^2}{2m} + V(\mathbf{r}) + \frac{1}{2m^2c^2}\frac{1}{r}\frac{dV}{dr}(\mathbf{Ls}) \tag{34.1}$$

In order to facilitate the integration of the Schrödinger equation we first look for all operators that commute with $\mathscr{H}$. As we may see immediately, these are $\mathbf{Ls}$, $\mathbf{L}^2$, $\mathbf{s}^2$, and hence $\mathbf{J}^2 = (\mathbf{L}+\mathbf{s})^2 = \mathbf{L}^2 + \mathbf{s}^2 + 2\mathbf{Ls}$.

We thus have an operator $\mathbf{J}$, the total angular momentum, the magnitude of which is constant with respect to time (i.e. commutable with $\mathscr{H}$). Furthermore, it may be verified that the individual components of $\mathbf{J}$ also commute with $\mathscr{H}$.

Using a similar procedure to that employed in the case of the central field alone, the spin and angle components can be separated; the radial part, for which $\mathbf{Ls}$ is a pure number, may then be treated by itself. We shall therefore look for functions that are eigenfunctions of $\mathbf{J}^2$, J_z, $\mathbf{L}^2$ or $\mathbf{s}^2$.

To illustrate the procedure, we shall consider two operators $\mathbf{L}_1$ and $\mathbf{L}_2$, together with the total angular momentum $\mathbf{J} = \mathbf{L}_1 + \mathbf{L}_2$. We shall investigate the eigenfunctions of $\mathbf{J}^2$ and J_z, knowing the common eigenfunctions of $\mathbf{L}_1^2$ and L_{1z}, and of $\mathbf{L}_2^2$ and L_{2z} respectively:

$$\mathbf{L}_1^2\, Y_{l_1m_1} = \hbar^2 l_1(l_1+1) Y_{l_1m_1} \qquad L_{1z}\, Y_{l_1m_1} = \hbar m_1\, Y_{l_1m_1}, \text{ where } |m_1| \leqq l_1$$

$$\mathbf{L}_2^2\, Y_{l_2m_2} = \hbar^2 l_2(l_2+1) Y_{l_2m_2} \qquad L_{2z}\, Y_{l_2m_2} = \hbar m_2\, Y_{l_2m_2}, \text{ where } |m_2| \leqq l_2$$

We now form the $(2l_1+1)(2l_2+1)$ products $Y_{l_1m_1} Y_{l_2m_2}$, corresponding to given l_1 and l_2; these are obviously also eigenfunctions of the operator J_z:

$$J_z\, Y_{l_1m_1} Y_{l_2m_2} = \hbar m_j\, Y_{l_1m_1} Y_{l_2m_2}, \text{ where } m_j = m_1 + m_2$$

In general, these products are not eigenfunctions of $\mathbf{J}^2$. However, since the application of a component of $\mathbf{L}_1$ or $\mathbf{L}_2$ to one of the products yields a function that still lies within the $(2l_1+1)(2l_2+1)$-dimensional Hilbert space that they span, the application of $\mathbf{J}^2$ must also lead to a function in this space, and since $\mathbf{J}^2$ and J_z commute, this function will be associated with the same value of m_j as that corresponding to the original product function.

Since there is only one function $Y_{l_1 l_1} Y_{l_2 l_2}$ corresponding to the maximum value of m_j ($m_j = l_1 + l_2$), it must be an eigenfunction of the operator $\mathbf{J}^2$ corresponding to the eigenvalue $\hbar^2 \bar{j}(\bar{j}+1)$, where $\bar{j} = l_1 + l_2$. Conversely, according to the general properties of angular-momentum operators there must be a total of $2\bar{j}+1$ eigenfunctions corresponding to the values $\bar{j}, \bar{j}-1, \dots, -\bar{j}$ of m_j; these are derived by repeated application of the operator $J_- = L_{1-} + L_{2-}$ to the function $Y_{l_1 l_1} Y_{l_2 l_2}$. We shall now consider the two eigenfunctions of the operator J_z belonging to the eigenvalue $m_j = \bar{j}-1$: these are $Y_{l_1 l_1 - 1} Y_{l_2 l_2}$ and $Y_{l_1 l_1} Y_{l_2 l_2 - 1}$. A linear combination of these two functions, $J_- Y_{l_1 l_1} Y_{l_2 l_2}$, belongs to the value $j = \bar{j}$; a second linear combination, orthogonal to the first one, must then belong to $j = \bar{j} - 1$, $m_j = j = \bar{j} - 1$. Similarly, linear combinations corresponding to $j = \bar{j}$ and $j = \bar{j} - 1$ may be formed from the three functions for which $m_j = \bar{j} - 2$; the third combination, orthogonal to the others, must then correspond to $j = \bar{j} - 2$. In this manner it is possible to separate the required functions.

We thus obtain the values $l_1 + l_2, l_1 + l_2 - 1, \dots, l_1 - l_2$, if $l_1 \geqq l_2$. The number of these functions,

$$\sum_{j=l_1-l_2}^{l_1+l_2} (2j+1) = (l_1+l_2+1)^2 - (l_1-l_2)^2$$

is equal to the number of the initial functions $(2l_1+1)(2l_2+1)$. The determination of the eigenvalues of $\mathbf{J}^2$ and their degree of degeneracy can be accomplished without any knowledge of the corresponding eigenfunctions; the explicit formulation of the latter is only necessary for the calculation of intensities (cf. Exercise 2, p. 238).

In the present case we are concerned with the quantum numbers $l_1 = l$ and $l_2 = s = \frac{1}{2}$, associated respectively with the orbital and spin angular momenta. For the total angular momentum we therefore obtain the two quantum numbers $j = l + \frac{1}{2}$ and $j = l - \frac{1}{2}$ when $l \neq 0$, and a single quantum number $j = s = \frac{1}{2}$ for $l = 0$.

The wave function ψ can therefore be defined by four quantum numbers n, l, j, m_j, designated as follows:

n: principal quantum number,
l: orbital angular momentum,
j: total angular momentum,
m_j: z-component of the total angular momentum.

Then

$$(\mathbf{Ls})\psi = \tfrac{1}{2}(\mathbf{J}^2 - \mathbf{L}^2 - \mathbf{s}^2)\psi = \tfrac{1}{2}\hbar^2 [j(j+1) - l(l+1) - s(s+1)]\psi$$

The equation for $\chi(r) = rR(r)$ is therefore

$$\left(-\frac{\hbar^2}{2m}\frac{d^2}{dr^2} + \frac{\hbar^2 l(l+1)}{2mr^2} + V + \right.$$
$$\left. + \frac{\hbar^2}{(2mc)^2}\frac{1}{r}\frac{dV}{dr}\{j(j+1) - l(l+1) - s(s+1)\}\right)\chi = E\chi \quad (34.2)$$

Spin-orbit interaction therefore vanishes in the case of s-terms, for which $l = 0$,* and when $l \neq 0$ it produces a small perturbation of $V(r)$. In the latter case the doublet energy levels can be represented as the sum of the unperturbed energy and the expectation value of the perturbation energy:†

$$E = E_{nl} + \frac{\hbar^2}{(2mc)^2}\overline{\frac{1}{r}\frac{dV}{dr}} \cdot \begin{cases} l & \text{for } j = l + \frac{1}{2} \\ -(l+1) & \text{for } j = l - \frac{1}{2} \end{cases} \quad (34.3)$$

If the difference between $V(r)$ and the Coulomb potential $-e^2/r$ is neglected in the spin-orbit correction term, then, using (29.14), we obtain

$$E = E_{nl} + \frac{e^2}{2a_0 n^2}\frac{\alpha^2}{(2l+1)n} \cdot \begin{cases} \dfrac{1}{l+1} & \text{for } j = l + \frac{1}{2} \\ -\dfrac{1}{l} & \text{for } j = l - \frac{1}{2} \end{cases} \quad (34.3a)$$

In the above expression $\alpha = e^2/\hbar c \approx 1/137$ is the dimensionless Sommerfeld fine-structure constant. The energy difference due to spin-orbit

* Dirac's relativistic theory of the electron provides a correction term (see §60, the term with div **E**) that ensures that, in the case of the hydrogen atom, the formula (34.3*a*) is also valid for $l = 0$ when $j = l + \frac{1}{2}$.

† The functions designated by n, l, j, m_j are the correct initial functions for the perturbation calculation.

interaction is therefore of the order of $\alpha^2 \approx 10^{-4}$ times smaller than E_{nl}. Theory predicts that the doublet energy separation should be proportional to $1/n^3$, and this is in good agreement with experiment for alkali atoms; the dependence on l is not very well confirmed, because the theoretical value is much affected by the deviation of $V(r)$ from the Coulomb potential $-e^2/r$.

In addition to the splitting of the energy levels as a result of spin-orbit interaction there is a further correction term of order of magnitude α^2, the relativistic variation of mass. If the relativistic formula for the energy

$$E_{kin} = mc^2\sqrt{\left(1+\frac{\mathbf{p}^2}{m^2c^2}\right)}-mc^2$$

is expanded as far as the fourth power of p, we obtain

$$E_{kin} = \frac{\mathbf{p}^2}{2m}-\frac{1}{2mc^2}\left(\frac{\mathbf{p}^2}{2m}\right)^2$$

The second term again represents a small perturbation. The energy perturbation is obtained by forming the expectation value from the unperturbed eigenfunctions:

$$-\frac{1}{2mc^2}\overline{\left(\frac{\mathbf{p}^2}{2m}\right)^2} = -\frac{1}{2mc^2}\overline{[E_{nl}-V(r)]^2}$$

In the case of the alkali atoms the term separations due to l are already large, and their values are imperceptibly altered by this effect. In the case of the hydrogen atom, on the other hand, the perturbation produces a separation of the originally degenerate terms corresponding to the same value of n. In order to determine the magnitude of this separation we introduce the appropriate values for hydrogen for E_{nl} and V in the above equation:

$$\Delta E_n = -\frac{1}{2mc^2}\left\{E_n^2+2E_n e^2\overline{\frac{1}{r}}+e^4\overline{\frac{1}{r^2}}\right\}$$

Then, using (29.12, 29.13) and the relation $e^2/a_0 = mc^2\alpha^2$:

$$\Delta E_n = E_n\left(\frac{2}{2l+1}-\frac{3}{4n}\right)\frac{\alpha^2}{n} \qquad (34.4)$$

We now combine (34.3) and (34.4) and replace l by j. Then strangely enough the terms with $j=l+\frac{1}{2}$ and $j=l-\frac{1}{2}$ coincide; i.e. in the case of hydrogen, terms corresponding to the same values of n and j are degenerate. The total energy, including the rest mass energy, is

$$E_{nj} = mc^2\left\{1-\frac{\alpha^2}{2n^2}-\frac{\alpha^4}{2n^4}\left(\frac{n}{j+\frac{1}{2}}-\frac{3}{4}\right)+\ldots\right\} \tag{34.5}$$

According to our method of derivation, the above approximation formula should only be valid for the case $l \neq 0$. However, if we compare it with the strictly correct Sommerfeld fine-structure formula,* which can be derived from Dirac's relativistic theory of the electron (Chapter F II), and which has been experimentally confirmed as far as terms of order $mc^2\alpha^5$, we find that (34.5) can also be employed in the case of s-terms. The Sommerfeld formula is as follows:

$$E_{nj} = mc^2\left\{1+\frac{\alpha^2}{[n-(j+\frac{1}{2})+\sqrt{\{(j+\frac{1}{2})^2-\alpha^2\}}]^2}\right\}^{-\frac{1}{2}} \tag{34.6}$$

If this formula is expanded in terms of α^2 and the series is terminated after the term in α^4, we obtain precisely the formula (34.5). The first term is obviously the rest-mass energy of the electron, the second term gives the Rydberg formula, and the third is derived from spin-orbit interaction and the relativistic variability of mass.

The third term in the approximation formula only amounts to a correction, in the case of the hydrogen terms. It is significantly greater, however, for the X-ray terms of the heavy elements. These result from the displacement of a valence electron that jumps into a previously produced gap in the lowest electron shell. The electrons in the inner shells move approximately in the Coulomb potential due to the nucleus of charge Z. The energy levels are then given by (34.5), in which e^2 is replaced by Ze^2, or α^2 by $Z^2\alpha^2$. The spin-orbit perturbation is therefore magnified relative to the Rydberg terms by a factor Z^2; for $Z \approx 30$ the factor is therefore as much as 10^3.

Exercises

1. *Detailed description of the Stern-Gerlach experiment for a neutral particle of spin* $\frac{1}{2}$

For the description of the experiment we assume that the wave function at time $t=0$ can be separated into position and spin components: $\Psi_0 = \phi_0(\mathbf{r})\chi_0$. Let the function of the coordinates $\phi_0(\mathbf{r})$ be a broad wave packet, the motion of which can be calculated by classical mechanics. Let χ_0 be an arbitrary spin function, e.g. an eigenfunction corresponding to σ_z or σ_y. Both functions are assumed to be normalized.

* Deviations from the Sommerfeld formula (e.g. the Lamb shift) occur as a result of interaction of the electron with the zero-point oscillations of the electromagnetic radiation field; this interaction is not taken into account in the treatment of the hydrogen atom according to Dirac's theory. See Lamb, W. E., and Retherford, R. C., *Phys. Rev.* 72 (1947), 241.

(*a*) Let the magnetic field be parallel to the z-axis, and let its inhomogeneity be represented by dH/dz, as in figure 32. The velocity of the wave packet is assumed to be parallel to the x-axis; the packet therefore travels along the ray paths shown in section in figure 32. How does the separation into two beams arise as a result of the equation of motion $\mathscr{H}\Psi = i\hbar\dot{\Psi}$? What are the probabilities of finding the particle in each beam?

(*b*) How are conditions altered if the apparatus is rotated through an angle θ about the beam direction? Consider the special cases $\theta = 0$ (case (*a*)) and $\theta = \frac{1}{2}\pi$, corresponding to a field direction parallel to the y-axis.

Hint: If **H** lies in the direction θ, then $\mathbf{H}\vec{\sigma} = H\sigma_\Theta$, where σ_Θ is the component of $\vec{\sigma}$ in the direction θ. Ψ may therefore be resolved in terms of the eigenfunctions $\kappa_{s'}{}^\Theta$ of σ_Θ:

$$\Psi = \Sigma\phi_{s'}(\mathbf{r}, t)\kappa_{s'}{}^\Theta \text{ with } \sigma_\Theta\kappa_{s'}{}^\Theta = s'\,\kappa_{s'}{}^\Theta,\; s' = \pm 1$$

(cf. Exercise 3, p. 152). The equation of motion $\mathscr{H}\Psi = i\hbar\dot{\Psi}$ is thus separated into two equations corresponding to $s' = \pm 1$. We finally obtain two separate wave packets, each associated with a given spin setting.

2. *Multiple Stern-Gerlach experiment*

If a beam is first passed through a magnetic field parallel to z, it is split into two component beams. If these are now analysed by means of a further Stern-Gerlach arrangement in which the field is inclined at an angle θ, each component beam is again split into two. Calculate the relative beam intensities, using the results of the previous exercise. Discuss the conditions in the case of a triple arrangement, in which the field is first parallel to z, then to x, and finally to z again. How does this affect the measurement of two non-commuting operators σ_x and σ_z?

3. *Spin precession in a magnetic field*

Give the general solution of (32.2) in operator form for a constant magnetic field, and deduce the rate of change of the state function by comparison with (23.2).

4. *Fine structure of the hydrogen spectrum*

Taking account of the relativistic corrections, give a qualitative diagram of the hydrogen spectrum as far as $n = 3$, and an accurate diagram of the fine structure of the H_α line ($n = 3 \rightarrow n = 2$).

CHAPTER CIII

The atom in the electromagnetic field

§35. The classical treatment of the motion of atomic electrons in a constant magnetic field

The effect of a superimposed magnetic field on the motion of the electrons in an atom constitutes the basis of an understanding of the Zeeman effect and diamagnetism. Both these phenomena are governed by a theorem due to Larmor.

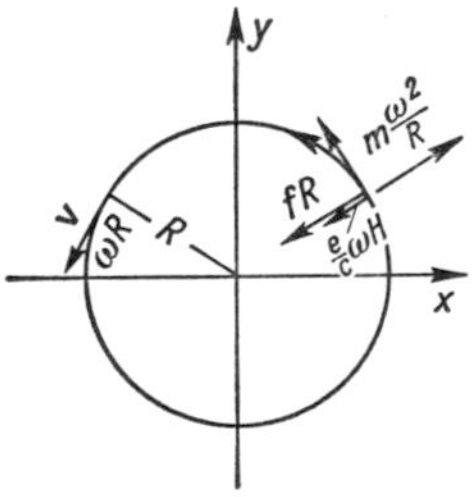

Fig. 34.—Forces acting on an elastically bound electron moving in an orbit normal to the magnetic field

We shall first consider the special case of an electron describing an orbit, which is elastically bound to an equilibrium position (figure 34). Let $-f\mathbf{r}$ be the elastic force of attraction directed towards the centre of the orbit. Then the angular frequency ω_0 follows from the condition that the attractive and centrifugal forces should be equal:

$$-f\mathbf{r}+m\omega_0^2\,\mathbf{r}=0, \text{ therefore } \omega_0=\sqrt{\frac{f}{m}} \tag{35.1}$$

If there is a magnetic field of strength $\mathbf{H}$ normal to the orbital plane, there arises an additional force $(e/c)\mathbf{v}\times\mathbf{H}$. In the present case the vector $\mathbf{v}\times\mathbf{H}$ also lies in the direction of $\mathbf{r}$, and is equal to $\omega H\mathbf{r}$ if ω is taken to be positive for an electron motion about the field direction in the sense of a right-handed screw. When the magnetic field is present we therefore obtain the following equation for the angular frequency ω:

$$-f+\frac{e}{c}\omega H+m\omega^2 = 0 \tag{35.2}$$

or in terms of the Larmor frequency $\omega_L = -eH/2mc$,

$$-\omega_0^2-2\omega_L\omega+\omega^2 = 0$$

Now let the magnetic field be so weak that ω_L is vanishingly small compared to ω_0. (In atomic problems this condition is satisfied except for the strongest fields that can be achieved in practice.) Then the two solutions of the quadratic equation in ω are

$$\omega_1 = -\omega_0+\omega_L \qquad \omega_2 = \omega_0+\omega_L \tag{35.3}$$

The electron rotating in a clockwise direction therefore experiences an increase ω_L in its orbital frequency, while the electron rotating in the opposite direction is retarded by the same amount. Therefore, if (35.1) represents a possible motion in the absence of the field, then (35.3) represents a possible motion when the field is present. We have not yet stated, however, whether in fact equation (35.1) is transformed into (35.3) when the field H is applied.

In order to answer this question we must take account of the following facts. We know that the force exerted by a magnetic field on an electron is always normal to the orbit. The field **H** can perform no work on the electron, and the kinetic energy of the latter therefore cannot change. In fact, however, the kinetic energy of the motion corresponding to ω_2, for instance, is greater than that of the initial motion, by an amount

$$\tfrac{1}{2}mr^2\{(\omega_0+\omega_L)^2-\omega_0^2\} \approx mr^2\omega_0\omega_L$$

How does this increase in kinetic energy arise? In answer, we must take into consideration the fact that when the magnetic field is applied an electric field must be created according to the equation of the law of induction

$$\operatorname{curl}\mathbf{E} = -\frac{1}{c}\dot{\mathbf{H}}$$

This electric field is capable of performing work. If the work performed by this field during one cycle is obtained by integrating over the period $\tau \approx 2\pi/\omega_0$, then, from Stokes's theorem,

$$\oint \mathbf{F} \,.\, d\mathbf{s} = e \oint \mathbf{E} \,.\, d\mathbf{s} = e \int (\text{curl}\,\mathbf{E})_n \, dS = -\frac{e}{c} \dot{H} \pi r^2$$

The work done per second is therefore

$$-\frac{e\dot{H}}{2c} r^2 \omega_0$$

and the total work performed as the field increases from 0 to H is

$$-\frac{eH}{2mc} mr^2 \omega_0 = mr^2 \omega_0 \, \omega_L$$

This is just the energy increase that we found above.

In the above derivation it is assumed that the orbital radius is almost constant over the period of one cycle. This condition is satisfied only if the rate of growth of the magnetic field is sufficiently slow to enable many cycles to occur during the interval; in this case the motion previously expressed by (35.1) is now represented by (35.3). Conversely, if the growth interval were short compared to the orbital period, completely different results would be obtained.

The two particular cases of a clockwise and an anticlockwise orbit are represented by (35.3), and may be summarized as follows. The influence of a slowly applied magnetic field on the motion of an electron is such that the latter possesses the same motion with respect to a co-ordinate system rotating with angular velocity ω_L as it had with respect to a system at rest before the field was applied. This is Larmor's theorem.

We must now verify that we have dealt with the general case of the elastically bound electron as a result of our previous consideration of the two orbits. For this purpose we shall consider the equation of motion of an elastically bound electron that is also subjected to a magnetic field of magnitude H, directed along the z-axis. Then the equation of motion contains not only the elastic force, but the Lorentz force as well:

$$m(\ddot{\mathbf{r}} + \omega_0^2 \mathbf{r}) = \frac{e}{c} \mathbf{v} \times \mathbf{H} \tag{35.4}$$

or in terms of the coordinates,

$$\ddot{x}+\omega_0^2 x = \frac{eH}{mc}\dot{y} \qquad \ddot{y}+\omega_0^2 y = -\frac{eH}{mc}\dot{x} \qquad \ddot{z}+\omega_0^2 z = 0$$

If the second equation is multiplied by i and added to the first, and the complex number $\xi = x+iy$ is introduced,

$$\ddot{\xi}+\omega_0^2 \xi = -i\frac{eH}{mc}\dot{\xi} = 2i\omega_L\dot{\xi} \tag{35.4a}$$

When $|\omega_L| \ll \omega_0$, the general solution of this equation is

$$\xi = e^{i\omega_L t}(A\,e^{i\omega_0 t}+B\,e^{-i\omega_0 t}) \tag{35.5}$$

where A and B are two arbitrary complex numbers.

We may immediately perceive the accuracy of the previous theorem: an oscillation in the direction of the magnetic field (the z-axis) is completely unaffected, whereas the motion in the plane normal to the field differs by a factor $e^{i\omega_L t}$ from the motion that takes place when $H=0$ (and therefore $\omega_L=0$). This factor represents a rotation of the coordinate system through an angle $\omega_L t$. *Therefore, when the field is applied, a constant rotation of angular frequency ω_L about the field direction is superimposed upon the original motion.*

From the above considerations, we should expect that, if the light emitted by an electron were spectrally analysed, it would be found that the magnetic field caused an originally single line of angular frequency ω_0 to be split into three lines of frequencies

$$\omega_0-\omega_L \qquad \omega_0 \qquad \omega_0+\omega_L \tag{35.6}$$

This separation,
$$\Delta\omega = \pm\omega_L = \mp\frac{eH}{2mc} \tag{35.7}$$

was first observed by Zeeman (somewhat qualitatively in the first place, and without a complete separation of the individual components); H. A. Lorentz immediately interpreted the phenomenon in the manner described above. The magnitude of the separation agrees with the result of the analysis given in §30.

Our analysis of the motion in the magnetic field enables us to predict the polarization of the three Zeeman components. The undisplaced vibration corresponds to a polarization of the electric vector parallel to the direction of the field, while each displaced component corresponds to a circularly polarized wave rotating respectively clockwise and anti-clockwise in a plane normal to the magnetic field. Therefore, if the light emitted by a radiating atom is observed along the direction of the lines of force, two lines are found, separated by an interval $|eH/mc|$, which are circularly polarized in a right- and left-hand sense: this is the longitudinal Zeeman effect. The undisplaced component is absent, because an oscillating dipole emits no light along the direction of its vibrations. In the transverse Zeeman effect, the light is observed from a direction at right angles to the field, and there is found to be an undisplaced line polarized parallel to the field, on either side of which at an interval $eH/2mc$ is a line polarized at right angles to the field (cf. § 30). It should be mentioned that this line-splitting, known as the normal Zeeman effect, occurs only exceptionally in the form described. Most lines exhibit a more complicated separation pattern (the anomalous Zeeman effect), the interpretation of which is only possible with the help of quantum theory, including electron spin.

The Larmor theorem may also be demonstrated for the case of several electrons. If the forces on the electrons are due to a potential,* and if the latter is cylindrically symmetrical about the field direction, the possible motions in the magnetic field are obtained by superimposing a rotation upon the motion in the absence of the field, involving a rotation about $\mathbf{H}$ at an angular velocity ω_L. The forces due to the potential are not affected by the additional motion of rotation, while the additional Coriolis forces $2m\vec{\omega}\times\mathbf{v}$ are compensated by the forces due to the magnetic field,† $(e/c)\mathbf{v}\times\mathbf{H}$, when $\vec{\omega}=\vec{\omega}_L=-(e/2mc)\,\mathbf{H}$.

In general, it is not possible to determine whether any given orbit is converted on application of the field into the corresponding orbit possessing the additional rotation; this only occurs with certainty when the field is applied slowly.

Since all electrons possess charges of the same sign, the rotational motion that sets in when the field is applied slowly must have an effect on the surroundings that is comparable to that of a current circulating about the atomic centre. Such a current produces a magnetic field that may be represented as due to a magnetic dipole situated in the atom. Therefore, if the atom possesses no magnetic moment in the absence of the field, it will exhibit such a moment when the latter is applied, as a result of the Larmor precession; the direction of this moment will be opposed to that of the field. The property of diamagnetism, which we shall now consider in further detail, is due to this moment which is induced by the magnetic field.

We start from the formula derived in Vol. I, § 47 for the magnetic moment of an atom in the interior of which the current density $\mathbf{j}$ is continuously distributed:

$$\mathbf{p}^{mag}=\frac{1}{2c}\int\mathbf{r}'\times\mathbf{j}(\mathbf{r}')\,d\mathbf{r}' \qquad (35.8)$$

* The potential includes that due to the nucleus and the electrostatic interaction between the electrons.

† It is again assumed that ω_L is small enough to enable the centrifugal force of the Larmor precession to be neglected in comparison with the Lorentz force.

If instead of the continuous current density $\mathbf{j}$ we introduce quasi point charges e_i situated at the points $\mathbf{r}_i$ and possessing velocities $\mathbf{v}_i$, the integral (35.8) is reduced to a sum of integrals taken over the individual point charges. The first electron makes a contribution $e_1\mathbf{r}_1\times\mathbf{v}_1/2c$; the total result is therefore

$$\mathbf{p}^{mag} = \frac{1}{2c}\sum_i e_i\overline{\mathbf{r}_i\times\mathbf{v}_i} \tag{35.9}$$

where the bar denotes a time average over the electron cycles.

We shall now investigate the manner in which this moment varies when a magnetic field is applied, as a result of the Larmor rotation. The vector $(\vec{\omega}_L\times\mathbf{r}_i)$ due to this rotation must be added to the velocities $\mathbf{u}_i$ of the electrons in the rotating coordinate system; the velocities of the electrons in the stationary system are therefore

$$\mathbf{v}_i = \mathbf{u}_i+\vec{\omega}_L\times\mathbf{r}_i \tag{35.9a}$$

If we insert these values in equation (35.9) we obtain

$$\mathbf{p}^{mag} = \frac{1}{2c}\sum_i e_i\overline{\mathbf{r}_i\times(\mathbf{u}_i+\vec{\omega}_L\times\mathbf{r}_i)} = \mathbf{p}^0+\frac{1}{2c}\sum_i e_i\overline{\mathbf{r}_i\times(\vec{\omega}_L\times\mathbf{r}_i)}$$

where $\mathbf{p}^0$ denotes the magnetic moment of the atom in the absence of the field. If we take the direction of the field to be parallel to the z-axis, the component of $\mathbf{p}^{mag}$ in this direction is

$$p_z^{mag} = p_z^0+\frac{1}{2c}\sum_i e_i\overline{(x_i^2+y_i^2)}\omega_L$$

If we insert the value of the Larmor precession $\omega_L = -eH/2mc$, then (if all $e_i = e$)

$$p_z^{mag} = p_z^0-\frac{e^2H}{4mc^2}\sum_i\overline{(x_i^2+y_i^2)}$$

For a spherically symmetrical electron distribution the time averages are

$$\overline{x_i^2} = \overline{y_i^2} = \overline{z_i^2} = \overline{r_i^2}/3, \qquad \overline{x_i\,y_i} = \overline{y_i\,z_i} = \overline{z_i\,x_i} = 0$$

hence in this case

$$p_z^{mag} = p_z^0-\frac{e^2H}{6mc^2}\sum_i\overline{r_i^2} \tag{35.10}$$

In contrast, the components at right angles to the field are not altered: the x-component, for instance, is

$$p_x^{mag} = p_x^0 + \frac{e\omega_L}{2c}\sum_i \overline{x_i z_i} = p_x^0$$

The above formulae for the dipole moment in the presence of a magnetic field are also correct on the average for atoms that are not spherically symmetrical, provided that the individual atoms are randomly orientated.

If the atoms do not possess a permanent magnetic moment $\mathbf{p}^0$, a material containing N atoms per cubic centimetre will acquire a moment

$$\left(-\frac{Ne^2}{6mc^2}\sum_i \overline{r_i^2}\right)H$$

when the field is applied. The factor occurring with H is termed the diamagnetic susceptibility per unit volume. As the formula indicates, its value is directly proportional to the mean square distance of the electrons from the centre of the atom. If we denote the number of electrons in the atom by Z and the mean square of their distance from the centre by a^2, then

$$\sum \overline{r_i^2} = Za^2$$

and the diamagnetic susceptibility is

$$\chi = -Ne^2Za^2/6mc^2$$

See §38 for experimental values of χ.

We must refer once more to our remarks in §8, when we pointed out that, strictly speaking, formula (35.10) is completely valueless in classical theory, since the thermal average of $\mathbf{p}^{mag}$ vanishes. Obviously, therefore, the term $\mathbf{p}^0$ must compensate the diamagnetism exactly; this may be verified by calculating the thermal average

$$\overline{\mathbf{p}^0} = \frac{e}{2c}\int \mathbf{r}\times\mathbf{u}\exp(-\mathscr{H}/kT)\,d\mathbf{p}\,d\mathbf{r}\Big/\int \exp(-\mathscr{H}/kT)\,d\mathbf{p}\,d\mathbf{r}$$

where, according to (7.5) and (35.9*a*),

$$\mathscr{H} = \left(\mathbf{p}-\frac{e}{c}\mathbf{A}\right)^2\Big/2m + V(r) \qquad \mathbf{p} = m\mathbf{v}+\frac{e}{c}\mathbf{A} = m\mathbf{u} \qquad \mathbf{A} = \mathbf{H}\times\mathbf{r}/2$$

In order that $\overline{\mathbf{p}^0}$ should contain terms of the first degree in $\mathbf{H}$, the exponential function is expanded in terms of $\mathbf{H}$ and the canonical angular momentum $\mathbf{M} = \mathbf{r}\times\mathbf{p}$ is introduced (cf. the second footnote on p. 187). Then

$$\overline{\mathbf{p}^0} = \frac{e^2}{2m^2c^2kT}\overline{(\mathbf{r}\times\mathbf{p})\,(\mathbf{pA})} = \frac{e^2}{4m^2c^2}\frac{\overline{\mathbf{M}(\mathbf{HM})}}{kT}$$

The mean values are formed by means of the weighting function exp $(\mathscr{H}_0/kT)$, where $\mathscr{H}_0$ is the Hamiltonian function in the absence of the magnetic field.

Putting $\overline{p_x^2} = \overline{p_y^2} = \overline{p_z^2} = mkT$ (from the law of equipartition) and $\overline{p_x p_y} = \overline{p_y p_z} = \overline{p_z p_x} = 0$, we obtain exactly the diamagnetic term, but with changed sign. In classical theory, therefore, paramagnetism is necessarily associated with diamagnetism, and exactly compensates the latter at the point of thermal equilibrium.

The situation is quite different in quantum theory. In this case the value of $\overline{\mathbf{M}(\mathbf{HM})}$ is not determined by the law of equipartition; on the contrary, the z-component and the square of $\mathbf{M}$ are quantized. At sufficiently low temperatures $\overline{\mathbf{M}(\mathbf{HM})}$ is independent of temperature, and $\overline{\mathbf{p}^0} = C\mathbf{H}/T$. This is Curie's law, which we shall consider in greater detail in §37.

In conclusion, we should mention another important phenomenon that follows from (35.8) and that is capable of being verified experimentally. The electric current $\mathbf{j}$ must clearly be associated with a particle current of magnitude $(m/e)\mathbf{j}$; the current system therefore possesses an angular momentum

$$\mathbf{L} = \frac{m}{e}\int \mathbf{r}\times\mathbf{j}(\mathbf{r})\,d\mathbf{r} = \frac{2mc}{e}\mathbf{p}^{mag} \qquad (35.11)$$

This mechanical effect may be detected in the course of the demagnetization of macroscopic specimens, i.e. when $\mathbf{p}^{mag}$ varies with respect to time; it was first observed by A. Einstein and J. de Haas. The first measurements resulted in a ratio of the angular momentum to the magnetic moment of the same order of magnitude as that predicted by (35.11). More precise measurements, in particular those due to S. J. Barnett, yielded the value mc/e for this ratio; as we have already indicated in §31, this points to the fact that ferromagnetism is due to electron spin.

§36. The anomalous Zeeman effect

In an external magnetic field both the orbital and the spin magnetic moments possess potential energy. Hence from (30.2), (32.2), and (34.1) we obtain the following expression for the Hamiltonian operator $\mathscr{H}_1$:

$$\mathscr{H}_1 = \mathscr{H}_0 + \frac{1}{2m^2c^2}\frac{1}{r}\frac{dV}{dr}(\mathbf{L}\,.\,\mathbf{s}) - \frac{e}{2mc}(\mathbf{H}\,.\,\mathbf{L}) - \frac{e}{mc}(\mathbf{H}\,.\,\mathbf{s}) \qquad (36.1)$$

If the field $\mathbf{H}$ is taken parallel to the z-axis,

$$\mathscr{H}_1 = \mathscr{H}_0 + \frac{1}{2m^2c^2}\frac{1}{r}\frac{dV}{dr}(\mathbf{L}\,.\,\mathbf{s}) - \frac{eH}{2mc}(J_z + s_z) \qquad (36.2)$$

The operator $\mathscr{H}_1$ no longer commutes with $\mathbf{J}^2$, because of the term in s_z; however, it still commutes with $\mathbf{L}^2$, $\mathbf{s}^2$, and J_z. Strictly speaking, therefore, we can use the quantum numbers n, l, s, and m_j only for the characterization of the states. However, the eigenfunctions of $\mathscr{H}_1$ are represented by a superposition of the solutions associated with the same value of m_j in the absence of the magnetic field. When $s=1/2$ they may be written in the form*

$$\phi_{nlm_j} = R_{nl}\{aY_{l,m_j-1/2}\cdot\alpha + bY_{l,m_j+1/2}\cdot\beta\} = R_{nl}\,\tilde{Y}_{lm_j} \quad (36.3)$$

The coefficients a and b depend on H, and are determined from the eigenvalue equation

$$\left\{E_{nl} + \left(R_{nl}, \frac{1}{2m^2c^2}\frac{1}{r}\frac{dV}{dr}R_{nl}\right)(\mathbf{L}\cdot\mathbf{s}) - \frac{eH}{2mc}(J_z+s_z)\right\}\tilde{Y}_{lm_j} = E\tilde{Y}_{lm_j} \quad (36.4)$$

Two limiting cases are of importance, and are easy to treat in the general case when s is free to assume any value.

(*a*) *The potential energy in the external field is small compared to the spin-orbit interaction*

In this case we may put $H=0$ in (36.2) as an approximation of zero order; the energy perturbation is the expectation value of $(-eH/2mc)(J_z+s_z)$, formed from the unperturbed eigenfunctions $\tilde{Y}_{ljm_j}$:

$$E_{nljm_j} = E_{nlj} + \mu_B m_j H(1+\bar{s}_z/\hbar m_j) = E_{nlj} + \mu_B m_j Hg \quad (36.5)$$

The factor in brackets is called the Landé splitting factor, g, or the Landé g-factor. In order to determine it, we require the expectation value of s_z, which is obtained as follows. Firstly, we require the following commutation relations, which may easily be verified.

$$\mathbf{L}(\mathbf{L}\cdot\mathbf{s}) - (\mathbf{L}\cdot\mathbf{s})\mathbf{L} = i\hbar\mathbf{s}\times\mathbf{L}, \qquad \mathbf{s}(\mathbf{L}\cdot\mathbf{s}) - (\mathbf{L}\cdot\mathbf{s})\mathbf{s} = -i\hbar\mathbf{s}\times\mathbf{L}$$

Since $\mathbf{J}=\mathbf{L}+\mathbf{s}$, it follows by addition that $\mathbf{J}$ commutes with $(\mathbf{L}.\mathbf{s})$. Hence, if we multiply the second of the above relations vectorially from the right by $\mathbf{J}$, the result may be written

$$\begin{aligned}(\mathbf{s}\times\mathbf{J})(\mathbf{L}\cdot\mathbf{s}) - (\mathbf{L}\cdot\mathbf{s})(\mathbf{s}\times\mathbf{J}) &= -i\hbar(\mathbf{s}\times\mathbf{L})\times\mathbf{J} \\ &= -i\hbar\{\mathbf{L}(\mathbf{s}\cdot\mathbf{J}) - \mathbf{s}(\mathbf{L}\cdot\mathbf{J})\} \quad (36.6) \\ &= i\hbar\{\mathbf{s}\cdot\mathbf{J}^2 - \mathbf{J}(\mathbf{s}\cdot\mathbf{J})\}\end{aligned}$$

* The functions Y_{lm} are functions of angle alone; the functions $\tilde{Y}_{lm}$ also contain the spin.

The last relation is due to the fact that **L** and **s** commute and that $\mathbf{L} = \mathbf{J} - \mathbf{s}$.

If we now form the expectation value of (36.6) in the state $\tilde{Y}_{ljm_j}$ the left side vanishes, because $(\mathbf{L}, \mathbf{s})$ is Hermitian and the $\tilde{Y}_{ljm_j}$ are the associated eigenfunctions. Hence

$$\overline{\mathbf{s}\mathbf{J}^2} = \overline{\mathbf{J}(\mathbf{s}, \mathbf{J})}, \text{ and in particular, } \overline{s_z \mathbf{J}^2} = \overline{J_z(\mathbf{s}, \mathbf{J})} \qquad (36.7)$$

Since $\tilde{Y}_{ljm_j}$ is also an eigenfunction of the operators $\mathbf{J}^2$, J_z, and $(\mathbf{s}, \mathbf{J}) = \frac{1}{2}(\mathbf{J}^2 + \mathbf{s}^2 - \mathbf{L}^2)$ with corresponding eigenvalues $\hbar^2 j(j+1)$, $\hbar m_j$, and $\frac{1}{2}\hbar^2[j(j+1) + s(s+1) - l(l+1)]$, it follows from (36.5) that the Landé factor is

$$g = 1 + \frac{j(j+1) + s(s+1) - l(l+1)}{2j(j+1)} \qquad (36.8)$$

In particular, when $s = \frac{1}{2}$,

$$g = \begin{cases} 1 + \dfrac{1}{2l+1} = \dfrac{2l+2}{2l+1} & \text{for } j = l + \frac{1}{2} \\[2ex] 1 - \dfrac{1}{2l+1} = \dfrac{2l}{2l+1} & \text{for } j = l - \frac{1}{2} \end{cases} \qquad (36.9)$$

When these values of g are introduced into the expression (36.5) for the energy, we obtain the term separation for single electron systems applicable to the anomalous Zeeman effect in weak magnetic fields. Figures 35 to 37 show the splitting of the sodium D lines both in the term scheme and on the frequency diagram of the possible transitions, including the polarizations observed transversally.

Equation (36.7) may be interpreted in terms of classical mechanics in a very simple manner. The spin-orbit interaction causes the vectors **L** and **s** to precess about the vector $\mathbf{J} = \mathbf{L} + \mathbf{s}$, the time rate of change of which is very small when the field is weak (figure 38). Therefore, if the vector **s** is resolved into components parallel and perpendicular to **J**,

$$\mathbf{s} = \frac{(\mathbf{s}, \mathbf{J})}{\mathbf{J}^2}\mathbf{J} + \left(\mathbf{s} - \frac{(\mathbf{s}, \mathbf{J})}{\mathbf{J}^2}\mathbf{J}\right) = \mathbf{s}_{\parallel} + \mathbf{s}_{\perp}$$

the mean value of $\overline{\mathbf{s}_{\perp}}$ over one precessional period is zero. Hence $\overline{s_z} = (\mathbf{s}, \mathbf{J})J_z/\mathbf{J}^2$, which corresponds exactly to (36.7).

(b) The potential energy in the external field is large compared to the spin-orbit interaction

In this case we obtain the approximation of zero order by eliminating the term in $(\mathbf{L},\mathbf{s})$ in (36.4); $\mathbf{L}^2$, L_z, $\mathbf{s}^2$, and s_z then commute with $\mathscr{H}_1$, and l, m_l, s, m_s may therefore be chosen as the quantum numbers. The energy is

$$E_{nlm_lm_s} = E_{nl} + \mu_B H(m_l + 2m_s) \qquad (36.10)$$

As in the case of equations (30.6*a*, 30.6*b*), it may be shown that the selection rules $\Delta l = \pm 1$ and $\Delta m_l = 0, \pm 1$ apply, together with the

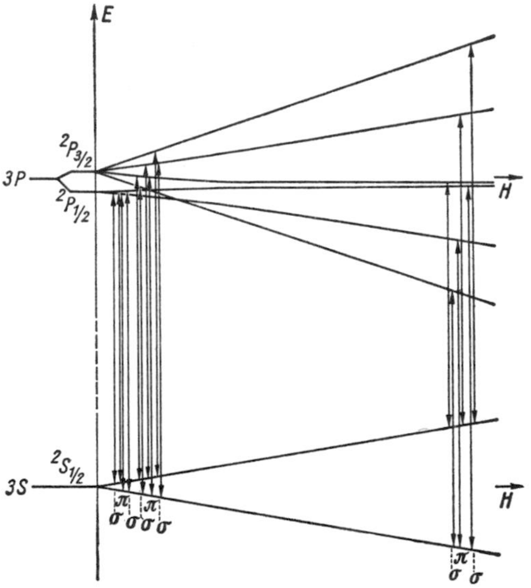

Fig. 35.—Displacement and splitting of the energy terms of the sodium D lines in the magnetic field. Each group of transitions refers to a single field strength, but for the sake of clarity the individual transitions are shown side by side.

additional rule $\Delta m_s = 0$. As a result of this last rule, only the normal Lorentz triplet (30.5) is observed.

This transition from the complicated pattern of the anomalous Zeeman effect in weak fields to the simple Lorentz triplet in strong fields has been verified experimentally and is termed the *Paschen-Back effect*.

In order to analyse the transition quantitatively it is necessary to solve the eigenvalue equation (36.4). When $m_j = \pm(l+\frac{1}{2})$, and hence $m_s = \pm\frac{1}{2}$, only one of the functions Y_{lm} in (36.3) is different from zero.

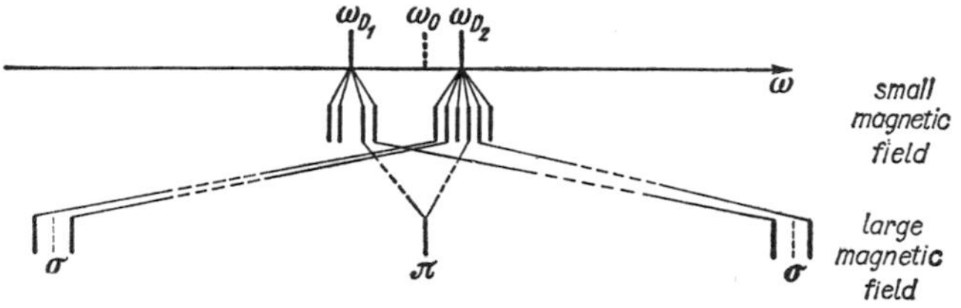

Fig. 36.—Zeeman effect: structure of the sodium D-lines in weak and strong magnetic fields

The expression for the energy is obtained directly from (36.4) by forming the scalar product with this function:

$$E = E_{nl} + (\Delta E_{nl})_{j=l+\frac{1}{2}} \pm \mu_B H(l+1) \quad \text{for} \quad m_j = \pm(l+\tfrac{1}{2}) \qquad (36.11)$$

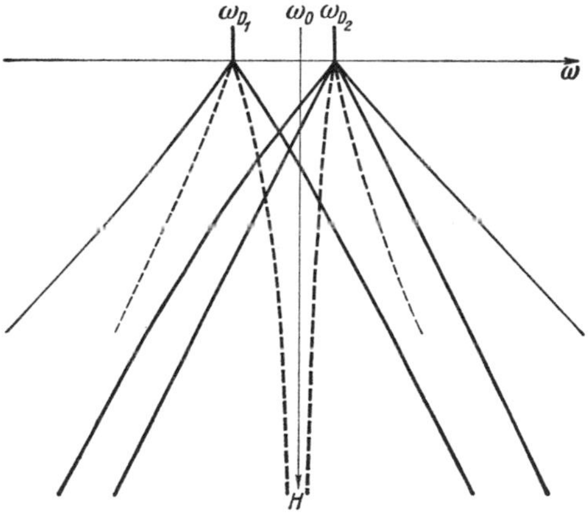

Fig. 37.—Zeeman effect: line shift and intensity as a function of field strength. The broken lines refer to the π-components. The thickness of the lines indicates the intensity

In the above expression $(\Delta E_{nl})_{j=l+\frac{1}{2}}$ denotes the energy separation when $H=0$, due to spin-orbit interaction, as calculated in §34, and including the additional effects mentioned there. When $m_j = \pm(l+\frac{1}{2})$, therefore, the displacement of the energy terms is proportional to H;

this result agrees with (36.5) and (36.10), and is valid in particular for all s-terms, for which $l = 0$, $m_j = m_s = \pm\frac{1}{2}$ (cf. fig. 35).

When $|m_j| < l + \frac{1}{2}$, both the functions Y_{lm} in (36.3) are different from zero, corresponding to the combined effect of the two states

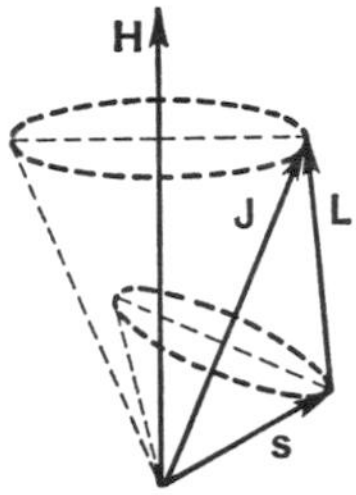

Fig. 38.—Vector model of the angular momenta

$j = l + \frac{1}{2}$ and $j = l - \frac{1}{2}$ possessing the same value of m_j. In this case forming the scalar product with $\phi_1 = Y_{l,m_j-\frac{1}{2}} \cdot \alpha$ and $\phi_2 = Y_{l,m_j+\frac{1}{2}} \cdot \beta$ yields a secular equation of the form

$$\begin{vmatrix} (\mathcal{H}_{11} - E) & \mathcal{H}_{12} \\ \mathcal{H}_{21} & (\mathcal{H}_{22} - E) \end{vmatrix} = 0$$

the solutions of which are

$$E_{1,2} = \tfrac{1}{2}(\mathcal{H}_{11} + \mathcal{H}_{22}) \pm [\tfrac{1}{4}(\mathcal{H}_{11} - \mathcal{H}_{22})^2 + |\mathcal{H}_{12}|^2]^{1/2}$$

In order to calculate the matrix elements $\mathcal{H}_{ik} = (\phi_i, \mathcal{H}\phi_k)$ we make use of (23.12), (23.13), and (24.8), and put $\sigma_\pm = \frac{1}{2}(\sigma_x \pm i\sigma_y)$. Then

$$2(\mathbf{L}, \mathbf{s}) = \hbar^2(\Lambda_x \sigma_x + \Lambda_y \sigma_y + \Lambda_z \sigma_z) = \hbar^2(\Lambda_+ \sigma_- + \Lambda_- \sigma_+ + \Lambda_z \sigma_z)$$

from which it follows as a result of (24.6) and (24.7) that

$$\mathcal{H}_{11} = E_{nl} + K_{nl}(m_j - \tfrac{1}{2}) + \mu_B H(m_j + \tfrac{1}{2})$$
$$\mathcal{H}_{22} = E_{nl} - K_n(m_j + \tfrac{1}{2}) + \mu_B H(m_j - \tfrac{1}{2})$$
$$\mathcal{H}_{12} = \mathcal{H}_{21} = +K_{nl}\sqrt{[(l + \tfrac{1}{2})^2 - m_j^2]}$$

where
$$K_{nl} = \frac{\hbar^2}{(2mc)^2} \int_0^\infty R_{nl} \frac{1}{r} \frac{dV}{dr} R_{nl} r^2 \, dr > 0$$

We finally obtain the following expression for the energy for the case in which $|m_j| \neq l + \frac{1}{2}$:

$$E_{1,2} = E_{nl} - \tfrac{1}{2}K_{nl} \pm \sqrt{[K_{nl}^2(l + \tfrac{1}{2})^2 + K_{nl}\mu_B H m_j + (\tfrac{1}{2}\mu_B H)^2]} + \\ + \mu_B H m_j \quad (36.12)$$

It may be verified that the energy expression (36.11) tends to (34.3) as H becomes vanishingly small; when H is small, it is converted into (36.5), where g is represented by (36.9); when H is very large the expression tends to (36.10) (cf. figs. 35, 36, 37). For strong fields, the doublet structure is preserved in the case of the σ-components, but vanishes in the case of the π-component (figure 36 and 37).

§37. Quantum theory of paramagnetism and diamagnetism

When a material is magnetizable, a magnetic moment is produced in it under the influence of a magnetic field. In the case of diamagnetism this moment is opposed to the field, while for paramagnetic materials it lies parallel to the field direction.

When calculating the magnetizability it is necessary to distinguish whether or not the individual molecules or atoms already possess a magnetic moment. In the latter case the magnetization arises as a result of the moment induced by the field in the atoms, as we have already seen in the classical treatment of §35. This induced moment always produces a diamagnetic effect; the latter is unaffected by the existence of any permanent moment, and is therefore a basic phenomenon occurring in all materials. However, when the individual molecules possess a permanent magnetic moment the resultant paramagnetism is generally much stronger, and the coexisting diamagnetism may therefore be neglected.

We give below a treatment of paramagnetism and diamagnetism of single-electron systems, or more precisely, of atoms with one valence electron which is almost entirely responsible for the magnetism. Such atoms possess a permanent magnetic moment as a result of the electron spin. There are also elements, such as boron in the ground state $^2P_{1/2}$, that possess a non-vanishing orbital moment. We shall, however, perform the analysis in a sufficiently general manner to enable the results to be easily extended to atoms with more than one electron, in which the permanent moment may vanish.*

The Hamiltonian operator for the atom in a constant external field is

$$\mathscr{H} = \mathscr{H}_0 - \frac{e}{mc}(\mathbf{A}, \mathbf{p}) + \frac{e^2}{2mc^2}\mathbf{A}^2 - \frac{e}{mc}(\mathbf{s}, \mathbf{H}) \quad \text{where } \mathbf{A} = \tfrac{1}{2}\mathbf{H}\times\mathbf{r} \tag{37.1}$$

* This may occur in the case of the so-called Russell-Saunders or L-S coupling, in which the spin-orbit interaction is so small that the orbital and spin angular momenta are each more strongly coupled among themselves than is the total spin with the total orbital moment. The resultant orbital, spin, and total angular momenta are represented by L, S, J in place of l, s, j.

In the above expression, $\mathscr{H}_0$ includes the kinetic, potential and spin-orbit energy terms that are independent of **H**. The magnetic moment consists of

$$\text{the spin component} \quad \bar{\vec{\mu}}_s = -\mu_0 \bar{\vec{\sigma}} \quad \text{and}$$

$$\text{the orbital component} \quad \bar{\vec{\mu}}_l = (e/2c)\overline{(\mathbf{r}\times\dot{\mathbf{r}})} \quad \text{(cf. 35.9).}$$

The averages represent the quantum-mechanical expectation values, and where applicable, mean values taken over the temperature distribution.

It may easily be verified that, since

$$\dot{\mathbf{r}} = \frac{i}{\hbar}(\mathscr{H}\mathbf{r} - \mathbf{r}\mathscr{H}) = \left(\mathbf{p} - \frac{e}{c}\mathbf{A}\right)\Big/ m$$

the expectation value of the moment for the state ϕ_i and energy E_i is given by

$$\bar{\mu}_z^i = \bar{\mu}_{lz}^i + \bar{\mu}_{sz}^i = -\frac{\overline{\partial \mathscr{H}}^i}{\partial H_z} = -\frac{\partial E_i}{\partial H_z} \tag{37.2}$$

with corresponding expressions for $\bar{\mu}_x$ and $\bar{\mu}_y$; in the following analysis, however, we shall put $H_x = H_y = 0$. Then by averaging over the temperature distribution we obtain

$$\bar{\mu}_z = \frac{\sum\limits_i \frac{\partial E_i}{\partial H} \exp - \beta E_i}{\sum\limits_i \exp - \beta E_i} \quad \text{where } \beta = \frac{1}{kT} \tag{37.3}$$

We shall restrict ourselves in the first instance to those cases in which the average thermal energy kT is large compared with the Zeeman energy separation. However, the temperature is assumed to be sufficiently low to enable practically all but the lowest multiplet state and its Zeeman separation to be neglected in cases where the ground state of the atom possesses an orbital moment and a consequent term separation as a result of spin-orbit interaction (figure 39).

The summation in (37.3) then merely extends over the $2j+1$ states of this separation. In addition, since we have assumed weak fields and comparatively high temperatures, we may restrict ourselves to terms of the first degree in β:

$$\bar{\mu}_z = -\sum_{m_j=-j}^{j} \frac{\partial E_{m_j}}{\partial H}(1-\beta E_{m_j}) \Big/ \sum_{m_j=-j}^{j} (1-\beta E_{m_j}) \tag{37.4}$$

In the above expression, the quantities E_{m_j} represent the portions of the multiplet energies E_{lsjm_j} that are dependent on H.

We are interested only in terms of the first degree in H; in the expression for E_{m_j}, therefore, we merely require terms as far as the

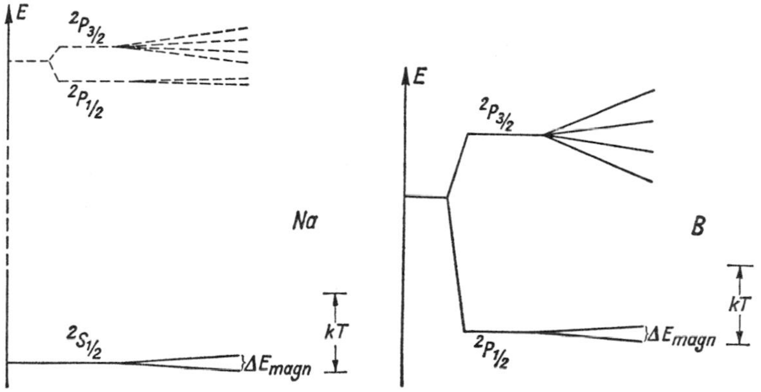

Fig. 39.—Ground-state thermal energy and Zeeman splitting, for sodium and boron

second degree in this quantity. These result firstly from the term separation calculated in §36: for the two cases $j=l+\frac{1}{2}$ and $j=l-\frac{1}{2}$ we have the following result, which follows from (36.11) and from (36.12) after expansion as far as terms of the second degree in H,

$$E^{(1)}_{m_j} = \mu_B H g m_j \pm \frac{\mu_B^2 H^2}{4K_{nl}(2l+1)}\left(1-\frac{4m_j^2}{(2l+1)^2}\right)$$

where the Landé factor g is given by (36.9).* Secondly, from the term in $\mathbf{A}^2$ in $\mathscr{H}$, which we have hitherto neglected,

$$E^{(2)}_{m_j} = \frac{e^2}{2mc^2}\overline{\mathbf{A}^2}^{m_j} = \frac{e^2}{8mc^2}\overline{(x^2+y^2)}^{m_j} H^2$$

Since $\sum m_j = 0$, $\sum m_j^2 = \frac{1}{3}j(j+1)(2j+1)$, after performing the summation in (37.4) we obtain the following expression for the mean

* When $j = l+\frac{1}{2}$, the term in H^2 obviously vanishes for $|m_j| = l+\frac{1}{2}$, in agreement with (36.11); the above formula is therefore also valid for s-terms. For $l > 0$, the doublet term with $j = l-\frac{1}{2}$ is the lowest, since $K_{nl} > 0$, and is the only one that requires to be considered.

magnetic moment in the direction of the field, for the cases $j = l \pm \frac{1}{2}$:

$$\bar{\mu}_z = \frac{\mu^2}{kT}\frac{j+1}{3j}H \mp \frac{\mu_B^2(2-g)}{3K_{nl}(2l+1)}H - \frac{e^2}{6mc^2}\overline{r^2}H \qquad (37.5)$$

where
$$\mu = -\mu_B g j$$

It should be noted that, when averaged over all values of m_j,

$$\overline{x^2} = \overline{y^2} = \overline{r^2}/3$$

where $\overline{r^2}$ denotes the average taken over the radial component of the wave function. When there are Z electrons present, the corresponding term in (37.5) is

$$-\frac{e^2}{6mc^2}\sum_{i=1}^{Z}\overline{r_i^2}H$$

The first term contains the theoretical basis of Curie's law, according to which the paramagnetic susceptibility per mole is

$$\chi_M = \frac{N\bar{\mu}_z}{H} = \frac{C}{T}$$

where N is Avogadro's number, and

$$C = \frac{\mu^2}{k}\frac{(j+1)}{3j}N$$

is the Curie constant.

The second term is strictly absent in the case of the s-terms (for which $g = 2$). In systems comprising a single electron j is never zero: in these cases the last two terms may be neglected in comparison with the first (for instance, the ratio of the first term to the second is of the same order of magnitude as that of the interaction term K_{nl} to kT). The first term may vanish in the case of systems with more than one electron, and the first and second terms vanish in particular for closed shells—a fact that we state without proof. In this last case the third term represents the normal diamagnetism (cf. §35). The reader is referred to §38 for experimental values of diamagnetic susceptibilities.

We shall now briefly investigate the situation in which μH and kT are of comparable magnitude. There are two limiting cases which we shall consider; in doing so we shall neglect the diamagnetic effect.

In the limiting case of classical mechanics, in which **J** may assume any orientation, the energy of a dipole of moment μ, making an angle

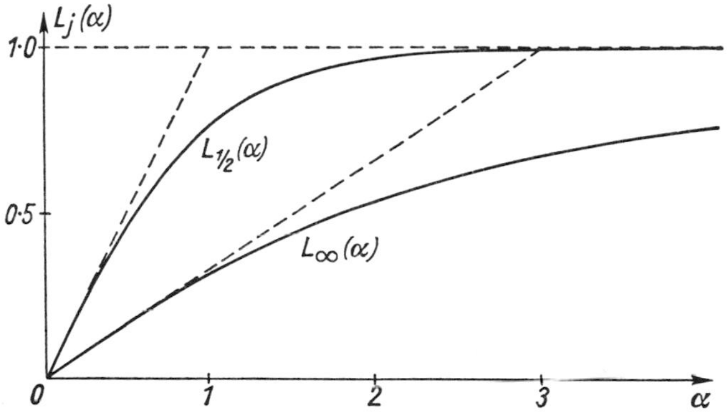

Fig. 40.—The Langevin functions $L_{\frac{1}{2}}(\alpha)$ and $L_\infty(\alpha)$

θ with the field direction, is $E = -\mu H \cos\theta$. Hence from Boltzmann's distribution law the mean moment is

$$\bar{\mu}_z = \frac{\int_0^\pi \mu \cos\theta \, e^{\beta\mu H \cos\theta} \sin\theta \, d\theta}{\int_0^\pi e^{\beta\mu H \cos\theta} \sin\theta \, d\theta} = \mu\left(\coth\alpha - \frac{1}{\alpha}\right) = \mu L_\infty(\alpha)$$

where
$$\alpha = \frac{\mu H}{kT}$$

Secondly, we consider the case $j = \frac{1}{2}$, for which

$$\bar{\mu}_z = \frac{\mu e^{\beta\mu H} - \mu e^{-\beta\mu H}}{e^{\beta\mu H} + e^{-\beta\mu H}} = \mu \tanh\alpha = \mu L_{1/2}(\alpha)$$

All the curves $L_j(\alpha) = \overline{\mu_z(j)}/\mu(j)$, where j is arbitrary and $\mu(j) = -\mu_B g j$, lie between the two limiting curves $L_\infty(\alpha)$ and $L_{1/2}(\alpha)$ (figure 40). The curves $L_j(\alpha)$ are called the Langevin functions.

In experimental work on paramagnetic materials it is usual to operate in the initial linear region of the Langevin curves (figure 40). In the measurements of susceptibility undertaken by Kammerlingh

Onnes and his collaborators on gadolinium sulphate, it was possible to cover a large part of the Langevin curve only by reducing the temperature to that of liquid helium and increasing the field strength to 22,000 gauss.

§38. The induced electrical dipole moment

An atom in which the centroids of the positive and negative charges coincide produces no external electrical effect. If an external electric field is applied, however, the centroids of the charges are drawn apart and a dipole moment is produced. This moment lies in the direction of the applied field, which we shall denote by **F** in order to avoid confusion with the energy. The factor of proportionality between the dipole moment and the field is called the polarizability α.

In §4 we saw that, in the case of the Thomson model, the polarizability is proportional to the atomic volume; the only effect of quantum mechanics is to alter the numerical factor (§28). This result is also approximately valid in the case of more complicated atoms and molecules. In the present context we shall confine ourselves to mentioning that the atomic volume enters into several very different effects, such as the volume correction term in the van der Waals equation, and the free path (and therefore the viscosity) in gases. A satisfactory agreement is found to exist between the values of the atomic volumes as determined from polarizability, the gas equation, and viscosity; this is particularly true in all cases in which a dipole moment exists only in the presence of a field.

In the special classical case of the Thomson model of §4, in which the electron is elastically bound and possesses an angular frequency ω_0, the dipole moment $\mathbf{p}^{el}$ induced in an atom by a field $\mathbf{F}=(F,0,0)$ is

$$p_x^{el} = ex = \frac{e^2}{m}\frac{1}{\omega_0^2}F = \alpha F, \qquad \alpha = a_0^3 \tag{38.1}$$

It will be shown in the next paragraph that, for the general case of an atom posessing one valence electron, quantum mechanics leads to the very similar formula

$$e\bar{x} = \frac{e^2}{m}\sum_{j\neq 0}\frac{f_{j0}}{\omega_{j0}^2}F \quad \text{where} \quad \hbar\omega_{j0} = E_j - E_0 \tag{38.2}$$

In the above expression the angular frequency ω_0 of the classical oscillator is replaced by a summation over all the Bohr transition frequencies from the ground state to the highest excited states. The so-called "oscillator strengths" f_{j0} indicate how much each frequency ω_{j0} contributes to the total dipole moment; it will be shown in the next paragraph that these strengths have the values

$$f_{j0} = \frac{2m\omega_{j0}}{\hbar} |x_{j0}|^2, \text{ and in particular, } f_{00} = 0 \qquad (38.3)$$

The oscillator strengths also occur in the theory of dispersion, absorption, and emission, and are accordingly considered in detail in §§41 and 50. In §41 we give the proof of the summation theorem:

$$\sum_j f_{j0} = 1 \qquad (38.4)$$

The polarizability may easily be evaluated with the help of this theorem. In (38.2) we put

$$\sum_{j \neq 0} \frac{f_{j0}}{\omega_{j0}^2} = \frac{1}{\overline{\omega^2}} \sum_j f_{j0} = \frac{1}{\overline{\omega^2}}$$

where $\overline{\omega^2}$ is an appropriate mean value of the ω_{j0}^2. In the case of the hydrogen atom the *f*-values decrease comparatively slowly as j increases, so that an appreciable fraction (about 40 per cent) of the sum in (38.4) lies in the continuous part of the spectrum.

We therefore tentatively replace $\sqrt{(\overline{\omega^2})}$ by the Rydberg frequency $\omega_R = e^2/2\hbar a_0$, and obtain

$$e\bar{x} = 4a_0^3 F, \quad \text{i.e.} \quad \alpha = 4a_0^3 \qquad (38.5)$$

A somewhat better estimate was given in §28 with the help of the method of variations. This method also provided comparatively simple expressions for systems containing more than one electron (cf. Exercise 5, p. 176 and Exercise 6, p. 238). In order to compare the theory with experimental results we shall neglect the correlation terms, i.e. the mean values $\overline{x_i x_k}$ for $i \neq k$, that occur in the above-mentioned formulae, since they may be expected to be small compared to $\overline{x_i^2}$. (If the wave function were separable into a product of functions of a single particle they would even vanish.) Hence for spherically symmetrical atoms

$$\alpha = \frac{4}{9} \frac{1}{N a_0} \left(\sum_i \overline{r_i^2} \right)^2 \qquad (38.6)$$

Since the wave functions of complex atoms are generally unknown, the $\overline{r_i^2}$ cannot be calculated. However, we recall that the same quantity occurs in the expression for the diamagnetic susceptibility (§37):

$$\chi = -e^2 \sum_i \overline{r_i^2}/6mc^2$$

We thus have a relationship between χ and α in which only experimentally verifiable quantities occur:

$$\chi = -\frac{e^2}{4mc^2}\sqrt{(N\alpha a_0)} \qquad (38.7)$$

ELECTRIC AND MAGNETIC POLARIZABILITY OF THE INERT GASES

N	$\alpha(10^{-24}\text{cm}^3)$ observed*	$-\chi(10^{-29}\text{cm}^3)$ observed**	$-\chi$ calculated
He 2	0·216	0·316	0·33
Ne 10	0·398	1·2	1·0
Ar 18	1·63	3·22	2·8
Kr 36	2·48	4·65	4·8
Xe 54	4·01	7·15	7·5

* Landolt-Börnstein I. 1 401 (1950).
** Landolt-Börnstein I. 1 394 (1950).

In the above table numerical values are given for the inert gases which show that (38.6) is a very good approximation.

§39. The Stark effect

Using quantum-mechanical methods, we shall calculate the effect of an external electric field on the energy levels of an atom (the Stark effect). If we take the x-axis of our coordinate system to be parallel to the field, the Hamiltonian operator is

$$\mathcal{H} = \mathcal{H}_0 - eFx \qquad (39.1)$$

In the above expression $\mathcal{H}_0$ is the Hamiltonian operator of the unperturbed atom, with eigenfunctions ϕ_j and eigenvalues E_j. The expression for the dipole moment in the direction of x is similar to the formula (37.2) for the magnetic moment:

$$e\bar{x} = -\overline{\frac{\partial \mathcal{H}}{\partial F}} = -\frac{\partial \varepsilon}{\partial F} \qquad (39.2)$$

We shall determine the energy ε by means of Schrödinger's perturbation method. We are interested only in the terms of $\bar{x}$ that are of the first degree in F, and consequently need to carry through the perturbation calculation only to the second-order approximation. Using (26.12), and noting that $W_{00} = -ex_{00}F = 0$, we obtain the following expression for the energy of the ground state, in the case of a spherically symmetrical charge distribution:

$$\varepsilon = E_0 + \sum_{j \neq 0} \frac{e^2 |x_{j0}|^2}{E_0 - E_j} F^2 \tag{39.3}$$

In view of the relation (39.2), differentiation of the above expression with respect to F gives equation (38.2), if f_{j0} is substituted from (38.3).

In the derivation of (39.3) it is important that the unperturbed energy value E_j should not be degenerate. This is generally the case for the ground state, but not for the excited states.

Consider, for instance, the first excited level of the hydrogen atom, for which $n = 2$, and which is fourfold degenerate. The quantum numbers (l, m) have the values (0,0), (1,0), (1,1), (1, −1).* For these states, all elements z_{jk} except $z_{(0,0),(1,0)} = z_{(1,0),(0,0)}$ vanish (cf. (25.11) regarding the selection rules $\Delta l = \pm 1$, $\Delta m = 0$ for the z-component of the matrix element). This gives

$$\begin{aligned} -eFz_{(0,0),(1,0)} &= -eF \int \phi_{210}(\mathbf{r}) z \phi_{200}(\mathbf{r})\, d\mathbf{r} \\ &= -\frac{eF}{16a_0^4} \int_0^\infty \int_{-1}^1 r^4 \left(2 - \frac{r}{a_0}\right) \exp\left(-\frac{r}{a_0}\right) \cos^2\theta\, d(\cos\theta)\, dr \\ &= 3ea_0 F \end{aligned}$$

In the subspace of the functions (0,0) and (1,0) we therefore have to solve another secular equation of the form of (26.9), in order to remove the degeneracy. In the present case we obtain

$$\begin{vmatrix} H_{11} - \varepsilon & H_{12} \\ H_{21} & H_{22} - \varepsilon \end{vmatrix} = \begin{vmatrix} E_1 - \varepsilon & 3ea_0 F \\ 3ea_0 F & E_1 - \varepsilon \end{vmatrix} = 0$$

the two solutions of which are

$$\varepsilon_1 = E_1 - 3ea_0 F \qquad \varepsilon_2 = E_1 + 3ea_0 F \tag{39.4}$$

* We temporarily take F to be parallel to the z-axis (although the latter is more usually employed as the polar axis); the field F is assumed to be strong enough to enable the term separation due to spin-orbit interaction to be neglected.

When no degeneracy is present, therefore, the energy merely decreases proportionately to the square of F (the quadratic Stark effect); in the degenerate case, however, the energy separation is directly proportional* to F, as though the atom possessed a permanent dipole moment (linear Stark effect) (see figure 41).

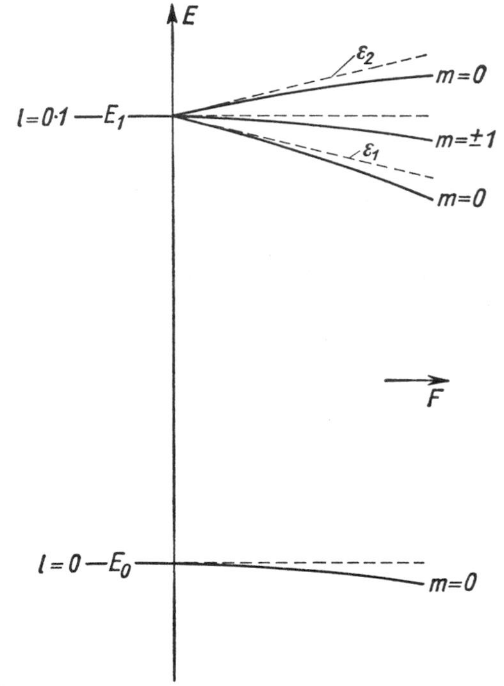

Fig. 41.—The Stark effect for the hydrogen atom. The broken lines illustrate the linear Stark effect; the full lines show the quadratic corrections. (These corrections are magnified by a factor of 10 relative to the linear terms, and are therefore really much smaller than shown.) The ground state and the state $l=1$, $m=\pm 1$ exhibit only the quadratic Stark effect

The correct eigenfunctions of zero-order approximation corresponding to the energy values (39.4) are $\phi_{200} \pm \phi_{210}$. These two functions give a charge density with a dipole moment parallel to the positive or the negative z-axis. The electrostatic interaction of this dipole moment with the external field gives the additional terms in (39.4). If the l-degeneracy is removed when the field is absent (e.g. in the case of sodium), only the quadratic Stark effect is obtained.

* In strong fields the quadratic Stark effect is naturally superimposed on the linear effect.

The validity of the previous perturbation calculation might be open to question, for the following reason. The potential energy, plotted as a function of x, exhibits a form as shown in figure 67, p. 384. Now the potential barrier can be penetrated by the electron in virtue of the tunnel effect (§16); the atom cannot therefore possess any stationary bound states, although these are clearly predicted by equation (39.3).

The use of (39.3) is justifiable, however, in spite of the above considerations, provided that the field is not too strong and that the atom is not too highly excited. The Hamiltonian operator (39.1) refers to a literally permanent field, whereas in fact in any experiment the field is switched on and off. If the atom is in the ground state and the field is not too strong, the probability of the electron tunnelling through the potential hill is so small that it remains in the bound state until the field is switched off. The situation is different for strong fields and excited states; in such cases, as we might expect on classical grounds (cf. Exercise 3, p. 238), the atom can be ionized much sooner as a result of the tunnel effect.

§40. The classical theory of dispersion

We refer again to the concept of the elastically bound atomic electron, which we have already used on a number of occasions. The equation of motion of such an electron, under the influence of an electric field $F_x = F\cos\omega t$, is

$$m(\ddot{x}+\omega_0 x) = eF\cos\omega t \tag{40.1}$$

if we neglect the effect of damping for the time being. The general solution of this equation is

$$x(t) = A\cos\omega_0 t + B\sin\omega_0 t + \frac{e}{m}F\frac{\cos\omega t}{\omega_0^2-\omega^2}$$

If we take the initial conditions $x=0$, $\dot{x}=0$ at $t=0$, the dipole moment is

$$p_x^{el}(t) = ex = \frac{e^2F}{m}\frac{\cos\omega t-\cos\omega_0 t}{\omega_0^2-\omega^2} \tag{40.1a}$$

Owing to the damping which is always present (but which has been neglected here for the sake of simplicity), the term in $\cos\omega_0 t$ resulting from the initial conditions soon decays; in the condition of "forced oscillation" the dipole moment is therefore

$$p_x^{el}(t) = \frac{e^2 F}{m(\omega_0^2 - \omega^2)} \cos \omega t \tag{40.2}$$

In the case of a not too highly compressed gas possessing N atoms per cubic centimetre, the electric displacement in an alternating field of angular frequency ω is

$$D_x = F_x + 4\pi N p_x^{el} = \left(1 + \frac{4\pi e^2 N}{m(\omega_0^2 - \omega^2)}\right) F_x$$

The refractive index $n = \sqrt{\varepsilon}$ is therefore given by

$$n^2 = 1 + \frac{4\pi N e^2}{m(\omega_0^2 - \omega^2)}$$

If N is so small that $|n^2 - 1| \ll 1$, the dispersion formula becomes

$$n - 1 = 2\pi \frac{N e^2}{m(\omega_0^2 - \omega^2)} \tag{40.3}$$

Apart from a numerical factor and an additional term, the above formula represents the function $n(\omega)$ in the resonance region $\omega \sim \omega_0$, in a manner that is very satisfactorily confirmed by experiment. When equation (40.1) is supplemented by a frictional term, it leads to the relation for $n(\omega)$ within the absorption line that is termed "anomalous dispersion".

The dispersion formula (40.3) soon proved to be inadequate in one respect: even in the simplest substances (such as a gas consisting of hydrogen atoms or sodium vapour, in which only one electron per atom can be concerned with dispersion), the absorption spectrum does not show a single line ω_0, but a very large number. If the atom is in the quantum state s, corresponding to an energy E_s, then on Bohr's theory all possible frequencies

$$\omega_{\nu s} = \frac{E_\nu - E_s}{\hbar} \qquad \nu = 0, 1, 2, 3, \ldots$$

can occur as absorption frequencies. Each of these frequencies contributes to the dispersion in the manner prescribed by the expression

(40.3). On the other hand, before the advent of quantum mechanics the oscillator model provided the only means of giving a fairly correct representation of dispersion phenomena. The idea thus came into being that the atom did not merely contain one single oscillator ω_0, but a whole series with characteristic frequencies $\omega_{\nu s}$, and that it was necessary to add the contributions of all these oscillators when calculating the quantities p_x^{el} and $n-1$. A simple summation of expressions of the form of (40.2) is out of the question, however, just because this would lead to abnormally large values of $p_x^{el}(t)$. To each *ad hoc* oscillator we must be prepared to assign a temporarily unknown "oscillator strength" $f_{\nu s}$ which indicates the extent to which it contributes to the dispersion.

The dispersion formula then becomes

$$n^2-1=\frac{4\pi Ne^2}{m}\sum_\nu \frac{f_{\nu s}}{\omega_{\nu s}^2-\omega^2} \tag{40.4}$$

and for the case in which $|n^2-1|\ll 1$

$$n-1=\frac{2\pi Ne^2}{m}\sum_\nu \frac{f_{\nu s}}{\omega_{\nu s}^2-\omega^2} \tag{40.5}$$

Using this model, we obtain the following expression for the dipole moment p_x^{el} of an atom in the state s:

$$p_x^{el}(t)=\frac{e^2F}{m}\sum_\nu \frac{f_{\nu s}}{\omega_{\nu s}^2-\omega^2}\cos\omega t \tag{40.6}$$

Soon after this formula was derived, Thomas and Kuhn put forward a hypothesis about the quantities $f_{\nu s}$. If the frequency ω is taken to be so high that ω^2 is large compared with all frequencies $\omega_{\nu s}^2$ (as in the case of X-rays, for instance), then (40.6) tends to the expression

$$p_x^{el}(t)=-\frac{e^2F}{m\omega^2}\left(\sum_\nu f_{\nu s}\right)\cos\omega t \tag{40.7}$$

The characteristic frequencies $\omega_{\nu s}$ do not appear in the above expression. We may assume that the old classical formula (40.2), in which

$$p_x^{el}=-\frac{e^2F}{m\omega^2}\cos\omega t$$

is valid in this limiting case; this formula simply describes the behaviour of a free electron. This can only be true if the relation

$$\sum_{\nu} f_{\nu s} = 1 \text{ for all } s \tag{40.8}$$

is satisfied. Equation (40.8) is termed the "summation theorem". The number 1 occurring in this theorem expresses the fact that we are dealing with only one electron in total; the individual quantities $f_{\nu s}$ indicate how the unit oscillator strength of the classical bound electron is to be distributed among the different "equivalent oscillators".

In the next paragraph we shall prove formula (40.6) using the methods of the quantum theory, and shall also investigate the actual numerical values of the quantities $f_{\nu s}$ in simple examples.

§41. The quantum-mechanical theory of dispersion

Let the unperturbed atom be described by the Hamiltonian operator $\mathscr{H}_0$, with associated eigenvalues E_ν and eigenfunctions ϕ_ν:

$$\mathscr{H}_0 \phi_\nu = E_\nu \phi_\nu \tag{41.1}$$

Let the effect of the light wave be represented by a time-dependent operator W. In the simplest particular case of an alternating electric field $F_x = F\cos\omega t$ parallel to the x-axis we may put*

$$W = -\tfrac{1}{2}xeF(\exp i\omega t + \exp - i\omega t) \tag{41.2}$$

We now take the Schrödinger equation

$$(\mathscr{H}_0 + W)\psi = -\frac{\hbar}{i}\dot{\psi} \tag{41.3}$$

and expand ψ in terms of the eigenfunctions ϕ_λ of the unperturbed equation:

$$\psi = \sum_{\lambda} a_\lambda(t) \exp\left(-\frac{i}{\hbar}E_\lambda t\right)\phi_\lambda \tag{41.3a}$$

* Strictly speaking, in place of $-exF$ we should use the expression

$$-\frac{e}{mc}p_x A_x \quad \text{where} \quad A_x = -\frac{c}{\omega}F\sin\omega t \tag{41.2a}$$

However, the difference between these two quantities is unimportant, provided that the vector potential A_x is nearly constant throughout the volume of the atom, so that a dipole approximation may be used. This may be directly verified from the expression (41.6), if we take into consideration the relation $p_{\nu s} = im\omega_{\nu s}x_{\nu s}$.

If we then form the scalar product of (41.3) and ϕ_ν we obtain

$$\dot{a}_\nu(t) = -\frac{i}{\hbar}\sum_\lambda W_{\nu\lambda}\exp\left(\frac{i}{\hbar}(E_\nu - E_\lambda)t\right)a_\lambda(t) \qquad (41.4)$$

where
$$W_{\nu\lambda} = (\phi_\nu, W\phi_\lambda) \qquad (41.5)$$

As in the case of the Dirac approximation described in §27, the integration of (41.4) is subject to the initial condition that the perturbation W is applied at time $t = 0$, and that until that moment the atom is in the state s, i.e. $a_\nu(0) = \delta_{s\nu}$. Then when $\nu \neq s$ we obtain

$$a_\nu(t) = \frac{eFx_{\nu s}}{2\hbar}\left\{\frac{\exp i(\omega_{\nu s}+\omega)t - 1}{\omega_{\nu s}+\omega} + \frac{\exp i(\omega_{\nu s}-\omega)t - 1}{\omega_{\nu s}-\omega}\right\} \qquad (41.6)$$

It is clear from the above expression that, whenever ω is in the neighbourhood of one of the resonance frequencies $\omega_{\nu s}$, the approximation assumed in the Dirac method ($|a_\nu| \ll 1$) is no longer satisfied even when F is small. We must therefore restrict ourselves in the present instance to frequencies for which the approximation is valid; the reader is referred to §50 for the discussion of the case for which $\omega \approx \omega_{\nu s}$. Using (41.3*a*) and (41.6) we obtain the following expression for ψ:

$$\psi = \exp\left(-\frac{i}{\hbar}E_s t\right)\phi_s + \sum_{\nu \neq s} a_\nu \exp\left(-\frac{i}{\hbar}E_\nu t\right)\phi_\nu \qquad (41.7)$$

We are concerned with the expectation value of the dipole moment, which is calculated by means of (41.7):

$$\overline{p_x^{el}(t)} = e(\psi, x\psi) \qquad (41.8)$$

(The mean-value symbol over p_x^{el} denotes a spatial, not a time average.) When calculating (41.8) we shall restrict ourselves in the approximation to terms of the first degree in a_ν. Then

$$(\psi, x\psi) = x_{ss} + \sum_\nu (a_\nu \exp(i\omega_{s\nu}t)x_{s\nu} + a_\nu^* \exp(-i\omega_{s\nu}t)x_{s\nu}^*)$$

If we now introduce the quantities a_ν as given by the expression (41.6), we obtain the following expression for the dipole moment in place of formula (40.1*a*), which was calculated from classical theory:

$$\overline{p_x^{el}(t)} = ex_{ss} + \frac{e^2F}{\hbar}\sum_\nu \frac{2\omega_{\nu s}|x_{\nu s}|^2}{\omega_{\nu s}^2 - \omega^2}(\cos\omega t - \cos\omega_{\nu s}t) \qquad (41.9)$$

We shall omit the contribution of $\cos\omega_{sv}t$ in the above expression, as we did in the case of the corresponding term in the classical treatment of §40. The first term in (41.9), ex_{ss}, denotes a constant dipole moment corresponding to an atom in the state s, and contributing nothing to the dispersion. The remainder of (41.9) corresponds exactly to formula (40.4), which was derived on semi-classical grounds; it possesses the great advantage, however, that the quantities f_{vs} can now be specified by a fundamental relation. Comparison of (40.6) and (41.9) gives (cf. (38.3))

$$f_{vs} = \frac{m}{\hbar} 2\omega_{vs} |x_{vs}|^2 \qquad (41.10)$$

This result enables us to prove the summation theorem $\sum_v f_{vs} = 1$. We first write (41.10) in the form

$$f_{vs} = \frac{m}{\hbar}(\omega_{vs} x_{vs} x_{sv} - \omega_{sv} x_{sv} x_{vs})$$

The matrix elements of the momentum are

$$p_{vs} = im\omega_{vs} x_{vs}$$

hence

$$f_{vs} = \frac{1}{i\hbar}(x_{sv} p_{vs} - p_{sv} x_{vs})$$

Now the summation theorem requires that the following relation should hold for all s:

$$\sum_v (p_{sv} x_{vs} - x_{sv} p_{vs}) = \frac{\hbar}{i}$$

This is just the matrix form of the term $r = s$ in the fundamental commutation relation

$$(px - xp)_{rs} = \frac{\hbar}{i}\delta_{rs}$$

the latter may therefore be considered as in a sense a consequence of the summation theorem for f.

According to (41.10), the sign of f_{vs} is the same as that of $\omega_{vs} = (E_v - E_s)/\hbar$. If s represents the ground state of the atom, then E_v is always greater than E_s, and f_{vs} is positive for all values of v; this is the usual situation in the case of dispersion measurements. If s represents an excited state, however, negative values of f_{vs} occur when

E_v is less than E_s. A "negative dispersion" of this type may be observed, for instance, in the case of excited (metastable) neon atoms in a neon arc.*

The behaviour of a linear harmonic oscillator is of interest. In this case, $E_s = \hbar\omega_0(s+\frac{1}{2})$. The only non-zero matrix elements x_{vs} occur when $v = s+1$ and $v = s-1$:

$$x_{s+1,s} = (s+1)^{1/2}\left(\frac{\hbar}{2m\omega_0}\right)^{1/2} \quad \text{and} \quad x_{s-1,s} = s^{1/2}\left(\frac{\hbar}{2m\omega_0}\right)^{1/2}$$

Hence from (41.10), putting

$$\omega_{s+1,s} = \omega_0 \quad \text{and} \quad \omega_{s-1,s} = -\omega_0:$$
$$f_{s+1,s} = s+1 \quad \text{and} \quad f_{s-1,s} = -s$$

The sum of the contributions of the positive and negative dispersion is unity; hence the value of the dipole moment due to forced oscillations is the same as that given by the classical formula (40.2), for all s including $s = 0$.

As an example, the values of f for the principal series of lithium and sodium are calculated from (41.10), and compared with the observed values; the results are extracted from the excellent compilation contained in A. Unsöld, *Physik der Sternatmosphären*, Berlin (1938), pp. 191 ff., 205 ff.

Lithium principal series	λ(Å)	f (calc.)	f (obs.)	
$n = 2$	6708	0·750	0·750	Absolute measurement
$n = 3$	3233	0·0055	0·0055	Relative measurements referred to $n = 2$
$n = 4$	2741	0·0052	0·0048	
$n = 5$	2563	0·0025	0·0032	

Sodium principal series	λ(Å)	f (calc.)	f (obs.)	
$n = 3$	5893	0·975	1·00	Absolute measurement
$n = 4$	3303	0·0144	0·0144	Relative measurements
$n = 5$	2853	0·00241	0·00211	
$n = 6$	2680	0·00098	0·00065	

* Cf. for instance H. Kopfermann and R. Ladenburg, *Z. Phys.* **65**, (1930), 167.

It should be noted that only the product $Nf_{\nu s}$ can be obtained from dispersion measurements in the neighbourhood of an absorption line, using the relation

$$n-1 = 2\pi N \frac{e^2}{m} \sum_{\nu} f_{\nu s}/(\omega_{\nu s}^2 - \omega^2)$$

Considerable uncertainty is involved in the determination of N (the number of atoms per cubic centimetre), and relative measurements are therefore often preferred. Further, the theoretical determination of the quantities $f_{\nu s}$ is strictly possible in the case of the hydrogen atom alone; all other atoms can only be treated by somewhat laborious approximation procedures, such as Hartree's method. The errors in the calculated transition probabilities are estimated to be 20 per cent. See Exercise 4 below for the calculation of the oscillator strengths in the case of the hydrogen atom.

Exercises

1. *Zeeman effect for the sodium D-line*

Is it possible to produce the Paschen-Back effect in the case of the sodium D-line, having regard to the fields that can be achieved in practice?

2. *Doublet eigenfunctions*

Determine the eigenfunctions

$$Y_{ljm_j} = a Y_{l, m_j - 1/2}\, \alpha + b Y_{l, m_j+1/2}\, \beta$$

and use them to calculate the relative intensities of the Zeeman components of the sodium D-lines in a weak magnetic field.

3. *Ionization due to the tunnel effect*

Make a rough estimate of the lifetime of a hydrogen atom in the ground state, acted on by an electric field of order of magnitude 10^6 V/cm.

4. *Spectral line intensities*

Calculate the oscillator strengths for the transition $2p \rightarrow 1s$ in the hydrogen atom. What is the lifetime of the excited $2p$ states?

5. *Oscillator strengths for the principal series of sodium*

In the table on p. 237 the sum of the experimental values of the oscillator strengths for sodium is obviously greater than 1. Does this conflict with the summation theorem for f? What is the sum in the case of lithium? See figure 30, p. 186 for the lithium and sodium terms entering into the sums of the f-values.

6. *Polarizability of the alkali atoms*

In the alkali atoms the oscillator strengths for the resonance lines corresponding to the transition from the ground state to the first excited state are nearly equal to 1. The polarizability is practically entirely due to the valence electron. Since the ground-state configurations are spherically symmetrical, the energy in an electric field F parallel to x is

$$E = E_0 + \sum_{i \neq 0} \frac{|W_{i0}|^2}{E_0 - E_i}$$

as in the case of the hydrogen atom ($W = -eFx$). The eigenfunctions of the first-order approximation are

$$\phi = \phi_0 + \sum_{i \neq 0} \frac{W_{i0}}{E_0 - E_i} \phi_i$$

Making the assumption that W_{i0} differs from zero only for transitions to the first excited state, show that

(1) the perturbed function ϕ is produced by a displacement of ϕ_0 by an amount β:

$$\phi = \phi_0 - \beta \frac{\partial}{\partial x} \phi_0$$

(2) the polarizability α is determined from β; it is expressed in terms of universal constants and the excitation energy E_a.

(3) Compare the calculated values of α with the values determined experimentally from the Stark effect.*

	Li	Na	K	Rb	Cs
E_a (eV)	1·84	2·10	1·61	1·56	1·39
α_{exp} (10^{-24} cm^3)	27	27	46	50	61

7. *Refractive index of free electrons*

Determine the refractive index $n(\omega)$ of a rarefied "gas" consisting of free electrons, neglecting radiation damping and ohmic resistance. If n is imaginary, total reflection occurs. For what wavelengths are alkali-metal foils transparent, assuming one free electron per atom? (The specific volumes of the body-centred alkali metals are given by $1/N = \frac{1}{2}a^3$, where $a = 3{\cdot}5$, $4{\cdot}3$, $5{\cdot}3$, $5{\cdot}6$, $6{\cdot}1$ respectively for Li, Na, K, Rb, Cs.) What is the density of the free electrons in the ionosphere, if total reflection occurs when $\nu \approx 10$ Mc/s $= 10^7$ s^{-1}?

* Landolt-Börnstein, I/1, 6th ed., Berlin, 1950.

D

Problems involving several electrons

CHAPTER DI

Problems involving several electrons

§42. Pauli's exclusion principle

So far we have considered systems possessing only a single electron. The treatment of systems containing more than one electron requires new concepts in order to make the properties of such systems comprehensible.

If we omit the effect of the electron spin and the electrostatic interaction of the electrons, the Hamiltonian operator for n electrons,

$$\mathscr{H} = \sum_{i=1}^{n} \left(\frac{1}{2m} \mathbf{p}_i^2 + V(\mathbf{r}_i) \right) = \sum_{i=1}^{n} \mathscr{H}_i \tag{42.1}$$

consists of the sum of the operators $\mathscr{H}_i$, each of which acts on a single set of electron coordinates $\mathbf{r}_i$. If the eigenfunctions $\phi_\mathbf{q}$ of $\mathscr{H}_i$ are known,*

$$\mathscr{H}_i \phi_\mathbf{q} = \varepsilon_\mathbf{q} \phi_\mathbf{q} \tag{42.2}$$

then the complete set of eigenfunctions of $\mathscr{H}$ can be given:

$$\mathscr{H} \Phi_Q(\mathbf{r}_1, \mathbf{r}_2, \ldots, \mathbf{r}_n) = E_Q \Phi_Q \tag{42.3}$$

where $\quad \Phi_Q = \phi_{\mathbf{q}_1}(\mathbf{r}_1) \phi_{\mathbf{q}_2}(\mathbf{r}_2) \ldots \phi_{\mathbf{q}_n}(\mathbf{r}_n)$ and $E_Q = \sum_{i=1}^{n} \varepsilon_{\mathbf{q}_i} \quad$ (42.3a)

The validity of equation (42.3) may easily be verified. Since $\mathscr{H}_i$ acts only on $\phi_{\mathbf{q}_i}(\mathbf{r}_i)$ and leaves the remaining functions unchanged, $\mathscr{H}_i \Phi_Q = \varepsilon_{\mathbf{q}_i} \Phi_Q$, from which (42.3) follows directly. Thus all solutions may be obtained, since the functions Φ_Q constitute a complete orthogonal system in the coordinate space $\mathbf{r}_1, \mathbf{r}_2, \ldots, \mathbf{r}_n$, if this is true for $\phi_\mathbf{q}(\mathbf{r})$ in the coordinate space of $\mathbf{r}$.

When dealing with atoms possessing more than one electron, it is generally possible as a first approximation to neglect the spin energy,

* The symbol q represents an abbreviation for a set of three quantum numbers, such as n_r, l, and m in the case of a central potential.

which is small. The electrostatic interaction of the electrons can be represented by taking $V(\mathbf{r}_i)$ in the ith equation to be the sum of the potential due to the nucleus and that due to the effect of the other electrons in the atom. The Hamiltonian operator then takes the form (42.1). If the system is further specified by the spin coordinates and spin quantum numbers, and if x is used to denote the space and spin coordinates $\mathbf{r}$ and s, then the eigenfunctions corresponding to the energy $E_\Lambda = \sum_i \varepsilon_{\lambda_i}$

$$\Psi_\Lambda(x_1, \ldots, x_n) = \Psi_{\lambda_1}(x_1)\Psi_{\lambda_2}(x_2)\ldots\Psi_{\lambda_n}(x_n) \qquad (42.4)$$

where λ represents the space quantum numbers $\mathbf{q}$ and the spin quantum numbers m_s. Each energy value E_Λ therefore exhibits spin degeneracy in addition to spatial degeneracy.

Investigation of the properties of atoms with more than one electron shows that the ground states are quite different from what we would expect in consequence of the above description. In the lowest energy state, all electrons should clearly be in the state $1s$. The corresponding spatial quantum numbers of all electrons would be equal.* In fact, even the simplest atoms behave quite differently. Spectroscopic observation shows that, whereas in helium the electrons occupy two $1s$ states, in lithium two $1s$ states and one $2s$ state are filled. Spectroscopic examination of the elements, and the shell-like electron structure of atoms, expressed by the periodic system, both lead inevitably to the hypothesis that each state can be occupied by only a single electron. This is Pauli's principle.

In consequence of this principle, equal sets of quantum numbers λ_i should not occur in the wave function Ψ_Λ. Using this assumption, it is possible to explain the construction of the periodic system of the elements. The ground state of an atom is obtained by filling the lowest states successively in the equivalent potential V, taking due account of the spin degeneracy.

For many reasons, however, the above formulation of Pauli's principle is untenable. For one thing, it is based on the assumption that the interaction of the electrons can be represented by an average potential. In general, however, individual sets of quantum numbers cannot be specified for each electron. Further, it may easily be shown that a perturbation gives rise to forbidden states produced from the

* Spin-spin and spin-orbit coupling would be absent. The energy would then be independent of the spin quantum numbers and the ground state would be 2^n-fold degenerate.

permitted ones. Finally, the above form of the Pauli exclusion principle can be only provisional, since it is based on the special properties of the Hamiltonian operator.

Heisenberg has shown how the Pauli principle may be expressed in general form. In order to understand the principle as expressed in Heisenberg's form we must first deal with the general properties of the Hamiltonian operator for many particles.

The Hamiltonian operator of a system of n electrons may depend in a very complicated manner on the operators $\mathbf{p}_i$, $\mathbf{r}_i$, $\vec{\sigma}_i$, but it possesses one simple property of decisive importance: it is symmetrical with respect to interchanges of the indices i, and is invariant for any such interchange. This is because the electrons are physically equivalent particles which are indistinguishable in all respects. All potentials, including the electron interaction, appear in the Hamiltonian operator in symmetrical form. (This may be seen in the case of the Hamiltonian operator in the absence of spin, which consists of the expression (42.1) together with the interaction terms

$$\left.\frac{1}{2}\sum_{i\neq i'}^{n}\frac{1}{|\mathbf{r}_i-\mathbf{r}_{i'}|}\right)$$

If P represents a permutation of the numbers $1,\ldots,n$ and P_i, the number replacing i after the permutation has been effected, this property of $\mathscr{H}$ may be represented as follows:

$$\mathscr{H}(\ldots,\mathbf{p}_i,\mathbf{r}_i,\vec{\sigma}_i,\ldots)=\mathscr{H}(\ldots,\mathbf{p}_{P_i},\mathbf{r}_{P_i},\vec{\sigma}_{P_i},\ldots) \qquad (42.5)$$

This may also be described by means of a permutation operator P:

$$P\Psi(x_1,\ldots,x_i,\ldots,x_n)=\Psi(x_{P_1},\ldots,x_{P_i},\ldots,x_{P_n}) \qquad (42.6)$$

$\mathscr{H}$ and P then commute:

$$P\mathscr{H}\Psi=\mathscr{H}P\Psi \quad \text{or} \quad P\mathscr{H}-\mathscr{H}P=0 \qquad (42.7)$$

Therefore if Ψ is an eigenfunction of $\mathscr{H}$, $P\Psi$ is also an eigenfunction, belonging to the same eigenvalue.

The simplest relations are those for the case of two particles, where the only permutation is the interchange of the numbers 1 and 2, denoted by P_{12}. If $\Psi(x_1,x_2)$ is an eigenfunction of $\mathscr{H}$, then so is $P_{12}\Psi(x_1,x_2)=\Psi(x_2,x_1)$. Since the double application of P_{12} gives the identity ($P_{12}.P_{12}=1$), the only possible eigenvalues of P_{12} are ± 1. Then the eigenfunctions of $\mathscr{H}$, that are also eigenfunctions of P_{12}, are evidently symmetric and antisymmetric functions Ψ^S and Ψ^A; when acted upon by P_{12}, these functions either remain unaltered or suffer a change of sign:

$$\mathscr{H}\Psi = E\Psi, \quad \mathscr{H}\Psi^A = E\Psi^A, \quad \mathscr{H}\Psi^S = E\Psi^S$$

$$P_{12}\Psi^A = -\Psi^A, \quad P_{12}\Psi^S = \Psi^S \tag{42.8}$$

where $$\Psi^A = \Psi - P_{12}\Psi \quad \text{and} \quad \Psi^S = \Psi + P_{12}\Psi$$

The symmetric or antisymmetric nature of a state does not change in the course of time; if a state is antisymmetric at time $t = 0$, it remains so for all time. This is because the unitary transformation that converts $\Psi(0)$ to $\Psi(t)$ (cf. §27) only contains the operator $\mathscr{H}$; the transformation operator therefore commutes with P even when $\mathscr{H}$ contains arbitrary (but necessarily symmetric) perturbations that are functions of time.

In the present problem, involving two particles, the following conditions apply. A symmetric and an antisymmetric eigenfunction are associated with each energy value E denoted by λ_1 and λ_2, where $\lambda_1 \neq \lambda_2$; when $\lambda_1 = \lambda_2$, however, there is only one symmetric function. We may therefore forbid the occurrence of a doubly occupied state by admitting antisymmetric functions only. This leads to the postulate that the wave function must be antisymmetric in the coordinates of both electrons. This form of Pauli's principle is free from objection; it reduces to the original form for the case in which no interaction is present. It does not depend on any special form of the Hamiltonian operator, but imposes a condition on the wave function. Since by § 19 any arbitrary quantum numbers may be introduced by resolving in terms of the corresponding eigenfunction system of commuting operators, the prohibition of identical sets of quantum numbers is quite general. In the Fourier expansion, for instance, no two wave-number vectors can be equal when the spin is the same in each case; the amplitude vanishes when $x_1 = x_2$, as does the antisymmetric wave function $\Psi(x_1, x_2)$.

For the case of several electrons, it is clearly necessary only to postulate that the wave function for each pair of electron coordinates is antisymmetric in order to express Pauli's principle in its general form. If P_{ik} represents the interchange of two electron coordinates, the following relation must hold:

$$P_{ik}\Psi(x_1, \ldots, x_n) = -\Psi(x_1, \ldots, x_n) \text{ for any } i \neq k \tag{42.9}$$

Now if we have an eigenfunction corresponding to a given eigenvalue,

$$\mathscr{H}\Psi = E\Psi \tag{42.10}$$

then in general, $n!$ functions $P\Psi$ belong to the same eigenvalue, since there are $n!$ different permutations. Since every permutation can be expressed as a product of interchanges of two quantities, the antisymmetric function Ψ^A associated with E can be represented as follows:

$$\Psi^A = \sum_P (-1)^P P\Psi, \quad \text{where} \quad \mathscr{H}\Psi^A = E\Psi^A \tag{42.11}$$

In the above expression the summation is to be taken over all permutations; the value of $(-1)^P$ is -1 when P contains an odd number of interchanges, and $+1$ when this number is even. Then Ψ^A is an antisymmetric eigenfunction, though it vanishes whenever the procedure for generating an antisymmetric function yields the value 0, as in the case, for instance, when Ψ is completely symmetrical. The energy values remain unchanged by this procedure; however, some states are excluded in virtue of Pauli's principle, and the degree of degeneracy of others is appreciably reduced.

According to Slater, the procedure for making the wave function (42.4) antisymmetric may be expressed in a simple manner as a determinant, known as the Slater determinant:

$$\Psi^A_\Lambda - \begin{vmatrix} \Psi_{\lambda_1}(x_1) & \Psi_{\lambda_1}(x_2) \ldots \Psi_{\lambda_1}(x_n) \\ \Psi_{\lambda_2}(x_1) & \vdots \\ \vdots & \vdots \\ \Psi_{\lambda_n}(x_1) \ldots\ldots\ldots & \ldots \Psi_{\lambda_n}(x_n) \end{vmatrix} \tag{42.4a}$$

It is clear that the interchange of two coordinates (or two quantum numbers) changes the sign of the above expression, since this corresponds to the interchange of two columns (or two rows) in the determinant. A single eigenfunction is associated with each set of quantum numbers $\lambda_1 \neq \lambda_2 \neq \lambda_3 \ldots \neq \lambda_n$.

As in the case of two particles, Pauli's principle is completely valid; the antisymmetry property expressed by (42.9) does not change in the course of time, and naturally still holds good when expressed in terms of other coordinates.

It is important to realize that Pauli's principle does not complicate the situation, but that on the contrary it represents a very great simplification. If the principle were not valid, it would for instance be possible to have completely symmetric functions,* $P_{ik}\Psi^s = \Psi^s$. However, the symmetric nature of the Hamiltonian operator implies that transitions between symmetric and antisymmetric states are strictly forbidden and can never take place. In the case of two particles, for instance, the Hilbert space is resolved into two completely independent components, one of which is symmetric, and the other antisymmetric. As a result, we should expect to find a symmetric and an antisymmetric "world", between which there would be no connection. It follows that any theory of thermodynamic statistics would be impossible, since it is assumed in all such statistics that every state is possible, starting from the ground state. We should therefore be compelled to treat the symmetric and antisymmetric components separately in the statistical theory. Fortunately, only one simple function group exists in nature, that of the antisymmetric states.

In the next sections we shall show by means of simple examples how fundamental the Pauli principle is to the physics of atoms and molecules.

The electron coordinates always appear in symmetrical form in physical quantities. For instance

$$|\Psi^A(\mathbf{r}_1, s_1, \mathbf{r}_2, s_2, \ldots)|^2 \, d\mathbf{r}_1 \ldots d\mathbf{r}_n$$

is the probability of finding electron 1 in the element of space $d\mathbf{r}_1$ and with spin coordinate s_1, electron 2 in $d\mathbf{r}_2$ with spin s_2, etc.; this quantity is symmetric in the electron coordinates $x_1, \ldots, x_n$ and independent of the numbering of the electrons. In this case there is no possibility of distinguishing between the individual electrons; it would therefore be more correct to say that $|\Psi^A|^2 \, d\mathbf{r}_1 \ldots d\mathbf{r}_n$ represents the probability of finding an electron in $d\mathbf{r}_1$ with spin s_1, another in $d\mathbf{r}_2$ with spin s_2, etc. In equation (42.4) the state Ψ_Λ represents electron 1 in state λ_1, electron 2 in state λ_2, etc.; the physical interpretation of $\Psi_\Lambda{}^A$, on the other hand, is that there is an electron in state λ_1, another in state λ_2, etc. Pauli's principle therefore implies that the physical equivalence of the electrons is expressed by the equivalence of the different states when the electrons are permuted.

In principle, all the electrons of the universe should be handled together in a single antisymmetric wave function; this would of course be an impossibly complicated matter. In the case of spatially separate

* When there are more than two electrons, other groups of functions exist in addition to antisymmetric and symmetric functions; they are associated with other forms of representation of the permutation group.

physical systems, however, it may easily be shown that the process of obtaining the antisymmetric wave function has no outside effect; when discussing the hydrogen atom, for instance, it is permissible to consider a single electron. The situation is perhaps best illustrated by taking the case of two electrons bound to two widely separated protons a and b; the states of the electrons are denoted by λ_a and λ_b. Then $\Psi=\Psi_{\lambda_a}(x_1)\Psi_{\lambda_b}(x_2)$ and $\Psi^A=(1/\sqrt{2})\left[\Psi_{\lambda_a}(x_1)\Psi_{\lambda_b}(x_2)-\Psi_{\lambda_a}(x_2)\Psi_{\lambda_b}(x_1)\right]$ are both normalized functions, if $(\Psi_{\lambda_a},\Psi_{\lambda_a})=(\Psi_{\lambda_b},\Psi_{\lambda_b})=1$, and if $(\Psi_{\lambda_a},\Psi_{\lambda_b})$ vanishes as it certainly does when the separation is great. Physically, Ψ and Ψ^A are quite indistinguishable, and all physical quantities, which must necessarily be symmetric in x_1, x_2, are the same whether calculated from Ψ or Ψ^A. The expectation values of all operators A are the same, whether formed from Ψ or Ψ^A, but the degree of degeneracy may well be reduced; two different Ψ functions are associated with λ_a and λ_b, but only one function Ψ^A. It is therefore immaterial whether Ψ or Ψ^A is employed, provided that Ψ is initially chosen so that, when $x_1=x_2$ and the Pauli principle would take effect, this function vanishes simply on account of the large interval between the two systems.

Pauli's principle applies not only to electrons, but to all elementary particles that possess half-integral spin, such as protons and neutrons whose spin is $\frac{1}{2}$; for all these particles, the principle requires that the corresponding wave functions should be antisymmetric. Such particles are called Fermi particles or fermions, and are subject to Fermi-Dirac statistics, so-called because E. Fermi was the first to develop a relation between the term selection given by Pauli's principle and statistical thermodynamics.

Finally, we must refer to the behaviour of composite particles. We may consider these as single particles of appropriate spin, provided that the binding energy is high, that the interaction is not too great, and that the inner state of the compound structure remains unchanged. The Hamiltonian operator corresponding to such particles is symmetric, and the particles themselves are indistinguishable. With regard to the behaviour of the wave function, it is necessary to distinguish between particles composed of an even number of fermions, e.g.

Deuteron:	1 neutron, 1 proton, spin 1
α-particle:	2 neutrons, 2 protons, spin 0
He^4 atom:	2 neutrons, 2 protons, 2 electrons, spin 0

and those composed of an odd number, such as

Triton: 2 neutrons, 1 proton, spin $\frac{1}{2}$

He^3 nucleus: 1 neutron, 2 protons, spin $\frac{1}{2}$

He^3 atom: 1 neutron, 2 protons, 2 electrons, spin $\frac{1}{2}$

In the first of these groups, the sign of the wave function remains the same when two identical particles are interchanged; in the second group, however, the sign changes when this occurs. If X_i are the co-ordinates of the centre of mass and the spin, then

$$P_{ik}\Psi(\ldots X_i \ldots) = \Psi \quad \text{for an even number of fermions} \qquad (42.12a)$$

$$P_{ik}\Psi(\ldots X_i \ldots) = -\Psi \quad \text{for an odd number of fermions} \qquad (42.12b)$$

Particles whose wave functions behave according to (42.12*b*) obey the Fermi-Dirac statistics, while those whose wave functions are given by (42.12*a*) are said to be governed by the Bose-Einstein statistics. Since all particles behaving according to (42.12*b*) possess half-integral values of the spin, while the spin of those governed by (42.12*a*) is an integral number or 0, the behaviour of the corresponding wave functions can be characterized by the spin; Fermi-Dirac and Bose-Einstein statistics apply respectively in the cases of half-integral and integral values of the spin. The wave functions obeying Bose-Einstein statistics are completely symmetric with respect to permutations of the co-ordinates. (Light quanta also belong to the family of Bose particles, or bosons.) It is important to note, however, that the above description is only valid when all the composite particles are in the ground state and excited states are excluded; an excited helium atom, for instance, would be physically distinguishable from such an atom in the ground state.

§43. The helium atom

(*a*) *General properties of the eigenfunctions*

In order to provide a simple illustration of the application of the Pauli principle, we shall discuss the properties of a system of two electrons in the Coulomb field of a nucleus of charge $Ze_0 = -Ze$. For the helium atom $Z = 2$; we shall use the general value of Z at first, however, so as to be able to treat simultaneously the cases of the negative hydrogen ion ($Z = 1$) and the positive lithium ion ($Z = 3$).

If we disregard the small contribution of the spin in the Hamiltonian operator, then

$$\mathscr{H} = \frac{1}{2m}(\mathbf{p}_1^2+\mathbf{p}_2^2) - Ze^2\left(\frac{1}{r_1}+\frac{1}{r_2}\right)+\frac{e^2}{r_{12}} \tag{43.1}$$

$\mathscr{H}$ is symmetric in $\mathbf{r}_1$ and $\mathbf{r}_2$; the spatial components of the eigenfunctions of $\mathscr{H}$ can therefore be chosen to be symmetric and antisymmetric:

$$P_{12}\Phi^S(\mathbf{r}_1,\mathbf{r}_2) = \Phi^S(\mathbf{r}_2,\mathbf{r}_1) = \Phi^S(\mathbf{r}_1,\mathbf{r}_2) \tag{43.2a}$$

$$P_{12}\Phi^A(\mathbf{r}_1,\mathbf{r}_2) = \Phi^A(\mathbf{r}_2,\mathbf{r}_1) = -\Phi^A(\mathbf{r}_1,\mathbf{r}_2) \tag{43.2b}$$

Since the entire wave function must be antisymmetric in all the electron coordinates, the spin component must be chosen to be symmetric for Φ^A [$\chi^S(s_1,s_2)$, where $P_{12}\chi^S=\chi^S$], and antisymmetric for Φ^S [$\chi^A(s_1,s_2)$, where $P_{12}\chi^A=-\chi^A$].* Thus the only total wave functions to occur are the two combinations

$$\Psi(x_1,x_2) = \Phi^S\chi^A \tag{43.3a}$$

$$\Psi(x_1,x_2) = \Phi^A\chi^S \tag{43.3b}$$

(*b*) *Properties of the spin functions χ^S and χ^A*

One antisymmetric and three symmetric functions can be formed from the two normalized and mutually orthogonal spin functions α and β (cf. §§24, 32) that are available for an electron:†

	s_z	$\mathbf{s}^2$	
$\chi^A = \frac{1}{\sqrt{2}}\{\alpha(s_1)\beta(s_2)-\alpha(s_2)\beta(s_1)\}$	0	0	(43.4*a*)
$\chi_1^S = \alpha(s_1)\alpha(s_2)$	$\hbar$	$2\hbar^2$	
$\chi_0^S = \frac{1}{\sqrt{2}}\{\alpha(s_1)\beta(s_2)+\alpha(s_2)\beta(s_1)\}$	0	$2\hbar^2$	(43.4*b*)
$\chi_{-1}^S = \beta(s_1)\beta(s_2)$	$-\hbar$	$2\hbar^2$	

* The spin and spatial components can be separated only in the case of systems comprising two electrons, since there is then only one permutation operator P_{12}. A further condition is that it should be possible to neglect the spin-orbit interaction.

† The factors in (43.4) are so chosen that the spin functions are normalized to unity. In addition they are mutually orthogonal since they belong to different eigenvalues of $\mathbf{s}^2$ and s_z, as can be immediately verified.

It may readily be verified that the above functions are both eigenfunctions of the square of the angular-momentum operator for a total spin $\mathbf{s}^2 = (\mathbf{s}_1 + \mathbf{s}_2)^2$ as well as eigenfunctions of the latter's z-component $s_z = s_{1z} + s_{2z}$: for this purpose we make use of the representation of the operator $\mathbf{s}$ given in §24, and note that $\mathbf{s}_1$ acts only on functions of s_1.

It follows that χ^A corresponds to a total spin of value 0, whereas in χ^S the spins of the two electrons, each of value $\frac{1}{2}$, combine to give a total spin of value 1. In the states represented by (43.4a), therefore, the angular momentum and the associated magnetic moment are due solely to the orbits of the two electrons.

Transitions between the states represented by (43.3a) and (43.3b) are very rare. Since $(\Phi^S, \Phi^A) = (\chi^S, \chi^A) = 0$, any perturbation W that could produce such transitions must contain spatial and spin components (e.g. spin-orbit interaction), in order that the matrix element $(\Phi^S\chi^A, W\Phi^A\chi^S)$ should be different from zero. Transitions in the optical region (for which W would be approximately proportional to $\mathbf{r}_1 + \mathbf{r}_2$) do not occur. From the optical point of view the term systems corresponding to (43.3a) and (43.3b) behave as though they were almost completely separate. The prohibition of transitions in the optical region is admittedly not a strict one, since as a result of the spin-orbit interaction the exact eigenfunctions do contain small components of both groups of functions.* No prohibition exists in electron collision processes, since the addition of a further electron to the two atomic electrons completely alters the symmetry conditions.

The helium atom states (43.3a), in which the spins are "antiparallel" ($\mathbf{s}^2 = 0$) are called *parhelium*, and the states (43.3b) in which the spins are "parallel" ($\mathbf{s}^2 = 2\hbar^2$) are termed *orthohelium*; the reason for this nomenclature is that it was originally sought to explain the different optical behaviour of the two types of helium by means of two different modifications of the helium atom. The terms belonging to the parhelium system are also called *singlet* terms, those belonging to orthohelium, *triplet* terms, since each ortho term can generally split into three terms as a result of the spin-orbit interaction.

* Thus there is for instance a weak line due to intercombination between the $2p$ ortho- and the $1s$ para-state (cf. figure 42).

(*c*) *The spatial components of the eigenfunctions in the presence of a perturbation* e^2/r_{12}

If we treat the electrostatic interaction of the electrons e^2/r_{12} as a perturbation, then the eigenfunctions of zero-order approximation are the products of eigenfunctions in the Coulomb field, which were treated in detail in §29 for the case of the hydrogen atom, and which may be taken to be real functions:

$$\Phi_Q = \phi_{\mathbf{q}_1}(\mathbf{r}_1)\,\phi_{\mathbf{q}_2}(\mathbf{r}_2) \tag{43.5}$$

In the above expression, $\mathbf{q}$ represents the three quantum numbers n, l, and m occurring in the hydrogen problem. Neglecting the perturbation, the energy then consists of the sum of the two components:

$$E_Q = \varepsilon_{\mathbf{q}_1} + \varepsilon_{\mathbf{q}_2}, \quad \text{where} \quad \varepsilon_{\mathbf{q}} = -\frac{m(Ze^2)^2}{2\hbar^2 n^2} = -\frac{Z^2 I_H}{n^2} \tag{43.6}$$

(I_H is the energy of ionization of the hydrogen atom.)

In the above approximation, the ground state of helium would possess the energy $E_0 = -8I_H$ ($n_1 = n_2 = 1$); the energy of ionization would be $4I_H$, which is the energy difference between the helium ground state and the energy ($-4I_H$) of the singly ionized helium atom in the ground state, characterized by $n_1 = 1$, $n_2 = \infty$ (or $n_1 = \infty$, $n_2 = 1$). States in which both electrons are excited (such as $n_1 = n_2 = 2$, for which $E_Q = -2I_H$) are situated above the helium ionization limit and may be disregarded in any discussion of the discrete spectrum of eigenvalues. In what follows, therefore, we shall consider only those states for which one of the n-values is unity; the corresponding wave function ϕ_{100} will be denoted by ϕ_0.

$$\Phi_{nlm} = \phi_0(\mathbf{r}_1)\phi_{nlm}(\mathbf{r}_2) \tag{43.5a}$$

The symmetric and antisymmetric functions formed from (43.5*a*)

$$\left.\begin{aligned} \Phi^S_{nlm} &= \frac{1}{\sqrt{2}}\{\phi_0(\mathbf{r}_1)\phi_{nlm}(\mathbf{r}_2) + \phi_0(\mathbf{r}_2)\phi_{nlm}(\mathbf{r}_1)\} \qquad (43.6a)\\ \Phi^A_{nlm} &= \frac{1}{\sqrt{2}}\{\phi_0(\mathbf{r}_1)\phi_{nlm}(\mathbf{r}_2) - \phi_0(\mathbf{r}_2)\phi_{nlm}(\mathbf{r}_1)\} \qquad (43.6b)\end{aligned}\right\} n = 2, 3, 4, \ldots$$

$$\Phi^S_{100} = \phi_0(\mathbf{r}_1)\phi_0(\mathbf{r}_2) \quad \text{for} \quad n = 1 \tag{43.7}$$

are the correct normalized initial eigenfunctions for the perturbation; they yield the following first-order approximation for the total energy:

$$E_{nl}^S = (\Phi_{nlm}^S, \mathscr{H}\Phi_{nlm}^S) \tag{43.8a}$$

$$E_{nl}^A = (\Phi_{nlm}^A, \mathscr{H}\Phi_{nlm}^A) \tag{43.8b}$$

This follows because $\mathscr{H}$, as given by (43.1), commutes with P_{12}, and with the components of the total angular momentum $\mathbf{L} = \mathbf{L}_1 + \mathbf{L}_2$, and therefore also with $\mathbf{L}^2$. The same applies to the perturbation $e^2/r_{12} = \mathscr{H} - \mathscr{H}_0$, since the unperturbed operator commutes in a trivial manner with these three operators. The functions (43.6) are chosen in such a manner that they are eigenfunctions of L_z, $\mathbf{L}^2$, and P_{12}:

	L_z	$\mathbf{L}^2$	P_{12}
Φ_{nlm}^S	$\hbar m$	$\hbar^2 l(l+1)$	$+1$
Φ_{nlm}^A	$\hbar m$	$\hbar^2 l(l+1)$	-1

(43.9)

(Note that each component of $\mathbf{L}_1$ when applied to $\phi_0(\mathbf{r}_1)$ gives the result 0.) The different functions corresponding to the same initial energy (i.e. a fixed value of n) belong to different eigenvalues of operators that commute with $\mathscr{H}$ and e^2/r_{12} (cf. §26). This implies the vanishing of the perturbation matrix elements composed of the different functions; the latter are therefore the correct initial functions for the perturbation calculation. The factors are so chosen that the functions are normalized, using the same criteria as for the hydrogen functions.

It can be shown that the energies given by (43.8) do not depend on m. The proof is most simply effected by introducing operators applicable to two particles that are the counterparts of (24.6) or (24.7); such operators change m by one unit and commute with $\mathscr{H}$.

The ground state is the parhelium state (43.7*a*) with zero spin, since there is no antisymmetric spatial function corresponding to it. This state is spherically symmetrical and possesses neither spin nor orbital angular momentum. Apart from this, the unperturbed energies are the same for the parhelium and orthohelium states; however, the orthohelium states possess the triple degeneracy of the corresponding parhelium states since three independent spin functions are associated with each orthohelium term.

The effect of the perturbation can easily be seen qualitatively. Since the perturbation e^2/r_{12} is positive, the first-order perturbation energy is also positive, and all the unperturbed energy values are displaced upwards. The perturbation effect is stronger for Φ^S than for Φ^A, because Φ^A vanishes in the region for which $r_{12} \approx 0$, where the perturbation is strongest. The parhelium energy terms are generally

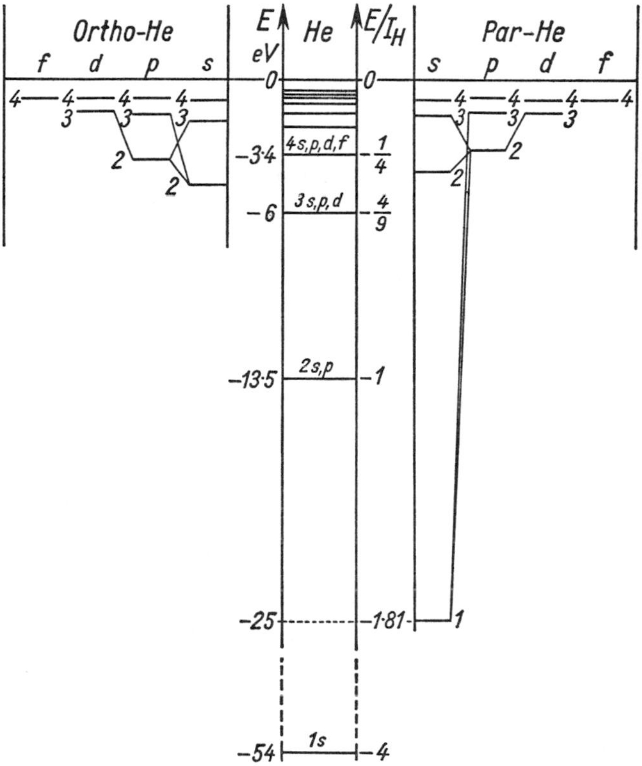

Fig. 42.—Term scheme of the helium atom. The centre column shows the unperturbed energies (43.6) up to the ionization level. On either side are shown the experimental term schemes of ortho- and parhelium

higher than the corresponding energy terms for orthohelium. Figure 42 shows the unperturbed energy values in comparison with the experimental term values. The deviation from the unperturbed energies is quite considerable, which suggests that the method of treating the electron interaction as a perturbation is not a particularly good approximation.

According to (43.6, 43.8) the perturbation energy $(\Phi, (e^2/r_{12})\Phi) = \delta E$ consists of two parts:

$$\delta E_{nl}^S = C_{nl} + A_{nl} \tag{43.10a}$$

$$\delta E_{nl}^A = C_{nl} - A_{nl} \tag{43.10b}$$

In the above expression C_{nl} is the "Coulomb integral"

$$C_{nl} = \int \frac{\rho_0(\mathbf{r}_1)\rho_{nl}(\mathbf{r}_2)}{|\mathbf{r}_1 - \mathbf{r}_2|} d\mathbf{r}_1\, d\mathbf{r}_2 \tag{43.11}$$

where $\rho_0(\mathbf{r}) = e\phi_0^2(\mathbf{r}), \quad \rho_{nl}(\mathbf{r}) = e\phi_{nl0}^2(\mathbf{r})$

This integral represents the Coulomb interaction energy between the charge densities in the states ρ_0 and ρ_{nl}. The "exchange integral"*

$$A_{nl} = \int \frac{\rho_{nl}^A(\mathbf{r}_1)\rho_{nl}^A(\mathbf{r}_2)}{|\mathbf{r}_1 - \mathbf{r}_2|} d\mathbf{r}_1\, d\mathbf{r}_2 \tag{43.12}$$

where $\rho_{nl}^A(\mathbf{r}) = e\phi_0(\mathbf{r})\phi_{nl0}(\mathbf{r})$

is the Coulomb energy of the charge distribution ρ_{nl}^A. Both integrals are positive: the orthohelium terms are therefore less than the corresponding parhelium terms by an amount $2A_{nl}$.

The perturbation calculation using e^2/r_{12} is not accurate enough for it to be worth while employing it to calculate the terms quantitatively. In particular, the perturbation in the case of the excited states is fairly large. It seems reasonable when selecting the initial functions to take $\phi_0(\mathbf{r})$ with $Z = 2$, but $\phi_{nlm}(\mathbf{r})$ with $Z = 1$, because the nuclear charge is so screened from the outer orbits by ϕ_0 that its effective value is practically 1; the excited states therefore resemble those of hydrogen. Better results are obtained by this method.

(*d*) *The ground state*

The calculation of the ground-state energy needs to be discussed in some detail. The first-order approximation for the energy calculated by the perturbation method is

$$E_0^{(1)} = E_0 + C_0 \tag{43.13}$$

where the unperturbed energy $E_0 = -2Z^2 I_H$, and the Coulomb integral C_0 is given by

$$C_0 = \int \frac{\rho_0(\mathbf{r}_1)\rho_0(\mathbf{r}_2)}{|\mathbf{r}_1 - \mathbf{r}_2|} d\mathbf{r}_1\, d\mathbf{r}_2 \tag{43.14}$$

* The physical meaning and nomenclature of this integral are discussed in the following paragraphs.

From (29.11),

$$\phi_0 = \frac{1}{\sqrt{(\pi a^3)}} \exp -\frac{r}{a} \quad \text{where} \quad a = \frac{1}{Z}\frac{\hbar^2}{me^2} = \frac{a_0}{Z}$$

hence

$$\rho_0(\mathbf{r}) = \frac{e}{\pi a^3} \exp -\frac{2r}{a} \tag{43.15}$$

depends only on the magnitude of r, as does $\Phi(\mathbf{r})$, the potential of the charge distribution $\rho_0(\mathbf{r})$. Instead of calculating Φ from the usual integral

$$\Phi(\mathbf{r}) = \int \frac{\rho_0(\mathbf{r}')}{|\mathbf{r}-\mathbf{r}'|} d\mathbf{r}' \tag{43.16}$$

let us determine this quantity from the equation for the potential

$$\nabla^2\Phi = -4\pi\rho_0, \text{ hence } \frac{1}{r}\frac{d^2}{dr^2} r\Phi(r) = -4\pi\rho_0(r) \tag{43.17}$$

Φ must vanish like e/r at infinity. Integration of (43.17) gives

$$\Phi = \frac{e}{r}\left\{1-\left(1+\frac{r}{a}\right)\exp -\frac{2r}{a}\right\}$$

then

$$C_0 = \int_0^\infty \rho_0(r)\Phi(r) 4\pi r^2\, dr = \frac{5}{8}\frac{e^2}{a}$$

hence

$$C_0 = \frac{5}{8} \times 4I_H \text{ for } Z = 2 \tag{43.14a}$$

The ionization energy would therefore be $1{\cdot}5I_H$, instead of $4I_H$ as in the case of the initial approximation; the experimental value is $1{\cdot}82I_H$. The value calculated by the first approximation is therefore still about $0{\cdot}3I_H$ or 4 eV too high; however, in view of rough approximation used, the agreement is surprisingly good.

A better approximation is obtained if the perturbation W is kept as small as possible. If it can be arranged that the first-order perturbation energy actually disappears, the effect of the perturbation is particularly small and the approximation procedure is optimal. For this purpose the Hamiltonian operator (43.1) is artificially split into two parts,

$$\mathscr{H} = \underbrace{\frac{1}{2m}(\mathbf{p}_1^2+\mathbf{p}_2^2) - Z'e^2\left(\frac{1}{r_1}+\frac{1}{r_2}\right)}_{\mathscr{H}_0} + \underbrace{e^2\left\{\frac{1}{r_{12}} - (Z-Z')\left(\frac{1}{r_1}+\frac{1}{r_2}\right)\right\}}_{W} \tag{43.18}$$

by introducing an effective nuclear charge Z' of such magnitude that, when the average value of W is formed from the eigenfunctions of $\mathscr{H}_0$, it vanishes. The eigenfunctions and eigenvalues of $\mathscr{H}_0$ are those

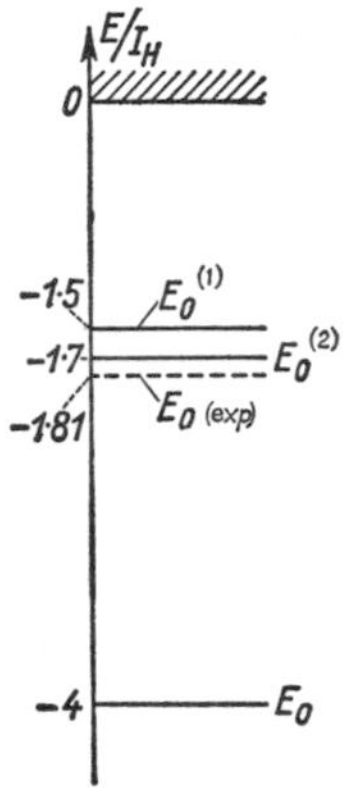

Fig. 43.—Comparison of the various energy values found for the ground state of the helium atom.

E_0(exp): experimental value
E_0: unperturbed value
$E_0^{(1)}$: value with perturbation e^2/r_{12}
$E_0^{(2)}$: value obtained from method of variations with optimum Z'

occurring in the analysis of the hydrogen atom, but with nuclear charge Z' and with $a' = a_0/Z'$. The unperturbed energy is

$$E_0 = -2Z'^2 I_H \tag{43.19a}$$

and the mean value of the perturbation energy is

$$\overline{W} = \frac{5}{8}\frac{e^2}{a'} - (Z-Z')\frac{2e^2}{a'} \tag{43.19b}$$

It follows from the requirement that $\overline{W}=0$ that the best choice of Z' is

$$Z' = Z - \tfrac{5}{16} \tag{43.20}$$

The above approximation leads to a value of about $1{\cdot}7 I_H$ for the ionization energy of helium; this is appreciably nearer the experimental value than the results of the previous approximation (figure 43).

The same choice for Z' can also be substantiated on other grounds. From (43.19), it is clear that $E_0 + \overline{W}$ is simply the expectation value of $\mathscr{H}$, formed from the hydrogen functions with a nuclear charge Z:

$$\overline{\mathscr{H}}(Z') = -\frac{e^2}{a_0}\{Z'^2 - \tfrac{5}{8}Z' + 2Z'(Z-Z')\} \qquad (43.21)$$

Z' is a parameter entering into the wave functions. In accordance with the procedure of §28, the best approximation for the ground state is obtained by choosing Z' so that $\overline{\mathscr{H}}(Z')$ is a minimum: this leads once more to the value for Z' given by (43.20). The energy found by a variational method of this sort must be higher than the exact value. We can also see that the perturbation calculation using e^2/r_{12} must yield an even higher value, since the total energy found by this procedure is $\overline{\mathscr{H}}(Z)$, which is the expectation value of $\mathscr{H}$ when the wave function is not an optimum. If we include still more parameters (say 9 in total) in the trial solution used in the variational method, and in particular, terms containing both $\mathbf{r}_1$ and $\mathbf{r}_2$, it is possible to calculate the position of the ground state with almost spectroscopic accuracy.* The result given by (43.20) can also be expressed as follows: the distributed charge of an electron screens the field of the nucleus to such an extent that the effective nuclear charge for the other electron is just $Z'e$.

From (43.19*a*) and (43.20), the ionization energy I_Z of a nucleus of charge Z with two electrons (i.e. the work of separation of an electron from an ion with positive charge $Z-2$) is

$$I_Z = I_H(2Z'^2 - Z^2) = I_H\{Z^2 - \tfrac{5}{4}Z + 2(\tfrac{5}{16})^2\} \qquad (43.22)$$

A comparison between theoretical and experimental values is given in the following table.

Ionization energy of helium-like ions, from equation (43.22)

Ion	Z	I/I_H theor.	I/I_H exp.†
H^-	1	−0·055	+0·053
He	2	+1·70	1·81
Li^+	3	5·45	5·57
Be^{++}	4	11·20	11·32
B^{3+}	5	18·95	19·08
C^{4+}	6	28·70	28·84
N^{5+}	7	40·45	40·61
O^{6+}	8	54·20	54·39
F^{7+}	9	69·95	70·12

* F. A. Hylleraas, *Z. f. Phys.* 54 (1929), 347.

† Landolt-Börnstein, 6th ed. (1950), Vol. I, part 1, p. 211.

Apart from the case of the negative hydrogen ion the agreement is good. The negative sign of I_1 would mean that the negative hydrogen ion could not exist, since the calculated energy of its ground state is higher than the energy of the hydrogen atom in the ground state. In the present approximation, the electrostatic repulsion exceeds the Coulomb attraction of the single nuclear charge. However, this approximation is not sufficiently accurate to enable the existence of the negative hydrogen ion to be excluded. This ion does in fact exist, and possesses a comparatively small ionization energy* of $0{\cdot}05 I_H$.

§44. The hydrogen molecule

The Hamiltonian operator for the hydrogen molecule may be expressed as follows:

$$\mathscr{H} = \frac{\mathbf{P}_a^2 + \mathbf{P}_b^2}{2M} + \frac{\mathbf{p}_1^2 + \mathbf{p}_2^2}{2m} + e^2 \left\{ \frac{1}{R} + \frac{1}{r_{12}} - \frac{1}{r_{a_1}} - \frac{1}{r_{a_2}} - \frac{1}{r_{b_1}} - \frac{1}{r_{b_2}} \right\} \tag{44.1}$$

In the above expression, a and b refer to the nuclei, 1 and 2 to the electrons, and $R = r_{ab}$ is the distance between the two nuclei (figure 44). Since we have neglected the spin-orbit interaction, the wave function may be expressed as the product of the spin and orbital functions:†

$$\Psi = \psi(\mathbf{R}_a, \mathbf{R}_b, \mathbf{r}_1, \mathbf{r}_2)\chi(s_a, s_b)\eta(s_1, s_2) \tag{44.2}$$

Since $\mathscr{H}$ commutes with the permutation operators P_{ab} and P_{12}, the eigenfunctions of $\mathscr{H}$ can be simultaneously chosen to be eigenfunctions of P_{ab} and P_{12}. Therefore $\psi(\mathbf{R}_a, \ldots)$ is either symmetric or antisym-

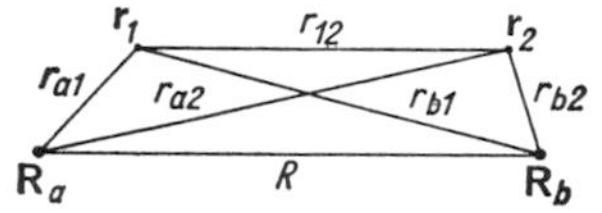

Fig. 44.—Distances between electrons and nuclei in the hydrogen molecule

metric in a,b and $1,2$; in virtue of Pauli's principle, the spin functions χ and η must always have the opposite symmetry to ψ. As in the case of the helium atom, therefore, singlet and triplet states exist due to both nuclear and electron spin.

* The quantity I_1 relating to the negative hydrogen ion is called the *electronic affinity*, by analogy with other atoms such as the halogens, which form negative ions. This affinity is the energy obtained when an electron is picked up by the neutral atom.

† This is possible because there are only two similar particles. When there are several particles the functions (44.2) must be made antisymmetric in their spin and orbital components together.

It is not possible to solve the Schrödinger equation $\mathscr{H}\psi = E\psi$ exactly, but good approximate solutions exist.

We shall now consider the adiabatic approximation due to M. Born and R. Oppenheimer (1927). It is based on the great difference in mass between electrons and protons, as a result of which the latter may be considered to move slowly relative to the electrons in stationary bound states, according to the classical concept of the atom. We shall therefore assume that at each instant the electrons are disposed according to the instantaneous positions of the nuclei, and accordingly express the wave function as follows:

$$\psi(\mathbf{R}_a, \mathbf{R}_b, \mathbf{r}_1, \mathbf{r}_2) = \kappa(\mathbf{R}_a, \mathbf{R}_b)\phi(\mathbf{r}_1, \mathbf{r}_2; \mathbf{R}_a, \mathbf{R}_b) \qquad (44.3)$$

In the above expression ϕ is the wave function for fixed values of $\mathbf{R}_a$ and $\mathbf{R}_b$, and $|\kappa(\mathbf{R}_a, \mathbf{R}_b)|^2 d\mathbf{R}_a d\mathbf{R}_b$ is the probability of finding $\mathbf{R}_a$ and $\mathbf{R}_b$ in $d\mathbf{R}_a$ and $d\mathbf{R}_b$ respectively. ϕ must therefore satisfy the equation

$$\begin{aligned}\mathscr{H}_{el}\phi &= \left\{\frac{\mathbf{p}_1^2+\mathbf{p}_2^2}{2m} + e^2\left(\frac{1}{r_{12}} - \frac{1}{r_{a_1}} - \frac{1}{r_{a_2}} - \frac{1}{r_{b_1}} - \frac{1}{r_{b_2}}\right)\right\}\phi \qquad (44.4)\\ &= E_{el}(R)\phi\end{aligned}$$

In this equation $E_{el}(R)$ is the energy of the electrons expressed as a function of the positions of the nuclei: for reasons of symmetry this quantity must be a function of the interval $|\mathbf{R}_a - \mathbf{R}_b| = R$ alone.

If we insert (44.3) in the Schrödinger equation $\mathscr{H}\psi = E\psi$, and then multiply by ϕ^* and integrate over $\mathbf{r}_1$ and $\mathbf{r}_2$, we obtain

$$\int \phi^* \left\{\frac{\mathbf{P}_a^2+\mathbf{P}_b^2}{2M} + \frac{e^2}{R} + \mathscr{H}_{el}\right\}\phi\kappa \, d\mathbf{r}_1 \, d\mathbf{r}_2 = E\kappa \int |\phi|^2 \, d\mathbf{r}_1 \, d\mathbf{r}_2$$

ϕ may be assumed to be real and normalized without loss of generality. Then since

$$\mathbf{P}_a^2 \kappa\phi = \phi \mathbf{P}_a^2 \kappa + \kappa \mathbf{P}_a^2 \phi + 2(\mathbf{P}_a \kappa)(\mathbf{P}_a \phi)$$

and
$$\int \phi^* \mathbf{P}_a \phi \, d\mathbf{r}_1 \, d\mathbf{r}_2 = \mathbf{P}_a \tfrac{1}{2} \int \phi^2 \, d\mathbf{r}_1 \, d\mathbf{r}_2 = \frac{\hbar}{2i}\frac{\partial}{\partial \mathbf{R}_a} 1 = 0$$

we obtain from (44.4) the following result:

$$\left\{\frac{\mathbf{P}_a^2+\mathbf{P}_b^2}{2M} + \int \phi^* \left(\frac{\mathbf{P}_a^2+\mathbf{P}_b^2}{2M}\right)\phi \, d\mathbf{r}_1 \, d\mathbf{r}_2 + E_{el}(R) + \frac{e^2}{R}\right\}\kappa = E\kappa \qquad (44.5)$$

We shall see later that ϕ depends essentially only on the differences $\mathbf{R}_a-\mathbf{r}_1$, etc. The order of magnitude of the second term in (44.5) is therefore $(\phi, [(\mathbf{p}_1^2+\mathbf{p}_2^2)/2M]\phi)$, i.e. smaller than the kinetic energy $(\phi, [(\mathbf{p}_1^2+\mathbf{p}_2^2)/2m]\phi)$ of the electrons by a factor m/M; this term can therefore be neglected in comparison with $E(R)$. Hence from (44.5)

$$\left\{\frac{\mathbf{P}_a^2+\mathbf{P}_b^2}{2M}+E_{el}(R)+\frac{e^2}{R}\right\}\kappa = E\kappa \tag{44.6}$$

It is evident that the total energy of the electrons appears as the potential energy of the nuclei. The solution of the problem reduces approximately to the solution of equations (44.4) and (44.6).

The translational and rotational motions can be separated in the usual way in equation (44.6). We introduce the coordinates $\mathbf{R}_s = \frac{1}{2}(\mathbf{R}_a+R_b)$ and $\mathbf{R}=\mathbf{R}_a-\mathbf{R}_b$, and put

$$\kappa = \exp(i\mathbf{K}\mathbf{R}_s)Y_{lm}(\Theta,\Phi)\frac{u(R)}{R}$$

Substituting for κ in (44.6) yields the following equation for u:*

$$-\frac{\hbar^2}{M}u''+\left\{\frac{\hbar^2 l(l+1)}{MR^2}+E_{el}(R)+\frac{e^2}{R}\right\}u = \left(E-\frac{\hbar^2\mathbf{K}^2}{4M}\right)u \tag{44.7}$$

In order that the molecule should possess a bound state, the function $V(R)=E_{el}(R)+e^2/R$ must possess a minimum corresponding to a definite equilibrium interval a. In the lowest energy states of the molecule only small vibrations can occur about the equilibrium position. We may therefore expand the expression in curly brackets in (44.7) about a:

$$\frac{\hbar^2 l(l+1)}{MR^2}+V(R) = \frac{\hbar^2 l(l+1)}{Ma^2}+V(a)+\tfrac{1}{4}M\omega^2(a-R)^2$$

If we neglect the displacement of the minimum of $V(R)$ due to the centrifugal force, we have the following relations:

$$\left.\frac{dV(R)}{dR}\right|_{R=a} = 0;\quad \tfrac{1}{4}M\omega^2 = \frac{1}{2}\frac{d^2}{dR^2}V(R)\bigg|_{R=a}$$

Then from (44.7) we obtain the equation of a harmonic oscillator with energy levels $E_{osc} = \hbar\omega(n+\frac{1}{2})$.

* Note that the reduced mass $\frac{1}{2}M$ occurs in place of M in the equation of relative motion.

Thus we arrive at the result that the total energy of the molecule may be divided as follows:

$$E = E_{trans} + E_{rot} + E_{osc} + V(a) \tag{44.8}$$

We wish to compare the order of magnitude of each of the above terms:

$E_{trans} = \dfrac{\hbar^2}{4M}\mathbf{K}^2 \approx \dfrac{\hbar^2}{M\lambda^2}$, where λ is the de Broglie wavelength corresponding to the translational momentum.

$E_{rot} = \dfrac{\hbar^2 l(l+1)}{Ma^2} \approx \dfrac{\hbar^2}{Ma^2}$, where a is the molecular equilibrium distance.

$$E_{osc} = \hbar\omega(n+\tfrac{1}{2}) \approx \hbar\sqrt{\frac{E''_{el}(a)}{M}} \approx \left(\frac{M}{m}\right)^{1/2}\frac{\hbar^2}{Ma^2}$$

$$V(a) \approx \frac{\hbar^2}{ma^2} = \frac{M}{m}\frac{\hbar^2}{Ma^2}$$

(We have assumed that $V(a)$ is of the same order of magnitude as the kinetic energy, since the potential energy is approximately equal to this quantity. $E''_{el}(a)$ is of the same order of magnitude as $\hbar^2/ma^4$.) In a gas consisting of diatomic molecules, translational motion is first produced, followed by rotational motion, and then by molecular vibrations, as the temperature is increased. With a further increase in temperature electron transitions may be excited; however, dissociation often occurs first.

The dissociation energy is given by $D = 2\varepsilon_0 - E_0$, where ε_0 is the energy of a free atom and the energy of the ground state of the molecule is $E_0 = V(a) + \frac{1}{2}\hbar\omega$.

There is a further point with regard to Pauli's principle, in connection with the rotational spectrum. The wave function $Y_{lm}(\Theta, \Phi)$ is symmetric in $\mathbf{R}_a$ and $\mathbf{R}_b$ if l is even, and antisymmetric if l is odd (cf. Exercise 1, p. 152). Since $\mathbf{R}_s$ is symmetric in $\mathbf{R}_a$ and $\mathbf{R}_b$ and the same is true of the wave function $\phi(\mathbf{r}_1, \mathbf{r}_2;\ \mathbf{R}_a, \mathbf{R}_b)$ of the bound states (as we shall see in §45), nuclear-spin function triplets correspond to odd values of l, and singlets to the even values; this is a consequence of Pauli's principle. The nuclear triplet states are called *orthohydrogen*, and the singlets *parahydrogen*, by analogy with the terminology used for helium. At high temperatures molecular hydrogen is a mixture of ortho- and parahydrogen in the ratio of 3 to 1; in this case all rotation states are excited with equal probability and the ratio depends only on the relative weights of the spin functions. At low temperatures no rotation terms are excited, and the hydrogen molecule should therefore occur in the para form. However, as a result of the almost total prohibition of singlet to triplet transitions, it takes many days before the pure gas reaches the new state of equilibrium after its temperature is lowered. Once this equilibrium has been achieved and the temperature is raised once more, it takes equally long for orthohydrogen to appear, which it does as a result of the weak nuclear spin interactions during molecular collisions.

The difference between the rotational terms of ortho- and parahydrogen is particularly noticeable experimentally, both in the rotation spectrum and in the rotational contribution to the specific heat. The specific heat of a 3:1 mixture of ortho- and parahydrogen is obtained by cooling below room temperature; heating pure parahydrogen from very low temperatures gives the specific heat of this form alone. It is clear from the above account that Pauli's principle can entail quite surprising and far-reaching experimental results.

§45. Chemical bonds

In §44 we assumed that the total potential energy $V(R)$ of the nucleus possessed a minimum; we now wish to know how this comes about.

While many questions concerning the heteropolar or ionic bond had been successfully dealt with before the advent of the quantum theory, the homopolar or covalent bond had obstinately resisted every attempt at explanation in terms of classical physics. We shall see that the quantum theory, without requiring any additional assumptions, provides both qualitative and quantitative answers to the problem of the nature of the homopolar bond.

Firstly, we must consider equation (44.4): an exact solution is not available, but approximations to the lowest energy states may be formed from the functions of the hydrogen atom, which have the following form:

$$\phi_0(\mathbf{r}-\mathbf{R}_a), \quad \phi_0(\mathbf{r}-\mathbf{R}_b), \quad \text{where} \quad \phi_0(\mathbf{r}) = \frac{1}{\sqrt{(\pi a_0^3)}} \exp -\frac{r}{a_0}$$

We shall make use of the abbreviations

$$a(1) = \phi_0(\mathbf{r}_1-\mathbf{R}_a), \quad b(1) = \phi_0(\mathbf{r}_1-\mathbf{R}_b)$$

together with similar abbreviations $a(2)$ and $b(2)$.

Four functions of two particles can be constructed from these single-particle functions:

$$a(1)a(2), \quad a(1)b(2), \quad b(1)a(2), \quad b(1)b(2)$$

The complete wave function $\phi(\mathbf{r}_1, \mathbf{r}_2; \mathbf{R}_a, \mathbf{R}_b)$ is expressed as a linear combination of these functions.

The form of these linear combinations is largely determined by the condition that they must be eigenfunctions of P_{ab} and P_{12}. It may easily be verified that this condition is satisfied only by the following combinations:*

$$\phi_A = c_1 \{a(1)b(2) - a(2)b(1)\} \quad P_{ab}\phi_A = P_{12}\phi_A = -\phi_A \tag{45.1}$$

$$\phi_S = c_2 \{a(1)b(2) + a(2)b(1)\} + c_3 \{a(1)a(2) + b(1)b(2)\}$$
$$P_{ab}\phi_S = P_{12}\phi_S = \phi_S \tag{45.2}$$

$$\phi_{AS} = c_4 \{a(1)a(2) - b(1)b(2)\}$$
$$P_{ab}\phi_{AS} = -\phi_{AS} \qquad P_{12}\phi_{AS} = \phi_{AS} \tag{45.3}$$

The subscripts S and A mean symmetric and antisymmetric respectively.

The coefficients c_3 and c_4 multiply functions representing two electrons associated with each nucleus: the corresponding states are termed "polar", although in contrast to the heteropolar or ionic bond the charge of the two electrons is always symmetrically distributed about both nuclei.

We shall omit any consideration of these states in the first instance, and shall investigate the lowest energy state of the two remaining combinations. For this purpose we shall require the mean particle density

$$\rho(\mathbf{r}) = \int |\phi(\mathbf{r}, \mathbf{r}')|^2 \, d\mathbf{r}'$$

for the two states

$$\phi_A = c_1 \{a(1)b(2) - a(2)b(1)\}, \quad \phi_S = c_2 \{a(1)b(2) + a(2)b(1)\} \tag{45.4}$$

The result is

$$\rho_A(1) = \frac{\rho_a(1) + \rho_b(1) - 2S\rho_{ab}(1)}{2(1 - S^2)}, \rho_S(1) = \frac{\rho_a(1) + \rho_b(1) + 2S\rho_{ab}(1)}{2(1 + S^2)} \tag{45.5}$$

* It is not possible to construct a function ϕ_{SA} from the above two-particle functions.

The coefficients c_1 and c_2 are chosen so as to normalize the functions ϕ_A and ϕ_S. Further,

$$\rho_a(1) = a^2(1) \qquad \rho_b(1) = b^2(1) \qquad \rho_{ab}(1) = a(1)b(1)$$

$$S = \int \rho_{ab}(1)\, d\mathbf{r}_1$$

Figure 45 illustrates the variation of the "overlap" integral S with the separation between the nuclei.

In classical physics the expected result would be simply $\rho = \frac{1}{2}(\rho_a + \rho_b)$; the expressions (45.5), on the other hand, exhibit additional terms containing the "exchange density" ρ_{ab}. These are due to the requirement

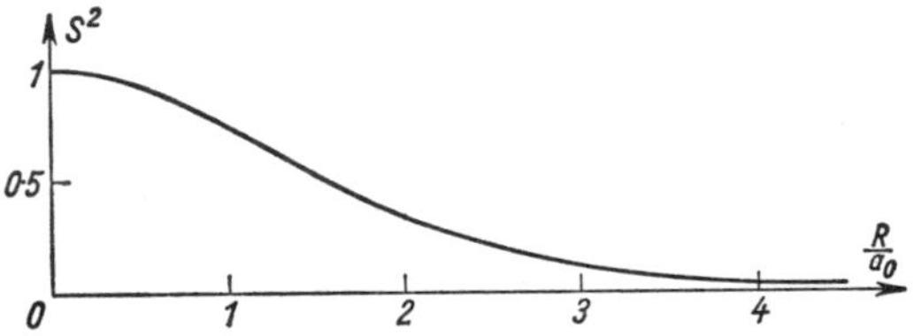

Fig. 45.—The square of the "overlap integral" S as a function of distance from the nucleus

that the stationary states should be eigenfunctions of the symmetry operators P_{ab} and P_{12}; they have no analogue in classical physics. Since the function $\rho_{ab}(\mathbf{r})$ is greatest along the line joining the nuclei ***a***, ***b***, the function ρ_A represents a reduction of the charge density between the nuclei in comparison with the classical value, while ρ_S represents an increase (cf. figure 46). The effect on the nuclei is that ρ_A involves an additional force of repulsion and ρ_S an additional force of attraction. We should therefore expect to find that ϕ_S relates to the bound state of the molecule, and this is in fact the case.

We are now provided with an interpretation of the chemical valency symbols in the case of covalent bonds. Owing to a symmetry effect of quantum mechanics* the electron charge accumulates between the nuclei in the case of those states possessing antisymmetric electron spin; it then acts electrostatically as a "cement" holding the nuclei together.

We now return to the "polar" states. These involve a reduction of the kinetic energy, since they enable each electron to spread over the

* Not to be confused with Pauli's principle.

whole molecule independently of the other. This can perhaps be seen most clearly if we put $c_3 = c_2$ in (45.2); we can then express this equation as follows:

$$\tilde{\phi}_S = c_2 [a(1)+b(1)] [a(2)+b(2)] \tag{45.6}$$

This means that both electrons move around the two nuclei completely independently of each other; this involves an increase in the de Broglie wavelengths of the individual electrons, corresponding to a reduction

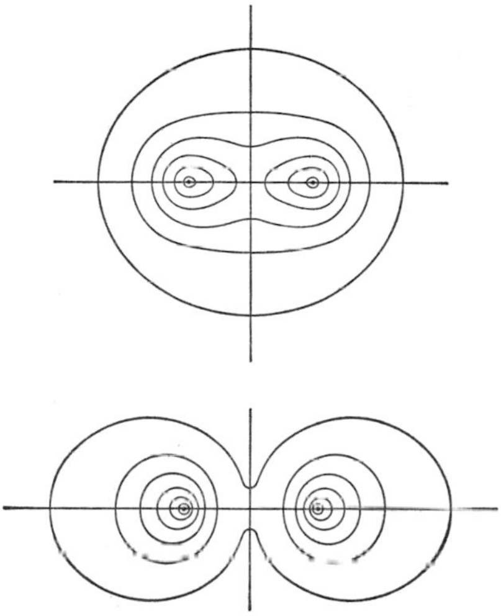

Fig. 46.—Electron density distribution, from (45.5)

of the kinetic energy. On the other hand the potential energy is increased as a result of the Coulomb repulsion between the electrons, since in comparison with ϕ_S as given by (45.4), there is a higher probability of finding two electrons associated with the same nucleus.

If the constants c_2 and c_3 are determined so as to make the energy a minimum, a comparatively small admixture of polar states to ϕ_S is obtained ($c_3 = 0{\cdot}26c_2$). For heavier molecules the proportion of the admixture is higher; in particular, the polar states provide appreciable contributions in the case of metallic bonds.

We shall neglect the polar states in our further discussion of the hydrogen molecule, in which we shall now consider the approximate treatment of W. Heitler and F. London (1927). The energy $E_{el}(R)$ is equal to the expectation value of $\mathscr{H}_{el}$ in the states ϕ_A and ϕ_S. Using (44.4) we obtain

$$E_S(R) = 2\varepsilon_0 + \frac{C+A}{1+S^2} \tag{45.7}$$

$$E_A(R) = 2\varepsilon_0 + \frac{C-A}{1-S^2} \tag{45.8}$$

in which

$$C(R) = e^2 \int \left(\frac{1}{r_{12}} - \frac{1}{r_{a2}} - \frac{1}{r_{b1}} \right) \rho_a(1)\, \rho_b(2)\, d\mathbf{r}_1\, d\mathbf{r}_2$$

is the Coulomb integral,

$$A(R) = e^2 \int \left(\frac{1}{r_{12}} - \frac{1}{r_{a2}} - \frac{1}{r_{b1}} \right) \rho_{ab}(1)\, \rho_{ab}(2)\, d\mathbf{r}_1\, d\mathbf{r}_2$$

the "exchange integral", and

$$\varepsilon_0 = \left(a(1), \left(\frac{\mathbf{p}_1^2}{2m} - \frac{e^2}{r_{a1}} \right) a(1) \right)$$

the energy of the ground state of the hydrogen atom.

As regards the term "exchange integral", it should be realized that it is meaningless to speak of an exchange of electrons, because such an interchange cannot be observed. On the other hand it is quite permissible to say that the two atoms exchange their spins; the frequency of this exchange is actually given by $A/\hbar$ (cf. Exercise 5, p. 272).

For the simple but rather long calculation of the integrals C and A the reader is referred to the original literature;* the results are given in figure 47. As we should expect, the symmetric state provides a bond as a result of the negative sign of $A(R)$.

Agreement with experiment is quite good, but can be appreciably improved by refinements in the expression for the wave function. Firstly, we can treat the nuclear charge number as a parameter in the method of variations (45.4), as we did in the case of helium (§43). This gives an energy level of about 17 per cent below the simple Heitler-London function, when the effective atomic number Z' is 1·166.† In addition, the constant c_3 occurring in (45.2) can also be included as a parameter; this implies that allowance is made for the polar states. We then obtain a further reduction in the energy of 10 per cent, when

* Y. Sugiura, *Z. Phys.* **45** (1927), 484.

† Note that in the present case $Z' > Z = 1$, in contrast to the situation for the helium atom.

$Z' = 1{\cdot}19$ and $c_3 = 0{\cdot}256c_2$. The remaining 25 per cent difference was accounted for by H. M. James and A. S. Coolidge: by making a more accurate allowance for the correlation between the electrons and the

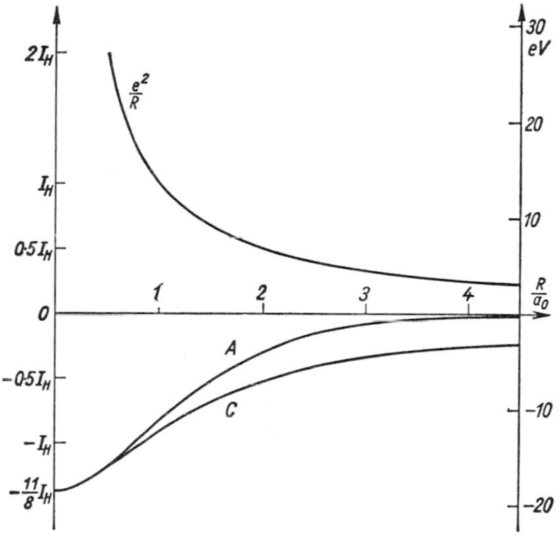

Fig. 47.—Coulomb integral C, exchange integral A, and electrostatic energy of the nuclei e^2/R. When $R \gtrsim 1{\cdot}5a_0$, $-C \approx e^2/R$

factors in the wave function depending explicitly on r_{12}, they obtained values for the energy of dissociation and the inter-nuclear equilibrium distance that agreed with experimental data to within 1 per cent (cf. figure 48).

We now refer to another way of expressing equations (45.7) and (45.8), of importance in connection with ferromagnetism. Owing to the Pauli principle, the symmetric spin function of the electron is associated with ϕ_A and the antisymmetric function with ϕ_S. We may therefore say that the potential energy of the nuclei depends on the setting of the electron spins. Equations (45.7) and (45.8) are put into a new form to make this more apparent:

$$P^s{}_{12}\,\eta_S(s_1, s_2) = \eta_S, \qquad P^s{}_{12}\,\eta_A(s_1, s_2) = -\eta_A \qquad (45.9)$$

In the above equations $P^s{}_{12}$ represents the permutation operator of the spin variables, and η_S and η_A are the symmetric and antisymmetric spin functions. Equations (45.7) and (45.8) can therefore be combined as follows:

$$\mathscr{H}^s(R)\eta = \tfrac{1}{2}\{(1+P^s{}_{12})E_A+(1-P^s{}_{12})E_S\}\eta$$

$$= 2\varepsilon_0\,\eta + \left\{\frac{C-AS^2}{1-S^4} - P^s{}_{12}\,\frac{A-CS^2}{1-S^4}\right\}\eta = E_{el}(R)\eta \qquad (45.10)$$

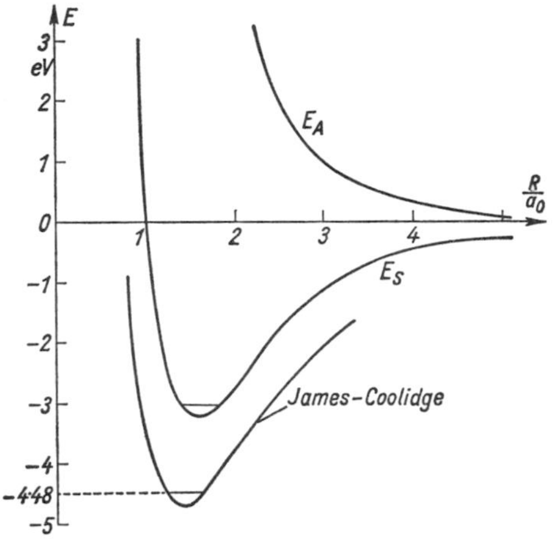

Fig. 48.—The Heitler-London approximation for the potential energy between the two nuclei in the singlet state (E_S) and the triplet state (E_A), compared with the result obtained by H. M. James and A. S. Coolidge for E_S. The lowest state, allowing for the zero-point energy of the oscillation, is shown in each case by a horizontal line. The experimental value for the energy of dissociation is 4·48 eV

η_A and η_S are eigenfunctions of $\mathscr{H}^s$, with respective eigenvalues E_S and E_A. In (45.9) we can replace $P^s{}_{12}$ by $\frac{1}{2}\{1+(\vec{\sigma}_1, \vec{\sigma}_2)\}$, where $\vec{\sigma}_1$ and $\vec{\sigma}_2$ are the Pauli spin operators acting on s_1 and s_2 (cf. Exercise 6, p. 272). Then

$$\mathscr{H}^s(R) = K(R) - \tfrac{1}{2}J(R)(\vec{\sigma}_1,\vec{\sigma}_2) \tag{45.11}$$

where

$$K(R) = 2\varepsilon_0 + \frac{C-AS^2}{1-S^4} - \frac{1}{2}\frac{A-CS^2}{1-S^4}, \qquad J(R) = \frac{A-CS^2}{1-S^4} < 0 \tag{45.12}$$

Since η_A and η_S are eigenfunctions of $\mathscr{H}^s(R)$, the correct spin functions and energies are obtained by solving the eigenvalue equation (45.10) for the spin function η.

Equation (45.10) implies that, for a given internuclear distance R, there is an interaction between the spins that tends to set them antiparallel, since η_A is the ground state. This is clearly expressed by the term $-\frac{1}{2}J(\vec{\sigma}_1, \vec{\sigma}_2)$ in (45.11).

This interaction is purely electrostatic in character and occurs indirectly as a result of Pauli's principle. It has no connection with the magnetic spin-spin interaction (which is also present). Heisenberg advanced the hypothesis (in 1928) that ferromagnetism was due to an exchange interaction of this sort between the spins. According to this theory, the difference between the "ferromagnetic electrons" of iron, cobalt, nickel, etc. (i.e. the electrons of the incomplete inner shells) and the electrons of the hydrogen molecule lies in the fact that J is positive for the former at the equilibrium distance, which is largely determined by the valence electrons (i.e. the electrons of the outer shell). It is not yet possible to decide conclusively whether the situation is really as described, but it is assumed that Heisenberg's theory is correct in its essentials.

Exercises

1. *Energy of an ideal Fermi "gas"*

The spatial components of the eigenfunctions corresponding to the particles of an ideal gas enclosed in a periodicity volume $V = L^3$ are $e^{i\mathbf{kr}}/\sqrt{V}$, where $\mathbf{k} = 2\pi\mathbf{n}/L$ and n_x, n_y, n_z are integers. These functions may also contain a spin function α or β if the particles possess a spin of value $\frac{1}{2}$. The energy is $E = \sum_{j=1}^{n} \hbar^2 \mathbf{k}_j{}^2/2m$, where n is the total number of particles and $\mathbf{k}_1, \ldots, \mathbf{k}_n$ are the propagation vectors represented in the eigenfunctions. In consequence of Pauli's exclusion principle, the $\frac{1}{2}n$ values of $\mathbf{k}$ with the lowest energies contain both α and β spins. What is the maximum value of the magnitude of $\mathbf{k}$, denoted by k_0? What is the energy of the ground state? (Since the $\mathbf{k}$-values lie very close together when the volume is large, the summation should be replaced by integrals.)

2. *Correlations for the ideal Fermi gas*

The single particle functions for the ideal Fermi gas are $\Psi_\lambda(x) = e^{i\mathbf{kr}}\kappa_s/\sqrt{V}$, where x represents the spatial and spin coordinates and λ the quantum numbers $\mathbf{k}$ and s, and

$$\kappa_s = \begin{cases} \alpha \text{ when } s = 1 \\ \beta \text{ when } s = -1 \end{cases}$$

The functions $\Psi_\lambda(x)$ are normalized and orthogonal. The ground state of the gas is

$$\Psi_\Lambda{}^A = \frac{1}{\sqrt{(n!)}} \Sigma(-1)^P \Psi_{\lambda_{P_1}}(x_1) \ldots \Psi_{\lambda_{P_n}}(x_n)$$

The indices λ_i extend over all values of $\mathbf{k}$ corresponding to those of Exercise 1 and the values ± 1 of s. $\Psi_\Lambda{}^A$ is normalized (see below). By integrating over all x_i except x_1 and x_2, we obtain the probability $w(\mathbf{r}_1, s_1, \mathbf{r}_2, s_2)d\mathbf{r}_1 d\mathbf{r}_2$ of finding an electron with spin s_1 in $d\mathbf{r}_1$ and an electron with spin s_2 in $d\mathbf{r}_2$:

$$w = \frac{1}{n!} \int dx_3 \ldots dx_n \Sigma(-1)^P(-1)^{P'} \Psi^*_{\lambda_{P'_1}}(x_1) \ldots \Psi^*_{\lambda_{P'_n}}(x_n) \Psi_{\lambda_{P_1}}(x_1) \ldots \Psi_{\lambda_{P_n}}(x_n)$$

Since the functions Ψ_λ are orthogonal, the only contributing permutations are those for which $P_i = P_i'$ where $i \geqq 3$. The permutations P and P' can therefore differ only in the case of the first two indices: this means that P and P' are either identical or that they simply differ through an interchange $P_1' = P_2$, $P_2' = P_1$. In the first case $(-1)^P(-1)^{P'} = 1$, in the second, -1. (It follows that Ψ_Λ is normalized. When integrating over all x_i we are only concerned with the case $P = P'$; this gives $n!$ times 1.) Hence

$$w = \frac{1}{n!} \sum_P \left(\Psi^*_{\lambda_{P_1}}(x_1) \Psi^*_{\lambda_{P_2}}(x_2) - \Psi^*_{\lambda_{P_2}}(x_1) \Psi^*_{\lambda_{P_1}}(x_2) \right) \Psi_{\lambda_{P_1}}(x_1) \Psi_{\lambda_{P_2}}(x_2)$$

The summation $\sum_P$ may be replaced by a factor $(n-2)!$ corresponding to the number of permutations that leave P_1 and P_2 unchanged, and by a summation over the range of quantum numbers:

$$w = \frac{1}{n(n-1)} \sum_{\lambda, \lambda'} \left(\Psi^*_\lambda(x_1) \Psi^*_{\lambda'}(x_2) - \Psi^*_{\lambda'}(x_1) \Psi^*_\lambda(x_2) \right) \Psi_\lambda(x_1) \Psi_{\lambda'}(x_2)$$

(*a*) Calculate w, replacing the summations over $\mathbf{k}$ by integrals.

(*b*) w is a function of the interval $|\mathbf{r}_1-\mathbf{r}_2| = r$. If $\mathbf{r}_1$, s_1 are fixed, then apart from a normalization factor, $wd\mathbf{r}$ is the probability of finding an electron with spin s_2 at a distance $\mathbf{r}$ from a given electron with spin s_1. Multiplication by the number $\frac{1}{2}n$ of electrons with spin s_2 gives the density $\rho_{s_1 s_2}(\mathbf{r})$ at the distance $\mathbf{r}$ from the electron with spin s_1; in this derivation the small difference between n and $n-1$ is neglected.

$$\rho_{s_1 s_2}(\mathbf{r}) = \tfrac{1}{2}nw(\mathbf{r}_1, s_1; \mathbf{r}_1+\mathbf{r}, s_2)/\int w\,d\mathbf{r} \approx 2Vnw$$

Discuss the densities $\rho_{1,1}$ and $\rho_{1,-1}$, and the total density $\rho_{1,1}+\rho_{1,-1}$ as observed from an electron. Illustrate them diagrammatically.

3. *Polarizability of helium*

Using the formula given in Exercise 5, p. 176, evaluate the polarizability of a helium atom by deriving an approximation to the exact eigenfunction of the ground state in the form of a product of hydrogen functions with an optimum value of Z.

4. *Rotation terms of the deuterium molecule*

The heavy hydrogen isotope, deuterium, has a spin of value 1, and therefore obeys Bose-Einstein statistics. Give the relative weights of the rotation states of D_2 for the different values of l, using a similar argument to that employed in the case of the hydrogen molecule.

5. *The exchange integral and spin interchange in the hydrogen molecule*

A state consisting of the combination

$$\begin{aligned}\phi &= c\{[a(1)b(2)-a(2)b(1)][\alpha(1)\beta(2)+\alpha(2)\beta(1)]+ \\ &\qquad +[a(1)b(2)+a(2)b(1)][\alpha(1)\beta(2)-\alpha(2)\beta(1)]\} \\ &= f_A+f_S\end{aligned}$$

at time $t = 0$ depends on time as follows (cf. §45):

$$\phi(t) = f_A \exp(-iE_A t/\hbar)+f_S \exp(-iE_S t/\hbar)$$

Show that this wave function represents the oscillation of an α and a β spin to and fro between the atoms a and b, and that the frequency of this exchange of spin is approximately given by $A/\hbar$, where A is the exchange integral.

6. *Dirac's identity for the spin vector*

Let $P^s\chi(s_1,s_2) = \chi(s_2,s_1)$. Show that

$$P^s \equiv \tfrac{1}{2}\{1+(\vec{\sigma}_1\vec{\sigma}_2)\}$$

7. *Eigenfunctions of* $\mathbf{S}^2$

Using the identity proved in the previous exercise, determine the eigenfunctions and eigenvalues of

$$\mathbf{S}^2 = \tfrac{1}{4}\hbar^2(\vec{\sigma}_1+\vec{\sigma}_2)^2$$

8. *Van der Waals potential for the Thomson atomic model*

According to §44, the potential energy between the two atoms of the hydrogen molecule decreases exponentially and is negligibly small at distances of a few Bohr radii. The energy calculated in that paragraph is essentially a first-order approximation, in which allowance is made only for the ground states of the hydrogen atoms. At great distances the main contribution is due to the second-order approximation, in which excited states are taken into account in the trial solution for the wave function; this contribution takes the form of a decreasing potential proportional to $1/R^6$ (the van der Waals potential). This potential is to be evaluated for a simple molecular model. Each atom is represented by a Thomson model of radius R_A (figure 49). Electron 1 ($\mathbf{r}_1$) is in nucleus a, electron 2 ($\mathbf{r}_2$) in nucleus b. Symmetrizing effects are unimportant when the inter-nuclear interval R is large.

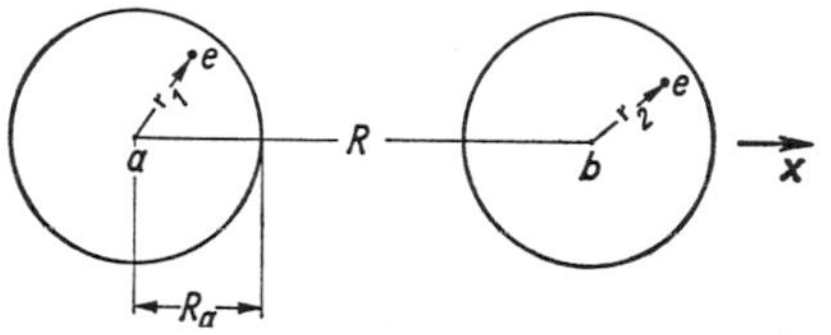

Fig. 49.—Two Thomson atoms

(*a*) Set up the classical equations of motion for each electron. (Since the displacements $\mathbf{r}_1$ and $\mathbf{r}_2$ are assumed to be small, it does not matter whether the field of dipole b is calculated at a or at $\mathbf{r}_1$.) The equation of motion for $\mathbf{r}_1$ contains a component proportional to $\mathbf{r}_1$ and $\mathbf{r}_2$, and similarly for $\mathbf{r}_2$. We thus obtain a system of differential equations for coupled oscillators.

(*b*) Calculate the eigenfrequencies ω_ν.

(*c*) Find the energy of the ground state, $V(R)$. It is the sum of the zero-point energies $\sum_{\nu=1}^{6} \frac{1}{2}\hbar\omega_\nu$. Derive an approximate expression for $V(R)$ for great distances.

(*d*) Obtain the eigenfunction corresponding to the ground state, and calculate the mean values of the individual coordinates and their products. Discuss the significance of the sign of the correlation product $\overline{x_1 x_2}$.

9. *Forces between two helium atoms*

Calculate the potential energy arising between two helium atoms, using the same method as was employed in the case of the hydrogen molecule. The ground state of the atom is assumed to be represented by products of the hydrogen functions a, b with the optimum value of Z. The present calculation is simpler because the ground state is not degenerate. The initial function Ψ^A is the antisymmetric function

$$\Psi^A = \sum_P (-1)^P P\Psi$$

where $\Psi = a(1)\alpha(1)a(2)\beta(2)b(3)\alpha(3)b(4)\beta(4)$
Hence

$$E_{el}(R) = (\Psi^A, \mathscr{H}_{el}\Psi^A)/(\Psi^A, \Psi^A) = (\Psi^A, \mathscr{H}_{el}\Psi)/(\Psi^A, \Psi)$$

In addition, there is the electrostatic interaction of the two nuclei. Express E_{el} in terms of the Coulomb and exchange integrals that were used in the case of the hydrogen molecule; in order to simplify the calculation, assume that the overlap integral S may be neglected except in the exchange integral itself. As a result of this assumption $(\Psi^A, \Psi) \approx 1$; it should also be noted that, in addition to the identical permutation, only P_{13}, P_{24}, and $P_{13}P_{24}$ (with appropriate sign) occur in $(\Psi^A, \mathscr{H}_{el}\Psi)$ because the spin functions are orthogonal.

E

The theory of radiation

CHAPTER EI

Black-body radiation

§46. Thermodynamics of black-body radiation

(a) Kirchhoff's proof of the existence of a universal function $u_\omega(\omega, T)$

If the walls of a completely evacuated enclosure are brought to a definite temperature T, electromagnetic radiation is produced in its interior. A state of equilibrium is attained when the material of the walls absorbs as much radiation energy per unit time as it emits. This radiation is represented by its energy density u; since the radiation is electromagnetic this density has the value

$$u = \frac{1}{8\pi}(\mathbf{E}^2 + \mathbf{H}^2) \tag{46.1}$$

The spectral distribution of the radiation energy is denoted by a function u_ω of ω; $u_\omega d\omega$ represents the portion of the energy density in the elementary angular frequency range $\omega, \omega + d\omega$. Naturally, the following relation is always valid:

$$u = \int_0^\infty u_\omega \, d\omega \tag{46.2}$$

It was found by G. R. Kirchhoff that, at a given temperature, the function u_ω does not depend at all on the nature of the material forming the enclosure; u_ω is determined solely by the temperature, and is completely independent of the material constants of the walls.

Kirchhoff's proof of this law is based on the following argument. Let us assume that there were two enclosures A and B formed within different materials, in which different values of u_ω arose at some point of the spectrum when they were each brought into contact with a heat source of temperature T. Then we could make use of this situation to produce a finite temperature difference between the two heat sources that were originally at the same temperature T, without performing any work. To do this, we should have to place enclosure A in contact with one source and enclosure B in contact with the other; we should then have to reflect (by means of a suitable optical arrangement) a small aperture constructed in A into a similar small aperture in B. The apertures would be covered by filters passing only the "colour" ω for which there is a difference between the two values of u_ω. If for instance u_ω were greater in A than in B, these measures would lead to more energy being radiated into B from A than would be radiated back. In consequence, energy would be abstracted from enclosure A; the temperature of the heat source surrounding A would therefore drop, and that of the source in contact with B would rise. These changes would continue until the value of u_ω was the same for each enclosure. The temperature difference so created could be used to perform mechanical work by means of a heat engine. A difference between the values of u_ω in A and B would therefore permit the construction of a *perpetuum mobile* of the second kind. Therefore by the second law of thermodynamics the value of u_ω in each enclosure must be the same at all frequencies. Since u_ω depends only on ω and on the temperature T, there must be a universal function $u_\omega(\omega, T)$ which gives the spectral distribution of the energy of the black-body radiation at temperature T.

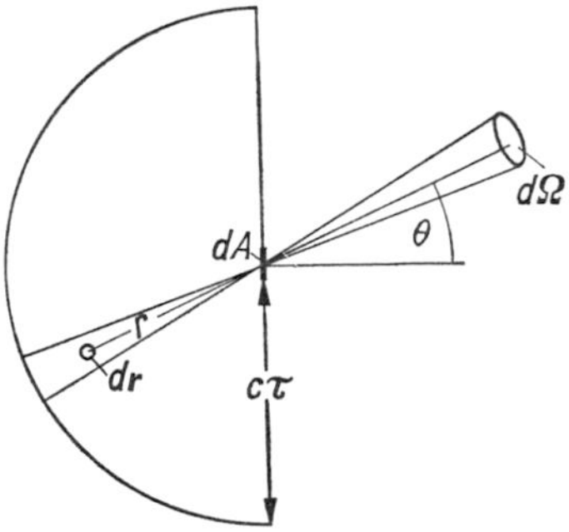

Fig. 50.—Calculation of the radiation intensity

Kirchhoff assigned to physical research the task of discovering this universal function; the stage-by-stage solution of the problem is associated with the names of L. Boltzmann, W. Wien, and M. Planck. When putting forward his law, Kirchhoff did not need to make any assumption regarding the physical nature of the black-body radiation.

Boltzmann and Wien merely used the fact that, for electromagnetic radiation, energy and momentum differ by the factor c. The complete solution was first produced by Planck with the help of his quantum hypothesis.

For further thermodynamic analysis, we need to know the relation between the radiation pressure P and intensity K, and the radiation energy density. Let us consider the radiation energy incident during a small time interval τ on a small element of surface dA of the enclosure boundary (figure 50). Since the energy is propagated with the velocity of light, all points for which $r \leqq c\tau$ contribute to the radiation through dA. A certain fraction $u\,d\mathbf{r}$ of the radiation energy present in the small element of volumc $d\mathbf{r}$ will strike dA. For isotropic radiation, which we shall assume, this fraction is given by the ratio of the solid angle $dA\cos\theta/r^2$ subtended by the element of surface at $d\mathbf{r}$, divided by the total solid angle 4π:

$$u\,d\mathbf{r}\frac{dA\cos\theta}{4\pi r^2}$$

The radiation incident on dA from a given solid angle $d\Omega$ is obtained by integrating over the volume of the cone $d\Omega$ contained in the hemisphere $r < c\tau$:

$$u\frac{c}{4\pi}dA\cos\theta\,d\Omega\tau = K\,dA\cos\theta\,d\Omega\tau, \quad \text{i.e.} \quad K = u\frac{c}{4\pi} \tag{46.3}$$

The total radiation incident on dA is obtained by integrating over the complete hemisphere:

$$u\frac{c}{4}dA\,\tau = S\,dA\,\tau, \quad \text{i.e.} \quad S = u\frac{c}{4} \tag{46.4}$$

$K\cos\theta$ is the energy radiated from the solid angle $d\Omega$, per unit time and per unit area of the boundary wall; S is the corresponding total energy. If dA is a small aperture in the enclosure K and S denote the energy emitted into $d\Omega$ and the total energy, respectively. Equations (46.3) and (46.4) are naturally also valid for each spectral component:

$$K_\omega = u_\omega\frac{c}{4\pi}, \qquad S_\omega = u_\omega\frac{c}{4} \tag{46.5}$$

Since the radiation energy and momentum differ by a factor $1/c$, we can now derive the momentum transferred to the wall, and hence the radiation pressure P. If we assume that the boundary wall is an ideal reflector, the radiation incident at an angle θ will be reflected at the same angle θ to the normal, in accordance with the law of reflection

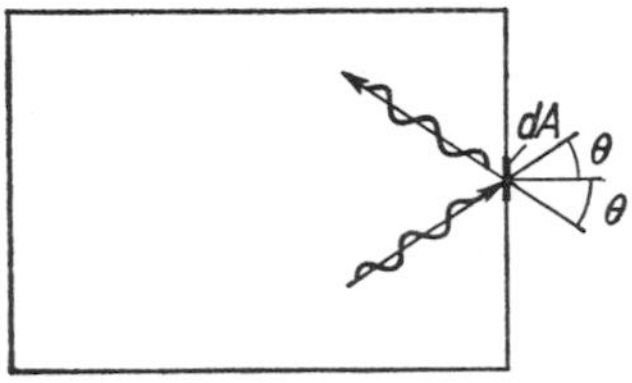

Fig. 51.—Ideal reflection at cavity wall

(figure 51). The momentum in the direction of the normal that is transferred to dA during the interval τ is clearly

$$dA\,\tau \int \frac{K}{c} \cos\theta \,.\, 2\cos\theta \, d\Omega = dA\,\tau \frac{4\pi K}{3c} = dA\,\tau \frac{u}{3}$$

The radiation pressure is therefore

$$P = \frac{u}{3} \tag{46.6}$$

This relation can also be derived from the hypothesis of light quanta (cf. Exercise 1, p. 296).

(*b*) *The Stefan-Boltzmann law and Wien's law*

The laws of Stefan-Boltzmann and of Wien are necessary consequences of the second law of thermodynamics.

In order to derive the Stefan-Boltzmann law we make use of the fact that a reversible heat engine working between two heat sources at temperature T and $T-\delta T$ possesses an efficiency $\delta T/T$. We wish to perform work by making use of the radiation pressure P; we know from (46.6) and Kirchhoff's law that this quantity is a function of temperature alone. The enclosure is provided with a frictionless moving piston and brought into contact with the heat source T. If the volume V is now increased by an amount v as a result of the slow motion outwards of the piston, the radiation pressure performs an amount of work Pv. This results in the extraction of a quantity of heat Q from the heat source, consisting of the energy equivalent of the work performed, Pv, and the increase in the energy content of the enclosure, uv. In total, therefore, $Q=(P+u)v$. We now remove the enclosure from the heat source and lower its temperature by an amount δT by means of an adiabatic expansion of amount δv. We now compress the system isothermally at temperature $T-\delta T$ to the point from which a succeeding adiabatic compression brings it back to the initial state. The net external work performed in this cycle is found from the $P-V$ diagram* (figure 52) to be $\delta P.v$, where δP is the difference in pressure at temperatures T and $T-\delta T\,[\delta P=(dP/dT)\,\delta T]$. From the second law of thermodynamics, this net work must be equal to $Q\,\delta T/T$; hence

$$\frac{dP}{dT}=\frac{P+u}{T}$$

If we put $P=\frac{1}{3}u$ (from (46.6)) in the above equation, integration gives

$$u=\text{constant}\times T^4 \tag{46.7}$$

which expresses the Stefan-Boltzmann law.

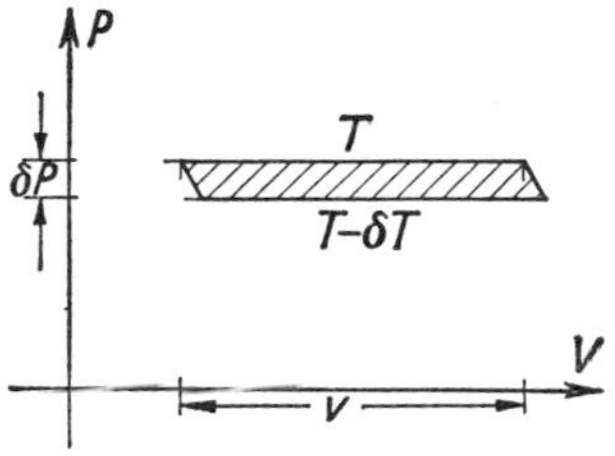

Fig. 52.—*P–V* diagram for the Stefan-Boltzmann law. The work performed is equal to the shaded area

The proof of Wien's law is based on the following argument. We imagine a cavity with a movable piston, and with walls composed of perfectly reflecting material. Only reflections can take place in such a cavity; there can be no absorption or emission processes. When any radiation has once been introduced into the cavity, therefore, the corresponding spectral distribution of energy would exist indefinitely. However, as soon as we introduce a "black" particle capable of absorbing and emitting energy, it will exchange energy with the radiation until the Kirchhoff distribution $u_\omega(\omega,T)$ is established, T being determined by the original total energy of the radiation and the particle.

* The difference between the area shown in figure 52 and the expression $\delta P.v$ is a small quantity of higher order.

The heat capacity of the latter is assumed to be vanishingly small compared with that of the enclosure, so that the total radiation energy uV remains unchanged by this process of producing a "black" distribution. After the Kirchhoff distribution u_ω has thus been established in the enclosure, the particle is removed and the radiation in the cavity is compressed by pressing in the piston with a constant and very small velocity v. This naturally alters the spectral distribution of the energy, since by the Doppler principle a light wave of frequency ω incident on the piston at an angle θ is reflected with an increased frequency

$$\tilde{\omega} = \omega\alpha(\theta) = \omega\left(1+\frac{2v}{c}\cos\theta\right) \tag{46.8}$$

The energy is also increased as a result of reflection at the moving piston, since work is performed by the piston on the radiation to the extent of the factor $\alpha(\theta)$, as we can see from the argument leading to equation (46.6).

The second law of thermodynamics requires that the radiation in the enclosure should retain the form of the Kirchhoff distribution during the course of the compression, as the following argument will show. Let us assume that a radiation density $u'(\omega)$ were to exist in the enclosure after the compression. We could then compare this density with the Kirchhoff radiation $u_\omega(\omega, T')$ at the temperature for which the total energy density is the same, i.e.

$$\int_0^\infty u'(\omega)\,d\omega = \int_0^\infty u_\omega(\omega, T')\,d\omega$$

If $u'(\omega)$ is not equal to $u_\omega(\omega, T')$ at all frequencies, there must be at least one frequency ω_1 for which $u'(\omega_1) > u_\omega(\omega_1, T')$, and another frequency ω_2 for which $u'(\omega_2) < u_\omega(\omega_2, T')$. Now let A and B once more represent two enclosures filled with "black" radiation at temperature T and placed in a heat source at temperature T'. We could then bring A and B into contact with our working enclosure as far as the respective "colours" ω_1 and ω_2 are concerned, using our previous optical arrangement together with coloured filters; by this means, energy would be introduced into enclosure A and extracted from enclosure B. By a suitable choice of exposure times we could always ensure that the total energy in the working enclosure remained unaltered, merely suffering a change in the spectral distribution. Then the pressure inside the working enclosure would also remain unchanged, so that after removal of the optical contact we should obtain exactly the same amount of work from an adiabatic expansion that we previously expended on the compression. The final result would simply be that we would have produced a temperature difference between the two heat sources in contact with A and B, and this is impossible to accomplish without performing work.

We shall now calculate the change in the spectral distribution of the energy $U_\omega d\omega = Vu_\omega d\omega$ in the enclosure in the interval τ, when a piston of area A is inserted with velocity v. If we consider a fixed frequency interval $d\omega = \Delta$, the change in $U_\omega \Delta$ is

$$dU_\omega \Delta = -A\tau\pi K_\omega \Delta + \int_{\omega \leq \tilde{\omega}' \leq \omega+\Delta} A\tau K_{\omega'}\, d\omega' \cos\theta \, d\Omega \, \alpha(\theta) \qquad (46.9)$$

The first term is the total energy in the interval that is incident on the surface A, in accordance with (46.4); as a result of the Doppler effect it will be converted into a different frequency and U_ω will be reduced. The integrand of the second term contains the energy contributions from the various intervals $d\omega'$ that are converted into radiation of frequency $\tilde{\omega}'$, their frequency and energy being altered by a factor $\alpha(\theta)$ on reflection. The fraction of this radiation for which $\omega \leqq \tilde{\omega}' \leqq \omega + \Delta$ produces an increase in U_ω. When Δ is small we have, from (46.9),

$$dU_\omega = -\pi A\tau K_\omega + \int A\tau K\left(\frac{\omega}{\alpha}\right) \cos\theta \, d\Omega \qquad (46.9a)$$

If we expand

$$K\left(\frac{\omega}{\alpha}\right) = K\left(\omega \Big/ \left(1 + \frac{2v}{c}\cos\theta\right)\right) \approx K(\omega) - \frac{\partial K_\omega}{\partial \omega}\omega\frac{2v}{c}\cos\theta$$

and neglect the terms of the second degree in v, the first term of (46.9*a*) cancels, and after integrating over the solid angle 2π there remains

$$dU_\omega = -\frac{4\pi}{3}\frac{\omega v A\tau}{c}\frac{\partial K_\omega}{\partial \omega} \qquad (46.10)$$

Since $vA\tau$ represents the decrease in volume $-dV$ as the piston is moved inwards during the interval τ, (46.10) may also be expressed in the form

$$dU_\omega = \frac{\omega}{3}\frac{\partial U_\omega}{\partial \omega}\frac{dV}{V} = \frac{\omega}{3}\frac{\partial u_\omega}{\partial \omega}dV \qquad (46.11)$$

using the relation (46.5). Equation (46.11) can be looked upon as a partial differential equation of the first order that must be satisfied by the function $U_\omega(V)$:

$$\frac{\omega}{3V}\left(\frac{\partial U_\omega}{\partial \omega}\right)_V = \left(\frac{\partial U_\omega(V)}{\partial V}\right)_\omega \tag{46.12}$$

This implies that $U_\omega(V)$ can only be a function $\psi(\omega^3 V)$, arbitrary in the first instance, of the argument $\omega^3 V$:

$$U_\omega(V) = V u_\omega = \psi(\omega^3 V) \tag{46.13}$$

or putting

$$\psi(\xi) = \xi\phi(\xi)$$

$$u_\omega = \omega^3 \phi(\omega^3 V) \tag{46.13a}$$

From this equation we can deduce the form of the function of interest to us, $u_\omega(T)$. From the first law of thermodynamics, $dU = -P\,dV$ for the adiabatic compression; this equation also follows immediately from (46.11) if we integrate over all ω and put $P = \frac{1}{3}u$. Then since $u =$ const. T^4 it follows that

$$d(VT^4) + \tfrac{1}{3}T^4\,dV = 0 \quad \text{or} \quad VT^3 = \text{const.}$$

Therefore, if we replace V in (46.13*a*) by const./T^3, we obtain

$$u_\omega(T) = \omega^3 f(\omega/T) \tag{46.14}$$

This is Wien's equation, by means of which Kirchhoff's problem is reduced to the determination of the function $f(\omega/T)$ of the single variable ω/T. Integration of (46.14) over the range of ω yields the Stefan-Boltzmann law (46.7); the equation also leads to Wien's displacement law, which states that ω_{max}/T or $\lambda_{max}T$ must possess a fixed universal numerical value at the maxima of the spectral distributions.

The Stefan-Boltzmann law and Wien's equation follow purely as a result of the general laws of thermodynamics and the electromagnetic nature of the radiation. In the next section we shall be concerned with the additional concepts required for the complete evaluation of the function $u_\omega(T)$.

§47. Mathematical model for black-body radiation

According to Kirchhoff's law, the function $u_\omega(T)$ representing the spectral distribution of the radiation energy density in the enclosure is independent of the nature of the enclosure walls and of the manner in which contact is established with the temperature bath T. We are therefore free to choose both in such a way as to make the theoretical treatment as clear as possible. We shall adopt the following model.

The bounding surface of the cavity is assumed to consist of perfectly reflecting walls. Inside the cavity there is assumed to be a linear oscillator in the form of a particle of charge e and mass m, capable of performing elastic oscillations parallel to the x-axis, about an equilibrium position. If E_x is the x-component of the electrical field strength at the particle, and

$$\gamma = \frac{2e^2\omega^2}{3mc^3} \tag{47.1}$$

is the radiation damping (cf. §5), then the equation of motion of the particle is

$$\ddot{x}+\gamma\dot{x}+\omega_0^2 x = \frac{e}{m}E_x \tag{47.2}$$

In order to define the temperature of the system we assume that the cavity contains an electrically neutral gas; this gas interacts with the boundary surface which is heated to the temperature T and thus "imposes the temperature T" on the oscillator by means of molecular collisions with it. On its side, the oscillator maintains contact with the cavity radiation as a result of the properties described by (47.1) and (47.2).

When integrating (47.2) we must take account of the fact that both $x(t)$ and $E_x(t)$ vary greatly and irregularly with respect to time. We are not interested in the values of these functions at any given moment, but in their statistical representation. The most appropriate way of treating such functions is to represent them by means of a Fourier integral:

$$E_x(t) = \frac{1}{\sqrt{(2\pi)}}\int_{-\infty}^{\infty} C(\omega)\, e^{i\omega t}\, d\omega, \text{ where } C(-\omega) = C^*(\omega) \tag{47.3}$$

Substituting this expression for $E_x(t)$ in (47.2), the solution of that equation may be expressed in the form

$$x(t) = \frac{1}{\sqrt{(2\pi)}}\frac{e}{m}\int_{-\infty}^{\infty} \frac{C(\omega)}{-\omega^2+\omega_0^2+i\gamma\omega}\, e^{i\omega t}\, d\omega \tag{47.4}$$

In order to evaluate the above relations we have to make an assumption about the behaviour of the function $E_x(t)$ for large intervals of time. We stipulate that $E_x(t)$ shall only differ from 0 in a finite interval extending from $t = -\frac{1}{2}t_0$ to $t = +\frac{1}{2}t_0$; t_0 can then be arbitrarily large, though finite. Using this assumption, we obtain the following expression for the time average of E_x^2, from (47.3):

$$\overline{E_x^2} = \frac{1}{t_0}\frac{1}{2\pi}\iiint_{-\infty}^{\infty} C(\omega)\, e^{i\omega t}\, C^*(\omega')\, e^{-i\omega' t}\, d\omega\, d\omega'\, dt$$

Since

$$\frac{1}{2\pi}\int_{-\infty}^{\infty} e^{i(\omega-\omega')t}\, dt = \delta(\omega-\omega')$$

it follows that

$$\overline{E_x^2} = \frac{2}{t_0}\int_0^{\infty} |\,C(\omega)\,|^{\,2}\, d\omega$$

Using the abbreviation

$$E_\omega^2 = \frac{2}{t_0}|\,C(\omega)\,|^2 \tag{47.5}$$

we obtain the spectral distribution of the field strength

$$\overline{E_x^2(t)} = \int_0^{\infty} E_\omega^2\, d\omega \tag{47.6}$$

Similarly, from (47.4) and (47.5) we have

$$\overline{x^2} = \frac{e^2}{m^2}\int_0^{\infty}\frac{E_\omega^2\, d\omega}{(\omega^2-\omega_0^2)^2+\gamma^2\omega^2} \tag{47.7}$$

Now in general $\gamma \ll \omega_0$; hence the integral in (47.7) has such a steep maximum at $\omega = \omega_0$ that we may replace E_ω^2 by $E_{\omega 0}^2$. If we take $\mu = \omega - \omega_0$ as the variable of integration, the denominator becomes

$$(\omega-\omega_0)^2(\omega+\omega_0)^2+\gamma^2\omega^2 \approx 4\omega_0^2\,\mu^2+\gamma^2\omega_0^2$$

The approximate integration can then be performed between the limits $-\infty$ and $+\infty$; the result is

$$\overline{x^2} = E_{\omega 0}^2\,\frac{e^2\pi}{m^2\omega_0^2\, 2\gamma} \tag{47.8}$$

To obtain the relation between the mean oscillator energy $\overline{E_{osc}}$ and the spectral energy density $u_\omega d\omega$ in the cavity we must introduce into

(47.8) the value of γ given by (47.1), and the value $m\omega_0^2\overline{x^2}$ for $\overline{E_{osc}}$. For isotropic black-body radiation

$$u_\omega \, d\omega = \frac{1}{8\pi} E_\omega^2 \, . \, 6 \, d\omega$$

where the factor 6 is due to the fact that on average the squares of the three components of **E** and the three components of **H** are all equal. Since the relation (47.8) must hold for every oscillator frequency ω, it follows that for isotropic black-body radiation

$$\overline{E_{osc}} = u_\omega \frac{\pi^2 c^3}{\omega^2}$$

or

$$u_\omega \, d\omega = \overline{E_{osc}} \frac{\omega^2}{\pi^2 c^3} d\omega \tag{47.9}$$

We may observe the following relation, which we shall require later. From §5, the energy radiated per second by a linear oscillator is

$$S = \frac{2e^2\omega^2}{3mc^3} \overline{E_{osc}} \tag{47.9a}$$

Since the oscillator is in equilibrium with the black-body radiation, it must absorb the same amount of energy per second from the latter, at its characteristic frequency. From (47.9), therefore, the energy absorbed per second is

$$A = \frac{2\pi^2 e^2}{3m} u_\omega \tag{47.9b}$$

If we put $\overline{E_{osc}} = kT$ in (47.9), as required by classical statistical mechanics, we obtain the Rayleigh-Jeans formula for black-body radiation:

$$u_\omega(T) \, d\omega = kT \frac{\omega^2}{\pi^2 c^3} d\omega \tag{47.10}$$

This result is obtained from classical physics alone. It leads to the absurd statement that the spectral distribution of the energy density u_ω increases without limit as the frequency increases, and hence that the energy density

$$u(T) = \int_0^\infty u_\omega(T) \, d\omega$$

is infinitely great for all finite values of T. This is the celebrated "ultra-violet catastrophe".

The difficulty was overcome by the Quantum Hypothesis, put forward by Max Planck in the year 1900. If $\overline{E_{osc}}$ is replaced in (47.9) by the value required by the quantum theory,*

$$\overline{E_{osc}} = \frac{\hbar\omega}{\exp\frac{\hbar\omega}{kT} - 1} \tag{47.11}$$

(cf. §9), the result is Planck's formula, which remains finite even when ω tends to infinity:

$$u_\omega(T)\,d\omega = \frac{\hbar\omega}{\exp\frac{\hbar\omega}{kT} - 1}\,\frac{\omega^2}{\pi^2 c^3}\,d\omega \tag{47.12}$$

The above derivation is admittedly open to the objection that we have essentially retained formula (47.9), which was deduced from the arguments of classical physics, in spite of the fact that the inadequacy of these arguments is demonstrated by the mere necessity for the postulate represented by (47.11). The rigour of this objection may be somewhat modified by considering a totally different form of (47.9). This is obtained from a consideration of the characteristic electro-magnetic oscillations in a cavity (such as a cube of side L), and in particular, the number $z(\omega)\,d\omega$ of the oscillations contained in the frequency interval $\omega, \omega + d\omega$. A simple calculation shows that

$$z(\omega)\,d\omega = L^3 \frac{\omega^2}{\pi^2 c^3}\,d\omega \tag{47.13}$$

Equation (47.9) may therefore be written as

$$L^3 u_\omega\,d\omega = \overline{E_{osc}}\,z(\omega)\,d\omega \tag{47.14}$$

In the above expression, the left-hand side denotes the mean energy of all oscillations taking place inside the volume L^3 and lying within the

* Quantum theory also yields the zero-point energy, in addition to (47.11). Strictly speaking, making allowance for this energy also leads to an "ultra-violet catastrophe". However, this is not so important as the difficulty inherent in the classical theory; we must remember that any experimental statement regarding emission and radiation pressure refers only to differences between the radiation cavity and its external surroundings. In the "balance-sheet", the zero-point energy drops out in each frequency interval, and therefore in total. $u_\omega(T)$ as given by (47.12) is the energy density which may be used in conjunction with (46.2) and (46.4) to give the radiation and the pressure in a cavity at temperature T, in comparison with a vacuum at the temperature of absolute zero.

interval $d\omega$. Equation (47.14) therefore simply states that the mean energy of any characteristic oscillation in the cavity is equal to the mean energy $\overline{E_{osc}}$ of a material oscillator with the same frequency.

To provide a strict proof of the above statement, we must first put Maxwell's equations for the cavity into their Hamiltonian form and apply to them the established propositions of statistical mechanics and the quantum theory. We then find that each characteristic oscillation behaves just as if it were a linear oscillator of the corresponding frequency; this result will be proved in detail in §51.

We shall now discuss Planck's formula (47.12) in greater detail, and establish a connection between it and the two familiar laws of black-body radiation, Wien's displacement law and the Stefan-Boltzmann law of total radiation.

Wien's displacement law

If the spectral distribution of the energy is expressed in terms of the wavelength λ instead of the frequency ω, (47.12) gives the following result:

$$u_\lambda \, d\lambda = \frac{16\pi^2 \hbar c}{\lambda^5} \frac{1}{\exp \dfrac{2\pi\hbar c}{\lambda k T} - 1} d\lambda \tag{47.15}$$

We wish to determine the wavelength λ_m for which u_λ is a maximum for any given value of T. The condition for this is $\partial u_\lambda / \partial \lambda = 0$; taking this into account, and using the abbreviation $y = 2\pi\hbar c/\lambda_m kT$, we obtain the equation

$$5(1 - e^{-y}) = y$$

The root of this transcendental equation may be seen to lie in the neighbourhood of $y = 5$. If we put $y = 5 - \eta$ we then obtain the relation

$$5e^{-5} e^{\eta} = \eta$$

Since η is a small number we can replace e^{η} by $1 + \eta$; we then obtain the approximation

$$\eta = \frac{1}{\frac{1}{5}e^5 - 1} = 0{\cdot}035$$

The constant of Wien's displacement law is therefore given by

$$\lambda_m T = \frac{2\pi\hbar c}{ky} = \frac{2\pi\hbar}{k} \frac{c}{4{\cdot}965} \tag{47.16}$$

Simultaneous measurements of λ_m and T on a black body will therefore give the ratio $\hbar/k$ of the two universal constants, named after Planck and Boltzmann. The fact that the maximum for solar radiation lies in the green region, for which $\lambda \approx 0{\cdot}5 \times 10^{-4}$ cm, and that the corresponding value of T is about 6000° K, enable us to determine an approximate figure for the ratio $\hbar/k$.

The Stefan-Boltzmann law of total radiation

The total energy density of black-body radiation is obtained by integrating (47.12):

$$u = \frac{\hbar}{\pi^2 c^3} \int_0^\infty \frac{\omega^3 \, d\omega}{\exp \dfrac{\hbar\omega}{kT} - 1}$$

Introducing $x = \hbar\omega/kT$ as a new variable,

$$u = \frac{\hbar}{\pi^2 c^3} \left(\frac{kT}{\hbar}\right)^4 \int_0^\infty \frac{x^3 \, dx}{e^x - 1}$$

The numerical value of this integral is $\pi^4/15$; this gives

$$u = \frac{\hbar}{\pi^2 c^3} \frac{\pi^4}{15} \left(\frac{kT}{\hbar}\right)^4 \tag{47.17}$$

We have thus determined the constant appearing in the Stefan-Boltzmann law as given by equation (46.7). As a rule direct measurements are not made on the energy density, but on the energy S emitted per second per unit area of the surface of a black body on one side (i.e. into a solid angle 2π). This quantity is related to u by equation (46.4):

$$S = \frac{c}{4} u$$

The energy emitted per second per square centimetre of a black body is therefore

$$S = \sigma T^4, \quad \text{where} \quad \sigma = \frac{\pi^2 k^4}{60 c^2 \hbar^3} \tag{47.18}$$

The measurement of S at a known temperature gives us the ratio $k^4/\hbar^3$; thus, merely by measuring the maximum and the total radiation we can determine the two fundamental constants $\hbar$ and k.

The experimental results are as follows:

$$\lambda_m T = 0{\cdot}290\,\text{cm deg},$$

$$\sigma = 5{\cdot}68 \times 10^{-5}\,\text{erg s}^{-1}\,\text{cm}^{-2}\,\text{deg}^{-4}$$

$$\hbar = 1{\cdot}05 \times 10^{-27}\,\text{erg s},$$

$$k = 1{\cdot}38 \times 10^{-16}\,\text{erg deg}^{-1}$$

A knowledge of Boltzmann's constant enables us to determine Avogadro's number N and the elementary electric charge e:

$$N = \frac{R}{k} = \frac{8{\cdot}31 \times 10^7}{1{\cdot}38 \times 10^{-16}} = 6{\cdot}02 \times 10^{23}$$

$$e = \frac{F}{N} = \frac{96{,}500}{6{\cdot}02 \times 10^{23}}\,\text{C} = 1{\cdot}60 \times 10^{-19}\,\text{C} = 4{\cdot}80 \times 10^{-10}\,\text{e.s.u.}$$

This method of Planck's for determining the elementary electric charge from radiation measurements alone deserves particular consideration, being by far the most accurate at the time (1900). It was only much later that it was surpassed in accuracy by the measurements of Millikan, which were described in Vol. I.

Planck's formula (47.12) may be expressed in a somewhat simpler form when the ratio $\hbar\omega/kT$ is either very large or very small compared with 1. The results for these two limiting cases are as follows.

$$\hbar\omega \gg kT: \quad u_\omega = \frac{\hbar\omega^3}{\pi^2 c^3} \exp -\frac{\hbar\omega}{kT} \tag{47.19}$$

$$\hbar\omega \ll kT: \quad u_\omega = \frac{\omega^2}{\pi^2 c^3} kT \tag{47.20}$$

Formula (47.19), known as Wien's radiation formula, had been established by W. Wien before Planck had put forward his hypothesis; however, it contained an undetermined numerical factor. The formula represents quite accurately the ultra-violet part of the energy distribution including the maximum. The other limiting case covered by Planck's formula, (47.20), is identical with the Rayleigh-Jeans radiation law (47.10); this is only to be expected in view of the method of derivation. When Planck's formula was put forward, therefore, it provided a connection between the experimentally verified equation (47.19) and the equation (47.20), which had been deduced from classical theory (cf. figure 53).

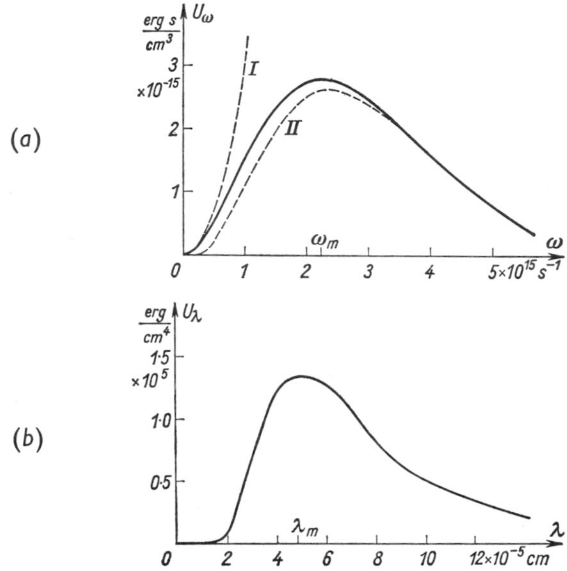

Fig. 53.—Spectral distribution of black-body radiation for $T = 6000°K$
(*a*) Planck's distribution, Rayleigh-Jeans law (I), and Wien radiation formula (II), as functions of the angular frequency ω.
(*b*) Planck's distribution as a function of the wavelength λ.

§48. Einstein's derivation of Planck's formula

Einstein, whose process of reasoning was of decisive importance in connection with the concepts of the quantum theory, successfully advanced a self-consistent proof of Planck's formula.* It is characteristic of the derivation that it demands a minimum number of basic assumptions. These are set out below.

1. If E_s and E_n are two non-degenerate energy levels of an atom ($E_n > E_s$), the latter reacts with the black-body radiation by emitting or absorbing light quanta of magnitude

$$\hbar\omega_{ns} = E_n - E_s \tag{48.1}$$

depending on whether it is in the state n or the state s.

* A. Einstein, *Phys. Z.* **18** (1917), 121.

2. Let there be a number of such atoms (e.g. free gas atoms) in a cavity at temperature T. In particular,

$$N_s = \text{number of atoms in the state } s,$$

$$N_n = \text{number of atoms in the state } n.$$

Then when the system is in thermal equilibrium it follows from a basic formula of statistical mechanics that

$$\frac{N_n}{N_s} = \frac{\exp -E_n/kT}{\exp -E_s/kT} \tag{48.2a}$$

and therefore

$$N_n = N_s \exp -\frac{\hbar\omega_{ns}}{kT} \tag{48.2b}$$

3. In the limiting case for which $\hbar\omega_{ns} \ll kT$ the laws of classical physics and hence the Rayleigh-Jeans formula

$$u(\omega_{ns}) \to \frac{\omega_{ns}^2}{\pi^2 c^3} kT \tag{48.3}$$

are valid.

We now consider in turn the number Z_{sn} of transitions from s to n taking place in the time dt, and the number Z_{ns} of opposite processes. At equilibrium, both numbers must be the same. We take the number of absorption processes Z_{sn} to be proportional to N_s and to the energy density $u(\omega_{ns})$ of the radiation at the corresponding frequency, and include a constant B_{sn} that is characteristic of the absorption:

$$Z_{sn} = N_s B_{sn} u(\omega_{ns})\, dt \tag{48.4}$$

The number of emission processes is proportional to N_n. We now have to distinguish between two types of emission. The first is spontaneous emission, which is independent of u, and which is represented by the probability $A_{ns} dt$ of a spontaneous transition from n to s in the interval dt. The second type is "forced" emission, proportional to $u(\omega_{ns})$, and expressed as $B_{ns} u(\omega_{ns})$. In total, therefore,

$$Z_{ns} = N_n [A_{ns} + B_{ns} u(\omega_{ns})]\, dt \tag{48.5}$$

The forced emission introduced here corresponds in classical physics to a vibrating oscillator which can extract energy from an incident electric wave, or convey energy to it, depending on the phase angle between the vibration and the electric field of the wave. Now it follows from the condition $Z_{ns}=Z_{sn}$, bearing in mind (48.2), that

$$\exp\frac{\hbar\omega_{ns}}{kT}B_{sn}\,u = A_{ns}+B_{ns}\,u$$

from which

$$u(\omega_{ns}) = \frac{A_{ns}}{B_{sn}\exp\dfrac{\hbar\omega}{kT}-B_{ns}} \tag{48.6}$$

where $\omega_{ns}=\omega$.

In order to apply our third postulate we take $\hbar\omega/kT \ll 1$. Then

$$u(\omega_{ns}) \rightarrow \frac{A_{ns}}{B_{sn}-B_{ns}+B_{sn}\dfrac{\hbar\omega}{kT}}$$

In order that this formula should be identical with (48.3) we must have

$$B_{sn} = B_{ns} \tag{48.7}$$

that is, the forced emission and the absorption constants must be equal. In addition we must have

$$\frac{A_{ns}}{\hbar\omega B_{sn}}kT = \frac{\omega^2}{\pi^2c^3}kT$$

i.e. the following relationship must exist between A_{ns} and B_{ns}:

$$\frac{A_{ns}}{B_{ns}} = \frac{\hbar\omega^3}{\pi^2c^3} \tag{48.8}$$

When the relations (48.7) and (48.8) between the initially arbitrary coefficients A and B are introduced into (48.6), Planck's formula

$$u(\omega) = \frac{\omega^2}{\pi^2c^3}\frac{\hbar\omega}{\exp\hbar\omega/kT-1}$$

is obtained.

The characteristic feature of the description of absorption and emission given by (48.4) and (48.5) is that it assumes that the occurrence of each elementary process is due to chance. Thus $A_{ns}dt$ is simply the probability that an atom in state n changes to the state s as a result of the spontaneous emission of a quantum $\hbar\omega_{ns}$, during the interval dt.

Most physicists were at first inclined to look upon this representation as a provisional expedient. It was only the further development of the quantum theory that showed that the physical situation was in a sense completely described by the statistical postulates (48.4) and (48.5). We shall see in §53 how the coefficients A_{ns} and B_{ns} can actually be calculated by means of the quantum theory.

Even without such a calculation, however, Einstein's relations (48.7) and (48.8) enable an important connection to be established between the coefficients A_{ns} and the oscillator strengths f_{ns} introduced in the theory of dispersion; this was first demonstrated by R. Ladenburg. We shall calculate the energy absorbed by an atom obeying the dispersion formula

$$n-1 = N\sum_s \frac{2\pi e^2}{m}\frac{f_{ns}}{\omega_{ns}^2-\omega^2}$$

in the neighbourhood of a given line ω_{ns} and over an interval dt, when it is in an isotropic radiation field of spectral energy density u_ω. From (47.9*b*) this energy is

$$f_{ns}\frac{2\pi^2 e^2}{3m}u(\omega_{ns})\,dt$$

Using Einstein's representation of the absorption process, the same energy is given by

$$\hbar\omega_{ns}B_{ns}u(\omega_{ns})\,dt$$

If the above expressions are equated to each other and the relation (48.8) is introduced, we obtain

$$A_{ns} = \frac{2}{3}\frac{e^2\omega_{ns}^2}{mc^3}f_{ns} = \gamma f_{ns} \tag{48.9}$$

This equation shows that it is possible to obtain quantitative estimates of spontaneous transition probabilities from measurements of dispersion. This method is much more exact and reliable than the one based on the duration of the luminosity of canal rays in Wien's well-known experiment.

If we introduce into (48.9) the value of f_{ns} given by (41.10),

$$f_{ns} = \frac{2m\,|x_{ns}|^2\,\omega_{ns}}{\hbar} \tag{48.10}$$

we obtain equation (11.9) for the probability of spontaneous emission, which we had previously inferred from the correspondence principle.

For the three-dimensional case we must add the contributions $|y_{ns}|^2$ and $|z_{ns}|^2$ due to the other two vibrational directions; the formula then becomes identical with (11.9*a*).

This agreement provides strong support for the validity of the argument of §11, based on the correspondence principle, and leading to equation (48.9). However, a self-consistent proof of this equation can be given only in terms of the quantum theory of the electromagnetic field (§53).

Exercises

1. *Pressure and energy density in an ideal gas*

A gas consisting of atoms of rest mass m is present in a container. The density of the atoms is n, and the distribution of the momentum is given by $f(\mathbf{p})d\mathbf{p}$, which is the number of atoms per cubic centimetre possessing a momentum in the range $(\mathbf{p}, d\mathbf{p})$ $(\int f d\mathbf{p} = n)$. The pressure P is defined as the momentum transferred to the container walls by collisions with the atoms, per unit time and per unit area. The collisions are assumed to be elastic, and the distribution $f(\mathbf{p})$ is isotropic. Show that

$$P = \frac{2}{3} n \overline{E_{kin}} \text{ in the non-relativistic limit,}$$

$$P = \frac{1}{3} n \overline{E} \text{ in the limit } \overline{E} \gg mc^2.$$

E is the total energy, E_{kin} the kinetic energy. The mean values are defined by

$$\overline{F} = \frac{\int F(\mathbf{p}) f(\mathbf{p}) d\mathbf{p}}{\int f(\mathbf{p}) d\mathbf{p}} = \frac{1}{n} \int F(\mathbf{p}) f(\mathbf{p}) d\mathbf{p}$$

The first relation gives the ideal gas equation if we put $\overline{E_{kin}} = \frac{3}{2} kT$; the second relation gives the connection between pressure and energy density (equation (46.6)) for a gas consisting of light quanta, for which $m = 0$.

2. *The solar constant*

The temperature of the sun's surface is about 6000°K. Using (47.17), calculate the solar constant S, i.e. the solar energy radiated per minute on to 1 cm^2 of the surface on the earth normal to the incident radiation. (The angle δ subtended by the sun at the earth is about $\frac{1}{2}$°.)

CHAPTER EII

Absorption and emission

§49. The classical treatment of absorption and anomalous dispersion

The theory of dispersion that was given in §40 applies only to the transparent region outside the spectral lines (i.e. $\omega \neq \omega_0$). In order to describe the behaviour within the lines, we must include the damping in the equation of motion for the electron. This equation then becomes

$$\ddot{\mathbf{r}}+\gamma\dot{\mathbf{r}}+\omega_0^2\mathbf{r} = \frac{e}{m}\mathbf{E} \tag{49.1}$$

If **E** depends on time through the factor $e^{i\omega t}$, the solution of (49.1) is given by

$$\mathbf{r}(t) = \frac{e}{m}\frac{1}{\omega_0^2-\omega^2+i\gamma\omega}\mathbf{E} \tag{49.2}$$

We shall first consider the balance of energy in the system. The work done by the field on the electron in the time interval dt is $e\mathbf{E}\dot{\mathbf{r}}dt$. From (49.1) the mean power due to **E** is therefore

$$e\overline{\mathbf{E}\dot{\mathbf{r}}} = m\gamma\overline{\dot{\mathbf{r}}^2} \tag{49.3}$$

since the mean values of

$$\ddot{\mathbf{r}}\dot{\mathbf{r}} = \frac{1}{2}\frac{d}{dt}\dot{\mathbf{r}}^2 \quad \text{and} \quad \mathbf{r}\dot{\mathbf{r}} = \frac{1}{2}\frac{d}{dt}(\mathbf{r}^2)$$

are equal to zero for periodic motion. This power is to be compared with the mean radiated power of the electron, which is

$$S = \frac{2}{3}\frac{e^2}{c^3}\overline{\ddot{\mathbf{r}}^2} = \frac{2}{3}\frac{e^2}{c^3}\omega^2\overline{\dot{\mathbf{r}}^2} \tag{49.4}$$

Now (49.3) represents the energy withdrawn from the field per second, while equation (49.4) gives the energy which is returned to the field in the form of radiation. Both these quantities are equal when γ has the usual value for the radiation damping

$$\gamma_{rad} = \frac{2}{3}\frac{e^2\omega^2}{mc^3}$$

If γ is greater than γ_{rad}, part of the power $e\mathbf{E}\dot{\mathbf{r}}$ is converted into heat, e.g. into kinetic energy of the atoms.

The order of magnitude of the ratio γ_{rad}/ω is of some interest: it is

$$\gamma_{rad}/\omega = \frac{2}{3}\frac{e^2/mc^2}{c/\omega} \approx \frac{R_{el}}{\lambda}$$

In the above expression, R_{el} is the classical electron radius ($\approx 10^{-13}$cm) and λ the wavelength employed ($\approx 10^{-5}$cm).

If we make use of (49.2) to express the current density $\mathbf{j} = Ne\dot{\mathbf{r}}$, and substitute in the first of Maxwell's equations,

$$\operatorname{curl}\mathbf{H} = \frac{4\pi}{c}\mathbf{j} + \frac{1}{c}\dot{\mathbf{E}}$$

we obtain

$$\operatorname{curl}\mathbf{H} = \frac{\varepsilon}{c}\dot{\mathbf{E}}, \text{ where } \varepsilon = 1 + 4\pi N\frac{e^2}{m}\frac{1}{\omega_0^2 - \omega^2 + i\gamma\omega} \tag{49.5}$$

We then obtain the following equations for a wave travelling parallel to the z-axis, and polarized parallel to the x-axis:

$$E_x = a\exp i\omega\left(t - \frac{\sqrt{\varepsilon}}{c}z\right), \qquad H_y = a\sqrt{\varepsilon}\exp i\omega\left(t - \frac{\sqrt{\varepsilon}}{c}z\right) \tag{49.6}$$

If we put

$$\sqrt{\varepsilon} = n - i\kappa \tag{49.7}$$

where n and κ are real, then the real part of the solution is

$$E_x = a\exp\left(-\frac{\omega\kappa}{c}z\right)\cos\omega\left(t - \frac{n}{c}z\right)$$

$$H_y = a(n^2+\kappa^2)^{1/2}\exp\left(-\frac{\omega\kappa}{c}z\right)\cos\left[\omega\left(t - \frac{n}{c}z\right) - \psi\right] \tag{49.8}$$

where $\tan\psi = \kappa/n$, $\sqrt{\varepsilon} = (n^2+\kappa^2)^{1/2}\,e^{-i\psi}$:

The time average of the Poynting vector $\mathbf{S} = (c/4\pi)\mathbf{E} \times \mathbf{H}$ is

$$S_z = S = \frac{c}{8\pi} n a^2 \exp - \frac{2\omega\kappa}{c} z$$

The reduction in intensity over the distance dz is thus

$$dS = -\frac{2\omega\kappa}{c} S\, dz \tag{49.9}$$

n is termed the (real) refractive index, and κ the extinction coefficient. If the gas is sufficiently rarefied it can be assumed that $|\varepsilon - 1| \ll 1$; then $\sqrt{\varepsilon} = 1 + \frac{1}{2}(\varepsilon - 1)$ approximately, whence

$$n = 1 + 2\pi N \frac{e^2}{m} \frac{\omega_0^2 - \omega^2}{(\omega_0^2 - \omega^2)^2 + \gamma^2\omega^2}$$

$$\kappa = 2\pi N \frac{e^2}{m} \frac{\gamma\omega}{(\omega_0^2 - \omega^2)^2 + \gamma^2\omega^2} \tag{49.10}$$

In order to see how the above quantities vary in the neighbourhood of a spectral line, we shall put

$$\omega = \omega_0 + \mu$$

When $|\mu| \ll \omega_0$, $\omega_0^2 - \omega^2 = -2\mu\omega_0$. Elsewhere we may replace ω by ω_0. Then

$$n = 1 + 2\pi N \frac{e^2}{m\omega_0} \frac{-2\mu}{4\mu^2 + \gamma^2}$$

$$\kappa = 2\pi N \frac{e^2}{m\omega_0} \frac{\gamma}{4\mu^2 + \gamma^2} \tag{49.11}$$

The manner in which κ and n vary with $\omega = \mu + \omega_0$ is shown in figure 54. Omitting the factor $2\pi N e^2/m\omega_0$ which is common to $n-1$ and κ, the latter quantity has a maximum of height $1/\gamma$ at $\mu = 0$, and half this value at $\mu = \pm\frac{1}{2}\gamma$. Now $n-1$ has a maximum at $\mu = -\frac{1}{2}\gamma$ and a minimum at $\mu = \frac{1}{2}\gamma$, the magnitudes of which are $1/2\gamma$. Between these two values, that is, within the spectral line, the refractive index decreases with increasing frequency, in contrast to its behaviour in the transparent region outside the spectral line. This property is termed *anomalous dispersion*.

The curve of κ becomes higher and narrower as γ decreases, but the area included under it is independent of the damping, and is equal to

$$\int_{-\infty}^{\infty} \frac{\gamma\, d\mu}{4\mu^2+\gamma^2} = \tfrac{1}{2}\pi$$

Therefore

$$\int_{-\infty}^{\infty} \kappa\, d\omega = 2\pi N \frac{e^2}{m\omega_0} \frac{\pi}{2} \qquad (49.12)$$

Using this result, the absorption in the case of a continuous spectrum may easily be calculated. Provided that the intensity (i.e. the energy

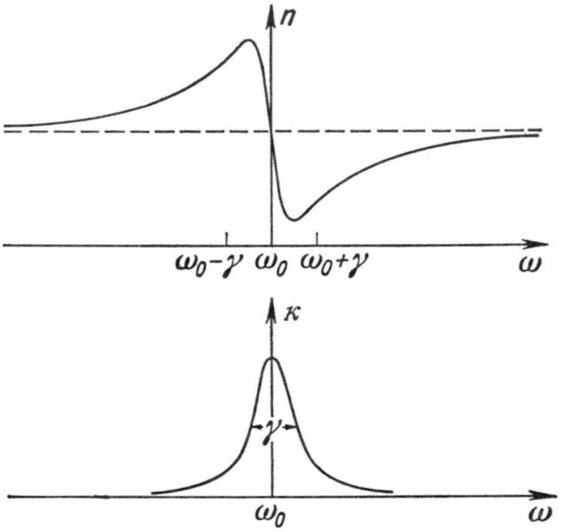

Fig. 54.—Refractive index and extinction coefficient in the neighbourhood of a spectral line

per second per square centimetre) of the incident radiation is not in the form of a sharp line, but extends over a continuous spectrum,

$$S = \int_0^{\infty} I(\omega)\, d\omega \qquad (49.13)$$

we should expect from (49.9) that the absorption over an interval dz would be

$$dS = -dz \int \frac{2\omega\kappa}{c} I(\omega)\, d\omega$$

Since κ has a sharp maximum at $\omega = \omega_0$, $\omega I(\omega)$ can be replaced by

$\omega_0 I(\omega_0)$ in the integrand provided that $I(\omega)$ remains nearly constant within the line width. Then from the last equation and (49.12)

$$dS = -N\,dz\frac{2\pi^2}{c}\frac{e^2}{m}I(\omega_0) \tag{49.14}$$

Equation (49.14) shows that the total energy absorbed by a line from the continuous spectrum is independent of the line width.

This equation may also be interpreted as follows. $N dz$ is the number of atoms contained in a layer of thickness dz and $1\,\text{cm}^2$ cross-section. Equation (49.14) therefore states that the energy absorbed per second by each oscillator from the spectrum represented by (49.13) is

$$\frac{2\pi^2 e^2}{cm}I(\omega_0) \tag{49.15}$$

If we represent the incident radiation by its energy density u(ergs per cm^3) instead of by its intensity S(ergs per second per cm^2), we have the following relation:

$$u(\omega) = \frac{1}{c}I(\omega)$$

The spectral energy density of the radiation field being $u(\omega)$, the energy absorbed from the field by a three-dimensional oscillator is therefore

$$\frac{2\pi^2 e^2}{m}u(\omega) \tag{49.15a}$$

A linear oscillator which is capable only of motion parallel to the x-axis can only react with the x-component of the field. For such an oscillator only one-third of the radiant energy of an isotropic field is effective, hence:

Energy absorbed by a linear oscillator is

$$\frac{2\pi^2 e^2}{3m}u(\omega) \tag{49.15b}$$

The damping constant does not appear in the above formulae for absorption in a continuous spectrum.

In view of the later treatment of the subject by means of the quantum theory, it is of interest to note that the same formulae for the absorption of energy by an oscillator can be obtained without introducing the damping. In §40, we gave the solution of the equation

$$\ddot{\mathbf{r}}+\omega_0^2\mathbf{r} = \frac{e}{m}\mathbf{F}\cos\omega t$$

(where **F** is the amplitude of the electric field), for initial conditions $\mathbf{r}=\dot{\mathbf{r}}=0$ at $t=0$:

$$\mathbf{r}(t) = \frac{e}{m}\mathbf{F}\frac{\cos\omega t-\cos\omega_0 t}{\omega_0^2-\omega^2} \tag{49.16}$$

(We may no longer omit the term $\cos\omega_0 t$, since we wish to perform the calculation when the damping is zero.) Using the identity $\cos\alpha-\cos\beta = 2\sin\frac{1}{2}(\beta+\alpha)\sin\frac{1}{2}(\beta-\alpha)$ we may express (49.16) as follows:

$$\mathbf{r}(t) = -\frac{e}{m}\mathbf{F}\frac{2\sin\frac{1}{2}(\omega+\omega_0)t\sin\frac{1}{2}(\omega-\omega_0)t}{(\omega_0+\omega)(\omega_0-\omega)} \tag{49.17}$$

The potential energy of the oscillator is $\frac{1}{2}m\omega_0^2\mathbf{r}^2$, which is equal to its mean kinetic energy; the total energy is therefore $m\omega_0^2\overline{\mathbf{r}^2}$. For the magnitude of this energy to be appreciable, ω must be nearly equal to ω_0. We shall therefore put $\omega_0+\omega\approx 2\omega_0$ in (49.17), and since the term $\sin^2\omega_0 t$ oscillates rapidly we shall replace it in the following expression by its mean value $\overline{\sin^2\omega_0 t}=\frac{1}{2}$. Then the energy absorbed by the oscillator in time t is

$$m\omega_0^2\mathbf{r}^2 = \frac{e^2}{m}\mathbf{F}^2\frac{1}{2}\frac{\sin^2\frac{1}{2}(\omega-\omega_0)t}{(\omega_0-\omega)^2}$$

The radiation intensity corresponding to a field amplitude **F** is

$$S = \frac{c}{8\pi}\mathbf{F}^2$$

If this intensity is distributed according to (49.13),

$$m\omega_0^2\overline{\mathbf{r}^2} = \frac{4\pi e^2}{mc}\int_0^\infty I(\omega)\frac{\sin^2\frac{1}{2}(\omega-\omega_0)t}{(\omega_0-\omega)^2}d\omega$$

Putting $\omega-\omega_0=\mu$ once more, we have for the function next to $I(\omega)$ in the integral

$$\phi(\mu) = \frac{\sin^2\frac{1}{2}\mu t}{\mu^2}$$

which we have already encountered in §27. When $\mu = 0$ it has the value $\frac{1}{4}t^2$, and its first zero is at $\mu_0 = 2\pi/t$. The area under the curve is approximately a triangle of base $2\mu_0$ and height $\frac{1}{4}t^2$, and is therefore equal to $\frac{1}{2}\pi t$. It may in fact easily be verified that

$$\int_{-\infty}^{\infty} \phi(\mu)\, d\mu = \tfrac{1}{2}\pi t$$

exactly. Now if t is so large that $I(\omega)$ does not change appreciably when ω changes by an amount π/t, we may take $I(\omega_0)$ out of the integral. We then have

$$m\omega_0^2 \overline{\mathbf{r}^2} = \frac{2\pi^2 e^2}{mc} I(\omega_0)t$$

in agreement with (49.15).

§50. The probability of an induced transition

In §41, an atom subject from time $t = 0$ to the effect of a perturbation was represented by the equation

$$\psi = \exp\left(-\frac{i}{\hbar}E_s t\right)\phi_s + \sum_{\nu \neq s} a_\nu \exp\left(-\frac{i}{\hbar}E_\nu t\right)\phi_\nu \qquad (50.1)$$

$|a_\nu(t)|^2$ is the probability of finding the atom in the state ν at time t, given the fact that it was in the state s at time $t = 0$. Provided that $|a_\nu| \ll 1$, it is permissible to say that $|a_\nu|^2$ represents the probability that a transition from s to ν took place during the interval t. In (41.6) we gave the following expression for $a_\nu(t)$ in the case of an alternating field $E_x = F\cos\omega t$:

$$a_\nu(t) = \frac{eFx_{\nu s}}{2\hbar}\left\{\frac{\exp i(\omega + \omega_{\nu s})t - 1}{\omega + \omega_{\nu s}} + \frac{\exp i(\omega - \omega_{\nu s})t - 1}{\omega - \omega_{\nu s}}\right\} \qquad (50.2)$$

The condition $|a_\nu| \ll 1$ is no longer satisfied when ω is nearly equal to $\omega_{\nu s}$; to deal with this case it is really necessary to take account of the damping. However, in the classical treatment of absorption it was shown that the total energy absorbed per second could be correctly deduced without taking the damping into account. In the present discussion we shall therefore limit ourselves to the calculation of the total absorption, making no allowance for damping.

We shall again consider the case of a continuous spectrum of incident radiation. The only frequencies contributing appreciably to

$|a_\nu(t)|^2$ are those for which one of the two denominators, $\omega_{\nu s}+\omega$ or $\omega_{\nu s}-\omega$, is very small. In particular, if ϕ_s denotes the ground state of the atom, $\omega_{\nu s}>0$, and only the term with $\omega_{\nu s}-\omega$ as denominator contributes significantly. On the other hand, if ϕ_s represents an excited state, $\omega_{\nu s}$ can be less than 0, and $|a_\nu(t)|^2$ then represents the probability that the radiation field induces a transition from ϕ_s to a state of lower energy ϕ_ν; this is termed *forced,* or *stimulated, emission.*

We now consider the case when $\omega_{\nu s}>0$. When monochromatic radiation is incident,

$$|a_\nu|^2 = \frac{e^2|x_{\nu s}|^2}{4\hbar^2}F^2\frac{\sin^2[\frac{1}{2}(\omega_{\nu s}-\omega)t]}{\frac{1}{4}(\omega_{\nu s}-\omega)^2} \tag{50.3}$$

(In the above equation we have used the relation $|e^{i\beta}-1|^2=4\sin^2\frac{1}{2}\beta$.) When the incident radiation is in the form of a continuous spectrum F^2 is replaced by $(8\pi/c)I_\omega\,d\omega$, and

$$|a_\nu|^2 = \frac{e^2|x_{\nu s}|^2}{4\hbar^2}\frac{8\pi}{c}\int I(\omega)\frac{\sin^2[\frac{1}{2}(\omega_{\nu s}-\omega)t]}{[\frac{1}{2}(\omega_{\nu s}-\omega)]^2}\,d\omega \tag{50.4}$$

When t is sufficiently great we can remove $I(\omega_{\nu s})$ from the integral, as we did in the previous paragraph; we then have

$$|a_\nu(t)|^2 = \frac{e^2|x_{\nu s}|^2}{\hbar^2}\frac{4\pi^2}{c}I(\omega_{\nu s})t \tag{50.5}$$

The energy of the atom increases by an amount $\hbar\omega_{\nu s}$ in the case of a transition from ϕ_s to ϕ_ν. The increase in energy per second is therefore

$$\frac{1}{t}\hbar\omega_{\nu s}|a_\nu(t)|^2 = \omega_{\nu s}\frac{e^2|x_{\nu s}|^2}{\hbar}\frac{4\pi^2}{c}I(\omega_{\nu s}) \tag{50.6}$$

This increase in energy may be compared with that found for the classical oscillator in (49.15), when the latter expression is multiplied by its appropriate f-value, as given by (48.10). In this case the increase in energy per second is

$$f_{\nu s}\frac{2\pi^2}{c}\frac{e^2}{m}I(\omega_{\nu s}) = \omega_{\nu s}\frac{e^2|x_{\nu s}|^2}{\hbar}\frac{4\pi^2}{c}I(\omega_{\nu s}) \tag{50.7}$$

The above expression is in complete agreement with the result given by equation (50.6).

§51. The Hamiltonian form of the Maxwell equations for a vacuum

Before we can make use of the quantum theory in the treatment of the radiation field, we must first put Maxwell's equations in their Hamiltonian form. The methods so far established cannot be directly employed because, unlike the position and momentum of a particle, the electromagnetic field is not represented by discrete numbers but by continuous functions of position. These methods become applicable, however, if we consider the fields inside a cavity such as an enclosure with reflecting walls.

As a result of the boundary conditions, which require the vanishing of the appropriate tangential and normal components of the fields, only a discrete number of plane waves can exist inside the enclosure, in contrast to the situation in infinite space. The fields can therefore be represented by means of a discrete set of wave amplitudes, dependent on time. Lagrangian or Hamiltonian differential equations may be derived for the latter, which can easily be made compatible with the postulates of the quantum theory.

We may obtain the results for continuous fields by proceeding to the limiting case of an infinitely large enclosure. In doing so, we may reasonably expect that the boundary conditions will not affect the final result; we are therefore free to choose them in the most appropriate manner for calculation. Instead of postulating ideally reflecting walls we shall therefore assume that all field quantities are periodic in the enclosure; for simplicity, we shall take the enclosure to be a cube, the sides of which are of length L and are parallel to the coordinate axes. More precisely, if $f(x,y,z,t)$ is any field quantity, then

$$f(x,y,z,t) = f(x+L,y,z,t) = f(x,y+L,z,t) = f(x,y,z+L,t) \tag{51.1}$$

The advantage of this procedure is that it permits the use of the more convenient exponential functions in the Fourier expansions occurring in the calculation, instead of sine and cosine waves.

In the first instance we shall consider fields in empty enclosures. The Maxwell equations

$$\operatorname{curl}\mathbf{E} = -\frac{1}{c}\dot{\mathbf{H}}, \quad \operatorname{div}\mathbf{E} = 0$$

$$\operatorname{curl}\mathbf{H} = \frac{1}{c}\dot{\mathbf{E}}, \quad \operatorname{div}\mathbf{H} = 0$$

are solved by putting

$$\mathbf{H} = \operatorname{curl} \mathbf{A}, \quad \mathbf{E} = -\frac{1}{c}\dot{\mathbf{A}}, \quad \operatorname{div} \mathbf{A} = 0 \tag{51.2}$$

giving the following equation for the vector potential **A**:

$$\nabla^2 \mathbf{A} - \frac{1}{c^2}\ddot{\mathbf{A}} = 0 \tag{51.3}$$

A is expanded in a Fourier series:

$$\mathbf{A}(\mathbf{r}, t) = \sum_{\mathbf{k},\lambda} A_{\mathbf{k}\lambda}(t)\, \mathbf{s}_{\mathbf{k}\lambda} \frac{e^{i\mathbf{kr}}}{L^{3/2}} \tag{51.4}$$

The quantities

$$\mathbf{s}_{\mathbf{k}\lambda} = \mathbf{s}_{-\mathbf{k}\lambda} \tag{51.4a}$$

are linearly independent unit vectors defining the polarization of the corresponding wave. Since $\operatorname{div} \mathbf{A} = 0$, $(\mathbf{s}_{\mathbf{k}\lambda}\mathbf{k}) = 0$, which implies that the waves are transverse. The summation over λ therefore extends only over the values 1, 2. The two vectors $\mathbf{s}_{\mathbf{k}1}$ and $\mathbf{s}_{\mathbf{k}2}$, which are normal to **k**, will also be chosen to be orthogonal to each other.

As a result of the postulate (51.1) **k** assumes only the discrete values

$$\mathbf{k} = \frac{2\pi}{L}(n_x, n_y, n_z), \quad \text{where } n_x, n_y, n_z = 0, \pm 1, \pm 2, \ldots \tag{51.5}$$

The summation over **k** in (51.4) therefore represents a triple summation over all integers n_x, n_y, n_z.

The proper variables to employ for the representation of the field are the amplitudes $A_{\mathbf{k}\lambda}(t)$. Since **A** is a real quantity,

$$A_{\mathbf{k}\lambda} = A^*_{-\lambda\mathbf{k}} \tag{51.4b}$$

in virtue of (51.4*a*).* From (51.3) we obtain the "equation of motion"

$$\ddot{A}_{\mathbf{k}\lambda} + \omega_{\mathbf{k}}^2 A_{\mathbf{k}\lambda} = 0, \quad \text{where } \omega_{\mathbf{k}} = c\,|\mathbf{k}| \tag{51.6}$$

This is the equation of a linear oscillator, for which the Hamiltonian formalism and quantization characteristics are already known. The equations (51.6) are not mutually independent, however, as a result of the accessory condition (51.4*b*), and the amplitudes are complex; we

* The relation of $s_{k\lambda}$ to $s_{-k\lambda}$ given by (51.4*a*) is arbitrary. Once it has been assumed, however, (51.4*b*) follows necessarily.

must therefore give further consideration to the problem of the Hamiltonian representation of the radiation field.

We shall assume that, as in the mechanics of particles, the total energy E of the field assumes the role of the Hamiltonian function. Then, taking account of the relation

$$\frac{1}{L^3}\int_0^L\int_0^L\int_0^L \exp i(\mathbf{k}-\mathbf{k}')\mathbf{r}\,dx\,dy\,dz = \begin{Bmatrix} 1 \text{ when } \mathbf{k}=\mathbf{k}' \\ 0 \text{ when } \mathbf{k}\neq\mathbf{k}' \end{Bmatrix} = \delta_{\mathbf{kk}'}$$

and the fact that $(\mathbf{ks}_{\mathbf{k}\lambda})=0$, we obtain from (51.2), (51.4), and (51.6):

$$E = \frac{1}{8\pi}\int(\mathbf{E}^2+\mathbf{H}^2)\,dV = \frac{1}{8\pi c^2}\sum_{\mathbf{k}\lambda}(\dot{A}^*_{\mathbf{k}\lambda}\dot{A}_{\mathbf{k}\lambda}+\omega_{\mathbf{k}}^2 A^*_{\mathbf{k}\lambda}A_{\mathbf{k}\lambda}) \qquad (51.7)$$

We must now form canonically conjugate variables q_j and p_j from the $A_{\mathbf{k}\lambda}$ and $\dot{A}_{\mathbf{k}\lambda}$ such that, when the field energy E is expressed in them, it may be employed as the Hamiltonian function $\mathscr{H}(p_j,q_j)$ in a canonical representation. This implies that the equations of motion (51.6) follow from the equations

$$\dot{p}_j = -\frac{\partial\mathscr{H}}{\partial q_j} \qquad \dot{q}_j = \frac{\partial\mathscr{H}}{\partial p_j} \qquad (51.8)$$

Now the amplitudes $A_{\mathbf{k}\lambda}$ themselves cannot be employed as coordinates in this canonical representation, because of the restriction imposed by (51.4*b*). However, if new amplitudes are introduced, defined by

$$a_{\mathbf{k}\lambda} = \frac{1}{2}\left(A_{\mathbf{k}\lambda}+\frac{i}{\omega_{\mathbf{k}}}\dot{A}_{\mathbf{k}\lambda}\right) \qquad a^*_{-\mathbf{k}\lambda} = \frac{1}{2}\left(A_{\mathbf{k}\lambda}-\frac{i}{\omega_{\mathbf{k}}}\dot{A}_{\mathbf{k}\lambda}\right) \qquad (51.9)$$

then

$$A_{\mathbf{k}\lambda} = a_{\mathbf{k}\lambda}+a^*_{-\mathbf{k}\lambda} \qquad (51.10)$$

Condition (51.4*b*) is thus automatically satisfied, while the amplitudes $a_{\mathbf{k}\lambda}$ and $a^*_{\mathbf{k}\lambda}$ are free from any further restriction. It would thus appear that the $a_{\mathbf{k}\lambda}$ could be employed as coordinates in the required representation; it can be shown immediately that this is in fact possible.

From (51.9) and (51.6) we first derive the new equations of motion:

$$\dot{a}_{\mathbf{k}\lambda}+i\omega_{\mathbf{k}}a_{\mathbf{k}\lambda}=0 \qquad \dot{a}^*_{\mathbf{k}\lambda}-i\omega_{\mathbf{k}}a^*_{\mathbf{k}\lambda}=0$$

Thus two differential equations of the first order have replaced the single equation of the second order (51.6). In addition,

$$\dot{A}_{\mathbf{k}\lambda} = -i\omega_{\mathbf{k}}(a_{\mathbf{k}\lambda}-a^*_{-\mathbf{k}\lambda}) \qquad (51.11)$$

The field energy E may now be expressed in terms of the $a_{\mathbf{k}\lambda}$ and $a^*_{\mathbf{k}\lambda}$ alone, in view of the definition (51.9):

$$E = \frac{1}{4\pi c^2}\sum_{\mathbf{k}\lambda}\omega_{\mathbf{k}}^2 (a^*_{\mathbf{k}\lambda}a_{\mathbf{k}\lambda}+a^*_{-\mathbf{k}\lambda}a_{-\mathbf{k}\lambda})$$

$$= \frac{1}{2\pi c^2}\sum_{\mathbf{k}\lambda}\omega_{\mathbf{k}}^2 a^*_{\mathbf{k}\lambda}a_{\mathbf{k}\lambda} \tag{51.12}$$

If the $a_{\mathbf{k}\lambda}$ are now identified with the canonical coordinates q_j, and the quantities $i\omega_{\mathbf{k}}a^*_{\mathbf{k}\lambda}/2\pi c^2$ with the conjugate momenta p_j, the energy may be expressed as the Hamiltonian function in the form

$$\mathscr{H} = -i\sum_{\mathbf{k}\lambda}\omega_{\mathbf{k}}q_j p_j \tag{51.12a}$$

The equations (51.11) then follow directly from the canonical equations of motion (51.8), thereby establishing the required connection with the canonical form of representation.*

In order that we may later form the necessary commutation relations as simply as possible, we shall replace the $a_{\mathbf{k}\lambda}$ by the quantities

$$b_{\mathbf{k}\lambda} = \frac{1}{c}\left(\frac{\omega_{\mathbf{k}}}{2\pi\hbar}\right)^{1/2} a_{\mathbf{k}\lambda} \tag{51.13}$$

following a similar procedure to that which we adopted in the case of the individual linear oscillator in §15. Then (51.12) becomes

$$E = \sum_{\mathbf{k}\lambda}\hbar\omega_{\mathbf{k}}b^*_{\mathbf{k}\lambda}b_{\mathbf{k}\lambda} \tag{51.14}$$

and the corresponding canonically conjugate coordinates and momenta are

$$b_{\mathbf{k}\lambda} \quad\text{and}\quad i\hbar b^*_{\mathbf{k}\lambda}$$

As before, it may easily be verified that equations (51.11) follow from (51.9).

We now express the vector potential (51.4) in terms of the $b_{\mathbf{k}\lambda}$. Using (51.10) and (51.13), we first obtain

$$\mathbf{A}(\mathbf{r},t) = \frac{c}{L^{3/2}}\sum_{\mathbf{k}\lambda}\left(\frac{2\pi\hbar}{\omega_{\mathbf{k}}}\right)^{1/2}\mathbf{s}_{\mathbf{k}\lambda}(b_{\mathbf{k}\lambda}+b^*_{-\mathbf{k}\lambda})\exp i\mathbf{kr}$$

* In the canonical equations of motion (51.8) the coordinates and momenta are complex conjugates, apart from a factor; however, they may be regarded as independent of each other in partial differentiation. This may be proved by resolving them into real and imaginary parts, and treating the latter as independent quantities.

If we replace $-\mathbf{k}$ by $\mathbf{k}$ in the second summation, and put

$$b_{\mathbf{k}\lambda} = b^0_{\mathbf{k}\lambda} \exp -i\omega_{\mathbf{k}} t \qquad b^*_{\mathbf{k}\lambda} = b^{0*}_{\mathbf{k}\lambda} \exp i\omega_{\mathbf{k}} t$$

in virtue of the relation (51.11), the expression becomes

$$\mathbf{A}(\mathbf{r}, t) = \frac{c}{L^{3/2}} \sum_{\mathbf{k},\lambda} \left(\frac{2\pi h}{\omega_{\mathbf{k}}}\right)^{1/2} \mathbf{s}_{\mathbf{k}\lambda} \times$$
$$\times \{b^0_{\mathbf{k}\lambda} \exp i(\mathbf{kr} - \omega_{\mathbf{k}} t) + b^{0*}_{\mathbf{k}\lambda} \exp -i(\mathbf{kr} - \omega_{\mathbf{k}} t)\} \qquad (51.15)$$

This is the sum of real waves of amplitude $|b^0_{\mathbf{k}\lambda}|$, travelling in the direction of $\mathbf{k}$. The result may be used to derive the number of waves occurring in the interval $d\omega$, which has already been given in (47.13). From (51.5) and the relation $\omega^2 = c^2\mathbf{k}^2$

$$\left(\frac{L}{2\pi}\right)^2 \frac{\omega^2}{c^2} = n_x^2 + n_y^2 + n_z^2$$

In the space of the n_x, n_y, n_z, the number of "lattice points" corresponding to integral values for which $n_x^2 + n_y^2 + n_z^2 \leq R^2$ is equal to the volume of the sphere of radius R, namely $(4\pi/3)R^3$, when R is large. Since two directions of polarization ($\lambda = 1,2$) are associated with each value of $\mathbf{k}$, the total number of waves of angular frequency less than ω is

$$s(\omega) = 2\frac{4\pi}{3}\left(\frac{L\omega}{2\pi c}\right)^3$$

The number of waves occurring in the interval $d\omega$ is therefore

$$z(\omega)\, d\omega = \frac{ds}{d\omega}\, d\omega = L^3 \frac{\omega^2}{\pi^2 c^3}\, d\omega$$

as stated in (47.13).

§52. The quantum theory of the radiation field

Now that Maxwell's equations have been expressed in canonical form with coordinates b and momenta $i\hbar b^*$, we may proceed to the quantum theory, replacing the numbers b^* and b by operators b^+ and b subject to the commutation relations†

$$i\hbar b^+_{\mathbf{k}\lambda} b_{\mathbf{k}'\lambda'} - b_{\mathbf{k}'\lambda'} i\hbar b^+_{\mathbf{k}\lambda} = \frac{\hbar}{i} \delta_{\mathbf{k}\mathbf{k}'} \delta_{\lambda\lambda'} \qquad b_{\mathbf{k}\lambda} b_{\mathbf{k}'\lambda'} - b_{\mathbf{k}'\lambda'} b_{\mathbf{k}\lambda} = 0$$

† The fact that b^* must be replaced in quantum theory by b^+ is best seen by resolving b into real and imaginary parts; these parts must become real numbers in Hermitian operators.

In other words, all operators b, b^+ commute except those with the same values of $\mathbf{k}$ and λ, for which

$$b_{\mathbf{k}\lambda}\, b^+_{\mathbf{k}\lambda} - b^+_{\mathbf{k}\lambda}\, b_{\mathbf{k}\lambda} = 1 \tag{52.1}$$

In terms of these operators, the Hamiltonian operator is

$$\mathscr{H} = \sum_{\mathbf{k}\lambda} \hbar\omega_{\mathbf{k}}\, b^+_{\mathbf{k}\lambda}\, b_{\mathbf{k}\lambda} \tag{52.2}$$

The transition to quantum theory is not quite free from ambiguity, since the Hamiltonian could equally well have been expressed as $\sum \hbar\omega_{\mathbf{k}} b_{\mathbf{k}\lambda} b^+_{\mathbf{k}\lambda}$. The expression (52.2) implies a particular choice of energy scale, corresponding in fact to a ground state of zero energy.

The vector potential now becomes the operator

$$\mathbf{A} = \sum_{\mathbf{k}\lambda} c \left(\frac{2\pi\hbar}{L^3}\right)^{1/2} \frac{\mathbf{s}_{\mathbf{k}\lambda}}{\sqrt{\omega_{\mathbf{k}}}} \{b_{\mathbf{k}\lambda}\, e^{i\mathbf{k}\mathbf{r}} + b^+_{\mathbf{k}\lambda}\, e^{-i\mathbf{k}\mathbf{r}}\} \tag{52.3}$$

We can now construct a Hilbert space from the eigenfunctions of $\mathscr{H}$, just as we did in the case of the linear oscillator in §15. If Φ is an eigenvector of $\mathscr{H}$ (cf. (15.11)) corresponding to the eigenvalue E,

$$\sum_{\mathbf{k}} \hbar\omega_{\mathbf{k}}\, b^+_{\mathbf{k}}\, b_{\mathbf{k}}\, \Phi = E\Phi \tag{52.4}$$

(The index λ has been temporarily omitted.) If we form the scalar product with Φ, taking account of the fact that b^+ is adjoint to b, we obtain

$$\sum_{\mathbf{k}} \hbar\omega_{\mathbf{k}}\, (b_{\mathbf{k}}\,\Phi, b_{\mathbf{k}}\,\Phi) = E \tag{52.4a}$$

All the terms on the left are positive or zero; therefore E is positive, and only equal to 0 if $b_{\mathbf{k}}\Phi$ is 0 for all $\mathbf{k}$. We now apply a particular operator $b_{\mathbf{k}'}$ to (52.4); it then follows from (52.1) that

$$\sum \hbar\omega_{\mathbf{k}}\, b^+_{\mathbf{k}}\, b_{\mathbf{k}}\, (b_{\mathbf{k}'}\,\Phi) = (E - \hbar\omega_{\mathbf{k}'})\, b_{\mathbf{k}'}\,\Phi \tag{52.4b}$$

If the operator $b_{\mathbf{k}'}$ is applied n times, the following result is obtained: either $b^n_{\mathbf{k}'}\Phi$ belongs to the eigenvalue $E - n\hbar\omega_{\mathbf{k}'}$, or it is equal to 0. The latter case must occur once for a finite value of n, since the eigenvalue certainly cannot be negative. Let the number $n_{\mathbf{k}'}$ be defined such that $b^{n_{\mathbf{k}'}}_{\mathbf{k}'}\Phi$ corresponds to the eigenvalue $E - n_{\mathbf{k}'}\hbar\omega_{\mathbf{k}'}$ but that $b^{n_{\mathbf{k}'}+1}_{\mathbf{k}'}\Phi = 0$. Now let us apply the same procedure to the equation

$$\sum_{\mathbf{k}} \hbar\omega_{\mathbf{k}}\, b_{\mathbf{k}}\, b^+_{\mathbf{k}}\, (b^{n_{\mathbf{k}'}}_{\mathbf{k}'}\Phi) = (E - n_{\mathbf{k}'}\,\hbar\omega_{\mathbf{k}'})\, b^{n_{\mathbf{k}'}}_{\mathbf{k}'}\Phi$$

forming the scalar product $n_{\mathbf{k}''}$ times with another operator $b_{\mathbf{k}''}$. Then the result,

$$\Psi = b_{\mathbf{k}''}^{n_{\mathbf{k}''}} b_{\mathbf{k}'}^{n_{\mathbf{k}'}} \Phi$$

corresponds to the eigenvalue

$$E - n_{\mathbf{k}'} \hbar\omega_{\mathbf{k}'} - n_{\mathbf{k}''} \hbar\omega_{\mathbf{k}''}$$

and

$$b_{\mathbf{k}''} \Psi = 0$$

We continue in this manner, taking each $b_{\mathbf{k}}$ in succession. We finally obtain an element

$$\Phi_0 = \left(\prod_{\mathbf{k}} b_{\mathbf{k}}^{n_{\mathbf{k}}} \right) \Phi$$

corresponding to the eigenvalue

$$E - \sum_{\mathbf{k}} \hbar\omega_{\mathbf{k}} n_{\mathbf{k}}$$

for which $b_{\mathbf{k}} \Phi_0 = 0$ for all $\mathbf{k}$. Then from (52.4*a*) the eigenvalue is equal to 0; the eigenvalue E in (52.4) must therefore have the form

$$E = \sum_{\mathbf{k}} \hbar\omega_{\mathbf{k}} n_{\mathbf{k}} \tag{52.5}$$

If the discrete sequence of $\mathbf{k}$ values is numbered in some way, say $\mathbf{k}_1, \mathbf{k}_2, \mathbf{k}_3, \ldots$, we may denote the eigenvector corresponding to the eigenvalue (52.5) as follows:

$$\Phi n_{\mathbf{k}_1}, n_{\mathbf{k}_2}, n_{\mathbf{k}_3}, \ldots \tag{52.6}$$

We can now take the rest of the argument directly from our earlier treatment of the linear oscillator. As in (15.12), if Φ is an eigenfunction corresponding to E, then $b_{\mathbf{k}}^{+} \Phi$ is an eigenfunction corresponding to $E + \hbar\omega_{\mathbf{k}}$. We can therefore construct the whole Hilbert space by means of the repeated application of the $b_{\mathbf{k}}^{+}$ to $\Phi_{0,0,0,\ldots} = \Phi_0$.* After once more introducing λ and normalizing, we obtain

$$\Phi_{\ldots, n_{\mathbf{k}\lambda}, \ldots} = \prod_{\mathbf{k}', \lambda'} \frac{b_{\mathbf{k}'\lambda'}^{+ n_{\mathbf{k}'\lambda'}}}{\sqrt{(n_{\mathbf{k}'\lambda'}!)}} \Phi_{0, 0, 0, \ldots}$$

* The ground state represented by Φ_0 corresponds to a vacuum; it still contains zero-point vibrations, however, as in the case of the linear oscillator (example 4, p. 108). Since we are dealing with an infinite number of oscillators the mean square values of the fields, $\overline{\mathbf{E}^2}$, $\overline{\mathbf{H}^2}$, must also be infinitely great. A completely satisfactory treatment of this anomaly does not yet exist (see p. 319).

The $n_{\mathbf{k}\lambda}$ form an infinite set of positive integers, and define the number of light quanta with wave number **k** and polarization λ that are present in the state $\Phi_{\dots,n_{\mathbf{k}\lambda},\dots}$ The energy corresponding to Φ is

$$E = \sum_{\mathbf{k}\lambda} \hbar\omega_{\mathbf{k}}\, n_{\mathbf{k}\lambda} \tag{52.7}$$

The operators b and b^+ have the same effect on the eigenfunctions as in the case treated in §15:

$$\begin{aligned} b^+_{\mathbf{k}\lambda}\,\Phi_{\dots,n_{\mathbf{k}\lambda},\dots} &= \sqrt{(n_{\mathbf{k}\lambda}+1)}\,\Phi_{\dots,n_{\mathbf{k}\lambda}+1,\dots} \\ b_{\mathbf{k}\lambda}\,\Phi_{\dots,n_{\mathbf{k}\lambda},\dots} &= \sqrt{(n_{\mathbf{k}\lambda})}\,\Phi_{\dots,n_{\mathbf{k}\lambda}-1,\dots} \end{aligned} \tag{52.8}$$

They can therefore be designated as the photon generating and annihilating operators.

This completes our description of the vectors forming the Hilbert space basis, and of the effect of the application of the operators $b^+_{\mathbf{k}\lambda}$ and $b_{\mathbf{k}\lambda}$ to them.

§53. Quantum mechanics of the atom in the radiation field

We shall now consider the case in which radiation and an atom with one valence electron are both present within the container. The stationary states ϕ_i of the electron satisfy a Schrödinger equation $\mathscr{H}_{el}\phi_i = \varepsilon_i\phi_i$; for the sake of simplicity they will be assumed to be non-degenerate. The index i represents the complete set of electron quantum numbers. The stationary states of the complete system, consisting of the electron and the radiation field, and neglecting their interaction, are given by

$$\Phi_\mu = \phi_i\,\Phi_{\dots,n_{\mathbf{k}\lambda},\dots} \quad \text{with energy } E_\mu = \varepsilon_i + \sum \hbar\omega_{\mathbf{k}}\, n_{\mathbf{k}\lambda} \tag{53.1}$$

(Greek subscripts represent the quantum numbers of the complete system, e.g. μ stands for the set of numbers $i,\dots,n_{\mathbf{k}\lambda},\dots$)

The interaction* between the field and the electron is

$$W = -\frac{e}{mc}\left(\mathbf{A},\frac{\hbar}{i}\,\mathrm{grad}\right) = -\frac{e}{mc}(\mathbf{A},\mathbf{p})$$

The states Φ_μ are no longer stationary, but functions of the time. Their dependence on time is determined by the Hamiltonian operator

$$\mathscr{H} = \mathscr{H}_0 + W$$

* The term in $\mathbf{A}^2$ is omitted, since it makes no contribution to the processes discussed below.

where $\mathscr{H}_0 = \mathscr{H}_{el} + \sum \hbar\omega_{\mathbf{k}}\, b^+_{\mathbf{k}\lambda} b_{\mathbf{k}\lambda}$

and $$W = -\frac{e}{m}\left(\frac{2\pi\hbar}{L^3}\right)^{1/2} \sum_{\mathbf{k}\lambda} \frac{(\mathbf{s}_{\mathbf{k}\lambda}, \mathbf{p})}{\sqrt{\omega_{\mathbf{k}}}} \{b_{\mathbf{k}\lambda} \exp i\mathbf{kr} + b^+_{\mathbf{k}\lambda} \exp -i\mathbf{kr}\}$$

If we take the general expression for a state to be

$$\Phi = \sum_\nu c_\nu(t) \exp\left(-\frac{i}{\hbar} E_\nu t\right) \Phi_\nu$$

then, since $\mathscr{H}\Phi = i\hbar\dot{\Phi}$, it follows that

$$\dot{c}_\mu(t) = -\frac{i}{\hbar} \sum_\nu (\Phi_\mu W \Phi_\nu) \exp(i\omega_{\mu\nu} t)\, c_\nu(t), \quad \text{where } \hbar\omega_{\mu\nu} = E_\mu - E_\nu$$

Therefore if the system is in the state $\Phi = \Phi_\nu$ at time $t = 0$, there is a probability $|c_\mu(t)|^2$ of finding other states Φ_μ at time t. This probability is found from Dirac's perturbation theory (§27) to be

$$|c_\mu|^2 = w_{\mu\nu} t = 2\pi \frac{|(\Phi_\mu W \Phi_\nu)|^2}{\hbar^2} \quad \frac{\sin^2 \frac{1}{2}\omega_{\mu\nu} t}{\frac{1}{2}\pi\omega^2_{\mu\nu} t} \quad t$$

where $w_{\mu\nu}$ is the "transition probability".

Since the vector potential and the operators b^+ and b only occur in linear form in the interaction W, the matrix element $W_{\mu\nu} = (\Phi_\mu, W\Phi_\nu)$ only differs from 0 if a single one of the $n_{\mathbf{k}\lambda}$ of the final state Φ_μ differs by unity from its corresponding value in the initial state Φ_ν. For instance: from (52.8),

$$(\Phi_\mu b^+_{\mathbf{k}\lambda} \Phi_\nu) = (\Phi \ldots, n_{\mathbf{k}\lambda}+1, \ldots,\ b^+_{\mathbf{k}\lambda}\Phi \ldots, n_{\mathbf{k}\lambda}, \ldots) = \sqrt{(n_{\mathbf{k}\lambda}+1)}$$

when Φ_μ and Φ_ν agree in all quantum numbers except $n_{\mathbf{k}\lambda}$. This means that, in the first-order approximation of Dirac's perturbation theory, the only transitions to occur are those in which a single light quantum is produced (i.e. emitted) or annihilated (absorbed).

When t is large enough, the function $\sin^2 \frac{1}{2}\omega t / \frac{1}{2}\pi\omega^2 t$ differs from 0 only in the immediate neighbourhood of $\omega = 0$. Since

$$\int_{-\infty}^{\infty} \frac{\sin^2 \frac{1}{2}\omega t}{\frac{1}{2}\pi\omega^2 t}\, d\omega = 1$$

the function may be replaced by $\delta(\omega)$ in all further integrations over ω. This implies that the only transitions to occur are those for which

$\omega_\mu \approx \omega_\nu$. Therefore, if $\omega_{\mathbf{k}}$ denotes the frequency of the emitted or absorbed quantum:

$$\underbrace{\varepsilon_i + \hbar\omega_{\mathbf{k}}}_{E_{initial}} = \varepsilon_j \quad \text{Absorption } (\varepsilon_j > \varepsilon_i)$$
$$\varepsilon_i = \underbrace{\varepsilon_j + \hbar\omega_{\mathbf{k}}}_{E_{final}} \quad \text{Emission } (\varepsilon_j < \varepsilon_i) \tag{53.2}$$

We shall now consider the case of emission. Using the relations (52.8), the transition probability is

$$w_{\mathbf{k}\lambda}^{i\to j} = \frac{(2\pi)^2}{L^3}\frac{e^2}{\hbar m^2}\frac{n_{\mathbf{k}\lambda}+1}{\omega_{\mathbf{k}}}\,|(\phi_j, \mathbf{s}_{\mathbf{k}\lambda}\,\mathbf{p}\exp(i\mathbf{kr})\,\phi_i)|^2\,\delta(\omega_{ij}-\omega_{\mathbf{k}}) \tag{53.3}$$

This may be expressed in words as follows: if an atom in the state ϕ_i is present at time $t=0$ in the radiation field $\Phi_{\ldots, n_{\mathbf{k}\lambda}, \ldots}$, then $w_{\mathbf{k}\lambda}^{i\to j}\,dt$ is the probability that after a time dt the atom should be in the state ϕ_j, having emitted a light quantum of wave number $\mathbf{k}$ and polarization λ. This probability consists of two components. One component contains the factor $n_{\mathbf{k}\lambda}$, and is therefore proportional to the intensity of the radiation field. It proves to be identical with the probability of the induced transition, which was introduced in §§48 and 50. The other term contains the factor 1, and is therefore quite independent of the radiation field, existing even when the field vanishes; this component gives the probability of the spontaneous emission. The formula that was derived in §48 on the basis of the correspondence principle is deducible in the present treatment as a natural consequence of the quantization of the radiation field. It is also apparent from the relations (52.8) and from the argument on which the construction of the Hilbert space was based that the figure 1 occurring next to $n_{\mathbf{k}\lambda}$ in (53.3) results directly from the commutation relations (52.1).

In order to deduce the familiar formulae (48.9) or (11.9) for the probability of spontaneous emission, we shall investigate the probability of a transition from i to j accompanied by the simultaneous emission of radiation into an element of solid angle $d\Omega$. In order to do this we must sum (53.3) over both polarizations and over all the $\mathbf{k}$ whose directions are contained in $d\Omega$. At the same time we proceed to the limit $L \to \infty$; as a result, the permitted values of $\mathbf{k}$ are packed closer and closer together, and the summation becomes an integral:

$$\sum_{\mathbf{k}} \Rightarrow \left(\frac{L}{2\pi}\right)^3 d\Omega \int k^2\,dk, \quad \text{where } k = |\mathbf{k}| = \frac{\omega}{c}$$

Owing to the δ-function in (53.3), the only value of $\mathbf{k}$ remaining after integration has the magnitude $|\mathbf{k}| = \omega_{ij}/c$.

In order to make the comparison with formula (11.9) complete we shall restrict ourselves to the case in which the wavelength of the emitted light is large compared with the diameter of the atom; we may then use the dipole approximation $e^{i\mathbf{kr}} = 1$. In addition,

$$(\phi_i, \mathbf{p}\phi_j) = im\omega_{ij}(\phi_i, \mathbf{r}\phi_j) = im\omega_{ij}\mathbf{r}_{ij}$$

We now take $\mathbf{s}_{\mathbf{k}1}$ to lie in the plane defined by the real or imaginary part of $\mathbf{r}_{ij}$ and by $\mathbf{k}$, and $\mathbf{s}_{\mathbf{k}2}$ normal to it. Then $(\mathbf{s}_{\mathbf{k}2}, \mathbf{r}_{ij}) = 0$, and there remains only

$$\frac{1}{2\pi}\frac{e^2\omega_{ij}^3}{\hbar c^3}|(\mathbf{s}_{\mathbf{k}1}, \mathbf{r}_{ij})|^2 \, d\Omega$$

From figure 55 we see that the scalar product $(\mathbf{s}_{\mathbf{k}1}, \mathbf{r}_{ij})$ contains the factor $\sin\theta$; hence after integrating over $d\Omega$ we obtain

$$w_{spont}^{i\to j} = \frac{4}{3}\frac{e^2\omega_{ij}^3}{\hbar c^3}|\mathbf{r}_{ij}|^2 \tag{53.4}$$

The energy emitted in connection with the transition $i \to j$ is obtained by multiplying (53.4) by $\hbar\omega_{ij}$. The results agree with the formulae based on the correspondence principle, (11.8, 11.9).

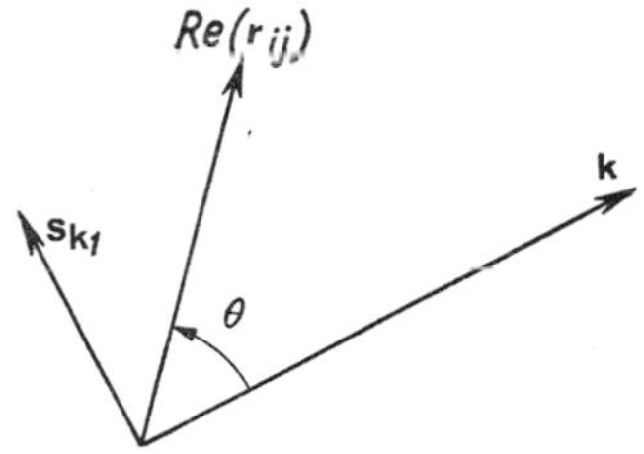

Fig. 55.—Polarization vector $\mathbf{s}_{\mathbf{k}_1}$, dipole moment Re $(\mathbf{r}_{ij})$, and propagation vector $\mathbf{k}$. The polarization vector $\mathbf{s}_{\mathbf{k}_2}$ is perpendicular to the plane of the diagram. To integrate over $[\mathbf{s}_{\mathbf{k}\lambda}, \text{Im}\,(\mathbf{r}_{ij})]^2$, $\mathbf{s}_{\mathbf{k}_1}$ is chosen to lie in the plane defined by Im $(\mathbf{r}_{ij})$ and $\mathbf{k}$

We shall now deal with the term containing the factor $n_{\mathbf{k}\lambda}$ in equation (53.3), in order to obtain the corresponding formula for the stimulated emission. In view of its application to the treatment of temperature radiation in a cavity we shall restrict ourselves to the case in which the radiation distribution is isotropic; in other words, we assume that the $n_{\mathbf{k}\lambda}$ depend only on the magnitude of **k**, but not on its direction or on the polarization λ.

We introduce once more a spectral energy density $u(\omega)$ such that $u(\omega)\,d\omega$ is the energy density of the radiation field in the frequency interval $d\omega$. Then in this interval there are $u(\omega)\,d\omega/\hbar\omega$ light quanta per unit volume of the cavity, each half of which is associated with one of the two independent polarization directions. We thus obtain the following expression for the probability of an induced dipole transition from i to j:

$$w_{induced}^{i\to j} = \sum_{\lambda} \int \frac{(2\pi)^2}{L^3} \frac{e^2}{m^2\hbar\omega} |(\phi_i, \mathbf{s}_{\mathbf{k}\lambda}\, \mathbf{p}\phi_j)|^2\, \delta(\omega_{ij}-\omega) \frac{L^3 u(\omega)}{2\hbar\omega} d\omega \frac{d\Omega}{4\pi}$$

This integral is evaluated as above, and gives

$$w_{induced}^{i\to j} = \frac{4}{3}\frac{\pi^2 e^2}{\hbar^2} u(\omega_{ij})\, |\mathbf{r}_{ij}|^2$$

which agrees with the result (50.6) when we put $I(\omega) = cu(\omega)$ in that equation.

The above analysis also covers the case of absorption, since the transition probability has the same form as (53.3), with the factor $(n_{\mathbf{k}\lambda}+1)$ replaced by $n_{\mathbf{k}\lambda}$. We thus have the familiar relation

$$w_{induced}^{i\to j} = w_{absorp}^{j\to i}$$

A comparison with the coefficients A and B introduced in Einstein's derivation of the Planck radiation formula yields the following relations:

$$A_{i\to j} = w_{spont}^{i\to j} = \frac{4}{3}\frac{e^2\omega_{ij}^3}{\hbar c^3} |\mathbf{r}_{ij}|^2$$

$$B_{i\to j} = \frac{4}{3}\frac{\pi^2 e^2}{\hbar^2} |\mathbf{r}_{ij}|^2 = B_{j\to i}$$

$$B_{i\to j}\, u(\omega_{ij}) = w_{induced}^{i\to j}$$

As we can see, the relation (48.8)

$$A_{i\to j} = B_{j\to i} \frac{\hbar\omega_{ij}^3}{\pi^2 c^3}$$

is in fact satisfied.

The natural width of spectral lines

In §5 we saw that the spectral line emitted by a classical oscillator possesses a certain width due to the radiation damping of the electron. The line intensity distribution is given by

$$I_\omega \, d\omega = \frac{\gamma_{cl}}{2\pi} \frac{I_0 \, d\omega}{(\omega-\omega_0)^2 + \frac{1}{4}\gamma_{cl}^2} \tag{53.5}$$

for which the half-value width is

$$\gamma_{cl} = \frac{2e^2\omega_0^2}{3mc^3}$$

On the other hand, the immediate result given by Dirac's perturbation calculation for the line width $\Delta\omega$ is the relation $\Delta\omega . t \approx 1$, from which it would appear that the quantum theory predicted infinitely sharp spectral lines in the limiting case of very large time intervals. This conclusion is false, however, because the Dirac approximation is not valid for arbitrary values of the time; on the contrary, it assumes that in the expansion

$$\Phi(t) = c_0(t)\,\Phi_0 + \sum_{\nu \neq 0} c_\nu(t)\,\Phi_\nu$$

the probability $|c_0|^2$ for the occurrence of the initial state is nearly 1. In view of the normalization condition $\sum_{\nu \neq 0} |c_\nu|^2 + |c_0|^2 = 1$, this implies that for a sufficiently weak radiation field $\sum_{\nu \neq 0} |c_\nu(t)|^2 \approx w_{\text{spont}} . t \ll 1$, where w_{spont} is the probability of a spontaneous transition from the initial state to some lower excited state of the atom. For greater time intervals, however, $c_0(t)$ will decrease as t increases; we shall attempt to allow for this in the perturbation calculation by making the initial assumption

$$c_0(t) = \exp - \tfrac{1}{2}\gamma t \tag{53.6}$$

instead of $c_0(t) \approx 1$.

For simplicity we shall restrict ourselves to the case of an atom in the first excited state ϕ_a in the absence of the radiation field; we shall neglect processes in which more than one light quantum is emitted, and shall use the dipole approximation. Then the light quantum wave number $\mathbf{k}$ is sufficient to denote uniquely the final states represented by the atom in the ground state ϕ_g and by one light quantum of frequency $\omega_{\mathbf{k}}$ in the radiation field. We thus have the following equation for the amplitudes $c_{\mathbf{k}}(t)$ of these states:

$$-\frac{\hbar}{i}\dot{c}_{\mathbf{k}}(t) = W_{\mathbf{k}0}\exp\left[i(\omega_{\mathbf{k}}-\omega_0)t\right]c_0(t) \tag{53.7}$$

where $$\hbar\omega_0 = E_a - E_g$$

and $$W_{\mathbf{k}0} = -\frac{e}{m}\left(\frac{2\pi h}{L^3}\right)^{1/2}\frac{im\omega_0}{\sqrt{\omega_{\mathbf{k}}}}(\mathbf{s}_{\mathbf{k}}, \mathbf{r}_{ag})$$

The vector $\mathbf{s}_{\mathbf{k}}$ is normal to $\mathbf{k}$ in the plane defined by $\mathbf{k}$ and the matrix element $\mathbf{r}_{ag}$ (see figure 55).

Substituting (53.6) and (53.7) and integrating,

$$c_{\mathbf{k}}(t) = W_{\mathbf{k}0}\frac{\exp\left[i(\omega_{\mathbf{k}}-\omega_0)t - \frac{1}{2}\gamma t\right]-1}{\hbar(\omega_0-\omega_{\mathbf{k}})-\frac{1}{2}i\hbar\gamma}$$

When $\gamma t \gg 1$, the probability distribution of the emitted quanta is

$$|c_{\mathbf{k}}(\infty)|^2 = \frac{|W_{\mathbf{k}0}|^2}{\hbar^2}\frac{1}{(\omega_0-\omega_{\mathbf{k}})^2+\frac{1}{4}\gamma^2}$$

The number of quanta present in the frequency interval $d\omega = c\,dk$ is

$$n(\omega)\,d\omega = \left(\frac{L}{2\pi}\right)^3 k^2\,dk\int|c_{\mathbf{k}}(\infty)|^2\,d\Omega$$

The above expression is integrated in the same manner as that leading to (53.4); the result is

$$n(\omega)\,d\omega = w_{spont}^{a\to g}\frac{\omega}{\omega_0}\frac{1}{2\pi}\frac{d\omega}{(\omega_0-\omega)^2+\frac{1}{4}\gamma^2} \tag{53.8}$$

The normalization condition is now

$$e^{-\gamma t}+\sum_{\mathbf{k}}|c_{\mathbf{k}}(t)|^2 = 1$$

Since this condition must hold good for all values of the time it follows that

$$\sum_{\mathbf{k}}|c_{\mathbf{k}}(\infty)|^2 = \int_0^\infty n(\omega)\,d\omega = 1$$

Since $\gamma \ll \omega_0$, the only appreciable contributions to this integral come from the range in the neighbourhood of $\omega = \omega_0$; its value is therefore

$$\int_0^\infty\frac{\omega}{\omega_0}\frac{d\omega}{(\omega_0-\omega)^2+\frac{1}{4}\gamma^2} \approx \int_{-\infty}^\infty\frac{d\omega}{(\omega_0-\omega)^2+\frac{1}{4}\gamma^2} = \frac{2\pi}{\gamma}$$

Then from (53.8) and the normalization condition we obtain the following relation for the lifetime of the excited state ϕ_a:

$$\gamma = w^{a \to g}_{spont} \tag{53.9}$$

Since the initial assumption $c_o = \exp -\frac{1}{2}\gamma t$ is not a strict solution of the Schrödinger equation, the normalization condition is not strictly fulfilled at all times. Further, γ is determined by the normalization condition only if it does not contain an imaginary part. It is therefore somewhat more satisfactory to determine γ from the equation of motion for $c_0(t)$,

$$-\frac{\hbar}{i}\dot{c}_0 = \sum_{\mathbf{k}} W_{0\mathbf{k}} \exp[i(\omega_0 - \omega_{\mathbf{k}})t] c_{\mathbf{k}}(t)$$

Using this procedure, we obtain the previous result (53.9) for the real part of γ, and an imaginary part which represents a displacement of the spectral line ω_0. Unfortunately, this imaginary part is a divergent integral.*

This divergence has for long been an insuperable difficulty of the quantum theory; it has not yet been completely overcome, but has been ingeniously circumvented through the concept of the mass renormalization of the electron (Kramers, 1945). The discussion of these developments lies outside the scope of this book. The reader is referred to such a book as Jauch and Rohrlich, *The Theory of Photons and Electrons*, Cambridge, Mass., 1955.

We give without proof the result for the case in which the electron is in some higher state ϕ_i; $w^{i \to j}$ denotes the probability of spontaneous transition to some lower state ϕ_j. From the correspondence principle we would expect the width γ_{ij} of the line ω_{ij} to be equal to $w^{i \to j}$. This is not the case, however; the result is

$$\gamma_{ij} = \gamma_i + \gamma_j = \sum_{k<i} w^{i \to k} + \sum_{k<j} w^{j \to k}$$

Each term ω_i is associated with a given width γ_i dependent on the probabilities of the transitions to lower terms; in the case of the transition ω_{ij} the widths of the terms γ_i and γ_j are to be added to give the width of the line ω_{ij}.

Exercises

1. *Fourier representation of Hertz's solution*

Integrate the equations

$$\nabla^2\mathbf{A} - \ddot{\mathbf{A}}/c^2 = -4\pi\mathbf{j}/c \qquad \nabla^2\phi - \ddot{\phi}/c^2 = -4\pi\rho$$

using the relations

$$\mathbf{A}(\mathbf{r}, t) = \int \mathbf{A}_{\mathbf{k},\omega} \exp i(\mathbf{kr} - \omega t)\, d\mathbf{k}\, d\omega \qquad \phi(\mathbf{r}, t) = \int \phi_{\mathbf{k},\omega} \exp i(\mathbf{kr} - \omega t)\, d\mathbf{k}\, d\omega$$

* This divergence is directly associated with the infinite field oscillations discussed on p. 311. See Weisskopf and Wigner, E., *Z. Phys.* 63 (1930); Heitler, *Quantum Theory of Radiation*, third ed., p. 181 (Oxford, 1954).

Perform the integration with respect to ω in the complex plane. How must the path of integration be taken with respect to the poles of $\mathbf{A}_{\mathbf{k},\omega}$ and $\phi_{\mathbf{k},\omega}$, in order to obtain the solutions of the retarded potentials?

2. *Total radiation momentum*

The momentum density of electromagnetic radiation is

$$\mathbf{g} = \frac{1}{4\pi c}\mathbf{E}\times\mathbf{H}, \quad \text{or} \quad \mathbf{g} = -\frac{1}{4\pi c^2}\dot{\mathbf{A}}\times\operatorname{curl}\mathbf{A}$$

Expressed in component form,

$$g_i = -\frac{1}{4\pi c^2}\sum_k \dot{A}_k\frac{\partial A_k}{\partial x_i} + \frac{1}{4\pi c^2}\sum_k \dot{A}_k\frac{\partial A_i}{\partial x_k} = g_i^{(1)} + g_i^{(2)}$$

Only the first term contributes to the total momentum $\mathbf{G} = \int \mathbf{g}\,d\mathbf{r}$. The contribution of the second term vanishes—this may be seen by integrating by parts, where the term outside the integral vanishes because of the periodicity assumed in (51.1), and the remaining integrand vanishes because $\operatorname{div}\mathbf{A} = 0$. Represent $\mathbf{G}$ in terms of $b_{\mathbf{k}\lambda}$ and $\overset{*}{b}_{\mathbf{k}\lambda}$, then proceed to the quantum theory and determine the eigenvalues of the operator $\mathbf{G}$.

Note the relations (51.4*a*) and (51.12), and express the result with b^+ to the left of b, as shown for the Hamiltonian operator (52.2).

3. *Angular momentum of the radiation*

The angular momentum $\mathbf{M}$ of electromagnetic radiation is $\mathbf{M} = \int \mathbf{r}\times\mathbf{g}\,d\mathbf{r}$, where $\mathbf{g}$ is the momentum density. If $\mathbf{g}$ is resolved into the two components $\mathbf{g}^{(1)}+\mathbf{g}^{(2)}$ of the previous exercise, the component $\mathbf{g}^{(2)}$ may be transformed by integration by parts, and we obtain

$$\mathbf{M} = \int \mathbf{r}\times\mathbf{g}^{(1)}\,d\mathbf{r} + \frac{1}{4\pi c^2}\int \mathbf{A}\times\dot{\mathbf{A}}\,d\mathbf{r}$$

The first term is of no interest; it clearly depends upon the choice of the origin of coordinates, and corresponds as it were to the "orbital angular momentum" of the radiation. It can always be made to vanish by a suitable choice of origin. In contrast, the second term is independent of the coordinate system, and corresponds to an intrinsic angular momentum, or "spin", of the radiation.

Represent
$$\mathbf{M} = \frac{1}{4\pi c^2}\int \mathbf{A}\times\dot{\mathbf{A}}\,d\mathbf{r}$$

in terms of the operators $b^+_{\mathbf{k}\lambda}$ and $b_{\mathbf{k}\lambda}$, taking due account of (51.9), and the remarks at the end of the previous exercise. As in the case of $\mathscr{H}$ and $\mathbf{G}$, $\mathbf{M}$ may be represented as a sum of terms, each of which is associated with a given value of $\mathbf{k}$: $\mathbf{M} = \sum_{\mathbf{k}} \mathbf{M}^{(\mathbf{k})}$.

In contrast to $\mathscr{H}^{(\mathbf{k})}$ and $\mathbf{G}^{(\mathbf{k})}$, however, the two polarizations $\lambda = 1, 2$ are still combined.

Introduce new operators in order to separate the polarizations in $\mathbf{M}^{(\mathbf{k})}$. What are the eigenvalues of $\mathbf{M}$? What classical waves correspond to the eigenstates? Express $\mathscr{H}$ and $\mathbf{G}$ in terms of the new operators. Describe the Hilbert space constructed from the eigenstates of $\mathscr{H}$, $\mathbf{G}$, and $\mathbf{M}$.

F

The relativistic theory of the electron

CHAPTER FI

Relativistic classical mechanics

§54. The equations of motion of the electron

We shall assume a knowledge of the principles of the theory of relativity that were derived in the first volume; the results required for our present purpose are summarized below.

The non-relativistic equation of motion of an electron in an electromagnetic field **E**, **H** is

$$\frac{d}{dt} m\mathbf{v} = e\left(\mathbf{E} + \frac{\mathbf{v}}{c} \times \mathbf{H}\right) \tag{54.1}$$

The energy equation is obtained by forming the scalar product with **v**:

$$\frac{d}{dt} \tfrac{1}{2} m\mathbf{v}^2 = e(\mathbf{E}\mathbf{v}) \tag{54.1a}$$

The relativistic analogue of the velocity $v_i = dx_i/dt$ is the four-velocity $u_\nu = dx_\nu/d\tau$, where x_ν stands for x, y, z, ict, and $d\tau = \sqrt{(1-v^2/c^2)}\,dt$ is the differential of the proper time. Since the x_ν constitute a four-vector and the proper time $d\tau$ is a scalar quantity, the u_ν also form a four-vector:

$$(u_1, u_2, u_3) = \frac{\mathbf{v}}{\sqrt{(1-v^2/c^2)}} \qquad u_4 = \frac{ic}{\sqrt{(1-v^2/c^2)}} \tag{54.2}$$

The length of this vector is

$$\sum_{\nu=1}^{4} u_\nu^2 = -c^2 \tag{54.2a}$$

In the relativistic case the field strengths* **E**, **H**, can be combined in an antisymmetric tensor of the second order:

$$F_{\mu\nu} = \left\{ \begin{array}{c|cccc} {}_\mu\diagdown^\nu & 1 & 2 & 3 & 4 \\ \hline 1 & 0 & H_z & -H_y & -iE_x \\ 2 & -H_z & 0 & H_x & -iE_y \\ 3 & H_y & -H_x & 0 & -iE_z \\ 4 & iE_x & iE_y & iE_z & 0 \end{array} \right\} \tag{54.3}$$

* Strictly, the magnetic induction **B** should be used instead of **H**, since **E** and this quantity together form a tensor. In what follows, however, we are only concerned with a vacuum, where **H** and **B** are identical.

If we form the vector of the four-force K_μ from $F_{\mu\nu}$ and u_ν,

$$K_\mu = \frac{e}{c}\sum_\nu F_{\mu\nu} u_\nu \tag{54.4}$$

then, substituting for u_ν according to (54.2), we obtain:

$$\begin{aligned}(K_1, K_2, K_3) &= e\left\{\mathbf{E}+\frac{\mathbf{v}}{c}\times\mathbf{H}\right\}\Big/\sqrt{(1-v^2/c^2)}\\ K_4 &= \frac{ie}{c}\mathbf{E}\mathbf{v}\Big/\sqrt{(1-v^2/c^2)}\end{aligned} \tag{54.5}$$

The above equations represent the relativistic generalization of the right-hand side of (54.1). The left-hand side becomes $dmu_\nu/d\tau$; the relativistic equation of motion therefore assumes the form

$$\frac{d}{d\tau} mu_\nu = \frac{e}{c}\sum_\nu F_{\mu\nu} u_\nu \tag{54.6}$$

Expressed in components:

$$\frac{d}{dt}\frac{m\mathbf{v}}{\sqrt{(1-v^2/c^2)}} = e\left(\mathbf{E}+\frac{\mathbf{v}}{c}\times\mathbf{H}\right) \tag{54.7}$$

$$\frac{d}{dt}\frac{mc^2}{\sqrt{(1-v^2/c^2)}} = e(\mathbf{E}\mathbf{v}) \tag{54.7a}$$

The spatial components (54.7) are the experimentally verified equations of motion that have already been discussed in §3. The fourth component (54.7*a*) provides the relativistic generalization of the theorem of the conservation of energy. Equations (54.6) therefore summarize and generalize equations (54.1) and (54.1*a*).

The energy of the electron is

$$E = mc^2/\sqrt{(1-v^2/c^2)} \tag{54.8}$$

For small velocities

$$E = mc^2 + \tfrac{1}{2}mv^2 + \dots$$

We thus obtain for E the kinetic energy of non-relativistic mechanics, apart from an additive constant which is the rest energy mc^2. It is apparent that in the non-relativistic limiting case, for which $v/c \ll 1$, the four equations (54.6) tend to the four equations (54.1, 54.1*a*).

If u_ν is multiplied by the electron mass m, a new four-vector is obtained,

$$p_\nu = mu_\nu, \text{ where } (p_1, p_2, p_3) = \frac{m\mathbf{v}}{\sqrt{(1-v^2/c^2)}} = \mathbf{p}, \; p_4 = \frac{i}{c}E \qquad (54.9)$$

the spatial parts of which are the components of the momentum. Then from (54.2*a*) we obtain the following relation between energy and momentum:

$$\mathbf{p}^2 - \frac{E^2}{c^2} = -m^2c^2 \qquad E = \sqrt{(p^2c^2 + m^2c^4)} \qquad (54.10)$$

§55. The Lagrangian and Hamiltonian functions

The relativistic Hamiltonian function can be obtained in its most concise form from the quantity $G = \int L\,dt$ which was introduced in (6.6). In non-relativistic mechanics the vanishing of the variation of G leads to a formulation of the equations of motion that is independent of the coordinates. G is a scalar, and if the relativistic equations of motion are based on a similar principle of the extremum, then G must be a scalar relativistic invariant.

Recollecting that the differential of the proper time $d\tau = dt\sqrt{(1-v^2/c^2)}$ is a scalar invariant, although dt is not, we may put

$$L\,dt = L'\,d\tau \qquad (55.1)$$

where L' is also to be invariant. Comparison with (7.3) suggests a form for L' which is deduced as follows. We consider the two four-vectors

$$\text{four-potential } (\Phi_1, \Phi_2, \Phi_3, \Phi_4) = (\mathbf{A}, i\phi) \qquad (55.2)$$

and four-velocity (u_1, u_2, u_3, u_4).

We assume that L' contains the scalar product of these two four-vectors, plus a scalar invariant. The latter must be equal to $-mc^2$, since in the non-relativistic case and in the absence of the field

$$L = L'\sqrt{(1-v^2/c^2)} \approx L'(1-v^2/2c^2)$$

This must reduce to the non-relativistic Lagrange function $L = \text{const} + \frac{1}{2}mv^2$. Hence for $\Phi_\nu \equiv 0$, L' must be equal to $-mc^2$. We therefore try the following solution:

$$L' = -mc^2 + \frac{e}{c}\sum_\nu u_\nu \Phi_\nu \qquad (55.3)$$

Our new Lagrange function L follows from this trial solution together with (55.1) and (55.2):

$$L = -mc^2\sqrt{(1-v^2/c^2)}+\frac{e}{c}(\mathbf{vA})-e\phi \tag{55.4}$$

Hence the relativistic canonical momentum is

$$p_x = \frac{\partial L}{\partial \dot{x}} = \frac{m\dot{x}}{\sqrt{(1-v^2/c^2)}}+\frac{e}{c}A_x, \text{ i.e. } \mathbf{p} = \frac{m\mathbf{v}}{\sqrt{(1-v^2/c^2)}}+\frac{e}{c}\mathbf{A} \tag{55.5}$$

It may easily be verified that the Lagrangian form of the equations of motion

$$\frac{dp_x}{dt} = \frac{\partial L}{\partial x} \qquad \frac{dp_y}{dt} = \frac{\partial L}{\partial y} \qquad \frac{dp_z}{dt} = \frac{\partial L}{\partial z} \tag{55.6}$$

agrees with (54.7).

For the Hamiltonian function $\mathbf{pv}-L$ it follows from (55.4) and (55.5) that

$$\frac{mv^2}{\sqrt{(1-v^2/c^2)}}+mc^2\sqrt{(1-v^2/c^2)}+e\phi = \frac{mc^2}{\sqrt{(1-v^2/c^2)}}+e\phi$$

We must now express the velocities in terms of the momenta, according to (7.4). Then from

$$\left(\mathbf{p}-\frac{e}{c}\mathbf{A}\right)^2 = \frac{m^2v^2}{1-v^2/c^2} = m^2c^2\left(\frac{1}{1-v^2/c^2}-1\right)$$

it follows that

$$\mathscr{H}(\mathbf{r},\mathbf{p},t) = c\sqrt{\left[\left(\mathbf{p}-\frac{e}{c}\mathbf{A}\right)^2+m^2c^2\right]}+e\phi \tag{55.7}$$

This is the relativistic Hamiltonian function for the motion of a particle of charge e and mass m in an electromagnetic field represented by the potentials $\mathbf{A}$ and ϕ.

This result may be expressed in the following form,

$$\left(\mathbf{p}-\frac{e}{c}\mathbf{A}\right)^2-\left(\frac{\mathscr{H}}{c}-\frac{e}{c}\phi\right)^2 = -m^2c^2$$

which brings the relativistic invariance into prominence when the four-vectors

$$(p_1, p_2, p_3, p_4) = \left(\mathbf{p}, \frac{i}{c}\mathscr{H}\right) \qquad (\Phi_1, \Phi_2, \Phi_3, \Phi_4) = (\mathbf{A}, i\phi)$$

are introduced. This gives the following result:

$$\sum_\nu \left(p_\nu - \frac{e}{c}\Phi_\nu\right)^2 = \sum_\nu (mu_\nu)^2 = -m^2c^2 \tag{55.8}$$

When the external fields vanish (55.8) is identical with (54.10) when the energy E is replaced by the Hamiltonian function.

Exercises

1. *The energy spectrum of electrons in β-disintegration, according to Fermi*

In the course of the β-disintegration of a nucleus, the latter emits an electron e and a neutrino ν. The energy of disintegration E_m is distributed between the two emitted particles. The only observable particles, the electrons, therefore possess different energies, depending on the share of the energy associated with each neutrino. In order to calculate the energy distribution of the electrons it is necessary to make an assumption concerning the distribution of the disintegration energy between the two particles. One obvious assumption drawn from statistical mechanics is that the number of disintegrations $n(\mathbf{p}_e, \mathbf{p}_\nu)\,d\mathbf{p}_e d\mathbf{p}_\nu$, for which the momenta of the two particles lie in the intervals $(\mathbf{p}_e, d\mathbf{p}_e)$ and $(\mathbf{p}_\nu, d\mathbf{p}_\nu)$, is proportional to $d\mathbf{p}_e d\mathbf{p}_\nu$. The nucleus itself may be assumed to be practically at rest in view of its large mass, and it is therefore unnecessary to take account of the conservation of momentum. The momenta are subject to the further condition that the energy of the two particles $\mathscr{H}_e(\mathbf{p}_e)+\mathscr{H}_\nu(\mathbf{p}_\nu)$ is equal to the energy of disintegration E_m, with an associated infinitesimal uncertainty ΔE_m which is introduced purely for convenience of calculation. Hence

$$n(\mathbf{p}_e, \mathbf{p}_\nu)\,d\mathbf{p}_e d\mathbf{p}_\nu = C\,d\mathbf{p}_e d\mathbf{p}_\nu, \quad \text{where} \quad E_m \leqq \mathscr{H}_e + \mathscr{H}_\nu \leqq E_m + \Delta E_m$$

The constant of normalization is determined from the total number N of observed disintegrations:

$$\int\limits_{E_m \leqq \mathscr{H}_e + \mathscr{H}_\nu \leqq E_m + \Delta E_m} n\,d\mathbf{p}_e d\mathbf{p}_\nu = N$$

The number of electrons in the interval $(\mathbf{p}_e, d\mathbf{p}_e)$ is obtained by integrating over $\mathbf{p}_\nu$, subject to the energy condition; the number of electrons $n(E_e)\,dE_e$ with energies in the interval (E_e, dE_e) is found by a further integration over $\mathbf{p}_e$ with $E_e \leqq \mathscr{H}_e \leqq E_e + dE_e$.

Evaluate $n(E_e)$: the calculation should be performed using the relativistic Hamiltonian function, first for a finite neutrino rest mass m_ν, then for the case $m_\nu = 0$.

2. *The relativistic Hamiltonian equations*

Derive the equations of motion (54.7) from the Hamiltonian function (55.7).

CHAPTER FII

Relativistic quantum mechanics

§56. Relativistic wave equations

In non-relativistic quantum theory momentum and energy are represented by operators as follows:

$$\mathbf{p} = \frac{\hbar}{i}\frac{\partial}{\partial \mathbf{r}} \qquad E = -\frac{\hbar}{i}\frac{\partial}{\partial t} \tag{56.1}$$

These operators act on a wave function ψ. Then, retaining the classical relation between $\mathscr{H}$ and $\mathbf{p}$, and applying the energy theorem $\mathscr{H} = E$, we obtain the Schrödinger equation

$$\mathscr{H}(\mathbf{p}, \mathbf{r})\psi = i\hbar\dot{\psi} \tag{56.2}$$

The relations (56.1) are also retained in the relativistic theory; they may be summarized by the four-vector p_μ in the form

$$p_\mu = \frac{\hbar}{i}\frac{\partial}{\partial x_\mu} \tag{56.1a}$$

which exhibits their invariant character.

We shall now attempt to establish a relativistic Schrödinger equation for the electron. The equation employed so far is not relativistically invariant. It contains derivatives of the second order with respect to the space coordinates, but a derivative of the first order with respect to time; the relativistically equivalent derivatives $\partial/\partial x_\mu$ are not treated in a symmetrical manner. If we wish to obtain a relativistic generalization of the original equation, there are two possibilities: the equation must either be of the second order in $\partial/\partial \mathbf{r}$ and so in $\partial/\partial t$ as well, or it remains linear in $\partial/\partial t$ and we must arrange to make it linear in $\partial/\partial \mathbf{r}$ also.

The first alternative together with (55.8) leads to the Klein-Gordon equation*

$$\sum_\mu \left(\frac{\hbar}{i}\frac{\partial}{\partial x_\mu} - \frac{e}{c}\Phi_\mu\right)^2 \psi = -m^2c^2\psi \tag{56.3}$$

or

$$\left\{\left(\mathbf{p} - \frac{e}{c}\mathbf{A}\right)^2 - \frac{1}{c^2}\left(\frac{\hbar}{i}\frac{\partial}{\partial t} + e\phi\right)^2\right\}\psi = -m^2c^2\psi \tag{56.3a}$$

* Klein, O., *Z. Phys.* **37** (1926), 895; Gordon, W., *Z. Phys.* **40** (1926), 117.

When the external forces vanish (i.e. $\Phi_\mu = 0$) the equation becomes

$$-\hbar^2\nabla^2\psi + \frac{\hbar^2}{c^2}\ddot{\psi} = -m^2c^2\psi \tag{56.3b}$$

If we now consider the second alternative, then following Dirac,* we can attempt to linearize the force-free form of equation (56.3) by assuming the following solution, which is known as Dirac's equation:

$$\left\{\sum_\mu \gamma_\mu p_\mu\right\}\psi \equiv \left\{\sum_\mu \gamma_\mu \frac{\hbar}{i}\frac{\partial}{\partial x_\mu}\right\}\psi = imc\psi \tag{56.4}$$

In the above expression the quantities γ_μ are constant operators that have yet to be determined. The manner of linearization must be such that the solutions of (56.4) also satisfy the force-free Klein-Gordon equation (56.3*b*), thus preserving the previous relation between energy and momentum (i.e. between the propagation vector and the frequency in the case of plane waves). If the operation $\sum_\mu \gamma_\mu p_\mu$ is again performed on (56.4) the result is

$$\sum_{\mu,\nu} \gamma_\mu \gamma_\nu p_\mu p_\nu \psi = -m^2c^2\psi \tag{56.5}$$

If this equation is to agree with (56.3*b*), this clearly requires that†

$$\tfrac{1}{2}(\gamma_\mu\gamma_\nu + \gamma_\nu\gamma_\mu) = \delta_{\mu\nu} \tag{56.6}$$

This equation cannot be satisfied by ordinary numbers γ_μ, but as we shall see, it can be by square matrices $\gamma_{\mu,mn}$ of at least four rows. This means that in (56.4) ψ must be a wave function consisting of a number of components: $\psi = (\psi_1, \psi_2, \ldots, \psi_n, \ldots)$. This is very satisfactory since the electron must be associated with additional degrees of freedom to take account of the spin. The γ_μ act on the components ψ_n in the manner with which we are already familiar from the discussion of spin:

$$(\gamma_\mu\psi)_m = \sum_n \gamma_{\mu,mn}\psi_n$$

Later on we shall encounter special representations of the γ_μ.

In the presence of external fields (56.4) is generalized to

$$\sum_\mu \gamma_\mu\left(p_\mu - \frac{e}{c}\Phi_\mu\right)\psi = imc\psi \tag{56.7}$$

* Dirac, P. A. M., *Proc. Roy. Soc.* **117** (1928), 610; **118**, 351.

† Only the symmetric part (56.6) occurs in (56.5), since $p_\mu p_\nu$ is symmetric in μ and ν.

While (56.4) together with the relation (56.6) leads to the Klein-Gordon equation, in the case of (56.7) the same procedure yields additional terms:

$$\sum_{\mu,\nu} \gamma_\mu \gamma_\nu \left(p_\mu - \frac{e}{c} \Phi_\mu \right) \left(p_\nu - \frac{e}{c} \Phi_\nu \right) \psi = -m^2 c^2 \psi \tag{56.8}$$

or after a simple transformation, taking account of (56.6),

$$\left\{ \sum_\mu \left(p_\mu - \frac{e}{c} \Phi_\mu \right)^2 - \sum_{\mu,\nu} \frac{\hbar e}{4ic} (\gamma_\mu \gamma_\nu - \gamma_\nu \gamma_\mu) F_{\mu\nu} \right\} \psi = -m^2 c^2 \psi \tag{56.8a}$$

where
$$F_{\mu\nu} = \frac{\partial \Phi_\nu}{\partial x_\mu} - \frac{\partial \Phi_\mu}{\partial x_\nu}$$

is the field strength tensor (54.2). Equation (56.8*a*) differs from (56.3) through an additional term that may be interpreted as the interaction of the spin with the external field.

In order to illustrate this more clearly, we introduce the vectors

$$\vec{\sigma}' = (\sigma_1', \sigma_2', \sigma_3') \quad \text{and} \quad \vec{\alpha} = (\alpha_1, \alpha_2, \alpha_3)$$

the components of which are

$$\begin{aligned} &\sigma_1' = i\gamma_3 \gamma_2, \quad &\sigma_2' = i\gamma_1 \gamma_3, \quad &\sigma_3' = i\gamma_2 \gamma_1 \\ \text{and} \quad &\alpha_1 = i\gamma_4 \gamma_1, \quad &\alpha_2 = i\gamma_4 \gamma_2, \quad &\alpha_3 = i\gamma_4 \gamma_3 \end{aligned} \tag{56.9}$$

and confine ourselves to the non-relativistic case. We now assume a solution $\psi = \tilde{\psi} \exp - imc^2 t/\hbar$ together with the approximation $|\dot{\tilde{\psi}}| \ll |mc^2 \tilde{\psi}|$. We can then neglect $\ddot{\tilde{\psi}}$ and consequently obtain

$$\left\{ \frac{1}{2m} \left(\mathbf{p} - \frac{e}{c} \mathbf{A} \right)^2 + e\phi - \frac{e\hbar}{2mc} \vec{\sigma}' \mathbf{H} + i \frac{e\hbar}{2mc} \vec{\alpha} \mathbf{E} \right\} \psi = i\hbar \dot{\psi} \tag{56.10}$$

This is the correct representation of the interaction between spin and field postulated in Pauli's theory of spin. The operators σ_i' are very similar to the Pauli spin matrices σ_i; this is shown by the fact that they satisfy the same commutation relations

$$\sigma_1' \sigma_2' - \sigma_2' \sigma_1' = 2i\sigma_3', \text{ etc., and } \sigma_k'^2 = 1 \tag{56.11}$$

(as may be verified from (56.6)), and that the three components of σ' can therefore have only the eigenvalues $+1$ and -1. In §60 we shall show that, apart from additional terms, (56.10) is actually identical with Pauli's spin theory.

It can be regarded as a great advance over the Schrödinger equation that the electron spin, including the commutation relations of the Pauli matrices, and the correct value of the magnetic moment follow automatically as it were from the relations (56.6) (cf. magneto-mechanical anomaly, p.194).

Nevertheless, serious difficulties are encountered in connection with the physical interpretation of the Klein-Gordon and Dirac equations as quantum-mechanical equations for the electron; that is, in taking ψ to represent a state vector, as in the non-relativistic theory. We shall give a qualitative discussion of these difficulties in the following pages.

The Klein-Gordon equation does not possess the established form $\mathscr{H}\psi = i\hbar\dot{\psi}$; on the contrary, it is of the second order in $\partial/\partial t$. A knowledge of the state at a given instant is therefore insufficient to determine the situation at a later time; for this purpose we require the initial values of ψ and $\dot{\psi}$. Again, it is not possible to define a probability density ρ (represented by $\psi^*\psi$ in the non-relativistic case): to see this, we shall attempt to determine ρ by establishing the relativistic generalization of the continuity equation $\dot{\rho} + \operatorname{div} \mathbf{j} = 0$ (which implies the maintenance of the normalization $\int \rho \, d\mathbf{r}$). Expressed in terms of the four-current* j_μ, the continuity equation is

$$\sum_\mu \partial j_\mu / \partial x_\mu = 0$$

The only possible equation of this type is obtained by a similar procedure to that used in the case of the non-relativistic Schrödinger equation in the absence of external forces:

$$j_\mu = \frac{\hbar}{2mi}\left\{\psi^* \frac{\partial \psi}{\partial x_\mu} - \psi \frac{\partial \psi^*}{\partial x_\mu}\right\}$$

It may easily be verified that the continuity equation is valid in virtue of (56.3*b*). The resultant density

$$\rho = j_4 / ic = \frac{i\hbar}{2mc^2}\{\psi^* \dot{\psi} - \dot{\psi}^* \psi\}$$

cannot be interpreted as a probability density because it can assume positive and negative values, and negative probability densities are obviously absurd.

This difficulty cannot be removed by restricting ψ and $\dot{\psi}$ to those values for which ρ is positive, because this positive value of ρ generally

* Cf. Vol. I, §81.

gives rise in the course of time to a density which is still negative in places. We cannot therefore make use of the Klein-Gordon equation to describe a particle.

However, this equation possesses meaning when considered as a classical wave equation in which $e\rho$ appears as a charge density (where the charges may be positive or negative). The normal quantization methods may then be applied to it, similar to the procedure employed in the case of Maxwell's equations (§§51, 52). Particles associated in quantum mechanics with the "Klein-Gordon field" possess a mass m, charge $\pm e$, and no spin; π-mesons are an example.

The above difficulties do not appear in the Dirac equation. This equation is linear in $\partial/\partial t$; further, the corresponding equation of continuity enables a value of ρ to be defined that is always positive (cf. following sections). On the other hand there is another difficulty, as we shall see later. It is found that the energy levels of the stationary states vary between $-\infty$ and $+\infty$; there is no state of lowest energy.* This means that it is impossible to find a completely positive expression for the energy density when the Dirac equation is interpreted as a classical wave equation; nor can the difficulty be eliminated by excluding the states of negative energy from consideration on the grounds that they are physically useless, because positive energy states can become states of negative energy in the presence of external fields.

Nevertheless, the Dirac equation may be "quantized" to provide a many-particle theory which at first sight also includes particles with negative energy possessing physically absurd properties (see §58). However, since the electrons satisfy Pauli's exclusion principle, Dirac was able to eliminate this difficulty by assuming that all the negative energy states were already filled and that therefore no transitions could take place between positive and negative states. This situation represents the vacuum state, that is, the state of lowest energy with zero charge and mass. An additional electron can assume only the unoccupied energy values, and a lowest state exists.†

The vacuum state is not empty; it possesses a lower stratum of occupied negative-energy levels which entail a number of physical

* The situation is different in the case of the Klein-Gordon equation. The energy density of the field theory is positive definite; in the quantized theory, therefore, the energy spectrum contains positive values only (in contrast to the frequency spectrum, which extends from $-\infty$ to $+\infty$).

† It may be shown directly that the occurrence of negative energies in the case of Dirac particles necessarily entails quantization in accordance with Pauli's principle. To some extent this proves the relation between spin and the statistics that was described in pp. 249-50.

properties. This can be most clearly seen from the fact that it is possible to produce electron and positron pairs. A light quantum of sufficient energy can raise an electron with negative energy into a positive energy state; the ground state is then short of a particle with negative energy and charge. What we should therefore be able to observe besides the excited electron is a new physical entity which, according to Dirac, behaves like a particle with positive energy and charge! It was in 1930 that Dirac advanced the hypothesis of the existence of "positrons"* on the strength of his bold and at first sight extremely surprising assumption with regard to the vacuum state. Such particles were in fact first observed two years later by Anderson in cosmic radiation.

Fundamentally, the Dirac and Klein-Gordon equations are similar in that each necessarily leads to the consideration of many particles. This is a general characteristic of all relativistic theories, which are represented in physical terms by quantized fields with many particles.

We shall, however, look upon the Dirac equation in an approximate manner as the Schrödinger equation for an electron, provided that we note that the states of negative energy are filled, and provided that we may neglect transitions from positive to negative energy states.

§57. The physical interpretation of Dirac's equation

We shall first put the Dirac equation

$$\left\{\sum_\mu \gamma_\mu\left(p_\mu - \frac{e}{c}\Phi_\mu\right) - imc\right\}\psi = 0 \tag{57.1}$$

into the usual form $\mathscr{H}\psi = i\hbar\dot{\psi}$. This is achieved by applying $ic\gamma_4$ to (57.1), since $\gamma_4\gamma_4 = 1$. Using the definitions (56.9) together with

$$\beta = \gamma_4 \qquad \alpha_l = i\beta\gamma_l \qquad (l = 1, 2, 3) \tag{57.2}$$

or

$$\vec{\alpha} = i\beta\vec{\gamma} \tag{57.2a}$$

we obtain the following equation:

$$\left\{\beta mc^2 + c\vec{\alpha}\left(\mathbf{p} - \frac{e}{c}\mathbf{A}\right) + e\phi\right\}\psi = i\hbar\dot{\psi} \tag{57.3}$$

* Dirac first thought that there was a connection between the "holes" in the ground state and the proton, which was then the only other particle known besides the electron. However, it was soon shown by R. Oppenheimer (*Phys. Rev.* 35 (1930), 461) and H. Weyl (1931) that the mass of a "hole" must be equal to the mass of the electron.

Thus in this expression the Hamiltonian operator is given by

$$\mathscr{H} = \beta mc^2 + c\vec{\alpha}\left(\mathbf{p} - \frac{e}{c}\mathbf{A}\right) + e\phi \qquad (57.3a)$$

$\mathscr{H}$ must be Hermitian in order to possess real eigenvalues. We therefore choose the matrices β and α_l to be Hermitian; the γ_μ are also Hermitian in consequence of the definitions (57.2):

$$\beta^+ = \beta \qquad \alpha_l^+ = \alpha_l \qquad \gamma_\mu^+ = \gamma_\mu \qquad (57.4)$$

or expressed in terms of the matrix elements,

$$\beta^*_{mn} = \beta_{nm} \qquad \alpha^*_{l,mn} = \alpha_{l,nm} \qquad \gamma^*_{\mu,mn} = \gamma_{\mu,nm} \qquad (57.4a)$$

In virtue of (57.2) and (56.6), the α_l and β satisfy the relations

$$\beta^2 = 1 \qquad \alpha_l\beta + \beta\alpha_l = 0 \qquad \alpha_l\alpha_k + \alpha_k\alpha_l = 2\delta_{kl} \qquad (57.5)$$

Hence in view of (57.4) and (57.5) the $\alpha_l, \beta, \gamma_\mu$ are unitary as well as Hermitian matrices.

We can now establish an equation of continuity, using a similar method to that employed in connection with the non-relativistic Schrödinger equation. Equation (57.3) is first expressed in terms of the components:

$$\sum_n \left\{\beta_{mn}\, mc^2 + c\vec{\alpha}_{mn}\left(p - \frac{e}{c}A\right) + e\phi\,\delta_{mn}\right\}\psi_n = i\hbar\dot{\psi}_m$$

This is multiplied by ψ^*_m, summed over m, and the conjugate complex removed. Then in view of the relations (57.4a) the result is

$$\frac{\partial\rho}{\partial t} + \operatorname{div}\mathbf{j} = 0$$

where
$$\rho = \sum_m \psi^*_m\psi_m \qquad \mathbf{j} = \sum_{m,n} c\vec{\alpha}_{mn}\psi^*_m\psi_n \qquad (57.6)$$

This continuity equation enables $\rho(\mathbf{r},t)d\mathbf{r}$ to be interpreted as the probability of the occurrence of the electron in the volume element $d\mathbf{r}$.

We can now calculate the centroid $\bar{\mathbf{r}} = \int \mathbf{r}\rho\, d\mathbf{r}$ of a wave packet together with its time rate of change $\dot{\bar{\mathbf{r}}}$. It is apparent from §22 that we merely need to form the operator $\dot{\mathbf{r}} = (i/\hbar)[\mathscr{H}, \mathbf{r}]$, when $\dot{\bar{\mathbf{r}}} = \bar{\dot{\mathbf{r}}}$. Then using (57.3$a$) and the usual commutation relations for $\mathbf{p}$ and $\mathbf{r}$ we obtain

$$\dot{\mathbf{r}} = \frac{i}{\hbar}[\mathscr{H}, \mathbf{r}] = c\vec{\alpha} \qquad (57.7)$$

Although this operator has exactly the form that we would expect from the continuity equation ($\bar{\mathbf{r}} = \int \mathbf{j}(\mathbf{r},t)\,d\mathbf{r}$), it has some unusual properties which we shall now describe.

Since the α_l are Hermitian and unitary, they can have only the eigenvalues ± 1; an exact measurement of a velocity component would therefore always yield the value $+c$ or $-c$. Further, the components $\dot{x}$, $\dot{y}$, $\dot{z}$ do not commute with each other or with $\mathscr{H}$ in the absence of the external forces Φ_μ. Thus there are no free particles with sharply defined velocity.

These properties of the operator $\dot{\mathbf{r}}$ indicate that it has very little in common with the corresponding operator $\{\mathbf{p}-(e/c)\mathbf{A}\}/m$ occurring in the non-relativistic theory, particularly since in experimental determinations of the velocity components any values may be found between $-c$ and $+c$.

We shall see in §60, however, that there is an operator $\mathbf{v}$ that is essentially different from $c\vec{\alpha}$, and which becomes the ordinary velocity operator in the non-relativistic case; this operator is directly connected with the experimentally determined velocity.

We shall now consider the time rate of change of the operator $\{\mathbf{p}-(e/c)\mathbf{A}\}$; since $c\vec{\alpha} = \dot{\mathbf{r}}$, this is

$$\frac{d}{dt}\left(\mathbf{p}-\frac{e}{c}\mathbf{A}\right) = \frac{i}{\hbar}\left[\mathscr{H}, \mathbf{p}-\frac{e}{c}\mathbf{A}\right] - \frac{e}{c}\frac{\partial \mathbf{A}}{\partial t} = e\mathbf{E} + \frac{e}{c}\dot{\mathbf{r}} \times \mathbf{H} \qquad (57.8)$$

Although the form of this equation is similar to that of the classical equation of motion (54.7) its significance is not the same, because of the difference mentioned above between the mean momentum and the velocity of the centroid multiplied by m (cf. §60).

For a free particle (i.e. one for which $\mathbf{A} = \phi = 0$):

$$\frac{d\mathbf{p}}{dt} = \frac{i}{\hbar}[\mathscr{H}, \mathbf{p}] = 0$$

Therefore although there are no free particles with a sharp value of $\dot{\mathbf{r}}$, such particles do exist with sharply defined values of $\mathbf{p}$; we shall consider these in more detail in the next paragraph.

We shall now investigate the conservation law for the orbital angular momentum of a free particle, $\mathbf{L} = \mathbf{r} \times \mathbf{p}$. Since $\mathscr{H}$ and $\mathbf{p}$ commute we have

$$\dot{\mathbf{L}} = \frac{i}{\hbar}[\mathscr{H}, \mathbf{L}] = \frac{i}{\hbar}[\mathscr{H}, \mathbf{r}] \times \mathbf{p} = \dot{\mathbf{r}} \times \mathbf{p} \qquad (57.9)$$

The above equation shows that the orbital angular momentum of a free particle is not constant in time. This is also true of the spin, for which we may tentatively assign the value $\mathbf{s} = \frac{1}{2}\hbar\vec{\sigma}'$, where $\vec{\sigma}'$ is defined by (56.9). Then from (57.5) and the relations $\sigma_1' = i\alpha_3\alpha_2$, etc., we obtain

$$\dot{\mathbf{s}} = \frac{i}{\hbar}[\mathscr{H}, \mathbf{s}] = -\dot{\mathbf{r}} \times \mathbf{p} \tag{57.10}$$

If we compare this result with (57.9) we see that the total angular momentum $\mathbf{J} = \mathbf{L} + \mathbf{s}$ is constant in time (cf. Exercise 1, p. 359).

We shall now derive the form of the matrices γ_μ, α_l, and β. These are merely required to satisfy the relations (56.6) and (57.5) and the Hermitian condition (57.4). It follows in the first instance that the matrices are determined except for unitary transformations $U\gamma_\mu U^+$ which leave (56.6) and (57.5) unchanged.

We can first choose U so that β is diagonal. Since β is unitary and Hermitian it can have only the eigenvalues ± 1, which can be so arranged that

$$\beta = \begin{pmatrix} 1 & 0 \\ 0 & -1 \end{pmatrix} = \left(\begin{array}{cccc|cccc} 1 & & & & 0 & \cdots & \cdots & 0 \\ & 1 & & & \vdots & & & \vdots \\ & & \ddots & & \vdots & & & \vdots \\ & & & 1 & 0 & & & 0 \\ \hline 0 & \cdots & \cdots & 0 & -1 & & & \\ \vdots & & & \vdots & & \ddots & & \\ \vdots & & & \vdots & & & \ddots & \\ 0 & \cdots & \cdots & 0 & & & & -1 \end{array}\right) \tag{57.11}$$

In the first matrix the figure 1 represents unit matrices, and the figure 0 stands for null matrices possessing an initially unknown number of rows and columns. Now it follows from the relations $\alpha_k\beta + \beta\alpha_k = 0$ and $\alpha_k\alpha_k^+ = 1$ that

$$\alpha_k \beta \alpha_k^+ = -\beta$$

Then, forming the matrix traces, we have

$$\operatorname{Tr}(-\beta) = \operatorname{Tr}\alpha_k\beta\alpha_k^+ = \operatorname{Tr}\alpha_k^+\alpha_k\beta = \operatorname{Tr}\beta, \text{ hence } \operatorname{Tr}\beta = 0$$

This means that, in (57.11), 1 and -1 have the same number of columns, and 0 is a square matrix. It then follows from the relations $\alpha_k\beta + \beta\alpha_k = 0$ and $\alpha_k = \alpha_k^+$ that α_k must have the form

$$\alpha_k = \begin{pmatrix} 0 & \alpha^{(k)} \\ \alpha^{(k)+} & 0 \end{pmatrix} \tag{57.12}$$

with corresponding square matrices $\alpha^{(k)}$ and 0. From (56.9) the σ'_k assume the form

$$\sigma'_k = \begin{pmatrix} \sigma_k & 0 \\ 0 & \tilde{\sigma}_k \end{pmatrix} \tag{57.13}$$

From (56.11) we know that the quantities $\frac{1}{2}\hbar\sigma'_k$ satisfy the familiar commutation relations for the angular momentum; so do $\frac{1}{2}\hbar\sigma_k$ and $\frac{1}{2}\hbar\tilde{\sigma}_k$ in view of (57.13). They must therefore be the usual angular-momentum matrices, in accordance with §24. Further, we know by definition that $\sigma_k'^2 = 1$, so that $\sigma_k^2 = \tilde{\sigma}_k^2 = 1$ also; therefore the only quantum number for the angular momentum arising is $l = \frac{1}{2}$. σ_k and $\tilde{\sigma}_k$ may then be put into the form of the Pauli spin matrices by means of a unitary transformation of σ'_k

$$U = \begin{pmatrix} U_1 & 0 \\ 0 & U_2 \end{pmatrix}$$

which leaves β unchanged: then*

$$\vec{\sigma}' = \begin{pmatrix} \vec{\sigma} & 0 \\ 0 & \vec{\sigma} \end{pmatrix} \tag{57.14}$$

The α_l may now be determined by introducing the matrix

$$\alpha_0 = -i\alpha_1\alpha_2\alpha_3 = \begin{pmatrix} 0 & \alpha^{(0)} \\ \alpha^{(0)+} & 0 \end{pmatrix} \tag{57.15}$$

This matrix is also unitary and Hermitian, and commutes with all α_l and σ_l, as may be shown from (56.9) and (57.5). Hence $\alpha^{(0)}$ can only have the form $e^{i\phi}\begin{pmatrix} 1 & 0 \\ 0 & 1 \end{pmatrix}$ (cf. Exercise 3, p. 360). Then by means of a unitary transformation

$$U = \begin{pmatrix} e^{i\phi/2}.1 & 0 \\ 0 & e^{-i\phi/2}.1 \end{pmatrix}$$

which leaves β and $\vec{\alpha}$ unchanged, α_0 may be put into the form

$$\alpha_0 = \begin{pmatrix} 0 & 1 \\ 1 & 0 \end{pmatrix} \tag{57.15a}$$

* Trivial generalizations of the form

$$\vec{\sigma}' = \begin{bmatrix} \vec{\sigma} & 0 & & \\ & \vec{\sigma} & & \\ 0 & & \vec{\sigma} & 0 \\ & & 0 & \vec{\sigma} \end{bmatrix}$$

would be conceivable; these would simply lead to two completely similar unconnected Dirac equations.

From (56.9) and (57.15) we finally obtain

$$\alpha_l = \alpha_0 \sigma_l' = \begin{pmatrix} 0 & \sigma_l \\ \sigma_l & 0 \end{pmatrix}$$

which completes our analysis.

We thus have the following result. The α_l, β, and γ_μ are uniquely determined by means of the relations (56.6) and (57.5), apart from unitary transformations (see footnote, p. 337). They are 4×4 matrices, and may be put into the form

$$\beta = \begin{pmatrix} 1 & 0 \\ 0 & -1 \end{pmatrix} \qquad \vec{\alpha} = \begin{pmatrix} 0 & \vec{\sigma} \\ \vec{\sigma} & 0 \end{pmatrix} \tag{57.16}$$

where $\vec{\sigma}$ represents the usual Pauli matrices (24.9).

In connection with later applications, it is useful to introduce the following designations. Matrices in the form of β and σ_l', which contain null matrices in their secondary diagonal, are called D-matrices, while those having the form of α_l with null matrices in the principal diagonal are termed A-matrices.* The following rules apply to the products of such matrices:

$$\beta A + A\beta = 0 \qquad \beta D - D\beta = 0 \tag{57.17}$$

$D.D'$ gives a D matrix, $A.A'$ gives a D matrix, $A.D$ gives an A matrix.

§58. The Dirac equation in the absence of an external field

We shall now look for solutions of the equation

$$(c\vec{\alpha}\mathbf{p} + \beta mc^2)\psi = i\hbar\dot{\psi} \tag{58.1}$$

We first investigate the stationary states $\psi = \phi e^{-i\omega t}$:

$$(c\vec{\alpha}\mathbf{p} + \beta mc^2)\phi = \hbar\omega\phi \tag{58.2}$$

Since $\mathbf{p}$ and $\mathcal{H}$ commute, as we have seen, ϕ may also be assumed to be an eigenfunction of $\mathbf{p}$, or expressed in terms of components:

$$\phi_n(\mathbf{k}, \mathbf{r}) = a_n(\mathbf{k})\, e^{i\mathbf{kr}} \tag{58.3}$$

In the above expression $\hbar\mathbf{k}$ is the eigenvalue of $\mathbf{p}$ and $\hbar\omega = E$ is the eigenvalue of $\mathcal{H}$.

When (58.3) is inserted in (58.2) we obtain the eigenvalue equation

$$\sum_n \{\vec{\alpha}c\hbar\mathbf{k} + \beta mc^2\}_{mn}\, a_n(\mathbf{k}) = Ea_m(\mathbf{k}) \tag{58.4}$$

* Translator's note: The German for "secondary diagonal" is "Ausserdiagonal".

Using the relations (57.16), this equation may be expressed in terms of components as follows:

$$\begin{aligned} (E-mc^2)a_1 - c\hbar k_3 a_3 - c\hbar(k_1-ik_2)a_4 &= 0 \\ (E-mc^2)a_2 - c\hbar(k_1+ik_2)a_3 + c\hbar k_3 a_4 &= 0 \\ (E+mc^2)a_3 - c\hbar k_3 a_1 - c\hbar(k_1-ik_2)a_2 &= 0 \\ (E+mc^2)a_4 - c\hbar(k_1+ik_2)a_1 + c\hbar k_3 a_2 &= 0 \end{aligned} \qquad (58.5)$$

The relativistic energy formula

$$E^2 = (c\hbar k)^2 + m^2c^4 \qquad (58.6)$$

results for the eigenvalues E, if the determinant of the above system of equations is set equal to 0, or if the operator $\{c\vec{\alpha}\hbar\mathbf{k}+\beta mc^2\}$ is simply applied again to (58.4), and the relations (57.5) are employed. Hence

$$E = \pm E(\hbar\mathbf{k}) = \pm\sqrt{\{(c\hbar\mathbf{k})^2+m^2c^4\}} \qquad (58.7)$$

Equating the determinant to zero yields an equation of the fourth degree in E; there are therefore four solutions, of which two pairs coincide.* These are designated (figure 56)

$$E_1 = E_2 = E(\hbar\mathbf{k}) \qquad E_3 = E_4 = -E(\hbar\mathbf{k})$$

Since the determinantal equation possesses double roots we are free to choose any two of the components a_n as we wish, the other two then being determined by (58.5). One possible choice is

$$\begin{pmatrix} a_1^1 \cdots\cdots a_1^4 \\ \vdots \qquad\quad \vdots \\ \vdots \qquad\quad \vdots \\ a_4^1 \cdots\cdots a_4^4 \end{pmatrix} = a \begin{pmatrix} 1 & 0 & \multicolumn{2}{c}{?} \\ 0 & 1 & & \\ & & 1 & 0 \\ \multicolumn{2}{c}{?} & 0 & 1 \end{pmatrix}$$

where the a_n^s are the components associated with E_s. The as yet undetermined factor a is chosen so as to normalize a_n^s (i.e. $\sum_n |a_n^s|^2 = 1$). Then the solution of (58.5) gives

$$a_n^s = \frac{1}{\sqrt{\{2E(\hbar\mathbf{k})[E(\hbar\mathbf{k})+mc^2]\}}} b_n^s$$

* From (58.7) there are only two different eigenvalues E_i. In addition, $\sum_{i=1}^{4} E_i = 0$, because the trace of the secular matrix vanishes ($\mathrm{Tr}\,\beta = \mathrm{Tr}\,\alpha = 0$).

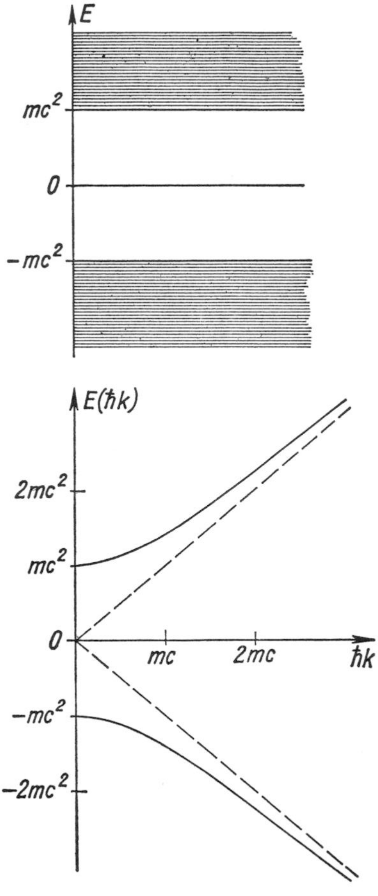

Fig. 56.—The energy spectrum of the Dirac equation for a free particle

where the values of b_n^s are given in the following table:

$n \backslash s$	1	2	3	4
1	$E(\hbar\mathbf{k})+mc^2$	0	$-c\hbar k_3$	$-c\hbar(k_1-ik_2)$
2	0	$E(\hbar\mathbf{k})+mc^2$	$-c\hbar(k_1+ik_2)$	$c\hbar k_3$
3	$c\hbar k_3$	$c\hbar(k_1-ik_2)$	$E(\hbar\mathbf{k})+mc^2$	0
4	$c\hbar(k_1+ik_2)$	$-c\hbar k_3$	0	$E(\hbar\mathbf{k})+mc^2$

The components a_n^s may be expressed more concisely, using the relations (57.16):

$$a_n^s(\hbar\mathbf{k}) = \left\{\frac{c\vec{\alpha}\hbar\mathbf{k}+\beta[E(\hbar\mathbf{k})+mc^2]}{\sqrt{\{2E(\hbar\mathbf{k})[E(\hbar\mathbf{k})+mc^2]\}}}\beta\right\}_{ns}$$

$$= \frac{\{\mathscr{H}\beta+E(\hbar\mathbf{k})\}_{ns}}{\sqrt{\{2E(\hbar\mathbf{k})[E(\hbar\mathbf{k})+mc^2]\}}} \tag{58.8}$$

The a_n^s clearly form an orthogonal system, since the matrix (58.8) is unitary because

$$[\mathscr{H}\beta+E(\hbar\mathbf{k})][\mathscr{H}\beta+E(\hbar\mathbf{k})]^+ = \mathscr{H}\beta^2\mathscr{H}+(\mathscr{H}\beta+\beta\mathscr{H})E(\hbar\mathbf{k})+E^2(h\mathbf{k})$$
$$= 2E(\hbar\mathbf{k})[E(\hbar\mathbf{k})+mc^2]$$

Further, we can see from (58.8) that the a_n^s satisfy equation (58.4), since

$$\mathscr{H}[(\mathscr{H}\beta+E(\hbar\mathbf{k})] = E^2(\hbar\mathbf{k})\beta+\mathscr{H}E(\hbar\mathbf{k}) = [\mathscr{H}\beta+E(\hbar\mathbf{k})]\beta E(\hbar\mathbf{k})$$

which is the same as (58.4) except for the factor

$$\sqrt{\{2E(\hbar\mathbf{k})[E(\hbar\mathbf{k})+mc^2]\}}$$

For our further calculations we shall again assume a periodicity box* of volume $V=L^3$. We can then represent all functions $\psi(\mathbf{r},t)$ in this box in terms of the complete system

$$\phi_n^s(\mathbf{k},\mathbf{r}) = a_n^s(\mathbf{k})\frac{e^{i\mathbf{k}\mathbf{r}}}{\sqrt{V}}, \quad \text{where} \quad \mathbf{k} = \frac{2\pi}{L}\mathbf{n} \tag{58.9}$$

$$\psi_n(\mathbf{r},t) = \sum_{\mathbf{k},s} b_s(\mathbf{k},t)\,\phi_n^s(\mathbf{k},\mathbf{r}) \tag{58.10}$$

The dependence on time of the coefficients $b_s(\mathbf{k},t)$ is found by introducing (58.10) into the Dirac equation. In the absence of external fields we obtain the following result:

$$E_s(\hbar\mathbf{k})b_s(\mathbf{k},t) = i\hbar\dot{b}_s(\mathbf{k},t)$$

or

$$b_s(\mathbf{k},t) = b_s(\mathbf{k},0)\,e^{-i\omega_s(\mathbf{k})t} \tag{58.11}$$

* This box distinguishes the system of reference in which it is at rest from all other systems. However, since we are not interested in the properties of the quantities subject to Lorentz transformations, this need not concern us any further.

We give below the expressions for the expectation values of the energy, momentum, charge density, and total charge, corresponding to (58.10):

$$\tilde{\mathscr{H}} = \int \sum_{m,n} \psi_m^* \{c\tilde{\alpha}\mathbf{p}+\beta mc^2\}_{mn} \psi_n \, d\mathbf{r} = \sum_{\mathbf{k},s} \hbar\omega_s(\mathbf{k}) b_s^*(\mathbf{k}) b_s(\mathbf{k}) \quad (58.12a)$$

$$\tilde{\mathbf{G}} = \int \sum_m \psi_m^* \mathbf{p} \psi_m \, d\mathbf{r} = \sum_{\mathbf{k},s} \hbar\mathbf{k} b_s^*(\mathbf{k}) b_s(\mathbf{k}) \quad (58.12b)$$

$$\tilde{\rho} = e\sum_m \psi_m^* \psi_m = e \sum_{\substack{m,\mathbf{k},\mathbf{k}' \\ s,s'}} b_s^*(\mathbf{k})\, b_{s'}(\mathbf{k}')\phi_m^{*s}(\mathbf{k},\mathbf{r})\, \phi_m^{s'}(\mathbf{k}',\mathbf{r}) \quad (58.12c)$$

$$\tilde{Q} = e\int \sum_m \psi_m^* \psi_m \, d\mathbf{r} = e\sum_{\mathbf{k},s} b_s^*(\mathbf{k})\, b_s(\mathbf{k}) \quad (58.12d)$$

We may summarize the foregoing analysis as follows. In the absence of external forces the solutions of the Dirac equation are superimposed plane waves. Four linear independent solutions are associated with a given value of **k**, of which two correspond to positive energy and two to negative energy: the spectrum is illustrated in figure 56. The negative energy states cannot be ignored, because they are definitely part of the complete system represented by (58.9), and when external fields are present transitions can take place between states of positive and negative energy.

In spite of the above remarks, the negative energy states are physically impossible systems, as will be seen from the following example. If we consider a wave packet consisting of such states, with wave numbers in the neighbourhood of $\mathbf{k}_0$, it moves with a group velocity $\mathbf{v}_0 = [\partial\omega_s(\mathbf{k})/\partial\mathbf{k}]_0$; this means that when $\mathbf{k}_0$ is small, $\mathbf{v}_0 = -\hbar\mathbf{k}_0/m$, and the momentum of the wave packet, $\hbar\mathbf{k}_0$, has the opposite direction to $\mathbf{v}$. If we consider a collision between the wave train and ordinary matter of mass M, at rest, the energy and momentum conservation laws yield the following equations for the velocities $\mathbf{v}$ and $\mathbf{V}$ of the wave packet and the mass (considering motion in one dimension only, and using the non-relativistic approximation):

$$-mv_0{}^2 = MV^2 - mv^2 \qquad -mv_0 = MV - mv$$

Hence

$$V = -\frac{2m}{M-m} v_0 \qquad v = -\frac{M+m}{M-m} v_0$$

This means that after the collision v is always greater than v_0 while M is now in motion. The wave packet is therefore accelerated by each collision with matter at rest. We indicated in §56 how Dirac was able to circumvent this difficulty, and shall now give a more precise account of his ideas on the subject of the quantization of the Dirac equation.

§59. The quantum theory of Dirac's field equations

If we interpret the Dirac equation as the classical field equation of a wave function ψ rather than as a quantum-mechanical equation representing a particle (as we did in the case of the wave equation in §16), it can then be quantized in the same way as Maxwell's equations, and the properties of the particles associated with the field may be studied. We are indeed forced to resort to this procedure, since only by so doing can we obtain a consistent representation of many particles required to eliminate the difficulty of the negative energy states. According to this interpretation, the expectation values given by (58.12) are the total energy, momentum, charge density, and charge of the ψ field, and the normalization condition $\int \rho\, d\mathbf{r} = e$ does not apply. Since the procedure was fully discussed in §52 for the Maxwell equations we can deal with it more briefly here.

The quantization is accomplished for the Dirac field alone, without taking any account of electromagnetic fields. For this purpose we make use of the Dirac field expansion given by (58.10). The equations of motion (58.11) for the coefficients of the expansion indicate that $\tilde{\mathscr{H}}$ in (58.12*a*) may be interpreted as a Hamiltonian function if $i\hbar b_s^*(\mathbf{k})$ is the momentum canonically conjugate to $b_s(\mathbf{k})$.

In proceeding to the quantum theory the time-dependent variables $b_s^*(\mathbf{k})$ and $b_s(\mathbf{k})$ of the field theory become the Hermitian conjugate operators $b_s^+(\mathbf{k})$ and $b_s(\mathbf{k})$ in the quantum field theory. Similarly, the physical quantities specified in (58.12) acquire the character of operators:

$$\tilde{\mathscr{H}} = \sum_{\mathbf{k},s} \hbar\omega_s(\mathbf{k})\, b_s^+(\mathbf{k})\, b_s(\mathbf{k}) \tag{59.1a}$$

$$\tilde{\mathbf{G}} = \sum_{\mathbf{k},s} \hbar\mathbf{k} b_s^+(\mathbf{k})_s\, b(\mathbf{k}) \tag{59.1b}$$

$$\tilde{\rho} = e \sum_{\mathbf{k},\mathbf{k}';\ s,s':n} b_s^+(\mathbf{k})\, b_{s'}(\mathbf{k}\ )\, \phi_n^{*s}(\mathbf{k},\mathbf{r})\, \phi_n^{s'}(\mathbf{k}',\mathbf{r}) \tag{59.1c}$$

$$\tilde{Q} = e \sum_{\mathbf{k},s} b_s^+(\mathbf{k})\, b_s(\mathbf{k}) \tag{59.1d}$$

If we were to employ the usual commutation relations between canonically conjugate quantities,

$$b_{s'}(\mathbf{k}')\, b_s^+(\mathbf{k}) - b_s^+(\mathbf{k})\, b_{s'}(\mathbf{k}') = \delta_{ss'}\,\delta_{\mathbf{k}\mathbf{k}'} \tag{59.2}$$

$$b_{s'}(\mathbf{k}')\, b_s(\mathbf{k}) - b_s(\mathbf{k})\, b_{s'}(\mathbf{k}') = b_{s'}^+(\mathbf{k}')\, b_s^+(\mathbf{k}) - b_s^+(\mathbf{k})\, b_{s'}^+(\mathbf{k}') = 0$$

we could construct the Hilbert space in which the operators act in the same way as we did in the case of light. As a result of the commutation relations the quantities $b_s^+(\mathbf{k})b_s(\mathbf{k})$ would have the integral eigenvalues $n_s(\mathbf{k}) = 0, 1, 2, 3, \ldots$ These would represent the occupation numbers of the states designated by $\mathbf{k}$ and s: at any given time there would be $n_s(\mathbf{k})$ particles of type s, $\mathbf{k}$ in a state $\psi_{\ldots n_s(\mathbf{k})\ldots}$

We can see at once, however, that this quantization procedure is useless for two reasons. For one thing the particles arising from it do not satisfy the Fermi statistics that must be postulated for electrons, and in which the only possible occupation numbers are $n_s(\mathbf{k}) = 0$ and 1. Further, as in the case of the solutions of the Dirac equation there is no state of lowest energy

$$E = \sum_{\mathbf{k}, s=1\ldots 4} \hbar\omega_s(\mathbf{k})\, n_s(\mathbf{k})$$

since the $\omega_s(\mathbf{k})$ can assume positive and negative values and the $n_s(\mathbf{k})$ can become arbitrarily great. In fact, the quantization procedure that we have described leads to the Bose-Einstein statistics. This can most easily be perceived by constructing the elements of Hilbert space by means of generating operators. The "vacuum state" $\tilde{\Psi}_0$, in which no particles are present, is defined by

$$b_s(\mathbf{k})\tilde{\Psi}_0 = 0 \text{ for all } s,\ \mathbf{k} \tag{59.3}$$

The general element

$$b_{s_1}^+(\mathbf{k}_1)\ldots b_{s_n}^+(\mathbf{k}_n)\tilde{\Psi}_0 \tag{59.4}$$

arises from the application of the generation operators to $\tilde{\Psi}_0$ and is symmetric in the quantum numbers s_i, $\mathbf{k}_i$ in virtue of the commutation relations (59.2).

Assuming the validity of the Fermi statistics, the general element (59.4) should be antisymmetric. Following P. Jordan and E. Wigner (1928), this can be achieved by substituting a plus sign for the minus sign everywhere in the commutation relations (59.2), which are thus radically altered:*

$$b_{s'}(\mathbf{k}')\,b_s^+(\mathbf{k}) + b_s^+(\mathbf{k})\,b_{s'}(\mathbf{k}') = \delta_{ss'}\,\delta_{\mathbf{k}\mathbf{k}'} \tag{59.5}$$

$$b_{s'}(\mathbf{k}')\,b_s(\mathbf{k}) + b_s(\mathbf{k})\,b_{s'}(\mathbf{k}') = b_{s'}^+(\mathbf{k}')\,b_s^+(\mathbf{k}) + b_s^+(\mathbf{k})\,b_{s'}^+(\mathbf{k}') = 0$$

* Note that in this case $b_s(\mathbf{k})b_s(\mathbf{k}) = 0$ and $b_s^+(\mathbf{k})b_s^+(\mathbf{k}) = 0$.

It can be seen that this arrangement is self-consistent from the fact that a Hilbert space can again be constructed in a similar manner to before. Equations (59.3) and (59.4) remain unchanged (see Exercise 4, p. 360). The element (59.4) is clearly antisymmetric; it differs from zero only for $s_1, \mathbf{k}_1 \neq s_2, \mathbf{k}_2 \neq \ldots \neq s_n, \mathbf{k}_n$, and the non-zero elements are normalized with $\tilde{\Psi}_0$. As before, $b_s^+(\mathbf{k})$ and $b_s(\mathbf{k})$ act as particle generating and annihilating operators, and the eigenvalues of the "particle number operator" $b_s^+(\mathbf{k})b_s(\mathbf{k})$ are $n_s(\mathbf{k}) = 0, 1$. (Cf. Exercise 4, p. 360.)

The difficulties associated with the states of negative energy may now be avoided by means of Dirac's postulate that these states are filled when the system is in the ground state. The ground or vacuum state Ψ_0 is then no longer defined by (59.3), but as follows:*

$$b_s(\mathbf{k})\Psi_0 = 0 \text{ for } s = 1, 2 \text{ and all } \mathbf{k} \tag{59.6a}$$

$$b_s^+(\mathbf{k})\Psi_0 = 0 \text{ for } s = 3, 4 \text{ and all } \mathbf{k} \tag{59.6b}$$

In the state Ψ_0, the expectation or eigenvalues of the operators (59.1) are undefined: for instance, we should obtain a "vacuum value" $-\infty$ for $\tilde{\mathscr{H}}$. On the other hand, if we wish to interpret Ψ_0 as the vacuum state, we must postulate that in this state the energy, momentum, and charge all vanish. In order to express this mathematically we subtract the appropriate vacuum expectation values from the operators (59.1), thus obtaining new operators, the values of which vanish in the state† Ψ_0. We shall illustrate the procedure by forming the new Hamiltonian operator $\mathscr{H}$, which we obtain from $\tilde{\mathscr{H}}$ by subtracting the vacuum expectation value $\sum_{\mathbf{k}, s=3,4} \hbar\omega_s(\mathbf{k})$:

$$\mathscr{H} = \tilde{\mathscr{H}} - \sum_{\mathbf{k}, s=3,4} \hbar\omega_s(\mathbf{k}) = \sum_{\mathbf{k}, s=1,2} \hbar\omega_s(\mathbf{k})\, b_s^+(\mathbf{k})\, b_s(\mathbf{k}) + \\ + \sum_{\mathbf{k}, s=3,4} \hbar\omega_s(\mathbf{k})\, \{b_s^+(\mathbf{k})\, b_s(\mathbf{k}) - 1\}$$

* The relation between Ψ_0 and $\tilde{\Psi}_0$ is given symbolically by

$$\Psi_0 = \prod_{\substack{\mathbf{k} \\ s=3,4}} b_s^+(\mathbf{k})\tilde{\Psi}_0$$

in which the product extends over all values of $\mathbf{k}$. If Ψ_0 is acted on by the operator $b_{s''}^+(\mathbf{k}'')$, where $s'' = 3, 4$, the result must be zero in view of the commutation relations. (Note that $b_s^+(\mathbf{k})b_s^+(\mathbf{k}) = 0$.)

† Since the vacuum values are mathematically undefined divergent expressions, this subtraction procedure is open to objection. It should be considered merely as a heuristic method for establishing a physically-rational relativistically-invariant system of equations (59.9) for many particles (cf. renormalization, p. 319).

Applying the commutation relation (59.5), we obtain

$$\mathcal{H} = \sum_{\mathbf{k},s=1,2} \hbar\omega(\mathbf{k})\, b_s^+(\mathbf{k})\, b_s(\mathbf{k}) + \sum_{\mathbf{k},s=3,4} \hbar\omega(\mathbf{k})\, b_s(\mathbf{k})\, b_s^+(\mathbf{k}) \tag{59.7a}$$

where $$\omega(\mathbf{k}) = \omega_{1,2}(\mathbf{k}) = -\omega_{3,4}(\mathbf{k})$$

We similarly obtain

$$\mathbf{G} = \sum_{\mathbf{k},s=1,2} \hbar\mathbf{k} b_s^+(\mathbf{k})\, b_s(\mathbf{k}) - \sum_{\mathbf{k},s=3,4} \hbar\mathbf{k} b_s(\mathbf{k})\, b_s^+(\mathbf{k}) \tag{59.7b}$$

$$\rho = e\sum_{\substack{\mathbf{kk}'\\ n}} \left\{ \sum_{\substack{s=1,2\\ s'=1,2}} + \sum_{\substack{s=1,2\\ s'=3,4}} + \sum_{\substack{s=3,4\\ s'=1,2}} \right\} b_s^+(\mathbf{k})\, b_{s'}(\mathbf{k}')\, \phi_n^{*s}(\mathbf{k})\, \phi_n^{s'}(\mathbf{k}') -$$

$$- e \sum_{\substack{\mathbf{k},\mathbf{k}'\\ s,s'=3,4\\ n}} b_{s'}(\mathbf{k}')\, b_s^+(\mathbf{k})\, \phi_n^{*s}(\mathbf{k})\, \phi_n^{s'}(\mathbf{k}') \tag{59.7c}$$

$$Q = e\sum_{\mathbf{k},s=1,2} b_s^+(\mathbf{k})\, b_s(\mathbf{k}) - e\sum_{\mathbf{k},s=3,4} b_s(\mathbf{k})\, b_s^+(\mathbf{k}) \tag{59.7d}$$

All the operators (59.7) now have zero expectation or eigenvalues in the state Ψ_0; in addition, the expectation value of $\mathcal{H}$ is always positive, and unlike $\tilde{Q}$, the new total charge operator Q can assume positive and negative values.*

We may simplify the above expressions by introducing new operators $c_{1,2}(\mathbf{k})$ in place of $b_{3,4}(\mathbf{k})$. These operators are defined as follows:

$$b_{3,4}^+(-\mathbf{k}) = c_{1,2}(\mathbf{k}) \tag{59.8}$$

Then

$$\mathcal{H} = \sum_{\mathbf{k},s=1,2} \hbar\omega(\mathbf{k})\{b_s^+(\mathbf{k})\, b_s(\mathbf{k}) + c_s^+(\mathbf{k})\, c_s(\mathbf{k})\}$$

$$\mathbf{G} = \sum_{\mathbf{k},s=1,2} \hbar\mathbf{k}\,\{b_s^+(\mathbf{k})\, b_s(\mathbf{k}) + c_s^+(\mathbf{k})\, c_s(\mathbf{k})\} \tag{59.9}$$

$$Q = e\sum_{\mathbf{k},s=1,2} \{b_s^+(\mathbf{k})\, b_s(\mathbf{k}) - c_s^+(\mathbf{k})\, c_s(\mathbf{k})\}$$

The definition of Ψ_0 now becomes

$$b_s(\mathbf{k})\Psi_0 = 0 \qquad c_s(\mathbf{k})\Psi_0 = 0 \text{ for } s = 1, 2 \text{ and all } \mathbf{k} \tag{59.10}$$

The states $b_s^+(\mathbf{k})\Psi_0$ and $c_s^+(\mathbf{k})\Psi_0$ (for $s = 1, 2$) are eigenstates of the energy and momentum operators $\mathcal{H}$ and $\mathbf{G}$ with respective eigenvalues $\hbar\omega(\mathbf{k})$ and $\hbar\mathbf{k}$, and belong respectively to the eigenvalues e and $-e$ of the charge operator Q. The operators $b_s^+(\mathbf{k})$ and $c_s^+(\mathbf{k})$ therefore create electrons and positrons respectively. Similarly, $b_s^+(\mathbf{k}) b_s(\mathbf{k}) = n_s^e(\mathbf{k})$ and $c_s^+(\mathbf{k}) c_s(\mathbf{k}) = n_s^{\bar{e}}(\mathbf{k})$ are the particle number operators of the

* This is not surprising; when an electron of charge e is removed from a negative energy state the resultant charge is $-e$.

electrons (e) and positrons ($\bar{e}=-e$). The total number of particles is associated with the operator

$$N=\sum_{\mathbf{k},s=1,2}\{n_s^e(\mathbf{k})+n_s^{\bar{e}}(\mathbf{k})\} \tag{59.11}$$

$N\Psi_0=0$ then defines the vacuum state.

The previous difficulties have now disappeared; the energy is always positive, but on the other hand we now have two sorts of particles with charges of different sign. The subtraction procedure employed is only possible for systems obeying Fermi statistics; it also satisfies the relativity requirements, but we shall not prove this.

The most general state is given by an expansion of the form

$$\begin{aligned}\Psi=F_0\Psi_0+&\sum_{\mathbf{k}_1,s_1=1,2}F_{1,0}(\mathbf{k}_1,s_1)\,b_{s_1}^+(\mathbf{k}_1)\Psi_0+\\&+\sum_{\mathbf{k}_1',s_1'=1,2}F_{0,1}(\mathbf{k}_1',s_1')\,c_{s_1'}^+(\mathbf{k}_1')\Psi_0+\\&+\sum_{\substack{\mathbf{k}_1,\mathbf{k}_1'\\ s_1,s_1'=1,2}}F_{1,1}(\mathbf{k}_1,s_1;\mathbf{k}_1',s_1')\,b_{s_1}^+(\mathbf{k}_1')\,c_{s_1'}^+(\mathbf{k}_1')\Psi_0+\ldots\end{aligned} \tag{59.12}$$

The Hilbert space elements in terms of which Ψ is expanded in (59.12) are normalized if Ψ_0 is assumed to be normalized (cf. Exercise 4, p. 360). Then $|F_{n,n'}(\mathbf{k}_1,s_1..;..,\mathbf{k}_{n'}',s_{n'}')|^2$ is the probability of finding n electrons in the state Ψ with quantum numbers $k_1,s_1,\ldots$ and n' positrons with numbers $k_1',s_1',\ldots$ For free particles* N commutes exactly with $\mathcal{H}$, while for slowly varying external fields it does so approximately; the number of particles is therefore constant. We can then limit ourselves to the consideration of states for which (e.g.) only $F_{1,0}$ (one electron) or only $F_{0,1}$ (one positron) differs from zero.

To proceed from the representation in momentum space to coordinate space representation, we introduce the Fourier transforms of the $F(\mathbf{k},s)$, which we denote by $G(\mathbf{r},s)$:

$$G_0=F_0$$

$$G_{1,0}(\mathbf{r},s)=\sum_{\mathbf{k}}F_{1,0}(\mathbf{k},s)\frac{e^{i\mathbf{kr}}}{\sqrt{V}}$$

$$F_{1,0}(\mathbf{k},s)=\int_V G_{1,0}(\mathbf{r},s)\frac{e^{-i\mathbf{kr}}}{\sqrt{V}}\,d\mathbf{r}$$

* In the quantization of the Dirac field we have not only neglected the external electromagnetic fields but the electromagnetic interactions of the field charges as well. This latter simplification is justifiable only if the particle densities are sufficiently low.

The general state then becomes

$$\Psi = G_0\Psi_0 + \sum_{s=1,2}\int_V d\mathbf{r}\, G_{1,0}(\mathbf{r},s)\sum_{\mathbf{k}} b_s^+(\mathbf{k})\frac{e^{-i\mathbf{kr}}}{\sqrt{V}}\Psi_0 + \dots \tag{59.13}$$

The norm of Ψ is

$$(\Psi,\Psi) = |F_0|^2 + \sum_{\mathbf{k},s=1,2} |F_{1,0}(\mathbf{k},s)|^2 + \dots$$

$$= |G_0|^2 + \sum_{s=1,2}\int_V d\mathbf{r}\,|G_{1,0}(\mathbf{r},s)|^2 + \dots \tag{59.14}$$

The expansion functions F and G are functions of time as well as of the variables shown above. Their equation of motion is obtained from the general equation $\mathscr{H}\Psi = i\hbar\dot{\Psi}$, which is valid for free particles because of the commutability of the particle number operators for each term of (59.12) and (59.13). A simple calculation gives the following results:

$$\begin{aligned} \dot{F}_0 &= 0, \qquad \hbar\omega(\mathbf{k})F_{1,0}(\mathbf{k},s) = i\hbar\dot{F}_{1,0}, \dots \\ \dot{G}_0 &= 0, \qquad E(\mathbf{p})G_{1,0}(\mathbf{r},s) = i\hbar\dot{G}_{1,0}, \dots, \end{aligned} \tag{59.15}$$

where $E(\mathbf{p})$ represents the operator

$$E(\mathbf{p}) = \{\mathbf{p}^2c^2 + m^2c^4\}^{1/2} = mc^2 + \frac{\mathbf{p}^2}{2m} - \frac{\mathbf{p}^4}{8m^3c^2} + \dots \tag{59.16}$$

and $$\mathbf{p} = \frac{\hbar}{i}\frac{\partial}{\partial\mathbf{r}}$$

These are relativistic Schrödinger equations for two-component "Schrödinger functions" $G_{1,0}(\mathbf{r},s)$, where $s = 1,2$.

What is the physical significance of these functions? At first sight we are inclined to assume that $|G_{1,0}|^2$ is the probability density for an electron; this is not the case, however, as we shall see immediately.

Let us examine the expectation value $\bar{\rho}(\mathbf{R})$ of the density $\rho(\mathbf{R})$ in a state in which only $G_{1,0}$ or $F_{1,0}$ is non-zero, and which therefore contains just one electron. The only terms in (59.7c) contributing to $\bar{\rho}$ are those for which $s,s' = 1,2$; it may easily be verified that the expectation values of the remaining terms vanish. Then $\bar{\rho}$ is the expectation value of

$$e\sum_{\substack{\mathbf{k},\mathbf{k}'n\\ s,s'=1,2}} b_s^+(\mathbf{k})\, b_{s'}(\mathbf{k}')\,\phi_n^{*s}(\mathbf{k},\mathbf{R})\,\phi_n^{s'}(\mathbf{k}',\mathbf{R})$$

in the state

$$\Psi = \sum_{\mathbf{k},s=1,2} F(\mathbf{k}, s)\, b_s^+(\mathbf{k})\,\Psi_0 = \sum_{s=1,2} \int_V d\mathbf{r}\, G(\mathbf{r}, s) \sum_{\mathbf{k}} b_s^+(\mathbf{k}) \frac{e^{-i\mathbf{k}\mathbf{r}}}{\sqrt{V}} \Psi_0$$

We obtain

$$\bar{\rho}(\mathbf{R}) = \sum_{\substack{\mathbf{k}\,\mathbf{k}'\mathbf{k}''\mathbf{k}'''n \\ s\,s's''s'''=1,2}} F^*(\mathbf{k}'', s'')\, F(\mathbf{k}''', s''')\, e\phi_n^{*s}(\mathbf{k}, \mathbf{R})\, \phi_n^{s'}(\mathbf{k}', \mathbf{R}) \times$$

$$\times \left(b_{s''}^+(\mathbf{k}'')\Psi_0,\, b_s^+(\mathbf{k})\, b_{s'}(\mathbf{k}')\, b_{s'''}^+(\mathbf{k}''')\Psi_0\right) \qquad (59.17)$$

It follows from the commutation relations (59.5), the definition (59.6*a*) and the fact that $(\Psi_0, \Psi_0) = 1$, that the second factor is $\delta_{s's'''}\,\delta_{\mathbf{k}'\mathbf{k}'''}\,\delta_{ss''}\,\delta_{\mathbf{k}\mathbf{k}''}$. Hence

$$\bar{\rho}(\mathbf{R}) = e \sum_{\substack{\mathbf{k},\mathbf{k}'n \\ s,s'=1,2}} \phi_n^{*s}(\mathbf{k}, \mathbf{R})\, \phi_n^{s'}(\mathbf{k}', \mathbf{R})\, F^*(\mathbf{k}, s)\, F(\mathbf{k}', s') \qquad (59.17a)$$

or inserting the values for ϕ_n^s given in (58.9),

$$\bar{\rho}(\mathbf{R}) = \frac{e}{V^2} \sum_{\substack{\mathbf{k},\mathbf{k}'n \\ s,s'=1,2}} \int d\mathbf{r}\, d\mathbf{r}'\, a_n^{*s}(\hbar\mathbf{k})\, a_n^{s'}(\hbar\mathbf{k}') \times$$

$$\times e^{i\mathbf{k}'(\mathbf{R}-\mathbf{r}') - i\mathbf{k}(\mathbf{R}-\mathbf{r})}\, G^*(\mathbf{r}, s)\, G(\mathbf{r}', s') \qquad (59.17b)$$

This result may be put into the form

$$\bar{\rho}(\mathbf{R}) = e \sum_{\substack{s,s'=1,2 \\ n=1\ldots4}} \int d\mathbf{r}\, d\mathbf{r}'\, G^*(\mathbf{r}, s)\, G(\mathbf{r}', s')\, K_n^{*s}(\mathbf{R}-\mathbf{r})\;\; K_n^{s'}(\mathbf{R}-\mathbf{r}') \qquad (59.17c)$$

The functions K_n^s in the above expression are defined by

$$K_n^s(\mathbf{r}) = \sum_{\mathbf{k}} a_n^s(\hbar\mathbf{k}) \frac{e^{i\mathbf{k}\mathbf{r}}}{V} \qquad (59.18)$$

or when V becomes infinite,

$$K_n^s(\mathbf{r}) = \frac{1}{(2\pi)^3} \int d\mathbf{k}\, a_n^s(\hbar\mathbf{k})\, e^{i\mathbf{k}\mathbf{r}} \qquad (59.18a)$$

When (59.18*a*) applies, the integrations in (59.17*c*) extend over all space, thus eliminating the arbitrarily introduced periodicity volume. The density is therefore not given by $|G|^2$, but is dispersed by a superposition of integral transforms in terms of the functions K_n^s. When the total charge is calculated by integrating over the range of **R** the K_n^s drop out, because the ϕ_n^s form an orthonormal system of functions.

In connection with the calculation of the charge distribution from $G(\mathbf{r}, s)$ a number of relativistic modifications of the previous rules are encountered.

(*a*) It is no longer possible to associate an operator **R** with the position coordinate $\underline{\mathbf{R}}$ such that

$$\int \mathbf{R}\bar{\rho}(\mathbf{R})\, d\mathbf{R} = e(G, \underline{\mathbf{R}}G)$$

and

$$\int f(\mathbf{R})\,\bar{\rho}(\mathbf{R})\, d\mathbf{R} = e\,(G, f(\underline{\mathbf{R}})\, G)$$

This is because the functions ϕ_n^s do not constitute a complete system when s ranges over the values 1,2 only.

In field theory, "position" does not correspond to any observable in the usual sense, but occurs as a parameter, as does the time. The observable quantities are all densities, such as energy, momentum, and charge density.

(*b*) The centroid of charge is displaced in a characteristic manner relative to the centroid of $|G|^2$. If we calculate the mean value

$$e\overline{\mathbf{R}}^{\rho} = \int \mathbf{R}\bar{\rho}(\mathbf{R})\, d\mathbf{R}$$

then after some intermediate calculations (see Appendix on p. 352) we obtain the non-relativistic approximation

$$\begin{aligned} \overline{\mathbf{R}} &= \int \sum_{s=1}^{2} G^*(\mathbf{r}, s)\,\mathbf{r}G(\mathbf{r}, s)\, d\mathbf{r} - \\ &\quad - \int \sum_{s} G^*(\mathbf{r}, s)\frac{\hbar}{4m^2c^2}\left(\vec{\sigma}\times\frac{\hbar}{i}\,\mathrm{grad}\right)G(\mathbf{r}, s)\, d\mathbf{r} \\ &= \overline{\mathbf{R}}^G - \frac{\hbar}{4m^2c^2}\,\overline{(\vec{\sigma}\times\mathbf{p})}^G \end{aligned} \qquad (59.19)$$

This result is very closely connected with the magnetic moment of the electron. We indicated in §34 that a moving magnetic moment behaves like an electric dipole. Now if we separate the Dirac current $\mathbf{j}_\nu = iec\psi^*\beta\gamma_\nu\psi$ into a "spin component" and an "orbital component" (see Exercise 5, p. 360), the spin portion $\bar{\rho}_s$ of the density $\bar{\rho}$ may be written in the form $\bar{\rho}_s = -\text{div}\,\bar{\mathbf{P}}$. This may be regarded as the density of the "dielectric polarization" $\bar{\mathbf{P}}$ of the electron. The mean value

$$e\overline{\mathbf{R}}^{\rho_s} = -\int \mathbf{R}\,\text{div}\,\bar{\mathbf{P}}\,d\mathbf{R} = \int \bar{\mathbf{P}}\,d\mathbf{R}$$

agrees with the above displacement, while the orbital portion $\bar{\rho}_b$ coincides with $\sum_{s=1,2} |G|^2$ in the non-relativistic limiting case. This displacement appears experimentally in the form of the spin-orbit interaction (§§34 and 60).

(*c*) The Dirac density is not only displaced relative to $\sum_{s=1,2} |\bar{G}|^2$, but is also "blurred". We can best see what is meant by this by comparing the quantities $\overline{\mathbf{R}^2}^{\rho}$ and $\overline{\mathbf{R}^2}^{G}$. The result is (see Appendix)

$$\overline{\mathbf{R}^2}^{\rho} = \overline{\mathbf{R}^2}^{G} + \frac{3}{4}\frac{\hbar^2}{m^2c^2} \tag{59.20}$$

The mean square deviation of the Dirac density is therefore greater than the Schrödinger-Pauli density by approximately the square of the Compton wavelength of the electron.

This result is associated with the fact that we have restricted ourselves to a pure electron state. It can readily be seen that, as in classical field theory, a sharply defined charge density must be represented by a superposition of solutions containing both positive and negative frequencies.

The effect on measurements would be as follows. If we attempt to determine the "position" of an electron, say with a microscope, to within less than the Compton wavelength, we must use γ-rays of wavelength $\lambda \ll \hbar/mc$, i.e. of energy $\varepsilon \gg mc^2$. Since this energy is sufficient to create electron-positron pairs, positrons will thus appear in any such accurate measurement of position.

The greater dispersion of the actual charge density compared with the Schrödinger density $|G|^2$ gives rise to an additional term in Pauli's equation that is experimentally observable (see following section).

(*d*) So far we have only considered states containing one particle. In the case where a number of particles are present, the densities of the individual particles are not simply additive; additional terms arise as a result of interference effects between electron and positron states (cf. the sums $\sum_{\substack{s'=1,2\\ s=3,4}}$ in (59.7*d*)). It would therefore be a mistake to think that, in the absence of external fields, quantization of the wave equation would lead to a system that was separated with regard to electrons and positrons. It is true that when the electromagnetic fields can be neglected the equations of motion are separated, but physical quantities such as the charge density are not.

Appendix

Calculation of the mean values of functions of position in the single electron state of the Dirac theory.

The most convenient representation of the expectation value of the charge density $\bar{\rho}(\mathbf{R})$ in the state described by the Schrödinger function $G(\mathbf{R},s)$ is

$$\bar{\rho}(\mathbf{R}) = e \sum_{\substack{s,s'=1,2\\ n}} \{a_n{}^s(\mathbf{p})\, G(\mathbf{R},s)\}^* \{a_n^{s'}(\mathbf{p})\, G(\mathbf{R},s')\} \tag{A.1}$$

where $\mathbf{p} = \dfrac{\hbar}{i}\dfrac{\partial}{\partial \mathbf{R}}$

This expression is obtained by passing to the limiting case of an infinite volume in (59.17*b*), expressing the arguments $\hbar\mathbf{k}$ of the components $a_n{}^s$ in terms of derivatives of the exponential functions, and transferring these derivatives to the functions G. The remaining integrals over $\mathbf{k}$ and $\mathbf{k}'$ give $\delta(\mathbf{R}-\mathbf{r})\,\delta(\mathbf{R}-\mathbf{r}')$, so that the integrations can be performed over $\mathbf{r}$ and $\mathbf{r}'$.

From (A.1), the mean value of any function $f(\mathbf{R})$ of weight $\bar{\rho}$ is

$$\bar{f}^{\rho} = \sum_{\substack{s,\, s'=1,\, 2\\ n=1\ldots 4}} \int d\mathbf{R}\, G^*(\mathbf{R},s)\, a_n^{+s}(\mathbf{p})\, f(\mathbf{R})\, a_n^{s'}(\mathbf{p})\, G(\mathbf{R},s') \tag{A.2}$$

The representation of the operators dependent on $\mathbf{p}$ is obtained from (58.8):

$$\begin{aligned} a_n{}^s(\mathbf{p}) &= \frac{c\{\vec{\alpha}\beta\}_{ns}\,\mathbf{p} + \delta_{ns}\,[E(\mathbf{p})+mc^2]}{\sqrt{\{2E(\mathbf{p})\,[E(\mathbf{p})+mc^2]\}}} \\ a_n^{+s}(\mathbf{p}) &= \frac{c\{\beta\vec{\alpha}\}_{sn}\,\mathbf{p} + \delta_{sn}\,[E(\mathbf{p})+mc^2]}{\sqrt{\{2E(\mathbf{p})\,[E(\mathbf{p})+mc^2]\}}} \end{aligned} \tag{A.3}$$

In addition

$$\sum_n a_n^{+s'}(\mathbf{p})\, a_n{}^s(\mathbf{p}) = \delta_{s's}$$

In order to deal with the non-relativistic limiting case we first expand the quantities in (A.3) in terms of powers of $1/mc$:

$$E(\mathbf{p}) = mc^2\left(1 + \frac{\mathbf{p}^2}{2m^2c^2} + \ldots\right)$$

$$a_n{}^s(\mathbf{p}) = \{\vec{\alpha}\beta\}_{ns}\frac{\mathbf{p}}{2mc}\left(1 - \frac{3\mathbf{p}^2}{8m^2c^2}\ldots\right) + \delta_{ns}\left(1 - \frac{\mathbf{p}^2}{8m^2c^2}\ldots\right) \tag{A.4}$$

with a corresponding expression for $a_n^{+s}(\mathbf{p})$. If we include terms to the second power of $1/mc$, we then have from (A.2):

$$\bar{f}^{\rho} = \sum_{\substack{s,\, s'=1,\, 2\\ n}} \int d\mathbf{R}\, G^*(\mathbf{R},s) \times \tag{A.2a}$$

$$\times\ [\delta_{ns}\delta_{ns'}f - \delta_{ns}\delta_{ns'}(\mathbf{p}^2 f + f\mathbf{p}^2)/8m^2c^2 + \{\beta\vec{\alpha}\}_{s'n}\,\mathbf{p} f\{\vec{\alpha}\beta\}_{ns}\ \mathbf{p}/4m^2c^2]\, G(\mathbf{R},s')$$

No term of the first degree in $1/mc$ appears, because $\bar{\alpha}\beta$ is a secondary diagonal matrix whose components vanish for the range $s, s' = 1, 2$. The first term in the square brackets gives $\bar{f}^G$; the other two terms give the deviations from the mean value to the required degree of approximation. The summation over n can then be performed; $\delta_{ss'}$ occurs in the first two terms, while in the third term it is necessary to take account of the relations (57.5). We then obtain

$$\bar{f}^\rho = \bar{f}^G + \sum_{s,s'=1,2} \int d\mathbf{R}\, G^*(\mathbf{R},s) \times$$
$$\times \left[\sum_{i,l=1,2,3} \{\alpha_l \alpha_i\}_{ss'} p_l f p_i / 4m^2c^2 - \delta_{ss'} (\mathbf{p}^2 f + f\mathbf{p}^2)/8m^2c^2 \right] G(\mathbf{R}, s') \tag{A.2b}$$

The second term in square brackets in (A.2*b*) may be conveniently transformed as follows:

$$\mathbf{p}^2 f + f\mathbf{p}^2 \rightarrow 2\mathbf{p}f\mathbf{p} + [\mathbf{p}, [\mathbf{p}, f]] = \sum_{i=1\ldots3} \{2p_i f p_i + [p_i, [p_i, f]]\}$$

We now combine the first term in the above expression with the term in $\alpha_l \alpha_i$ in

$$\sum_{i,l=1\ldots3} (\{\alpha_l \alpha_i\}_{ss'} - \delta_{il}\delta_{ss'}) p_l f p_i / 4m^2c^2$$

From (57.5) we can express this as

$$\sum_{i,l} \tfrac{1}{2}\{\alpha_l \alpha_i - \alpha_i \alpha_l\}_{ss'} p_l f p_i / 4m^2c^2$$

Since $fp_i = p_i f + i\hbar\, \partial f/\partial X_i$, this expression becomes

$$\sum_{i,l=1\ldots3} (\alpha_l \alpha_i - \alpha_i \alpha_l) p_l \frac{\partial f}{\partial X_i} i\hbar/8m^2c^2$$

because the contribution of $p_l p_i f$ vanishes owing to the symmetry in i, l. We then finally obtain

$$\bar{f}^\rho = \bar{f}^G + \overline{\sum_{i,l=1\ldots3} (\alpha_l \alpha_i - \alpha_i \alpha_l) p_l \frac{\partial f}{\partial X_i} i\hbar/8m^2c^2}^G$$
$$- \overline{\sum_{i=1\ldots3} [p_i, [p_i, f]]/8m^2c^2}^G \tag{A.2c}$$

In the calculation of the mean value of the position, $f = X_k$, the double commutation drops out, and since $\partial X_k/\partial X_i = \delta_{ik}$ we have

$$\bar{X}_k^\rho = \bar{X}_k^G + \overline{\sum_{l=1\ldots3} (\alpha_l \alpha_k - \alpha_k \alpha_l) p_l i\hbar/8m^2c^2}^G \tag{A.5}$$

In view of (57.16), this is identical with equation (59.19),

$$\bar{X}_k^\rho = \bar{X}_k^G - \overline{(\vec{\sigma} \times \mathbf{p})_k . \hbar/4m^2c^2}^G \tag{A.5a}$$

If the complete calculation is strictly performed, we obtain

$$\bar{\mathbf{R}}^\rho = \bar{\mathbf{R}}^G - \overline{\frac{(\vec{\sigma} \times \mathbf{p})\hbar c^2}{2E(\mathbf{p})\,[E(\mathbf{p}) + mc^2]}}^G \tag{A.6}$$

which tends to (A.5*a*) in the non-relativistic approximation.

If we calculate the mean square deviation ($f = \mathbf{R}^2$) for a G-function that is spherically symmetrical about $\mathbf{R}=0$ ($\overline{\mathbf{R}}^\rho=\overline{\mathbf{R}}^G=0$, $\overline{\mathbf{p}}=0$, $\overline{\mathbf{p}\times\mathbf{R}}^G=0$), the second term in (A.2c) contributes nothing. This follows either from the symmetry in l, i of the averaged expression $p_l\mathbf{R}^2p_i$, or from the fact that $\overline{\mathbf{p}\times\mathbf{R}} = 0$ for the spherically symmetrical state, because only the components of the "orbital angular momentum" $\mathbf{p}\times\mathbf{R}$ contribute to the second term. The value of the double commutation term is a constant, $6\hbar^2/m^2c^2$. In total we therefore obtain the result that was given in §59,

$$\overline{\mathbf{R}^2}^\rho = \overline{\mathbf{R}^2}^G + \frac{3}{4}\frac{\hbar^2}{m^2c^2} \tag{A.7}$$

This result does not apply to arbitrarily small values of $\overline{\mathbf{R}^2}^G$; on the contrary, a necessary condition is that $\overline{\mathbf{R}^2}^G \gg \hbar^2/m^2c^2$, since if it were not, the expansion (A.4) would be meaningless.

§60. The Pauli spin theory as an approximation

In the last paragraph we saw how the equations (59.15) for two-component functions can be set up, proceeding from the quantization of the Dirac field in the absence of external forces. In the non-relativistic case, for which $v/c \ll 1$, these equations become the ordinary Schrödinger equations for a free particle. When external fields are present and the interaction between particles must be taken into account, it is no longer possible to establish two-component equations of this sort, because electron-positron pairs can be produced by the external field. The operator N for the total number of particles no longer commutes with $\mathscr{H}$, and we cannot confine ourselves to a state in which only a single function $G_{nn'}(\mathbf{r}_1\ldots;\mathbf{r}_1'\ldots)$ differs from zero.

However, if the probability of pair production is small, we can attempt to treat the transitions between states with different numbers of particles as a perturbation of the independent two-component equations. The prerequisites for this procedure exist when the external field is almost constant* over a distance of the order of magnitude of the Compton wavelength $\hbar/mc$:

$$\frac{\hbar}{mc}\left|\frac{\partial\mathbf{E}}{\partial x}\right| \ll |\mathbf{E}| \qquad \frac{\hbar}{mc}\left|\frac{\partial\mathbf{H}}{\partial x}\right| \ll |\mathbf{H}| \tag{60.1}$$

In deriving the two-component equation it proves to be unnecessary to adopt the roundabout procedure involved in the quantization of the

*This results from a more exact discussion of the Dirac equation in the presence of external fields. The condition is plausible, since it states that the field contains only Fourier components of wavelength $\lambda \gg \hbar/mc$, and hence that the energies of the corresponding quanta $\hbar\omega \approx \hbar c/\lambda$ are small compared with $2mc^2$, the minimum energy necessary for the production of electron-positron pairs.

Dirac equation, provided that we restrict ourselves to correction terms in the Schrödinger equation that are of the second degree in $\hbar/mc$ and v/c. It is then sufficient to treat the original Dirac equation itself. As an illustration we shall again consider the case of a free particle.

We seek an equation that is equivalent to the Dirac equation

$$\mathscr{H}\psi = \{c\vec{\alpha}\mathbf{p}+\beta mc^2\}\,\psi = i\hbar\dot{\psi}$$

in which the posititive energy states are represented by functions $G(\mathbf{r}, s)$ of two components $(s = 1, 2)$. This is obviously equivalent to finding a unitary transformation $U\psi = G$ in which the transformed Hamiltonian operator $\mathscr{H}' = U\mathscr{H}U^+$ contains only D-type matrices (where D is defined by (57.17)), because A-type matrices mix the components (1,2) of the functions $\psi_n(\mathbf{r}, t)$ with the components (3,4).

For a free particle, the transformation U can be derived from (58.8):

$$U = \frac{c\beta\vec{\alpha}\mathbf{p}+E(\mathbf{p})+mc^2}{\sqrt{\{2E(\mathbf{p})\,[E(\mathbf{p})+mc^2]\}}} \tag{60.2}$$

Hence

$$\mathscr{H}' = \beta E(\mathbf{p})$$

and the eigensolutions for positive values of the energy are

$$G(\mathbf{r}, s) = \delta_{ss_z}\frac{e^{i\mathbf{k}\mathbf{r}}}{\sqrt{V}} \qquad s_z = 1, 2 \tag{60.3}$$

For $U\mathbf{r}U^+$ etc., we obtain comparatively involved expressions (see table on p. 356). The transformation of $\mathbf{r}$ was effectively performed in the previous section.* Those operators that transform to $\mathbf{r}$, $\dot{\mathbf{r}}$, etc., do not have the same physical significance as these quantities in their previous sense; the only exception is $\mathbf{p}$, because $U\mathbf{p}U^+ = \mathbf{p}$. In order to express this difference we shall designate the previous Dirac operators by the terms electron position $\mathbf{R}_{el}$, electron velocity $\dot{\mathbf{R}}_{el}$, etc., which indicates that they are associated with the electric charge ($e\overline{\mathbf{R}}_{el} = \int \mathbf{r}\bar{\rho}_{el}\,d\mathbf{r}$). In the case of the new operators, which possess a simple representation in the Schrödinger-Pauli theory, we shall retain the designations of position, velocity, etc. (see table on p. 356). We saw in the last paragraph that the "electron position" is both displaced and dispersed with respect to "position" as defined above. External fields do not "act"

* It is $(U\mathbf{r}U^+)_{ss'} = \sum_n a_n^{+s}(\mathbf{p})\mathbf{r}a_n^{s'}(\mathbf{p})$ for $s, s' = 1 \ldots 4$; see equation (A.2) in §59.

at the latter, but at the electron position. The centre of charge is given by $\overline{\mathbf{R}}_{el}$. On the other hand it is the operators $\mathbf{R}$, etc. which in the non-relativistic case become the corresponding operators x, y, z, etc., of the Schrödinger-Pauli theory. For instance, in the new representation

$$\mathscr{H}' = \beta E(\mathbf{p}) = \beta\left(mc^2 + \frac{\mathbf{p}^2}{2m} + \ldots\right)$$

$$\dot{\mathbf{r}} = \frac{i}{\hbar}[\mathscr{H}', \mathbf{r}] = \beta\frac{\partial E(\mathbf{p})}{\partial \mathbf{p}} = \beta\left(\frac{\mathbf{p}}{m} + \ldots\right)$$

$$\dot{\vec{\sigma}}' = \frac{i}{\hbar}[\mathscr{H}', \vec{\sigma}'] = 0$$

These are just the properties of the operators in the non-relativistic theory. In particular, $\dot{\mathbf{R}} = \mathbf{v}$ for the positive energy states,* and the state of a free particle can be chosen as an eigenfunction of $\mathbf{p}$ and $\vec{\sigma}$.

Quantity	Symbol	Representation according to Dirac	Representation according to Schrödinger-Pauli
Electron position	$\mathbf{R}_{el}$	$\mathbf{r}$	$\mathbf{r} - \frac{\hbar c^2 \vec{\sigma}' \times \mathbf{p} - i\hbar c^3 \beta(\vec{\alpha}\mathbf{p})\mathbf{p}/E(\mathbf{p})}{2E(\mathbf{p})[E(\mathbf{p}) + mc^2]} - \frac{i\hbar c}{2E(\mathbf{p})}\beta\vec{\alpha}$
Position	$\mathbf{R}$	$U^+\mathbf{r}U$	$\mathbf{r}$
Electron spin	$\vec{\Sigma}_{el}$	$\vec{\sigma}'$	$\vec{\sigma}' + \frac{i\beta\vec{\alpha} \times \mathbf{p}c}{E(\mathbf{p})} - \frac{\mathbf{p} \times (\vec{\sigma}' \times \mathbf{p})c^2}{E(\mathbf{p})[E(\mathbf{p}) + mc^2]}$
Spin	$\vec{\Sigma}$	$U^+\vec{\sigma}'U$	$\vec{\sigma}'$
State	ψ	$\psi_n(\mathbf{r})$	$\sum_n U_n^s \psi_n(\mathbf{r}) = G(\mathbf{r}, s)$
Mean values	$\overline{f(\mathbf{R}_{el})} = \bar{f}^\rho$	$\int f(\mathbf{r}) \sum_n \lvert\psi_n(\mathbf{r})\rvert^2 d\mathbf{r}$	$= \int \sum_{ss'} f_{ss'}(\mathbf{r}) G^*(\mathbf{r}, s) G(\mathbf{r}, s') d\mathbf{r}$
	$\overline{f(\mathbf{R})} = \bar{f}^G$	$\sum_{nn's} \int (U^+ f U)_{nn'}^{ss} \psi_n^* \psi_{n'} d\mathbf{r}$	$= \int f(\mathbf{r}) \sum_s \lvert G(\mathbf{r}, s)\rvert^2 d\mathbf{r}$

We shall now consider the case in which external fields are present, and attempt to bring the appropriate Hamiltonian operator into a form in which it contains only D-type matrices. Since the transformation that effects this contains the fields and possibly the time explicitly, we

* In § 57 we found that $\dot{\mathbf{r}} = c\vec{\alpha}$, $\dot{\vec{\sigma}}' = -2c(\vec{\alpha} \times \mathbf{p})/\hbar$.

must assume the following form for the transformed Hamiltonian operator:

$$\mathscr{H}' = U\mathscr{H}U^{+} - i\hbar U\frac{\partial U^{+}}{\partial t} \tag{60.4}$$

This is necessary to ensure that the equation

$$\mathscr{H}U^{+}G = i\hbar\frac{\partial}{\partial t}(U^{+}G)$$

takes the form

$$\mathscr{H}'G = i\hbar\dot{G}$$

in the new representation.

We now write

$$\mathscr{H} = \beta mc^2 + e\phi + c\vec{\alpha}\left(\mathbf{p} - \frac{e}{c}\mathbf{A}\right)$$

in the form

$$\mathscr{H} = \beta mc^2 + D + A$$

where A and D are defined by (57.17), and try the solution*

$$U_1 = \exp\frac{\beta A}{2mc^2} \tag{60.6}$$

We shall use this expression to determine the Hamiltonian operator as given by (60.4). In the final result we shall include only terms as far as $(v/c)^4$, since we are interested only in non-relativistic velocities and in slowly varying fields as defined by (60.1). When (60.6) is expanded and introduced into (60.4), we obtain the following result for $\mathscr{H}'$ after some intermediate calculations:

$$\mathscr{H}' = \beta mc^2 + D + \frac{\beta A^2}{2mc^2} - \frac{1}{8(mc^2)^2}\left[A, [A, D] + i\hbar\frac{\partial A}{\partial t}\right] - \frac{\beta A^4}{8(mc^2)^3} +$$
$$+ \frac{\beta}{2mc^2}\left\{[A, D] + i\hbar\frac{\partial A}{\partial t}\right\} - \frac{A^3}{3(mc^2)^2} + \dots \tag{60.7}$$

In view of the rules governing A- and D-matrices, the first line contains D-matrices only and the second line A-matrices only. Thus $\mathscr{H}'$ now has the form $\mathscr{H}' = \beta mc^2 + D' + A'$, where A' is only of order of magni-

* This solution is suggested by the non-relativistic expansion of the corresponding operator (60.2) in the case of the free particle: $U = 1 + \beta\vec{\alpha}\mathbf{p}/2mc + \frac{1}{2}(\beta\vec{\alpha}\mathbf{p}/2mc)^2 + \dots$ This agrees with the expansion of (60.6) apart from terms of the order of magnitude of $(v/c)^2$. Cf. Foldy, L. L., and Wouthuysen, S. A., *Phys. Rev.* **78** (1950), 29.

tude $(v/c)^3$. Using exactly the same procedure, these non-diagonal terms can be reduced by a further order of magnitude by means of another transformation $U_2 = \exp \frac{\beta A'}{2mc^2}$, etc. It may be verified that the use of U_2 supplies only correction terms to D' of higher order than the fourth in v/c; the first line of (60.7) therefore correctly represents the Hamiltonian operator to within terms in $(v/c)^4$.

In order to gain a more precise understanding of the significance of this approximation, we now introduce the quantities $D = e\phi$ and $A = c\vec{\alpha}\left(\mathbf{p} - \frac{e}{c}\mathbf{A}\right)$ into (60.7), when we obtain

$$\mathscr{H}' = \beta mc^2 + e\phi + \frac{\beta}{2m}\left(\mathbf{p} - \frac{e}{c}\mathbf{A}\right)^2 - \frac{e\hbar}{2m\,c}\beta\vec{\sigma}'\,\mathbf{H} - \frac{\beta}{8m^3c^2}\left(\mathbf{p} - \frac{e}{c}\mathbf{A}\right)^4 -$$
$$- \frac{e\hbar}{8m^2c^2}\vec{\sigma}'\left\{\mathbf{E}\times\left(\mathbf{p} - \frac{e}{c}\mathbf{A}\right) - \left(\mathbf{p} - \frac{e}{c}\mathbf{A}\right)\times\mathbf{E}\right\} -$$
$$- \frac{e\hbar^2}{8m^2c^2}\operatorname{div}\mathbf{E} + \ldots \tag{60.8}$$

The quantities $\mathbf{v}/c$ and $\frac{\hbar}{mc}\left|\frac{\partial \mathbf{E}}{\partial x}\right| \Big/ |\mathbf{E}|$ are independent of each other, but have the same order of magnitude for the lowest states of the hydrogen atom:

$$\overline{|\mathbf{v}|}/c \approx \frac{\hbar}{mc}\overline{\left|\frac{\partial \phi}{\partial x}\right| \Big/ |\phi|} \approx \frac{e^2}{\hbar c} \approx 1/137$$

We can see that the two terms in the second line of (60.8) are of the same order of magnitude, since the first is approximately $\frac{\hbar}{mc}\frac{\partial e\phi}{\partial x}\frac{v}{c}$ and the second is $\left(\frac{\hbar}{mc}\frac{\partial}{\partial x}\right)^2 e\phi$.

If we restrict ourselves to positive energy states and irrotational fields (when curl $\mathbf{E} = 0$, i.e. $-\mathbf{p}\times\mathbf{E} = \mathbf{E}\times\mathbf{p}$), (60.8) finally becomes

$$\mathscr{H}' = mc^2 + e\phi + \frac{1}{2m}\left(\mathbf{p} - \frac{e}{c}\mathbf{A}\right)^2 - \frac{e\hbar}{2mc}\vec{\sigma}\mathbf{H} - \frac{1}{8m^3c^2}\left(\mathbf{p} - \frac{e}{c}\mathbf{A}\right)^4 -$$
$$- \frac{e\hbar}{4m^2c^2}\vec{\sigma}\,\mathbf{E}\times\left(\mathbf{p} - \frac{e}{c}\mathbf{A}\right) - \frac{e\hbar^2}{8m^2c^2}\operatorname{div}\mathbf{E} \tag{60.9}$$

The physical significance of each term occurring in the above expression has been explained in §34, with the exception of the term $-\dfrac{e\hbar^2}{8m^2c^2}\operatorname{div}\mathbf{E}$, the origin of which, however, is quite clear as a result of our previous discussion. We have already seen that the quantity $\mathbf{r}$ occurring in the Schrödinger function $G(\mathbf{r},s)$ is not the point at which the fields act; the latter is displaced and dispersed relative to the Schrödinger "position" as previously defined. Hence if $e\phi(\mathbf{R}_{el})$ is expanded in terms of powers of $\mathbf{R}_{el}-\mathbf{R}$, the spin-field interaction* is given by the dipole term implied by the displacement (59.19). (This interaction is represented by the sixth term in (60.9).) For spherically symmetrical dispersion the quadrupole term is

$$\frac{1}{2}\sum_{ik}\frac{\partial^2 e\phi}{\partial x_i\,\partial x_k}\overline{x_i x_k}=\frac{\overline{\mathbf{r}^2}}{6}\nabla^2 e\phi=-\frac{e}{6}\overline{\mathbf{r}^2}\operatorname{div}\mathbf{E}$$

where $\overline{\mathbf{r}^2}$ is a measure of the dispersion of the electrical charge relative to the electron position. Comparison with (60.9) shows that

$$\overline{\mathbf{r}^2}=\frac{3}{4}\left(\frac{\hbar}{mc}\right)^2$$

in agreement with (59.20); the electron charge is therefore dispersed over a region of the order of magnitude of the Compton wavelength.

For the Coulomb field of the hydrogen nucleus $\operatorname{div}\mathbf{E}=-\nabla^2\phi=4\pi e\,\delta(\mathbf{r})$. The additional term therefore produces an energy perturbation (actually an increase) in the case of those states for which $|G(0,s)|^2\neq 0$, that is, for all s-states (cf. §34). However, when calculating the energy terms for an electron in a pure Coulomb field it is unnecessary to adopt the preceding approximation procedure, since in this case the Dirac equation can be integrated exactly. The result (which we shall not prove) is Sommerfeld's formula (34.6).

Exercises

1. *The spin operator of the Dirac equation*

Equation (57.10) indicated that the spin of a free particle is not constant with respect to time. Show that the component of spin parallel to the momentum is constant, however, and that the spin and electron spin components (using the terminology of §60) in this direction are the same.

* Cf. Becker, R.: *Akad. d. Wiss., Math. Phys.*, Göttingen 1945.

2. *The matrix trace as a unitary invariant*

Show that the trace $\sum_n A_{nn}$ of a matrix A remains unchanged in value when subjected to an arbitrary unitary transformation.

Derive an expression for the trace of a Hermitian matrix in terms of the matrix eigenvalues a_i.

3. *Commutation with the Pauli matrices*

Show that if a matrix $\begin{pmatrix} a & b \\ c & d \end{pmatrix}$ commutes with all three Pauli matrices σ_x, σ_y, σ_z, it must be a multiple of the unit matrix.

4. *Hilbert space for Fermi-Dirac statistics*

Describe the formation of Hilbert space for the operators $b_{\mathbf{k}}^+$ and $b_{\mathbf{k}}$ which have the following commutation relations:

$$b_{\mathbf{k}}^+ b_{\mathbf{k}'} + b_{\mathbf{k}'} b_{\mathbf{k}}^+ = \delta_{\mathbf{k}\mathbf{k}'}, \qquad b_{\mathbf{k}} b_{\mathbf{k}'} + b_{\mathbf{k}'} b_{\mathbf{k}} = b_{\mathbf{k}}^+ b_{\mathbf{k}'}^+ + b_{\mathbf{k}'}^+ b_{\mathbf{k}}^+ = 0$$

5. *The spin and orbital current of the Dirac electron*

Equation (57.6) may be written in abbreviated form as follows:

$$\rho = \psi^*\psi \qquad \mathbf{j} = c\psi^*\vec{\alpha}\psi$$

Putting $\rho = \frac{1}{2}(\psi^*\psi + \psi^*\psi)$, with a corresponding expression for $\mathbf{j}$, replace ψ and ψ^* once each by their value as given by the expression resulting from the Dirac equation,

$$c\vec{\alpha}\mathbf{p}\psi + \beta mc^2\psi = i\hbar\dot{\psi}$$

i.e.

$$\psi = \frac{\beta}{mc^2}(i\hbar\dot{\psi} - c\vec{\alpha}\mathbf{p}\psi)$$

Compare the two components of ρ and $\mathbf{j}$ with the Schrödinger expressions and with (56.10).

G

Solutions

Solutions

Chapter AI (p. 15)

1. *Rutherford's scattering formula*

(*a*) The three conservation laws are proved by differentiating out and taking account of the equation of motion. The laws of conservation of energy and angular momentum are valid for central forces in general; the third conservation theorem holds good only for a potential of the form $1/r$.

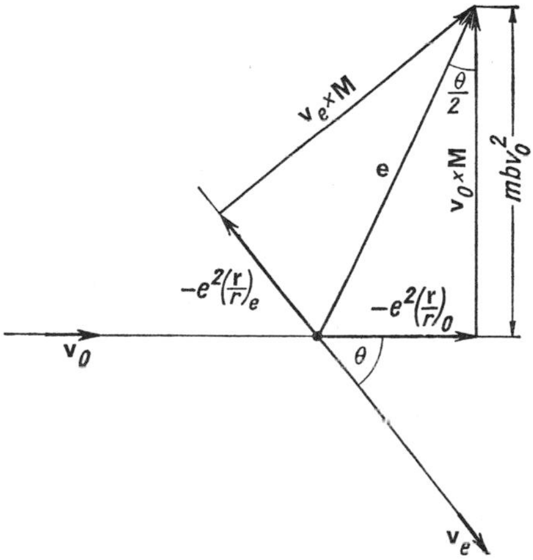

Fig. 57.—Graphical construction for the vector **e**

(*b*) The graphical construction for **e** is illustrated in figure 57. The relation $\tan \frac{1}{2}\theta = e^2/mv_0{}^2b$ is directly deduced from it. Note that the angular momentum **M** is normal to the plane of the diagram, that **M** has the magnitude mv_0b, and hence that $|\mathbf{v}_0 \times \mathbf{M}| = mv_0{}^2b$.

(*c*)
$$dQ = \pi\, db^2 = \pi \left(\frac{e^2}{mv_0{}^2}\right)^2 d \cot^2 \tfrac{1}{2}\theta = \left(\frac{e^2}{2mv_0{}^2}\right)^2 \frac{d\Omega}{\sin^4 \frac{1}{2}\theta}$$

2. *Aston's mass spectrograph*

The deflection in the electric field is

$$\delta v_z = \frac{e}{m}\, E\delta t = \frac{eEa}{mv_x} \rightarrow \theta \approx \frac{eEa}{mv^2}$$

The deflection in the magnetic field is

$$\delta v_z = \frac{ev_x}{mc} H\delta t = \frac{eHb}{mc} \to \phi \approx \frac{eHb}{mvc}$$

The equation for the path when $x > l$ is $z = -\theta x + \phi(x-l)$. Focusing takes place when

$$\left(\frac{\partial z}{\partial v}\right)_{z=z_f} = 0, \text{ i.e. when } z_f = \theta x_f = \frac{e}{mv^2} Eax_f = \frac{Ea}{2V} x_f$$

The photographic plate must therefore be inclined to the x-axis at an angle $\theta = Ea/2V$.

Chapter AII (p. 34)

1. *Broadening of spectral lines*

(*a*) $$\left(\frac{\Delta\omega}{\omega}\right)_{\text{radiation}} = \frac{2}{3}\frac{e^2\omega}{mc^3} \approx \frac{e^2/mc^2}{\lambda} \approx 10^{-8} \text{ for } \lambda \approx 10^{-5}\text{cm (visible light)}$$

(*b*) $$\left(\frac{\Delta\omega}{\omega}\right)_{\text{collision}} = \frac{2}{\tau\omega} \approx \frac{\bar{v}}{l}\frac{\lambda}{c} \approx \frac{\sigma^2\lambda}{V/N}\frac{\bar{v}}{c}$$

$$\approx \begin{cases} 10^{-7} \text{ for normal atmospheric pressure,} \\ 10^{-10} \text{ for } 10^{-2}\text{mm Hg} \end{cases}$$

σ is the atomic radius, l the mean free path, $\bar{v} = \sqrt{(kT/M)}$ the mean velocity of the atoms, V/N the specific volume.

(*c*) $\omega' = \omega_0\left(1+\frac{v_x}{c}\right)$ is the frequency observed along the x-direction. v_x is seldom greater than $\pm\bar{v}$; hence

$$\left(\frac{\Delta\omega}{\omega}\right)_{\text{Doppler}} \approx \frac{\bar{v}}{c} \approx 10^{-5}$$

(*d*) The broadening due to collisions can be made small compared with the width due to radiation damping by reducing the pressure; this latter width, however, is generally small compared with the Doppler width. Nevertheless, the radiation damping can be measured separately as a result of the different line form produced by the two effects. Taking account of the Maxwell distribution, we obtain the following expression for the spectral energy density in the emitted light:

$$S(\omega) = \frac{\gamma W_0}{2\pi}\int_{-\infty}^{\infty} \frac{\exp -\frac{Mv_x^2}{2kT}\, dv_x}{\left(\omega-\omega_0-\omega_0\frac{v_x}{c}\right)^2 + \frac{1}{4}\gamma^2} \Bigg/ \int_{-\infty}^{\infty} \exp -\frac{Mv_x^2}{2kT}\, dv_x$$

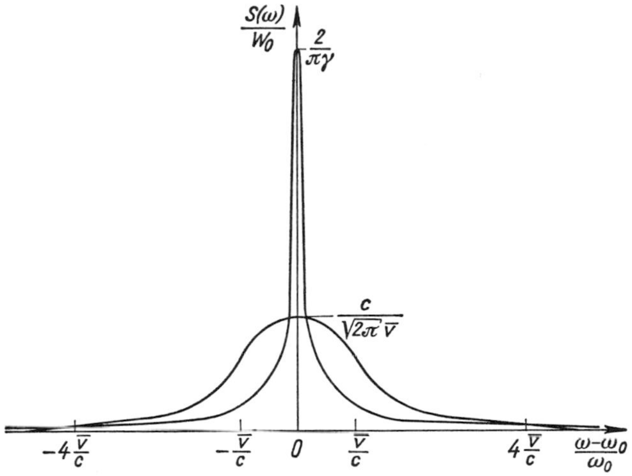

Fig. 58.—$S(\omega)/W_0$ for pure radiation damping and for pure Doppler broadening

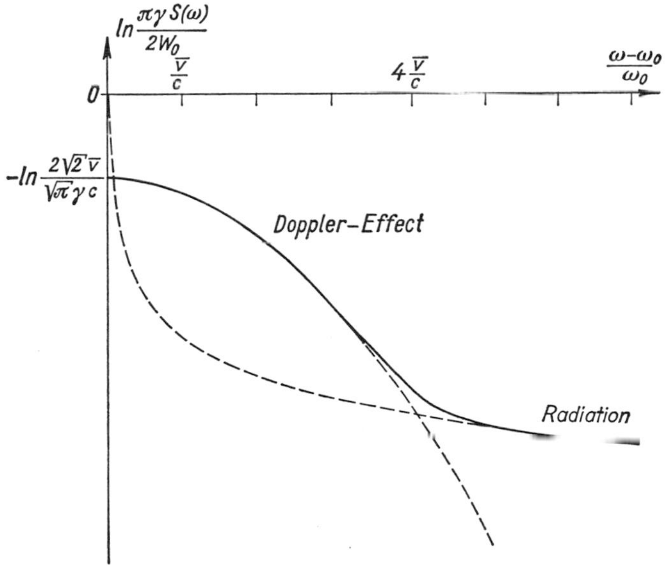

Fig. 59.—$S(\omega)/W_0$ for radiation and Doppler broadening on a logarithmic scale

Hence when $|\omega-\omega_0| \gg \frac{\omega_0}{c}\sqrt{\frac{kT}{m}}$

$$S(\omega) = \frac{\gamma W_0/2\pi}{(\omega-\omega_0)^2+\frac{1}{4}\gamma^2}$$

and when $|\omega-\omega_0| \ll \frac{\omega_0}{c}\sqrt{\frac{kT}{m}}$

$$S(\omega) = \frac{\gamma W_0 c}{2\pi\omega_0} \exp\left[-\frac{mc^2}{2kT}\left(\frac{\omega-\omega_0}{\omega_0}\right)^2\right] \times$$

$$\times \int_{-\infty}^{+\infty} \frac{\exp\left\{-\frac{mc^2}{2kT\omega_0{}^2}[\eta^2+2\eta(\omega_0-\omega)]\right\}}{\eta^2+\frac{1}{4}\gamma^2} d\eta \Bigg/ \int_{-\infty}^{+\infty} \exp -\frac{mv_x{}^2}{2kT} dv_x$$

The integral in η depends only slightly on $\omega-\omega_0$, because $\gamma \ll \frac{\omega_0}{c}\sqrt{\frac{kT}{m}}$, hence

$$S(\omega) \sim \exp -\frac{mc^2}{2kT}\left(\frac{\omega-\omega_0}{\omega_0}\right)^2$$

We therefore have practically pure Doppler line form within the Doppler width, while outside this width the line form is almost entirely due to the radiation damping.

2. *Radiation damping and the electron radius*

From the radiated power $S = \frac{2e^2}{3c^3}\overline{\ddot{x}^2}$, and the energy incident on the sphere, $s\pi R_{el}^2$, we have

$$R_{el}^2 = \frac{2e^2}{3\pi c^3}\frac{\overline{\ddot{x}^2}}{s} = \frac{8e^2}{3c^4}\frac{\overline{\ddot{x}^2}}{\overline{E^2}}$$

The equation of motion $m\ddot{x} = eE$ gives

$$\overline{\ddot{x}^2} = \frac{e^2}{m^2}\overline{E^2}$$

It follows that $R_{el} = \sqrt{(8/3)}.e^2/mc^2$, which agrees in order of magnitude with the value given in §4.

Chapter AIII (p. 46)

1. *The Hamiltonian function in polar coordinates*

$$L = \tfrac{1}{2}m\{\dot{r}^2+r^2\dot{\theta}^2+r^2\sin^2\theta\,\dot{\phi}^2\}-U(r)$$

therefore

$$p_r = m\dot{r} \qquad p_\theta = mr^2\dot{\theta} \qquad p_\varphi = mr^2\sin^2\theta\,\dot{\phi}$$

If these expressions are introduced into the sum of the kinetic and potential energies, we obtain

$$\mathscr{H} = \frac{1}{2m}\left\{p_r^2+\frac{1}{r^2}p_\theta^2+\frac{1}{r^2\sin^2\theta}p_\varphi{}^2\right\}+U(r)$$

2. *The Lagrangian function and the conservation of momentum*

$$\int_{t_0}^{t_1} L(\mathbf{r}_1 \ldots)dt = \int_{t_0}^{t_1} L(\mathbf{r}_1+\mathbf{R}_1, \ldots)dt$$

The second integral is evaluated in the same manner as on p. 37:

$$\int_{t_0}^{t_1} L(\mathbf{r}_1+\mathbf{R}_1, \ldots)dt$$

$$= \int_{t_0}^{t_1} L(\mathbf{r}_1, \ldots)dt + \int_{t_0}^{t_1} dt \sum_i \mathbf{R}_i \left\{-\frac{d}{dt}\frac{\partial L}{\partial \dot{\mathbf{r}}_i}+\frac{\partial L}{\partial \mathbf{r}_i}\right\} + \left[\sum_i R_i \frac{\partial L}{\partial \dot{\mathbf{r}}_i}\right]_{t_1} - \left[\sum_i \mathbf{R}_i \frac{\partial L}{\partial \dot{\mathbf{r}}_i}\right]_{t_0}$$

Since the initial path $\mathbf{r}_i$ was "correct", the second integral on the right-hand side vanishes, and we obtain the following condition for invariance:

$$\left[\sum_i \mathbf{R}_i \frac{\partial L}{\partial \dot{\mathbf{r}}_i}\right]_{t_1} = \left[\sum_i \mathbf{R}_i \frac{\partial L}{\partial \dot{\mathbf{r}}_i}\right]_{t_0} \quad \text{for all } t_1,\ t_0,$$

or

$$\frac{d}{dt}\sum_i \mathbf{R}_i \frac{\partial L}{\partial \dot{\mathbf{r}}_i} = 0 \qquad \frac{d}{dt}\sum_i \mathbf{R}_i m_i \mathbf{v}_i = 0$$

When $\mathbf{R}_i = \mathbf{R}_0$ we obtain the law of conservation of linear momentum:

$$\frac{d}{dt}\sum_i m_i \mathbf{v}_i = 0$$

$\mathbf{R}_i \to \mathbf{n} \times \mathbf{r}_i$ yields the law of conservation of angular momentum:

$$\frac{d}{dt}\sum_i \mathbf{r}_i \times m_i \mathbf{v}_i = 0$$

3. *Hamilton's principle of the extremum*

(*a*) In this case we have

$$G\{x+y\} - G\{x\} = \int_{t_0}^{t_1} \tfrac{1}{2} m \dot{y}^2 dt$$

The term of the first degree in y vanishes if $x(t)$ represents the correct path. G is therefore a minimum for this path, since

$$\int_{t_0}^{t_1} \tfrac{1}{2} m \dot{y}^2 dt > 0$$

(*b*) In this case

$$G\{x+y\} - G\{x\} = \int_{t_0}^{t_1} \tfrac{1}{2} m \{\dot{y}^2 - \omega^2 y^2\} dt$$

since the term of the first degree in y vanishes as in case (*a*). Since $y(t)$ must vanish at t_0 and t_1 it can be represented by a sine series:

$$y(t) = \sum_{n=1}^{\infty} a_n \sin n\pi \frac{t-t_0}{t_1-t_0} = \sum_{n=1}^{\infty} a_n \sin \omega_n (t-t_0)$$

The integral may then be performed, to give the result

$$G\{x+y\} - G\{x\} = \tfrac{1}{4} m (t_1 - t_0) \sum_{n=1}^{\infty} a_n^2 (\omega_n^2 - \omega^2)$$

If all $\omega_n > \omega$, i.e. $t_1 - t_0$ is smaller than the half-period of the oscillation, $\frac{1}{2}T$, G is a minimum. If $t_1 - t_0$ is greater than $\frac{1}{2}T$, angular frequencies ω_n with small values of n are smaller than ω, while the other ω_n are greater; G is then indeterminate in its behaviour. If we choose a variation γ that contains only small values of n, G is a maximum; otherwise it is a minimum. However, the coefficients a_n may be so chosen that G does not change at all.

Chapter BI (p. 107)

1. *Planck's radiation formula interpolation*

$$\Delta = \begin{cases} \varepsilon^2 & \text{Rayleigh-Jeans} \\ \alpha k \nu \varepsilon & \text{Wien} \end{cases}$$

The representation $\Delta = \varepsilon^2 + \alpha k \nu \varepsilon$ is a reasonable interpolation for the mean square deviation Δ, since the second term is small compared with the first in the Rayleigh-Jeans region, and vice versa in the Wien region. The differential equation for ε as a function of T possesses the solution

$$\varepsilon(\nu, T) = \frac{\alpha \nu k}{C \exp(\alpha \nu / T) - 1}$$

In the above expression the constant of integration C must be assumed to be 1, since for small values of ν in the Rayleigh-Jeans region we should have $\varepsilon = kT$. When $\alpha = h/k$ we obtain Planck's formula. The mean-square-deviation formula applicable to a small frequency range of the black-body radiation is obtained by multiplying the mean square deviation of the oscillator by the number of oscillations in the frequency interval. In the Wien region these deviations are identical with those of an ideal gas composed of particles of energy $h\nu$, while in the Rayleigh-Jeans region the deviations can clearly be interpreted in terms of the interference effects of the light waves. Planck's formula thus demonstrates most clearly both the wave and particle nature of light.

2. *Derivation of the hydrogen terms from the correspondence principle*

For a linear oscillator ω is independent of E, hence $E(n) = \text{const} + n\hbar\omega$. In a Coulomb field, and for an orbit of radius R,

$$E = -\tfrac{1}{2}mv^2 = -e^2/2R = -\tfrac{1}{2}e^2(m\omega^2/e^2)^{1/3}, \text{ hence } \omega = \{-8E^3/me^4\}^{1/2}$$

Therefore $$dE/\omega(E) = -d\{-2E/me^4\}^{-1/2} = \hbar\, dn$$

from which $$-me^4/2E = (\text{const} + \hbar n)^2$$

and $E = -me^4/2(\hbar n + \text{const})^2$, which gives the hydrogen terms when the constant of integration vanishes.

3. *First approximation to the energy of an anharmonic linear oscillator*

$$E_n = n\hbar\omega + \tfrac{3}{2}\lambda\left(\frac{n\hbar}{m\omega}\right)^2$$

4. *Vibrations of solid bodies at the absolute zero of temperature*

$$\overline{x^2}/a^2 = \hbar/2mca, \text{ hence } \sqrt{(\overline{x^2}/a^2)} \approx 1/30 \approx 3 \text{ per cent}$$

It should be realized that the disturbance is much greater than the displacements due to normal elastic stresses.

5. *Rate of change of total momentum in wave theory*

From (16.8):

$$\frac{d}{dt}\int \mathbf{j}_m\,d\mathbf{r} = \frac{m}{i\alpha}\int d\mathbf{r}\,\{\dot{\psi}^* \text{ grad } \psi + \psi^* \text{ grad } \dot{\psi} - \text{conjugate complex quantity}\}$$

$$= \frac{m}{i\alpha}\int d\mathbf{r}\,\left\{\frac{\beta}{i\alpha}\psi^*\psi \text{ grad } \Phi + \frac{1}{i\alpha}(\nabla^2\psi^* \text{ grad } \psi - \psi^* \text{ grad} \nabla^2\psi) - \text{conj. compl.}\right\}$$

using (16.1*a*). The second term of the integrand vanishes on integrating by parts. Then since $2m\beta \to e\alpha^2$,

$$\frac{d}{dt}\int \mathbf{j}_m\,d\mathbf{r} = -\frac{2m\beta}{\alpha^2}\int \psi^*\psi \text{ grad } \Phi\,d\mathbf{r} = \int \rho_e \mathbf{E}\,d\mathbf{r}$$

6. *Motion of the centroid of a wave packet*

The first relation is obtained from the equation of motion by integrating by parts. We can deduce from the previous exercise that v_0 is constant (since $\mathbf{E} = 0$), and hence that $\int \rho_m dx$ does not depend on the time. In addition

$$\psi(x,t) = \frac{1}{\sqrt{(2\pi)}}\int g(k,t)e^{ikx}\,dk,$$

$$x\psi(x,t) = \frac{1}{\sqrt{(2\pi)}}\int g(k,t)\left(\frac{\partial}{\partial k}e^{ikx}\right)dk = \frac{i}{\sqrt{(2\pi)}}\int \left(\frac{\partial}{\partial k}g(k,t)\right)e^{ikx}\,dk$$

integrating by parts once more. Accordingly,

$$x_s = i\int g^*(k,t)\frac{\partial}{\partial k}g(k,t)\,dk \bigg/ \int |g(k,t)|^2 dk$$

and
$$\dot{x}_s = \int |g(k,t)|^2 \frac{d\omega}{dk}\,dk \bigg/ \int |g(k,t)|^2 dk$$

using the relation $g(k,t) = g(k,0)\,e^{-i\omega(k)t}$

7. *Energy according to wave theory, and the Hamiltonian operator*

$$\int u\,d\mathbf{r} = \int \left(\frac{e}{\beta}\text{grad } \psi^* \text{ grad } \psi + e\Phi\psi^*\psi\right)d\mathbf{r}$$

$$= \int \psi^*\left\{-\frac{e}{\beta}\nabla^2\psi + e\Phi\psi\right\}d\mathbf{r} = \int \psi^*\mathscr{H}\psi\,d\mathbf{r}$$

Chapter BII (p. 137)

1. *Various representations of the δ-function*

$$\delta(x) = \lim_{b\to 0} \frac{1}{b} S(x/b), \text{ where}$$

(1) $S(\eta) = \dfrac{\exp -\eta^2}{\sqrt{\pi}}$ (2) $S(\eta) = \dfrac{1}{\pi(1+\eta^2)}$

(3) $S(\eta) = \begin{cases} 0 \text{ for } |\eta| > 1 \\ \frac{1}{2} \text{ for } |\eta| \leqq 1 \end{cases}$ (4) $S(\eta) = \dfrac{\sin^2 \eta}{\pi\eta^2}$

$$\int_{-\infty}^{+\infty} \frac{1}{b} S(x/b)\,dx = \int_{-\infty}^{+\infty} S(\eta)\,d\eta = 1$$

in all four representations. In addition:

$$\int_{-a}^{a'} f(x)\frac{1}{b} S(x/b)\,dx = \int_{-a/b}^{a'/b} f(b\eta)\,S(\eta)\,d\eta \underset{b\to 0}{\to} f(0) \int_{-\infty}^{+\infty} S(\eta)\,d\eta = f(0)$$

It can be seen from the graphical representation (figure 60) that the maximum heights are proportional to $1/b$ and that the widths are proportional to b; the total area under the curves is therefore independent of b.

2. *δ-function relations*

(1) This relation is most simply proved if the δ-function is represented by a Gaussian function as in the previous exercise. If x is replaced by Cx, the normalization must be adjusted by the factor C in order to yield $\delta(x)$ again.

(2) $\delta[(x-a)(x-b)]$ behaves like a δ-function at $x = a$ and $x = b$. When $x \approx a$, $x-b$ may be replaced by $a-b$ and removed, and similarly when $x \approx b$.

(3) Since $|\det \alpha_{ik}| \neq 0$, the left-hand side of the relation is only zero for $x_k = 0$, and may therefore be represented as the product of simple δ-functions. The factor is the functional determinant of the transformation of $\sum_k \alpha_{ik} x_k$ to the x_k; it is obtained by effecting the transformation, noting that

$$\int dx_1 \ldots dx_N \prod_k \delta(x_k) = 1$$

For orthogonal transformations $|\det \alpha_{ik}| = 1$, hence

$$\delta\left[\frac{1}{\sqrt{2}}(x+y)\right] \delta\left[\frac{1}{\sqrt{2}}(x-y)\right] = \delta(x)\,\delta(y)$$

3. *The Schrödinger equation in momentum space*

The operator effecting the transformation between position and momentum space is

$$U(p,x) = \frac{1}{\sqrt{(2\pi\hbar)}} \exp(ipx/\hbar)$$

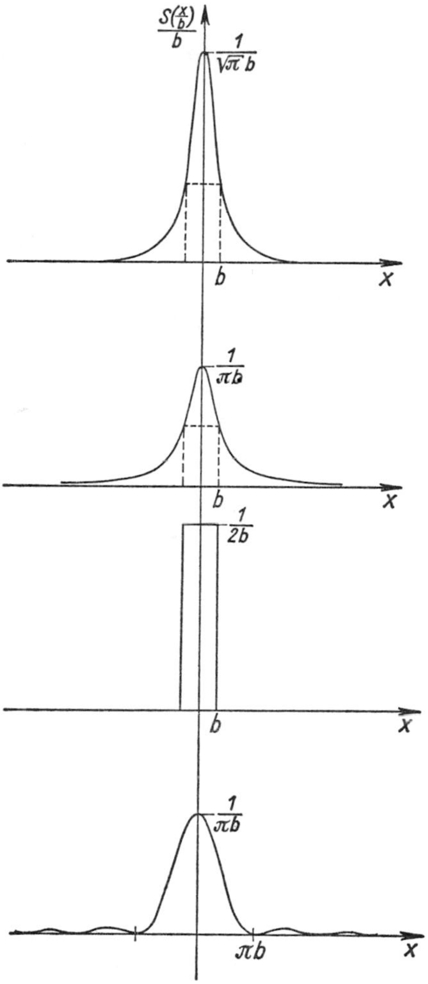

Fig. 60.—Various representations of the δ-function

The representation of $\phi(x,t)$ in momentum space is therefore

$$\psi(p,t) = \int U(p,x)\,\phi(x,t)\,dx$$

Hence
$$\mathscr{H}\phi = \int \mathscr{H}\exp(-ipx/\hbar)\frac{\psi(p,t)}{\sqrt{(2\pi\hbar)}}\,dp$$

Therefore

(a) $\dfrac{p^2}{2m}\psi(p,t)+\int V_{p-p'}\psi(p',t)\,dp' = i\hbar\dot{\psi};\quad V(x) = \int V_p \exp(-ipx/\hbar)\,dp$

(b) $\dfrac{p^2}{2m}\psi(p,t)+V\left(\dfrac{-\hbar}{i}\dfrac{\partial}{\partial p}\right)\psi(p,t) = i\hbar\dot{\psi}$

(c) $\dfrac{p^2}{2m}\psi-\dfrac{\hbar^2 m\omega^2}{2}\dfrac{\partial^2}{\partial p^2}\psi = i\hbar\dot{\psi}$

The form of equation (*c*) is therefore the same as in the *x*-representation.

4. *One-dimensional potential well*

$$S_g(k) = e^{2ikl}\frac{q\sin ql+ik\cos ql}{q\sin ql-ik\cos ql}$$

$$S_u(k) = e^{2ikl}\frac{q\cos ql-ik\sin ql}{q\cos ql+ik\sin ql}$$

The roots of these equations are obtained graphically (figure 61) from the intersections of the curves $q^2+\kappa^2 = 2mV_0 l^2/\hbar^2$ and $q\tan ql = \kappa$, $-q\cot ql = \kappa$ in the plane of q and κ. ($k = i\kappa$; $\kappa > 0$.) The energy of the bound states is $-\hbar^2\kappa^2/2m$, since $S(-i\kappa) = 0$ implies that ϕ has only exponentially decaying components, and may therefore be normalized. Even bound states also exist for any arbitrarily small potential V_0; in the case of odd functions V_0 must be greater than $\hbar^2/2ml^2$ in order that bound states may exist.

5. *Potential in δ-function form*

(*a*) In the limit $q^2 l \to 1/2\lambda$ and $ql \to 0$; hence

$$S_g \to \frac{1+2i\lambda k}{1-2i\lambda k}$$

$$\phi_g = \frac{2i}{1-2i\lambda k}(2\lambda k\cos kx - \sin k\,|\,x\,|)$$

with a bound state for $\kappa = -ik = 1/2\lambda$;

$$S_u \to 1 \qquad \phi_u = -2i\sin kx$$

with no associated bound state.

(*b*) If

$$-\frac{\hbar^2}{2m}\phi''(x) - \frac{\hbar^2}{2m\lambda}\delta(x)\,\phi(x) = \varepsilon\phi(x)$$

is integrated over a very small interval containing $x = 0$, it follows that

$$\phi'(+0)-\phi'(-0)+\phi(0)/\lambda = 0$$

The first derivative of ϕ therefore has a discontinuity $-\phi(0)/\lambda$ at $x = 0$, while $\phi(x)$ itself is continuous. If we seek once more to find the odd and even eigenfunctions we obtain the same solutions as in (*a*). $\phi(0) = 0$ for the odd functions; since there is a vanishing probability of finding the particle at the point at which $V(x) \neq 0$, the odd functions are those of a free particle.

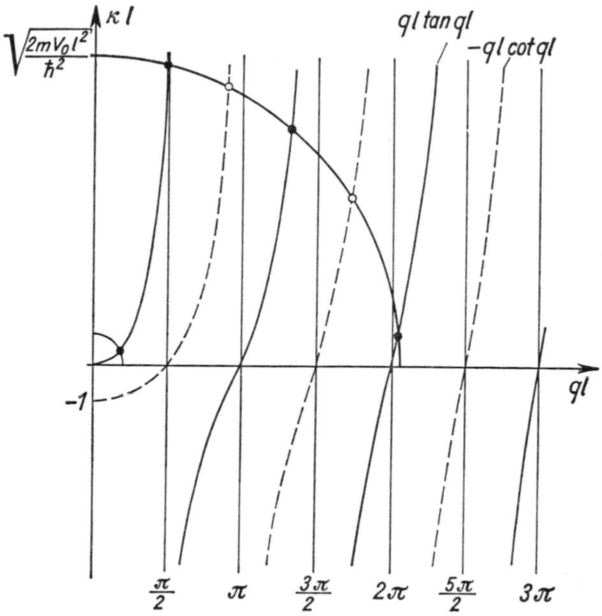

Fig. 61.—Determination of the bound states of the potential well. The intersections of the circular quadrant of radius $\{2mV_0l^2/\hbar\}^{\frac{1}{2}}$ with the curves $ql\tan ql$ and $-ql\cot ql$ give the values of κ for the bound states. (Dots correspond to even functions, circles to odd functions.) If the radius is less than $\pi/2$ there is only one even bound state

6. *Ehrenfest's theorem and the magnetic field*

In the presence of a magnetic field

$$\mathscr{H} = \frac{1}{2m}\left(\mathbf{p} - \frac{e}{c}\mathbf{A}(\mathbf{r},t)\right)^2 + e\phi(\mathbf{r},t);$$

hence the velocity operator is

$$\dot{\mathbf{r}} = \frac{i}{\hbar}(\mathscr{H}\mathbf{r} - \mathbf{r}\mathscr{H}) = \frac{1}{m}\left(\mathbf{p} - \frac{e}{c}\mathbf{A}\right)$$

and the x-component of $m\ddot{\mathbf{r}}$ is

$$m\ddot{x} = \frac{i}{\hbar}\left[\mathscr{H}\left(p_x - \frac{e}{c}A_x\right) - \left(p_x - \frac{e}{c}A_x\right)\mathscr{H}\right] - \frac{e}{c}\frac{\partial A_x}{\partial t}$$

$$= eE_x + \frac{e}{2c}\left[(\dot{y}H_z - \dot{z}H_y) + (H_z\dot{y} - H_y\dot{z})\right]$$

The following relations were used to derive the last expression (cf. § 7):

$$E_x = -\frac{\partial \phi}{\partial x} - \frac{1}{c}\frac{\partial A_x}{\partial t} \qquad H_x = \frac{\partial A_z}{\partial y} - \frac{\partial A_y}{\partial z}, \ldots$$

7. *Current and magnetic field*

As in (14.15), if we add $\phi^* \mathscr{H} \phi$ and $-\phi \mathscr{H} \phi^*$ we again obtain

$$\dot{\rho} + \operatorname{div} \mathbf{j} = 0$$

where $\rho = \phi^* \phi$ and $\mathbf{j} = \frac{\hbar}{2mi}(\phi^* \operatorname{grad} \phi - \phi \operatorname{grad} \phi^*) - \frac{e}{mc}\mathbf{A}\phi^*\phi$

In the presence of a magnetic field real functions also yield a current density $\mathbf{j} \neq 0$.

8. *The virial theorem*

For a Coulomb potential $V \sim 1/r$; hence $\mathbf{r} \operatorname{grad} V = r\partial V/\partial r = -V$. The total energy $E = \overline{E_{kin}} + \overline{V} = \frac{1}{2}\overline{V}$ is therefore equal to half the potential energy.

For the oscillator, $V \sim r^2$, i.e. $\mathbf{r} \operatorname{grad} V = 2V$. The mean values of the kinetic and potential energies are equal.

Chapter BIII (p. 152)

1. *Parity of the spherical harmonics*

(1) Let $P\phi = \lambda\phi$: then $P^2\phi = \lambda^2\phi$. Hence, since $P\phi(-\mathbf{r}) = \phi(\mathbf{r})$, $\lambda^2 = 1$.

(2) The relation $PY_{lm}(\theta, \phi) = Y_{lm}(\pi - \theta, \phi - \pi)$ is correct when $m = l$, since $Y_{ll} = \text{const} (\sin\theta)^l e^{il\varphi}$. Since $Y_{lm} = \text{const}\, \Lambda_-^{l-m} Y_{ll}$ and $P\Lambda_- - \Lambda_- P = 0$, it follows that the relation is valid for all m.

2. *Angular-momentum matrices*

$$M_x = \frac{\hbar}{\sqrt{2}}\begin{pmatrix} 0 & 1 & 0 \\ 1 & 0 & 1 \\ 0 & 1 & 0 \end{pmatrix} \quad M_y = \frac{\hbar}{\sqrt{2}}\begin{pmatrix} 0 & -i & 0 \\ i & 0 & -i \\ 0 & i & 0 \end{pmatrix} \quad M_z = \hbar\begin{pmatrix} 1 & 0 & 0 \\ 0 & 0 & 0 \\ 0 & 0 & -1 \end{pmatrix}$$

$$M^2 = M_x^2 + M_y^2 + M_z^2 = 2\hbar^2\begin{pmatrix} 1 & 0 & 0 \\ 0 & 1 & 0 \\ 0 & 0 & 1 \end{pmatrix}$$

Since $\overline{M_x} = (M_x)_{lm,\,lm} = 0$ for all m,

$$(\Delta M_x)^2 = \overline{M_x^2} = \sum_{l'm'} (M_x)_{lm,\,l'm'}(M_x)_{l'm',\,lm}$$

Since M_x possesses no matrix elements for which $l' \neq l$ the $\overline{M_x^2}$ are directly obtained as the diagonal elements in the squares of the above matrices. Hence

$$\Delta M_x = \Delta M_y = \begin{cases} \hbar/\sqrt{2} & \text{for } m = \pm 1 \\ \hbar & \text{for } m = 0 \end{cases}$$

for a total angular momentum $\hbar\sqrt{2}$.

In the case of a top with total angular momentum $M = \hbar\sqrt{2}$ precessing about the cones shown in figure 62, the time averages of $\overline{M_x^2}$ and $\overline{M_y^2}$ are equal to the above values.

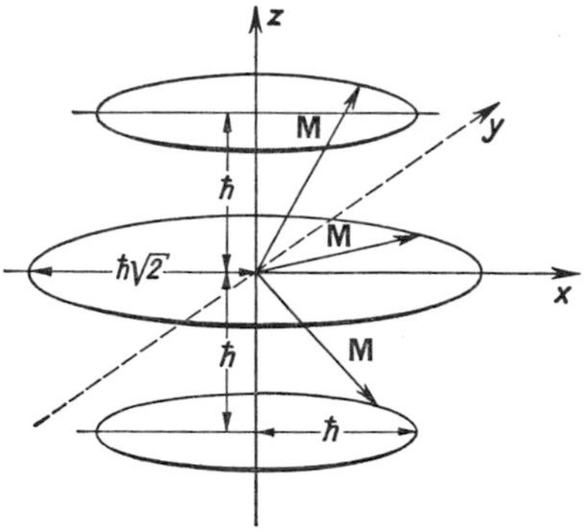

Fig. 62.—Representation of an angular-momentum vector and its dispersion due to a precessing moment about the z-axis

3. *Eigenfunctions of the electron spin*

(*a*) The matrix of $s_{\theta,\varphi}$ is

$$s_{\theta,\varphi} = \tfrac{1}{2}\hbar \begin{pmatrix} \cos\theta & \sin\theta\, e^{-i\varphi} \\ \sin\theta\, e^{i\varphi} & -\cos\theta \end{pmatrix}$$

The eigenvalues of this matrix are $\pm\frac{1}{2}\hbar$; this may be seen at once because the sum of the eigenvalues (the sum of the diagonal elements) is zero and the product (which is the determinant) is $-\frac{1}{4}\hbar^2$. Then the relations

$$\cos\theta . a + \sin\theta\, e^{-i\varphi} . b = \pm a, \qquad \sin\theta\, e^{i\varphi} . a - \cos\theta . b = \pm b$$

give the normalized eigenstates corresponding to the eigenvalues $\pm\frac{1}{2}\hbar$:

$$\begin{pmatrix} a_+ \\ b_+ \end{pmatrix} = \begin{pmatrix} \cos\frac{1}{2}\theta\, e^{-i\varphi} \\ \sin\frac{1}{2}\theta \end{pmatrix} \text{ and } \begin{pmatrix} a_- \\ b_- \end{pmatrix} = \begin{pmatrix} -\sin\frac{1}{2}\theta\, e^{-i\varphi} \\ \cos\frac{1}{2}\theta \end{pmatrix}$$

(*b*) The required rotation operator is

$$D = \exp -\frac{i}{\hbar}\phi s_z . \exp -\frac{i}{\hbar}\theta s_y = \exp -\tfrac{1}{2}i\phi\sigma_z . \exp -\tfrac{1}{2}i\theta\sigma_y$$

Now since $\sigma_y{}^2 = \sigma_z{}^2 = 1$,

$$\exp -\tfrac{1}{2}i\theta\sigma_y = \sum_\nu (-\tfrac{1}{2}i\theta)^\nu \frac{\sigma_y{}^\nu}{\nu!} = \sum_{\nu\ even} (-\tfrac{1}{2}i\theta)^\nu \frac{1}{\nu!} + \sum_{\nu\ odd} (-\tfrac{1}{2}i\theta)^\nu \frac{1}{\nu!}\sigma_y$$

$$= \cos\tfrac{1}{2}\theta - i\sin\tfrac{1}{2}\theta . \sigma_y$$

Hence $$D = (\cos\tfrac{1}{2}\phi - i\sin\tfrac{1}{2}\phi\sigma_z)(\cos\tfrac{1}{2}\theta - i\sin\tfrac{1}{2}\theta\sigma_y)$$

The application of this operator to $\alpha = \begin{pmatrix} 1 \\ 0 \end{pmatrix}$ and $\beta = \begin{pmatrix} 0 \\ 1 \end{pmatrix}$ gives

$$D\alpha = \begin{pmatrix} a_+ \\ b_+ \end{pmatrix} = \begin{pmatrix} \cos\frac{1}{2}\theta \exp -\frac{1}{2}i\phi \\ \sin\frac{1}{2}\theta \exp \frac{1}{2}i\phi \end{pmatrix} \qquad D\beta = \begin{pmatrix} a_- \\ b_- \end{pmatrix} = \begin{pmatrix} -\sin\frac{1}{2}\theta \exp -\frac{1}{2}i\phi \\ \cos\frac{1}{2}\theta \exp \frac{1}{2}i\phi \end{pmatrix}$$

(*c*) The two states thus determined are identical, differing only by a factor $\exp\frac{1}{2}i\phi$ of magnitude 1.

4. *Relation between Λ_+ and Λ_-*

The relation is proved by integrating by parts. Note the factor $\sin\theta$ in the normalization integral.

5. *A spherical harmonic relation*

We first show that the expression $\sum_{m=-l}^{l} Y_{lm}^* Y_{lm}$ remains unchanged when subjected to an arbitrary rotation. If D is the unitary rotation operator and DY_{lm} is the rotated function, then

$$D\,\Sigma\, Y_{lm}^* Y_{lm} = \Sigma\,(DY_{lm})^* D Y_{lm}$$

Since D commutes with $\mathbf{M}^2$, DY_{lm} contains only functions with the same value of l. If $D_{mm'}$ is the associated matrix defined by $D_{mm'} = (Y_{lm'}, DY_{lm})$, then

$$DY_{lm} = \sum_{m'} D_{mm'} Y_{lm'}$$

Making use of the unitariness property of the rotation matrices,

$$\Sigma\, D_{mm'}^* D_{mm''} = \delta_{m'm''}$$

we then obtain

$$D \sum_m Y_{lm}^* Y_{lm} = \sum_{mm'm''} D_{mm'}^* Y_{lm'}^* D_{mm''} Y_{lm''} = \sum_{m'} Y_{lm'}^* Y_{lm'}$$

We have thus proved that $\Sigma\, Y_{lm}^* Y_{lm}$ is invariant to rotation, and therefore independent of θ and ϕ:

$$\sum_m Y_{lm}^* Y_{lm} = C$$

The numerical value of the constant C is obtained by integrating the above relation over a unit sphere, taking account of the normalization condition $\int Y_{lm}^* Y_{lm} d\Omega = 1$:

$$\int \sum_m Y_{lm}^* Y_{lm} d\Omega = \sum_{m=-l}^{l} 1 = 2l+1, \qquad \int C d\Omega = 4\pi C$$

C therefore has the value $(2l+1)/4\pi$.

Chapter BIV (p. 175)

1. *First-order perturbation calculation for an anharmonic oscillator*

$$E_n = (n+\tfrac{1}{2})\hbar\omega + \frac{3\lambda}{2}\left(\frac{\hbar}{m\omega}\right)^2 \{(n+\tfrac{1}{2})^2 + \tfrac{1}{4}\}$$

Compare the solution of Exercise 3, p. 368.

2. *Quadratic secular equation*

$$E_{1,2} = \tfrac{1}{2}(\varepsilon_1+\varepsilon_2) + \tfrac{1}{2}\lambda(W_{11}+W_{22}) \pm \{[\tfrac{1}{2}(\varepsilon_1-\varepsilon_2)+\tfrac{1}{2}\lambda(W_{11}-W_{22})]^2 + \lambda^2|W_{12}|^2\}^{1/2}$$
$$= \tfrac{1}{2}(\varepsilon_1+\varepsilon_2) + \tfrac{1}{2}\lambda(W_{11}+W_{22}) \pm \left\{\tfrac{1}{2}(\varepsilon_1-\varepsilon_2)+\tfrac{1}{2}\lambda(W_{11}-W_{22}) + \lambda^2 \frac{|W_{12}|^2}{\varepsilon_1-\varepsilon_2}\right\} + \ldots$$

Perturbation theory gives the same result.

3. *A primitive model of the electron in a metal*

Put

$$\frac{1}{\sqrt{l}}e^{ikx} = \frac{1}{\sqrt{l}}e^{iKx}\,e^{i\kappa x} = \phi_{K\kappa}, \qquad K = \frac{2\pi}{a}n \qquad -\frac{\pi}{a} \leqq \kappa < \frac{\pi}{a}$$

Then

$$T_a\,\phi_{K,\kappa} = e^{i\kappa a}\,\phi_{K,\kappa}$$

Therefore all matrix elements $\mathscr{H}_{K\kappa\;K'\kappa'}$ of $\mathscr{H}$ vanish for $\kappa \neq \kappa'$, and

$$E_{K,\kappa} = \frac{\hbar^2}{2m}(K+\kappa)^2 + V_{00} + \sum_{K'\neq K}\frac{2m\,|V_{(K-K')}|^2}{\hbar^2\{(K+\kappa)^2-(K'+\kappa)^2\}}$$

$$V_{K\kappa,K'\kappa} = \frac{1}{l}\int V e^{i(K-K')x}\,dx = V_{(K-K')}$$

This expansion fails when $(K+\kappa)^2 \approx (K'+\kappa)^2$, i.e. when $K+K' \approx -2\kappa$, which only occurs when $\kappa \approx \pm\pi/a, 0$. The degeneracy is removed by setting up the following determinant and solving for ε:

$$\begin{vmatrix} \dfrac{\hbar^2}{2m}(K+\kappa)^2-\varepsilon & V_{(K'-K)} \\ V_{(K-K')} & \dfrac{\hbar^2}{2m}(K'+\kappa)^2-\varepsilon \end{vmatrix} = 0$$

whence

$$\varepsilon_{1,2} = \frac{\hbar^2}{2m}\frac{(K+\kappa)^2+(K'+\kappa)^2}{2} \pm \sqrt{\left[\hbar^4\left(\frac{(K+\kappa)^2-(K'+\kappa)^2}{4m}\right)^2 + |V_{(K-K')}|^2\right]}$$

The form of $\varepsilon(\kappa)$ is shown graphically in figure 63.

4. *Effective scattering cross-section for a screened Coulomb potential*

$$dQ = \left(\frac{2me^2}{\hbar^2}\right)^2 \frac{d\Omega}{\left(\dfrac{1}{a^2} + |\mathbf{k}_0' - \mathbf{k}_0|^2\right)^2} = \left(\frac{2me^2}{\hbar^2}\right)^2 \frac{d\Omega}{\left(\dfrac{1}{a^2} + 4k_0^2\sin^2\frac{1}{2}\theta\right)^2}$$

If a is allowed to tend to infinity and the kinetic energy $\hbar^2k^2/2m$ of the incident particle is represented by E as in the classical formula for scattering, we surprisingly obtain the same formula $dQ = \left(\dfrac{e^2}{4E}\right)^2 \dfrac{d\Omega}{\sin^4\frac{1}{2}\theta}$ as in the classical case. Further, the exact quantum-mechanical calculation always gives the classical result in the case of the Coulomb potential for any value of the energy. The total effective cross-section is

$$Q = \left(\frac{4me^2a^2}{\hbar^2}\right)^2 \frac{\pi}{1+4a^2k_0^2}$$

If $ak_0 \gg 1$, Q is proportional to the square of the wavelength. For a pure Coulomb potential the effective cross-section is divergent.

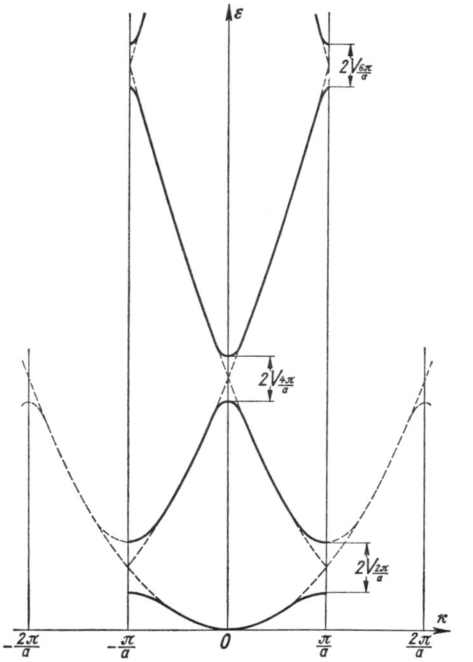

Fig. 63.—Energy perturbation of free electrons in a periodic potential field

5. *Polarizability of a spherically symmetrical atom*

The energy expressed as a function of β is derived as in §28, and is

$$E(\beta) = E_0 + 2\beta\overline{W^2} + \beta^2\{\overline{W\mathscr{H}_0 W} - E_0\overline{W^2}\}$$

Since the state ϕ_0 over which the average is taken satisfies the equation $\mathscr{H}_0\phi_0 = E_0\phi_0$, we may replace $E_0\overline{W^2}$ by $\overline{\mathscr{H}_0 W^2}$, $\overline{W^2\mathscr{H}_0}$, or $\frac{1}{2}(\overline{\mathscr{H}_0 W^2} + \overline{W^2\mathscr{H}_0})$ The factor of β^2 then only contains the commutations:

$$\overline{W\mathscr{H}_0 W} - \tfrac{1}{2}(\overline{\mathscr{H}_0 W^2} + \overline{W^2\mathscr{H}_0}) = \tfrac{1}{2}\overline{[[W, \mathscr{H}_0], W]} = \frac{e^2F^2\hbar^2N}{2m}$$

Only the kinetic part of $\mathscr{H}_0$ is of importance in $[W, \mathscr{H}_0]$ (i.e. $[W, \mathscr{H}_0] \sim \sum_i p_{x_i}$), and the remaining commutation then merely contains the simple commutation relations between p_{x_i} and x_i. The energy at the minimum is

$$E = E_0 - \frac{\{\overline{W^2}\}^2}{\overline{W\mathscr{H}_0 W} - E_0\overline{W^2}} = E_0 - \frac{2e^2m}{\hbar^2N}\{\overline{(\Sigma x_i)^2}\}^2F^2$$

$$= E_0 - \frac{2}{Na}\{\overline{(\Sigma x_i)^2}\}^2F^2$$

and the polarizability is thus $\alpha = 4/Na\{\overline{(\Sigma x_i)^2}\}^2$, where a is the Bohr radius. The mixed terms may not be omitted when forming the mean value of $(\Sigma x_i)^2$:

$$\overline{(\Sigma\, x_i)^2} = \sum_i \overline{x_i{}^2} + \sum_{i \neq k} \overline{x_i x_k}$$

It is true that $\Sigma\overline{x_i}$ vanishes for spherically symmetrical states, but $\sum_{i\neq k} \overline{x_i x_k}$ does not do so, because the electrons tend to avoid each other as a result of the mutual Coulomb repulsion. This effect is termed correlation, and is referred to in §38.

Chapter CI (p. 191)

1. *Energy terms and degree of degeneracy for a three-dimensional oscillator*

The Schrödinger equation gives

$$\sum_{\nu=0}^{\infty} \{r^{\nu-2}c_\nu[\nu(\nu-1) + 2\nu(l+1)] + r^\nu c_\nu[\beta - 2\alpha(\nu + l + 3/2)]\} = 0$$

where $\alpha = m\omega/\hbar$ and $\beta = 2mE/\hbar^2$. Comparison of the coefficients associated with the same powers of r shows that the odd coefficients $c_1, c_3, c_5, \ldots$ must vanish. When ν is even and equal to $2n_r$, the power series terminates only when $\beta = 2\alpha(2n_r + l + 3/2)$ or $E = \hbar\omega(2n_r + l + 3/2)$, where n_r and l can extend over all positive integers and zero. The number of terms corresponding to a given $n = 2n_r + l$ is $(n+1)(n+2)/2$. Even values of l are associated with even values of n, and similarly for odd values. The results for the first few terms are summarized in the following table:

Quantum number n:	0	1	2	3	4	5
Energy E, excluding zero point energy	0	$\hbar\omega$	$2\hbar\omega$	$3\hbar\omega$	$4\hbar\omega$	$5\hbar\omega$
Degeneracy	1	3	6	10	15	21
Term symbols	s	p	s, d	p, f	$s, d, g,$	$p, f, h,$

2. *Hermitian nature of the Hamiltonian operator expressed in polar coordinates*

$$\int \psi_1{}^*(p_r\psi_2)r^2 \sin\theta\, dr\, d\theta\, d\phi = \int \left(\frac{1}{r^2}\, p_r r^2 \psi_1\right)^* \psi_2 r^2 \sin\theta\, dr\, d\theta\, d\phi$$

as may be seen by integrating by parts. In order that the integrated part should vanish, the wave functions must vanish sufficiently strongly at infinity and be regular at $r = 0$. Then $p_r{}^+ = (1/r^2).p_r r^2$, and hence the radial component of the kinetic energy

$$-\frac{\hbar^2}{2m}\frac{1}{r^2}\frac{\partial}{\partial r} r^2 \frac{\partial}{\partial r} = \frac{1}{2m} p_r{}^+ p_r$$

is a Hermitian operator.

3. *Probability function and Bohr orbits of the hydrogen atom*

When $l = n - 1$ the radial component of the wave function takes the form

$$R = \text{const.}\, r^{n-1} \exp - \frac{r}{na_0}$$

Therefore $w(r) = (Rr)^2 = \text{const. exp } 2n(\log r - r/n^2a_0)$, with a maximum at $r_n = n^2a_0$, the radius of the nth Bohr orbit. The deviation is obtained by expanding the exponent about the maximum value:

$$w(r) \approx \text{const. exp } [-(r - r_n)^2/n^3a_0{}^2]$$

Hence
$$\Delta r/\bar{r} = 1/\sqrt{(2n)}$$

The relative deviations therefore decrease proportionately to $1/\sqrt{n}$.

Comparison with (29.12) and (29.13): since the deviations are small, we must have

$$\Delta\frac{1}{r}\bigg/\overline{\frac{1}{r}} \approx \Delta r/\bar{r}$$

this result may also be proved from the fact that

$$\Delta\frac{1}{r} = \sqrt{\left[\overline{\left(\frac{1}{r}\right)^2} - \overline{\frac{1}{r}}^2\right]}$$

and
$$\overline{\frac{1}{r^2}} = \frac{2}{(2l+1)n^3a_0{}^2} \approx \frac{1}{n^4a_0{}^2} + \frac{1}{2n^5a_0{}^2} \quad \text{for } n \gg 1$$

Chapter CII (p. 206)

1. *Detailed description of the Stern-Gerlach experiment for a neutral particle of spin* 1/2

(*a*) If the trial solution

$$\Psi(\mathbf{r}, t) = \sum_s \phi_s(\mathbf{r}, t)\, \kappa_s^z \text{ whereby } \sigma_z\kappa_s^z = s\kappa_s^z \text{ with } s = \pm 1$$

is introduced into the equation of motion, we obtain

$$\left(\frac{\mathbf{p}^2}{2m} + \mu_B H(z)s\right)\phi_s(\mathbf{r}, t) = i\hbar\dot{\phi}_s(\mathbf{r}, t) \text{ for } s = \pm 1$$

This result may be verified by inserting Ψ into the equation of motion and forming the scalar product with κ_1 or κ_{-1}; it follows from the orthogonal property of the two spin functions. In the two equations $\pm\mu_B H(z)$ occurs as the potential energy and $\pm\mu_B \partial H/\partial z$ as the force. The initial conditions are clearly

$$\phi_s(\mathbf{r}, 0) = \phi_0(\mathbf{r})(\kappa_s^z, \chi_0) = \phi_0(\mathbf{r})\chi_0(s)$$

In view of the breadth of the wave packet the resultant motion approximately follows the laws of classical mechanics; therefore, when $\partial H/\partial z$ is negative (as in figure 32), the wave packet ϕ_{+1} corresponding to $s = +1$ moves parallel to the positive x-axis like a particle of moment μ_B in this direction, and similarly in the case of ϕ_{-1} in the opposite direction. We finally obtain two spatially separated wave packets, each of which has an eigenfunction κ_s^z as factor. In view of the equation of motion, $\int |\phi_s|^2 d\mathbf{r}$ is independent of the time and equal to $|(\kappa_s^z, \chi_0)|^2$, since ϕ_0 is normalized. Therefore $|(\kappa_s^z, \chi_0)|^2 = |\chi_0(s)|^2$ is the probability of finding the particle in the component beam denoted by s; in experiments with many particles $|\chi_0(s)|^2$ is proportional to the intensity of the beam.

(*b*) In this case the two probabilities correspond to $|(\kappa_s^\theta, \chi_0)|^2$. As in Exercise 3, p. 375, $\kappa_{s'}^{\theta,\phi} = \kappa_{s'}^z \cos \frac{1}{2}\theta - s'\kappa_{-s'}^z \sin \frac{1}{2}\theta \exp is'\phi$ with $\sigma_z\kappa_s^z = s\kappa_s^z$.

In case (*a*), for $\theta = 0$, $\kappa_s^{\theta,\phi}$ becomes κ_s^z.

In case (*b*), when $\theta = \pi/2$, $\phi = \pi/2$, therefore we obtain the following values for the intensities:

$$\kappa_{s'}^{\pi/2} = (1/\sqrt{2})(\kappa_{s'}^z + i\kappa_{-s'}^z) \text{ and } \tfrac{1}{2}|\chi_0(+1) \pm i\chi_0(-1)|^2 \text{ for } s' = \pm 1$$

The above analysis applies to a hydrogen or alkali atom in the ground state (when the appropriate mass is introduced), since in these cases there is merely a spin moment, and no orbital moment is present. For charged particles such as electrons the Stern-Gerlach splitting is completely masked by the effect of the Lorentz force.

2. *Multiple Stern-Gerlach experiment*

From the previous exercise we see that, when the component beam s_z is again split by a magnetic field parallel to θ, the resultant relative intensities are

$$|(\kappa_s^z, \kappa_{s'}^\theta)|^2 = \cos^2 \tfrac{1}{2}\theta \text{ or } \sin^2 \tfrac{1}{2}\theta$$

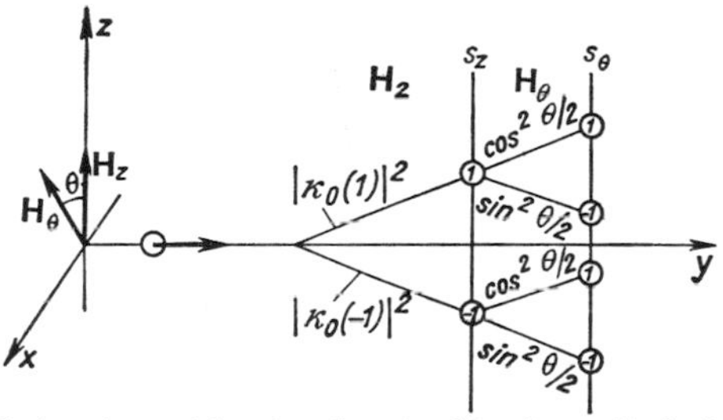

Fig. 64.—Relative intensities in the double Stern-Gerlach experiment

The value of these quantities is derived from the eigenfunctions $\kappa_{s'}^\theta$ of the previous solution (figure 64). In the case of the triple experiment we first have $|\kappa_s^z, \kappa_{s'}^x|^2 = \frac{1}{2}$, then $|\kappa_s^x, \kappa_{s'}^z|^2 = \frac{1}{2}$ (figure 65). We can see from this experiment that it is clearly impossible to make a simultaneous and precise determination of the values of two non-commuting quantities σ_z and σ_x. In the first experiment we

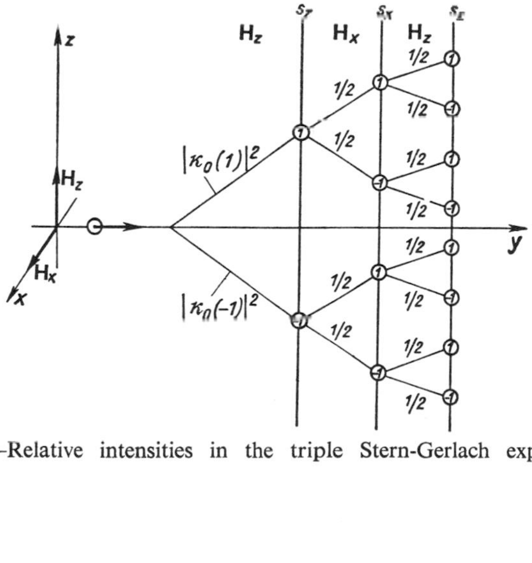

Fig. 65.—Relative intensities in the triple Stern-Gerlach experiment

measure σ_z, selecting the upper beam, for which σ_z is exactly equal to 1; in the second experiment we measure σ_x, again selecting the upper beam, for which $\sigma_x = 1$; if we now attempt to measure σ_z again in a third experiment we do not obtain a sharp result.

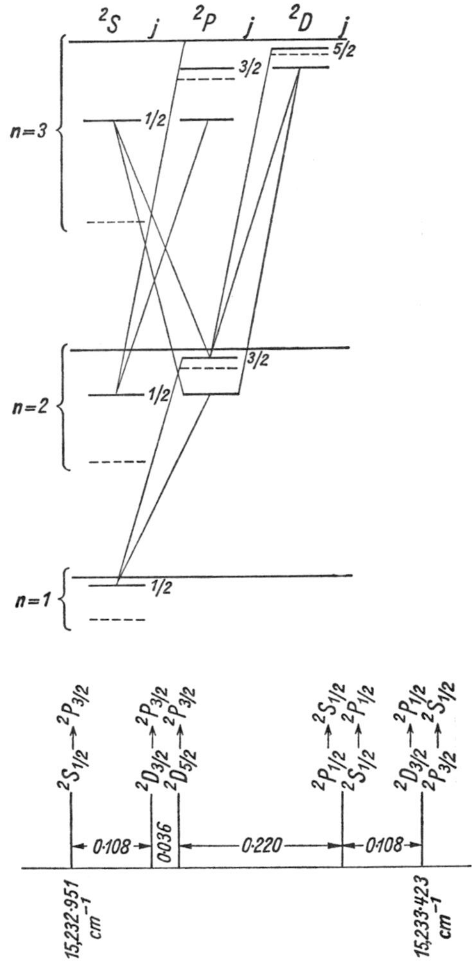

Fig. 66.—Fine-structure terms of hydrogen (not to scale), and fine structure of the H_α line. Long lines—Balmer terms. Short lines—fine-structure terms. Thin lines—permitted transitions. Broken lines—positions of the terms taking into account only the relativistic correction for mass (from Condon-Shortley, *The Theory of Atomic Spectra*, pp. 124–139, Cambridge 1953)

3. *Spin precession in a magnetic field*

The solution corresponding to the initial state $\chi(0)$ is

$$\chi(t) = \exp\left\{\frac{i}{\hbar}(\vec{\mu}\,\mathbf{H})t\right\}\chi(0) = \exp\left\{-\frac{2i}{\hbar}(\mathbf{s}\vec{\omega}_L)t\right\}\chi(0)$$

Comparison with (23.2) shows that $\chi(t)$ is produced from $\chi(0)$ by a rotation about **H** through an angle $2\omega_L t$.

4. *Fine structure of the hydrogen spectrum*

Note that $\Delta l = \pm 1$, $\Delta j = 0, \pm 1$. A study of equations (34.3) and (34.5) leads to the term scheme shown in figure 66.

Chapter C III (p. 238)

1. *Zeeman effect for the sodium D-line*

The Zeeman splitting and spin-orbit splitting are of approximately equal magnitude when $\Delta E_{\text{spin-orbit}} \approx \mu_B H$; ΔE is determined from the separation of the D-lines $\Delta\lambda = 6$ A.U. $\Delta E = hc\Delta\lambda/\lambda^2$, where $\lambda = 5893$ A.U. This leads to the result $H \approx 10^5$ oersteds.

2. *Doublet eigenfunctions*

The eigenfunctions are obtained by applying $(j - m_j)$ times the operator $J_- = L_- + \sigma_-$ to $Y_{ll}\alpha$ (for $j = l + \frac{1}{2}$), and by finding the orthogonal combinations for $j = l - \frac{1}{2}$. The result is:

$$Y_{ljm_j} = \begin{cases} Y_{00}\alpha \text{ and } Y_{00}\beta & \text{for } l=0 \\ \sqrt{\left(\dfrac{l+m_j+\frac{1}{2}}{2l+1}\right)}\, Y_{l,m_j-\frac{1}{2}}\alpha - \sqrt{\left(\dfrac{l-m_j+\frac{1}{2}}{2l+1}\right)}\, Y_{l,m_j+\frac{1}{2}}\beta & \text{for } l=j-\frac{1}{2} \\ \sqrt{\left(\dfrac{l-m_j+\frac{1}{2}}{2l+1}\right)}\, Y_{l,m_j-\frac{1}{2}}\alpha + \sqrt{\left(\dfrac{l+m_j+\frac{1}{2}}{2l+1}\right)}\, Y_{l,m_j+\frac{1}{2}}\beta & \text{for } l=j+\frac{1}{2} \end{cases}$$

The angular components of the matrix elements $(Y_{l'j'm'_j}|\mathbf{r}|\,Y_{ljm_j}) = r\mathbf{a}_{l'j'm'_j;\,ljm_j}$ are given for the sodium D-lines in the following table:

Transition	m_j'	m_j	$18a_x^2$	$18a_y^2$	$18a_z^2$
$2P_{3/2}$	3/2	1/2	3	3	0
↓	3/2	−1/2	0	0	0
	1/2	1/2	0	0	4
$2S_{1/2}$	1/2	−1/2	1	1	0
$2P_{1/2}$	1/2	1/2	0	0	2
↓ $2S_{1/2}$	1/2	−1/2	2	2	0

The intensities of the Zeeman components for a weak field are calculated in accordance with §§30 and 36, using the above table. Note that $\Delta m_j = 0, \pm 1$, $\Delta l = \pm 1$, $\Delta j = 0, \pm 1$.

3. *Ionization due to the tunnel effect*

From p. 105, the probability of ionization of a hydrogen atom owing to the tunnel effect is

$$w\,dt \approx \omega D\,dt \qquad \hbar\omega = \frac{e^2}{2a_0} \approx \hbar \times 10^{16}\text{s}^{-1}$$

$$D \approx e^{-\kappa l} \qquad \kappa \approx \sqrt{\left(\frac{2m}{\hbar^2}(V_0 - E_0)\right)}$$

From figure 67:

$$l \approx \frac{-e}{2a_0 F} \qquad \kappa \approx \frac{1}{a_0} \to D \approx \exp - \frac{e}{2a_0{}^2 F} \approx 10^{-10^3/F}$$

When $F = 10^6$ V/cm the lifetime is therefore of the order of 10^{1000}s (one year $\approx 10^7$s, age of the earth $\approx 10^9$ years). The state is therefore practically stationary.

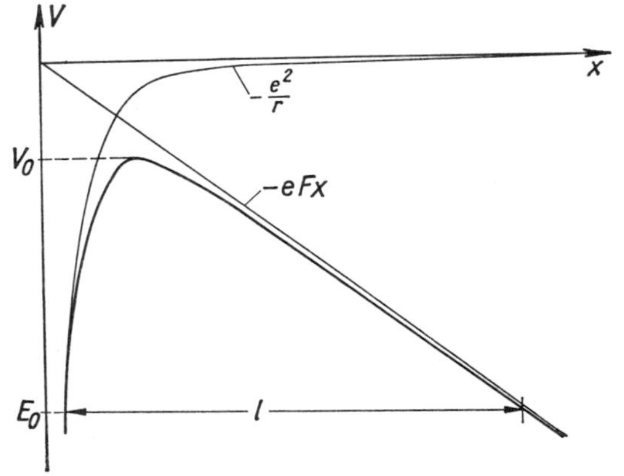

Fig. 67.—Potential of an electron in the electric field

4. *Spectral line intensities*

The x- and y-components of the transition elements, for which $m = \pm 1$, $m' = 0$, are $a_x{}^2 = a_y{}^2 = 1/6$, calculated from formulae (25.9/25.11); the z-component (for which $m = 0$, $m' = 0$) is $a_z{}^2 = 1/3$. From (29.11), the radial portion of the eigenfunction is

$$\int R_{10} r R_{21} r^2 dr = \frac{24}{\sqrt{6}}\left(\frac{2}{3}\right)^5 a_0$$

the x-, y-, and z-components of f therefore have the values f_{m0} shown in the table below:

m	x	y	z
1	0·21	0·21	0
0	0	0	0·42
−1	0·21	0·21	0

Hence
$$\underset{2p,1s}{f(x)} = \underset{2p,1s}{f(y)} = \underset{2p,1s}{f(z)} = \Sigma f_{m0} = 0{\cdot}42$$

The lifetime τ is given by

$$\frac{1}{\tau} = \frac{2}{3}\frac{e^2\omega^2}{mc^3}\frac{2m}{\hbar}\,\omega_{01}\,|\mathbf{r}_{01}|^2$$

and is about 10^{-9}s for all p-states (for which $m = \pm 1, 0$).

5. *Oscillator strengths for the principal series of sodium*

No.

The summation theorem $\sum_{\nu} f_{\nu\mu} = 1$ is valid only when ν extends over all quantum numbers of a complete system. For sodium, however, the initial state μ is $3s$. The transition from this state to the $2p$-state is forbidden by Pauli's principle, because the $2p$-level is occupied; this term is therefore absent from the sum of the f-values. Since the $2p$-energy level is lower than the $3s$-level this term is negative, and the experimental value of the f-sum is therefore greater than unity. For lithium, the f-value is zero for the transition of the valence electron to the ground state which is occupied by the electrons of the inner shell, as a result of the selection rule $\Delta l \neq 0$; in this case, therefore, the sum of the f-values must be unity.

6. *Polarizability of the alkali atoms*

$$\phi = \phi_0 + \sum_{i \neq 0} \frac{W_{i0}(E_i - E_0)}{(E_0 - E_i)(E_i - E_0)}\,\phi_i$$

From the above sum the square of the excitation energy can be removed from the denominator, and the summation can then be effected over all i:

$$\phi = \phi_0 + \frac{eF}{E_a{}^2}\sum_i x_{i0}(E_i - E_0)\phi_i$$

Since
$$x_{i0}(E_i - E_0) = (\mathscr{H}x - x\mathscr{H})_{i0} = -\frac{i\hbar}{m}p_{xi0}$$

$$\phi = \phi_0 - \frac{eFi\hbar}{E_a{}^2 m}\sum_i p_{xi0}\,\phi_i = \phi_0 - \frac{eFi\hbar}{E_a{}^2 m}p_x\phi_0$$
$$= \phi_0 - \beta\frac{\partial}{\partial x}\phi_0$$

where the displacement β is given by $\beta = eF\hbar^2/E_a{}^2 m$.

The polarizability α is the factor of F in the dipole moment $e\beta$:

$$\alpha = \frac{e^2\hbar^2}{mE_a{}^2} = 4a^3\left(\frac{I_{\rm H}}{E_a}\right)^2$$

where a is the Bohr radius and I_H the ionization energy of the hydrogen atom. The experimental and the calculated values agree very well:

	Li	Na	K	Rb	Cs
$\alpha_{th}(10^{-24}\text{cm}^3)$	32·6	25·2	43	45·5	57·2
$\alpha_{exp}(10^{-24}\text{cm}^3)$	27	27	46	50	61

7. *Refractive index of free electrons*

From the equation of motion $m\ddot{\mathbf{r}} = e\mathbf{E}_0 e^{i\omega t} = e\mathbf{E}$ we obtain $e\mathbf{r} = \alpha\mathbf{E}$, where $\alpha = -e^2/m\omega^2$. Hence $n = \sqrt{\varepsilon} = \sqrt{(1+4\pi N\alpha)}$ is imaginary when

$$\frac{\omega^2}{c^2} = \left(\frac{2\pi}{\lambda}\right)^2 \leqslant \frac{4\pi e^2}{mc^2}N$$

For the alkali metals Li, Na, K, Rb, Cs: $\lambda = 1560, 2100, 2900, 3100, 3550$ A.U. Cf. the experimental values (R. W. Wood, *Physical Optics*, New York, 1934, p. 560) 2050, 2150, 3150, 3600, 4400 A.U.

$N \approx 10^6\,\text{cm}^{-3}$ for the ionosphere.

Chapter DI (p. 271)

1. *Energy of an ideal Fermi gas*

The density of the **k**-values is $V/(2\pi)^3$. Hence the number of **k**-vectors within a sphere of radius k_0 is $(4\pi/3)k_0^3\,V/(2\pi)^3$, which must be equal to $n/2$ for the ground state; thus $k_0^3 = 3\pi^2 n/V$. The smallest wavelength is therefore of the same order of magnitude as the mean distance between particles $(V/n)^{1/3}$. In addition:

$$E_0 = 2\sum_{|\mathbf{k}|<k_0}\frac{\hbar^2}{2m}\mathbf{k}^2 = \frac{\hbar^2}{m}\frac{V}{(2\pi)^3}\int_{|\mathbf{k}|<k_0} k^4\,dk = n\frac{3}{5}\frac{\hbar^2 k_0^2}{2m}$$

The mean energy per particle is 3/5 of the maximum energy.

2. *Correlations for the ideal Fermi gas*

(*a*) $$w = \frac{1}{n(n-1)V^2}\sum_{\substack{|\mathbf{k}|<k_0\\|\mathbf{k}'|<k_0}}\{1 - \delta_{s_1 s_2}\exp\,[i(\mathbf{k}-\mathbf{k}')(\mathbf{r}_1-\mathbf{r}_2)]\}$$

When evaluating the summation it should be noted that $(\kappa_{s_1}, \kappa_{s_2}) = \delta_{s_1,s_2}, = \delta^2_{s_1,s_2}$, etc. Integrating over **k** and **k**′ we obtain

$$w = \frac{n}{4(n-1)V^2}\{1 - \delta_{s_1 s_2}F(k_0 r)\}$$

where $$F(k_0 r) = \left\{3\frac{\sin k_0 r - k_0 r\cos k_0 r}{(k_0 r)^3}\right\}^2$$

(*b*) $$\rho_{s_1,s_2}(r) = \frac{n}{2V}\{1 - \delta_{s_1 s_2}F(k_0 r)\}$$

$$\rho_{11} = \frac{n}{2V}\{1 - F(k_0 r)\}; \qquad \rho_{12} = \frac{n}{2V}; \qquad \rho_{11} + \rho_{12} = \frac{n}{V}\{1 - \tfrac{1}{2}F(k_0 r)\}$$

When observed from a particle of spin $s_1 = 1$, the particles with $s_2 = -1$ possess a constant density, unaffected by the presence of the first particle; in contrast, the density of the particles with the same spin is reduced almost to zero in the neighbourhood of the point of observation, up to distances of the order of $1/k_0$

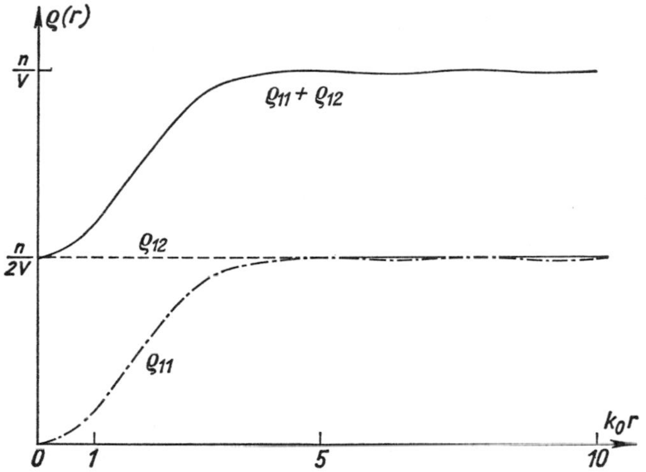

Fig. 68.—Densities in an ideal Fermi gas

(figure 68). (Note that $F(0) = 1$, corresponding to the "Fermi hole".) There is almost zero probability of finding two particles with the same spin at a distance less than $1/k_0$ from each other. Only half the "Fermi hole" occurs in the expression for the total density; the Fermi statistics therefore imply that the density in the neighbourhood of each particle is reduced by a factor of two, relative to the average density.

3. *Polarizability of helium*

From Exercise 5, p. 176:

$$\alpha = \frac{4}{2a_0}\{\overline{(x_1 + x_2)^2}\}^2 = \frac{8}{a_0} a'^4, \text{ since } \overline{x_1{}^2} = \overline{x_2{}^2} = a'^2, \ \overline{x_1 x_2} = 0$$

Therefore

$$\alpha = \frac{8}{Z'^4} a_0{}^3 \approx a_0{}^3 = 0{\cdot}15 \times 10^{-24} \text{ cm}^3$$

The experimental value is $0{\cdot}2 \times 10^{-24}$ cm^3. If we wish to make a more precise evaluation, using the method of variations and an initial function for the ground state with optimum Z', the calculation follows the same lines as that in Exercise 5, p. 176. It should be noted, however, that the initial function is not an exact eigenfunction of the Hamiltonian operator in the absence of the electric field. The result is practically identical with that given above.

4. *Rotation terms of the deuterium molecule*

The complete wave function must be symmetric in the coordinates of the nuclei. Symmetric spin functions correspond to even values of l, antisymmetric spin functions to odd values. Six symmetric spin functions may be constructed from the two spins of value 1; one function with five-fold degeneracy corresponding to spin 2, and one function corresponding to spin 0. In addition, there are three antisymmetric functions corresponding to spin 1.

5. *The exchange integral and spin interchange in the hydrogen molecule*

The wave function may be put into the form

$$\phi(t) = 2c \exp\left\{-\frac{it}{\hbar}(K + \tfrac{1}{2}J)\right\}\left\{[a(1)\,b(2)\,\alpha(1)\,\beta(2) - a(2)\,b(1)\,\alpha(2)\,\beta(1)] \cos\frac{Jt}{\hbar}\right.$$
$$\left. + \, i\,[a(1)\,b(2)\,\beta(1)\,\alpha(2) - a(2)\,b(1)\,\alpha(1)\,\beta(2)] \sin\frac{Jt}{\hbar}\right\}$$

K and J are given by (45.12). At the instant $t = 0$ atom a has an α-spin, atom b a β-spin, while at time $t = \pi\hbar/2J$ the situation is reversed. From (45.12), $J \approx A$ when S^4 and CS^2 can be neglected.

6. *Dirac's identity for the spin vector*

It is sufficient to prove the identity when the operator P^s is applied to the functions

$$\alpha(1)\,\alpha(2), \quad \alpha(1)\,\beta(2), \quad \beta(1)\,\alpha(2), \quad \beta(1)\,\beta(2)$$

because any function can be expressed in terms of them. Consider as an example the relation

$$\vec{\sigma}_1\,\vec{\sigma}_2 = 2(\sigma_1^+\,\sigma_2^- + \sigma_1^-\,\sigma_2^+) + \sigma_{1_z}\sigma_{2_z}$$

7. *Eigenfunctions of* $\mathbf{S}^2$

From the previous exercise:

$$(\vec{\sigma}_1 + \vec{\sigma}_2)^2 = \sigma_1^2 + \sigma_2^2 + 2\vec{\sigma}_1\,\vec{\sigma}_2 = 4(1 + P^s)$$

The eigenfunctions agree with those of P^s; they are

$$\alpha(1)\,\alpha(2), \quad \alpha(1)\,\beta(2) + \alpha(2)\,\beta(1), \quad \beta(1)\,\beta(2), \quad \alpha(1)\,\beta(2) - \alpha(2)\,\beta(1)$$

The eigenvalues are $2\hbar^2$ for the three symmetric functions and 0 for the antisymmetric one.

8. *Van der Waals potential for the Thomson atomic model*

(*a*)
$$m\ddot{x}_1 = -fx_1 + 2\gamma x_2 \qquad m\ddot{y}_1 = -fy_1 - \gamma y_2 \qquad m\ddot{z}_1 = -fz_1 - \gamma z_2$$
$$m\ddot{x}_2 = -fx_2 + 2\gamma x_1 \qquad m\ddot{y}_2 = -fy_2 - \gamma y_1 \qquad m\ddot{z}_2 = -fz_2 - \gamma z_1$$

where $\qquad f = e^2/R_A{}^3$ and $\gamma = e^2/R^3$

(*b*) The characteristic oscillations and eigenfrequencies are found by adding and subtracting the pairs of equations shown in (*a*). Only non-zero amplitudes are listed in the table below.

Oscillation state	Eigenfrequency
$x_1 + x_2 \neq 0$	$\omega_1 = \left\{\dfrac{f - 2\gamma}{m}\right\}^{1/2}$
$x_1 - x_2 \neq 0$	$\omega_2 = \left\{\dfrac{f + 2\gamma}{m}\right\}^{1/2}$
$y_1 + y_2 \neq 0$	$\omega_3 = \left\{\dfrac{f + \gamma}{m}\right\}^{1/2}$
$y_1 - y_2 \neq 0$	$\omega_4 = \left\{\dfrac{f - \gamma}{m}\right\}^{1/2}$
$z_1 + z_2 \neq 0$	$\omega_5 = \left\{\dfrac{f + \gamma}{m}\right\}^{1/2}$
$z_1 - z_2 \neq 0$	$\omega_6 = \left\{\dfrac{f - \gamma}{m}\right\}^{1/2}$

(*c*) $E(R) = \frac{1}{2}\hbar \sum_{\nu=1}^{6} \omega_\nu$. Expanding in powers of γ, we obtain

$$E(R) = \tfrac{1}{2}\hbar\omega_0 \left\{6 - \frac{3}{2}\frac{\gamma^2}{f^2}\right\}$$

where $\omega_0 = \sqrt{(f/m)}$ is the frequency of the unperturbed Thomson atom. The energy of the ground state E_0 of the two unperturbed atoms is $3\hbar\omega_0$. If we now put $\hbar\omega_0$ equal to the excitation or ionization energy of the atom, I, and substitute the polarizability α of the isolated atom for $R_A{}^3$, then

$$E(R) = E_0 - \frac{3}{4}\frac{I\alpha^2}{R^6}$$

This formula is of much more general validity, as might be expected from its method of derivation. In the case of two atoms, 1 and 2, the correct perturbation calculation by the methods of quantum mechanics leads to the following approximate formula, which is suitable for estimates:

$$E(R) \approx E_0 - \frac{3}{2}\frac{I_1 I_2}{I_1 + I_2}\frac{\alpha_1\alpha_2}{R^6}$$

In the classical model, $E(R)$ would be equal to 0 in the ground state since each electron would be at rest at the centre of its respective nucleus and no form of electrostatic interaction would occur. In quantum theory, on the other hand, the zero-point oscillations induce an attractive force, which can also be achieved according to classical mechanics by means of thermal motion.

(*d*) The ground-state function for a linear oscillator is $C \exp -\dfrac{m\omega}{2\hbar}x^2$. In the present case we obtain a product of six such functions:

$$C \exp \left\{-\frac{m\omega_1}{4\hbar}(x_1 + x_2)^2 - \frac{m\omega_2}{4\hbar}(x_1 - x_2)^2 - \frac{m\omega_3}{4\hbar}[(y_1 + y_2)^2 + (z_1 + z_2)^2] - \frac{m\omega_4}{4\hbar}[(y_1 - y_2)^2 + (z_1 - z_2)^2]\right\}$$

It should be noted that in the case of the oscillations for which $x_1 + x_2 \neq 0$, twice the mass and the coordinate $\frac{1}{2}(x_1 + x_2)$ are employed, while half the mass and the coordinate $x_1 - x_2$ enter into the oscillations for which $x_1 - x_2 \neq 0$.

Proof: If all ω_i are equal, as in the case of two separate atoms, the ground-state function must become $\exp\{(-m\omega_0/2\hbar)(\mathbf{r}_1{}^2 + \mathbf{r}_2{}^2)\}$.

We can immediately deduce from the above representation that all mean values of form $\overline{x_1}$, $\overline{x_2}$, $\overline{y_1}$ and $\overline{x_1y_1}$, $\overline{x_1y_2}$, . . . vanish.

The various correlation products such as $\overline{x_1x_2}$ are found from $\overline{(x_1+x_2)^2} = 2\hbar/m\omega_1$ and $\overline{(x_1-x_2)^2} = 2\hbar/m\omega_2$, etc.:

$$\overline{x_1x_2} = \frac{\hbar}{2m}\left(\frac{1}{\omega_1} - \frac{1}{\omega_2}\right) > 0; \quad \overline{y_1y_2} = \overline{z_1z_2} = \frac{\hbar}{2m}\left(\frac{1}{\omega_3} - \frac{1}{\omega_4}\right) < 0$$

The significance of the positive correlation $\overline{x_1x_2} > 0$ is as follows: for a given $x_1 > 0$, the chance of finding electron 2 in the region $x_2 > 0$ is greater than the chance of encountering it in the region $x_2 < 0$; similarly for $x_1 < 0$ and $x_2 < 0$. The reason is clear: when $x_1 > 0$ the force on electron 2 is directed towards the right, and therefore tends to give preference to positive values of x_2. The opposite situation exists in the case of the y- and z-components.

9. *Forces between two helium atoms*

The result is $E_{el}(R) = 2\varepsilon_0 + 4C - 2A$, where ε_0 is the energy of the ground state of the helium atom when calculated with the optimum value of Z, and C and A have the same significance as in the case of the hydrogen molecule, but are calculated from the modified hydrogen functions appropriate to helium. Further integrals appear when the overlap integral S cannot be neglected. The contribution of the Coulomb integral $4C$ is practically compensated by the electrostatic interaction $4e^2/R$, and the potential energy therefore consists almost entirely of the repulsion term $-2A$, where $A < 0$.

Chapter EI (p. 296)

1. *Pressure and energy density in an ideal gas*

The number of particles in the interval ($\mathbf{p}$, $d\mathbf{p}$) incident on an element of surface dS in time dt is $f(\mathbf{p})d\mathbf{p}v_x dS dt$ (cf. figure 69). In the course of a collision (assumed to be elastic) each particle transfers momentum $2p_x$ to the wall. Therefore

$$P dS dt = \int_0^\infty dp_x \iint_{-\infty}^{+\infty} dp_y dp_z 2p_x v_x f dS dt$$

since it is only permissible to integrate over those particles that actually strike the wall (i.e. p_x, $v_x > 0$). The general relations between the energy E, the momentum $\mathbf{p}$, and the velocity $\mathbf{v}$ are:

$$\mathbf{p} = \frac{m\mathbf{v}}{\sqrt{\left(1 - \frac{v^2}{c^2}\right)}} \qquad E = \frac{mc^2}{\sqrt{\left(1 - \frac{v^2}{c^2}\right)}}$$

$$E = \sqrt{(p^2c^2 + m^2c^4)} \qquad \mathbf{pv} = pv = \frac{E^2 - m^2c^4}{E}$$

Since the gas is assumed to be isotropic, the factor 2 may be replaced by integration over all values of p_x: hence $P = n\overline{p_x v_x}$. In addition,

$$\overline{p_x v_x} = \overline{p_y v_y} = \overline{p_z v_z} = \frac{1}{3}\overline{\mathbf{pv}} = \frac{1}{3}\overline{\left\{\frac{E^2 - m^2c^4}{E}\right\}}$$

Therefore

$$P = \frac{n}{3}\overline{\left\{\frac{(E-mc^2)(E+mc^2)}{E}\right\}} = \begin{cases} \frac{n}{3}\bar{E} \text{ for } E \gg mc^2, \text{ or } m = 0 \\ \frac{2}{3}n\overline{(E-mc^2)} = \frac{2}{3}n\bar{E}_{\text{kin}} \text{ for } E - mc^2 \ll mc^2 \end{cases}$$

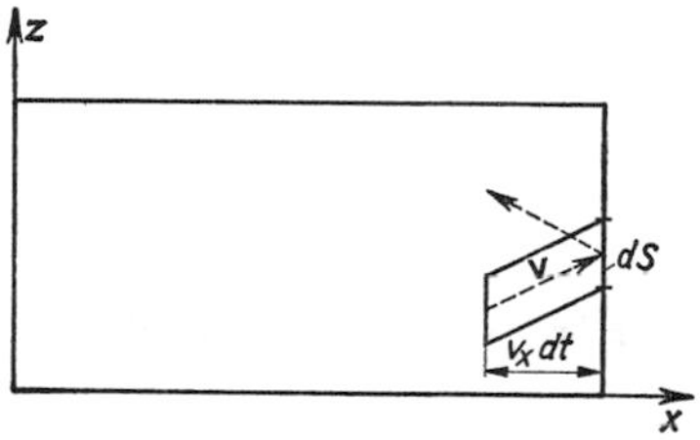

Fig. 69.—Calculation of the pressure of an ideal gas

2. *The solar constant*

From (46.4), the total energy emitted from the surface of the sun per unit time is $\sigma T^4.4\pi R_s{}^2$, where R_s is the sun's radius. This energy passes through the surface of a sphere of radius R_E, where R_E denotes the radius of the earth's orbit. At the earth, therefore, the incident energy per unit time and per unit area is

$$S = \sigma T^4\left(\frac{R_s}{R_E}\right)^2 = \sigma T^4\frac{\delta^2}{4}$$

The value of σ is $1{\cdot}4 \times 10^{\ 12}$ cal cm^{-2}s^{-1}deg^{-4}; putting $T = 6 \times 10^3$ and $\delta \approx 0{\cdot}009$ gives a value of about 2 cal cm^{-2}min^{-1} for the solar constant.

Chapter E II (p. 319)

1. *Fourier representation of Hertz's solution*

If the trial solution for ϕ, say, is introduced into the initial equation, we obtain

$$\phi = \frac{1}{(2\pi)^4}\int 4\pi\rho(\mathbf{r}', t')\frac{\exp\,[i\mathbf{k}(\mathbf{r}-\mathbf{r}') - i\omega\,(t-t')]}{k^2 - \omega^2/c^2}\,d\mathbf{k}\,d\omega\,d\mathbf{r}'\,dt'$$

The path of integration in the plane of ω should be taken as shown in figure 70.

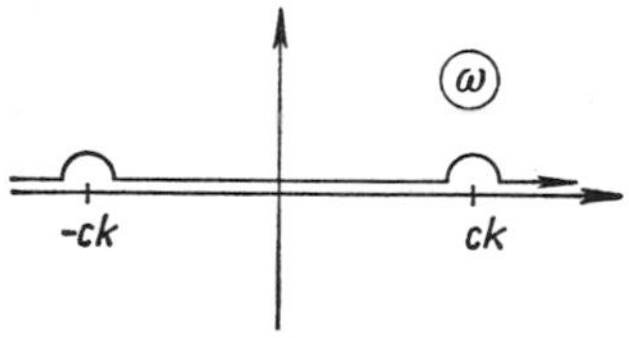

Fig. 70

When $t < t'$ the path of integration may be moved upwards into the positive imaginary region, and the integral round the contour is then zero. For $t > t'$ the path of integration must be moved downwards into the negative imaginary region, in which case it still includes the poles of the integrand at $\omega = -ck$ and $\omega = +ck$. Then from the theorem of residues:

$$\frac{4\pi}{(2\pi)^4}\int \frac{\exp\,[i\mathbf{k}(\mathbf{r}-\mathbf{r}')-i\omega(t-t')]}{k^2-\omega^2/c^2}d\mathbf{k}d\omega$$

$$=\frac{-ic}{(2\pi)^2}\int \exp i\mathbf{k}(\mathbf{r}-\mathbf{r}')\,\frac{\exp ick(t-t')-\exp -ick(t-t')}{k}d\mathbf{k}$$

$$=\frac{-c}{2\pi|\mathbf{r}-\mathbf{r}'|}\int_0^{\infty}\{\exp ik|\mathbf{r}-\mathbf{r}'|-\exp -ik|\mathbf{r}-\mathbf{r}'|\}\times$$
$$\times\{\exp ick(t-t')-\exp -ick(t-t')\}dk$$

$$=\frac{1}{|\mathbf{r}-\mathbf{r}'|}\int_{-\infty}^{+\infty}\left\{\exp\{ik|\mathbf{r}-\mathbf{r}'|-ick(t-t')\}-\exp\{ik|\mathbf{r}-\mathbf{r}'|+ick(t-t')\}\,d\frac{kc}{2\pi}\right.$$

$$=\frac{\delta\left(t'-t+\dfrac{|\mathbf{r}-\mathbf{r}'|}{c}\right)}{|\mathbf{r}-\mathbf{r}'|},\ \text{since}\ t-t'>0$$

When this result is introduced into the above integral and the integration is performed with respect to t' we obtain the familiar formula for the retarded potential. The calculation in the case of $\mathbf{A}(\mathbf{r}, t)$ is similar.

2. *Total radiation momentum*

Using the relations (51.10) and (51.12), we obtain

$$\mathbf{G} = \sum_{\mathbf{k},\lambda} \hbar\mathbf{k}b^{+}_{\mathbf{k}\lambda}b_{\mathbf{k}\lambda}$$

Equation (52.2) shows that $\mathbf{G}$ commutes with $\mathscr{H}$, and that it is therefore constant with respect to time. The eigenvectors (52.6) are also eigenvectors of $\mathbf{G}$ with eigenvalues

$$\sum_{\mathbf{k},\lambda} n_{\mathbf{k}\lambda}\hbar\mathbf{k}$$

This state therefore represents $n_{\mathbf{k}\lambda}$ light quanta with energy $\hbar\omega_{\mathbf{k}}$ and momentum $\hbar\mathbf{k}$.

3. *Angular momentum of the radiation*

We first obtain

$$\mathbf{M} = \sum_{\mathbf{k}}\sum_{\lambda,\lambda'} \tfrac{1}{2}i\hbar\{b^{+}_{\mathbf{k}\lambda}b_{\mathbf{k}\lambda'}-b^{+}_{\mathbf{k}\lambda'}b_{\mathbf{k}\lambda}\}(\mathbf{s}_{\mathbf{k}\lambda}\times\mathbf{s}_{\mathbf{k}\lambda'}) = \sum_{\mathbf{k}}\mathbf{M}^{(\mathbf{k})}$$

The vector product of the two mutually orthogonal polarization vectors is only non-zero if $\lambda \neq \lambda'$. $\mathbf{s}_{\mathbf{k}1} \times \mathbf{s}_{\mathbf{k}2} = \mathbf{e}_{\mathbf{k}}$ is a unit vector ($\mathbf{e}_{-\mathbf{k}} = \mathbf{e}_{\mathbf{k}}$) in the direction of $+\mathbf{k}$ if the vectors are chosen as in figure 71. Then

$$\mathbf{M}^{(\mathbf{k})} = \mathbf{e}_{\mathbf{k}} \cdot i\hbar\{b^{+}_{\mathbf{k}1} b_{\mathbf{k}2} - b^{+}_{\mathbf{k}2} b_{\mathbf{k}1}\}$$

In order to find the eigenvalues of a Hermitian operator in the form of $i(b^{+}_{1} b_2 - b^{+}_{2} b_1)$ we may introduce the new operators

$$b_{(\sigma)} = \frac{1}{\sqrt{2}}(b_1 + i\sigma b_2), \text{ where } \sigma = \pm 1$$

(It should be verified that the commutation relations for the $b_{\mathbf{k}(\sigma)}$ are identical with those for $b_{\mathbf{k}\lambda}$.) Then

$$\begin{aligned} & & & \text{Eigenvalues} \\ \mathbf{M}^{(\mathbf{k})} &= \mathbf{e}_{\mathbf{k}}\hbar(b^{+}_{\mathbf{k}(1)} b_{\mathbf{k}(1)} - b^{+}_{\mathbf{k}(-1)} b_{\mathbf{k}(-1)}) & \mathbf{e}_{\mathbf{k}}\hbar & \quad (n_{\mathbf{k}(1)} - n_{\mathbf{k}(-1)}) \\ \left.\begin{matrix} \mathscr{H}_{(\mathbf{k})} = \hbar\omega_{\mathbf{k}} \\ \mathbf{G}^{(\mathbf{k})} = \hbar\mathbf{k} \end{matrix}\right\} &\cdot (b^{+}_{\mathbf{k}(1)} b_{\mathbf{k}(1)} + b^{+}_{\mathbf{k}(-1)} b_{\mathbf{k}(-1)}) & \left.\begin{matrix} \hbar\omega_{\mathbf{k}} \\ \hbar\mathbf{k} \end{matrix}\right\} & \cdot (n_{\mathbf{k}(1)} + n_{\mathbf{k}(-1)}) \end{aligned}$$

Hence the eigenvalues of $\mathbf{M}^{(\mathbf{k})}$ are integral multiples of $\pm\mathbf{e}_{\mathbf{k}}\hbar$. The spin has the value $\hbar$ and is parallel or antiparallel to the propagation vector $\mathbf{k}$. The classical waves associated with $\sigma = 1$ clearly have corresponding amplitudes $b_{(1)} \neq 0$,

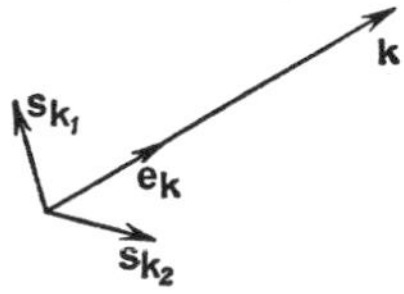

Fig. 71.—Polarization and propagation vectors

$b_{(-1)} = b_1 - ib_2 = 0$: i.e. the amplitudes b_1 and b_2 have the same magnitude and a phase difference of $\pi/2$. This is a circularly polarized wave (in the right-handed sense with respect to $\mathbf{k}$). It is evident from the above representation that $\mathscr{H}$, $\mathbf{G}$, and $\mathbf{M}$ commute. The Hilbert space is formed as in §52, except that the $b_{\mathbf{k}(\sigma)}$ are employed in place of the $b_{\mathbf{k}\lambda}$:

$\Phi_{\ldots, n_{\mathbf{k}(\sigma)}, \ldots}$ is an eigenfunction of the operator

$\mathscr{H}$ with eigenvalue	$\sum_{\mathbf{k},\sigma} \hbar\omega_{\mathbf{k}} n_{\mathbf{k}(\sigma)}$
$\mathbf{G}$ with eigenvalue	$\sum_{\mathbf{k},\sigma} \hbar\mathbf{k} n_{\mathbf{k}(\sigma)}$
$\mathbf{M}$ with eigenvalue	$\sum_{\mathbf{k},\sigma} \hbar\mathbf{e}_{\mathbf{k}} \sigma n_{\mathbf{k}(\sigma)}$

The Hilbert space is spanned by these eigenfunctions.

Chapter FI (p. 327)

1. *The energy spectrum of electrons in β-disintegration, according to Fermi*

$n(\mathbf{p}_e)\,d\mathbf{p}_e = C\,d\mathbf{p}_e \int d\mathbf{p}_\nu$ is first calculated, where $\mathbf{p}_\nu$ must be integrated subject to the condition $E_m - \mathscr{H}_e \leqslant \mathscr{H}_\nu \leqslant E_m - \mathscr{H}_e + \Delta E_m$. Since $\mathscr{H} = \{\mathbf{p}^2c^2 + m^2c^4\}^{1/2}$, this is the same as integrating in $\mathbf{p}_\nu$-space over a spherical shell of radius

$$\bar{p}_\nu = \left\{\frac{(E_m - \mathscr{H}_e)^2 - m_\nu^2c^4}{c^2}\right\}^{1/2}$$

and thickness
$$\Delta\bar{p}_\nu = \frac{E_m - \mathscr{H}_e}{p_\nu c^2}\,\Delta E_m$$

Therefore
$$n(\mathbf{p}_e)\,d\mathbf{p}_e = C'\{(E_m - \mathscr{H}_e)^2 - m_\nu^2c^4\}^{1/2}(E_m - \mathscr{H}_e)$$

where C' is a new constant.

If this distribution is again integrated over $\mathbf{p}_e$, with $E_e \leqslant \mathscr{H}_e \leqslant E_e + dE_e$, the result is

$$n(E_e)\,dE_e = C''\{E_e^2 - m_e^2c^4\}^{1/2}E_e\{(E_m - E_e)^2 - m_\nu^2c^4\}^{1/2}(E_m - E_e)$$

In particular, for $m_\nu = 0$:

$$n(E_e)\,dE_e = C''\{E_e^2 - m_e^2c^4\}^{1/2}E_e(E_m - E_e)^2$$

At values near the rest energy of the electron, $E_e = m_ec^2$, the distribution has the form $\sqrt{(E_e - m_ec^2)}$; at the maximum energy E_m the slope is horizontal. The

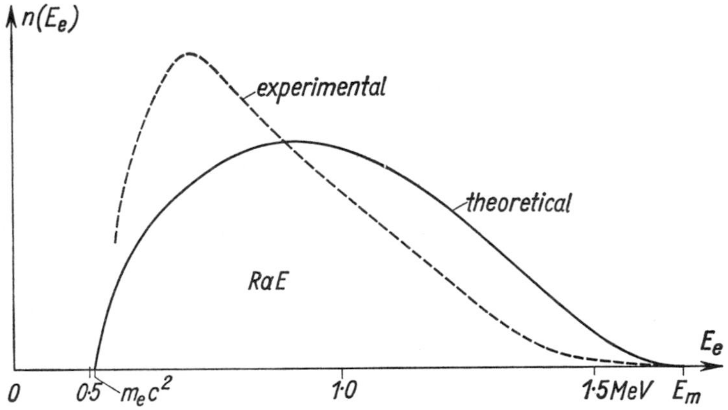

Fig. 72.—Experimental and theoretical distributions for β-disintegration of Ra E

theoretical distribution is compared with an experimental curve in figure 72. The theoretical curve is adjusted to E_m and normalized to make the area under each curve the same.

2. *The relativistic Hamiltonian equations*

The treatment is the same as in §7.

Chapter FII (p. 359)

1. *The spin operator of the Dirac equation*

From (57.10), $[\mathscr{H}, \vec{\sigma}'] = 2ic\vec{\alpha} \times \mathbf{p}$, whence on forming the scalar product with $\mathbf{p}$ it follows that

$$[\mathscr{H}, (\vec{\sigma}'\mathbf{p})] = 2ic\vec{\alpha}\mathbf{p} \times \mathbf{p} = 0$$

We can also see from the table on p. 356 that

$$\sigma'\mathbf{p} = (U\vec{\sigma}'U^+)\mathbf{p}$$

2. *The matrix trace as a unitary invariant*

For unitary transformations:

$$\tilde{A} = U^+AU \qquad \sum_m U^*_{nm} U_{lm} = \delta_{ln}$$

Therefore
$$\sum_m \tilde{A}_{mm} = \sum_{l,m,n} U^*_{nm} A_{nl} U_{lm} = \sum_n A_{nn}$$

If U is so chosen for Hermitian matrices that A is diagonal, then $\sum_n A_{nn} = \sum_i a_i$.

In addition:

$$\mathrm{Tr}\, AB = \sum_{mn} A_{mn} B_{nm} = \sum_{mn} B_{nm} A_{mn} = \mathrm{Tr}\, BA$$

3. *Commutation with the Pauli matrices*

It follows from the condition

$$\left[\sigma_z, \begin{pmatrix} a & b \\ c & d \end{pmatrix}\right] = \begin{pmatrix} a & b \\ -c & -d \end{pmatrix} - \begin{pmatrix} a & -b \\ c & -d \end{pmatrix} = 0$$

that $b = c = 0$; further, $a = d$ because

$$\left[\sigma_x, \begin{pmatrix} a & 0 \\ 0 & d \end{pmatrix}\right] = \begin{pmatrix} 0 & d \\ a & 0 \end{pmatrix} - \begin{pmatrix} 0 & a \\ d & 0 \end{pmatrix} = 0$$

Since $2i\sigma_y = \sigma_z\sigma_x - \sigma_x\sigma_z$, the commutation relation between the matrix and σ_y does not impose any further condition.

4. *Hilbert space for Fermi-Dirac statistics*

Since
$$b_\mathbf{k}^+ b_\mathbf{k} + b_\mathbf{k} b_\mathbf{k}^+ = 1 \quad \text{and} \quad b_\mathbf{k}^2 = 0$$

it follows that
$$(b_\mathbf{k}^+ b_\mathbf{k})^2 = b_\mathbf{k}^+(1 - b_\mathbf{k}^+ b_\mathbf{k}) b_\mathbf{k} = b_\mathbf{k}^+ b_\mathbf{k}$$

Hence the equation for the eigenvalues $n_\mathbf{k}$ of $b_\mathbf{k}^+ b_\mathbf{k}$ is $n_\mathbf{k}^2 = n_\mathbf{k}$, possessing the two solutions $n_\mathbf{k} = 0$ or 1. If there is an eigenstate ϕ of $b_\mathbf{k}^+ b_\mathbf{k}$, then

$$(b_\mathbf{k}\phi, b_\mathbf{k}\phi) = n_\mathbf{k}(\phi, \phi)$$

If $n_{\mathbf{k}} = 0$, then $b_{\mathbf{k}}\phi = 0$; if $n_{\mathbf{k}} = 1$, $b_{\mathbf{k}}\phi$ corresponds to the eigenvalue $n_{\mathbf{k}} = 0$ because

$$b_{\mathbf{k}}^{+} b_{\mathbf{k}}^{2} \phi = (b_{\mathbf{k}}^{+} b_{\mathbf{k}}) b_{\mathbf{k}} \phi = 0 \quad \text{and} \quad b_{\mathbf{k}}^{2} = 0$$

$b_{\mathbf{k}}$ therefore possesses the property of annihilating a particle of momentum $\hbar\mathbf{k}$ Similarly, it may be verified that the operator $b_{\mathbf{k}}^{+}$ generates a particle. Since $b_{\mathbf{k}}^{+2} = 0$, a particle of type **k** can only be created once.

5. *The spin and orbital current of the Dirac electron*

$$\rho = \rho_b - \operatorname{div} \mathbf{P} \qquad \mathbf{j} = \mathbf{j}_b + e \operatorname{curl} \mathbf{M} + \dot{\mathbf{P}}$$

$$\rho_b = \frac{i\hbar}{2mc^2}(\psi^* \beta \dot{\psi} - \dot{\psi}^* \beta \psi) \qquad \mathbf{P} = \frac{i\hbar}{2mc}(\psi^* \vec{\alpha} \beta \psi)$$

$$\mathbf{j}_b = \frac{i\hbar}{2m}(\operatorname{grad} \psi^* \beta \psi - \psi^* \beta \operatorname{grad} \psi) \qquad \mathbf{M} = \frac{\hbar}{2mc}(\psi^* \vec{\sigma}' \beta \psi)$$

$\mathbf{j}_b$ corresponds to the Schrödinger current, and ρ_b is the associated relativistic generalization of the density. **M** is the "magnetization" and **P** the "polarization" of the electron. (See Vol. I, §§ 26 and 47, and p. 216.)

H

Index

INDEX